FOUNDATIONS

DESIGN and PRACTICE

By ELWYN E. SEELYE

DATA BOOK for
CIVIL ENGINEERS

VOLUME ONE — DESIGN —
Second edition.

VOLUME TWO — SPECIFICATIONS
AND COSTS — Second edition.

VOLUME THREE — FIELD PRACTICE —
Second edition.

●

FOUNDATIONS — Design and Practice.

FOUNDATIONS
DESIGN and PRACTICE

ELWYN E. SEELYE

With special acknowledgment to

PHILIP P. PAGE, JR.

New York—JOHN WILEY AND SONS, Inc.

London — CHAPMAN AND HALL, Limited

Library of Congress Catalog Card Number: 56-9435

PRINTED IN THE UNITED STATES OF AMERICA

Dedicated to the association of foundation engineers and contractors known as The Moles, whose members risk their lives and fortunes delving into the earth's crusts, and particularly to Richard E. Dougherty, former President of The Moles.

Preface

Foundation engineering is not a "push-button" subject. More than any other area of construction engineering, it requires a knowledge of theoretical design principles and practical construction technique. Given a good foundation design, the remaining design work in buildings, bridges, dams, and sewers can be safely carried out in the office. But the foundation design must be related to field conditions. A full knowledge of field conditions is essential, from site geology to soil behavior on the particular site, and from cofferdamming to damage by vibration force.

This book is intended for the practicing designing engineer, the builder, the inspector, the architect, the teacher, and the student. All phases of this inexact engineering subject are covered, to assist engineers in subsurface exploration, inspection, foundation reports, specifications, estimates, contracts, and design. The engineer and architect will find these subjects arranged for reference to the particular problems facing them, and the teacher and student can use the book as a whole for study.

For convenience and clarity, *Foundations* is organized as follows:

1. The "push-button" design of simple elements such as plate footings and retaining walls.

2. More complex designs and consideration of various allied problems such as combined footings on problems of settlement.

3. Economic studies, to enable the engineer to choose between various types of structures (such as a wood pile versus a concrete pile).

4. A wide variety of structural types, ranging from a concrete building foundation to a bridge abutment, and from an embankment to a paving base.

Because it is assumed that the reader will be designing or inspecting one item at a time, a certain amount of repetition is necessary and desirable. For instance, the engineer or architect interested in embankments will want the design information and criteria at hand as much as possible, and not scattered throughout the book.

A set of typical foundation specifications is given.

The *field problems* are presented in juxtaposition to the corresponding design information, since they add to the design engineer's basic understanding. For instance, the *field methods* of underpinning and shoring are included with the discussion of underpinning design; an engineer cannot exercise judgment in deciding, say, between an open pier and a pile foundation to rock unless he has an understanding of the difficulty of underpinning which the open pier may involve.

On the other hand, *field practice,* which covers such points as an inspector's checking list, is not of direct interest to the designer, and it is therefore placed in a separate chapter.

The treatment of soil mechanics illustrates the flexibility of the book. The theoretical considerations of soil mechanics, such as time settlement, are separated from the immediate attention of the designer. Since, however, the designer and student should have at least a background of understanding of the significance of soil mechanics, the subject is prefaced by a unique discussion entitled "Soil Behavior" which furnishes them with a readable introduction to the subject.

It is hoped that the use of this book may enable the less-experienced reader to function as a well-rounded foundation engineer, as far as this is possible without years of office design work and field experience.

For this reason, discussions and "red-light warnings" are presented in addition to field methods and conditions.

Foundations, then, is designed in five dimensions:

Design

Design Data and Criteria

Costs

Specifications

Field Practice

All these five dimensions are necessary for the "compleat" foundation engineer.

Elwin E. Seelye

New York
February, 1956

Acknowledgments

The author wishes to acknowledge the assistance received from the following persons:

Mr. Edward P. Albright, MacLean-Grove & Co., Inc.

Mr. A. R. Bastone } Griffin Wellpoint Corporation.
Mr. H. J. Hush, President }

Mr. T. B. Breen, New York Roofing Co.

Mr. Jules R. Breuchaud, Underpinning & Foundation Co.

Mr. William F. Brostek, Housing Authority, City of New York.

Prof. Donald M. Burmister, Columbia University.

Mr. H. P. Burrell, C. L. Guild Construction Co., Inc.

Dr. Arthur Casagrande, Harvard University.

Dr. D. B. Chisholm, Fellow: American Geographical Society.

Mr. Irving B. Crosby, Geologist.

Mr. G. A. Fletcher, Raymond Concrete Pile Co.

Mr. Shortridge Hardesty } Hardesty and Hanover, Consulting Engineers.
Mr. Clinton D. Hanover }

Mr. R. B. Holtz, R. B. Holtz & Co., Inc.

Mr. Harry T. Immerman, Spencer, White & Prentis, Inc.

Maintenance Engineering Co., Inc., Bloomfield, New Jersey.

Mr. Ralph Mann, American Wood Preservers Association.

Mr. William H. Mueser } Moran, Proctor, Mueser & Rutledge.
Mr. Philip C. Rutledge }

Mr. O. J. Porter } Porter, Urquhart, McCreary & O'Brien.
Mr. L. C. Urquhart }

The Portland Cement Association.

Capt. E. H. Praeger, Praeger & Kavanagh.

Dr. Harry S. Rogers, President, Brooklyn Polytechnic Institute.

Mr. Ole Singstad, Singstad & Baillie.

Mr. Leon P. Sudrabin, Electro Rust-Proofing Corporation.

The late Prof. Donald W. Taylor, Massachusetts Institute of Technology.

The late Mr. Rudolph Triest, John Wiley & Sons, Inc.

The author wishes to make special mention of the assistance received from the following members of his organization:

Mr. Albert L. Stevenson, Mr. Stephen D. Teetor, Mr. Richard E. Dougherty, Mr. A. H. Jorgensen, Mr. Jack L. Staunton, Mr. Patrick H. Murphy, Mr. Paul Kluger, Mr. Frederick C. Zeigler, Mr. T. C. DiBlasi, Mr. M. C. Simmons, Mrs. Lucille Burnham, Miss Jean M. Luckett.

Contents

1

Introduction

COMMON TYPES AND ELEMENTS
OF SPREAD FOOTINGS

The following drawings will serve to familiarize
the user with common elements and designs of spread
footings and piles, and their nomenclature.

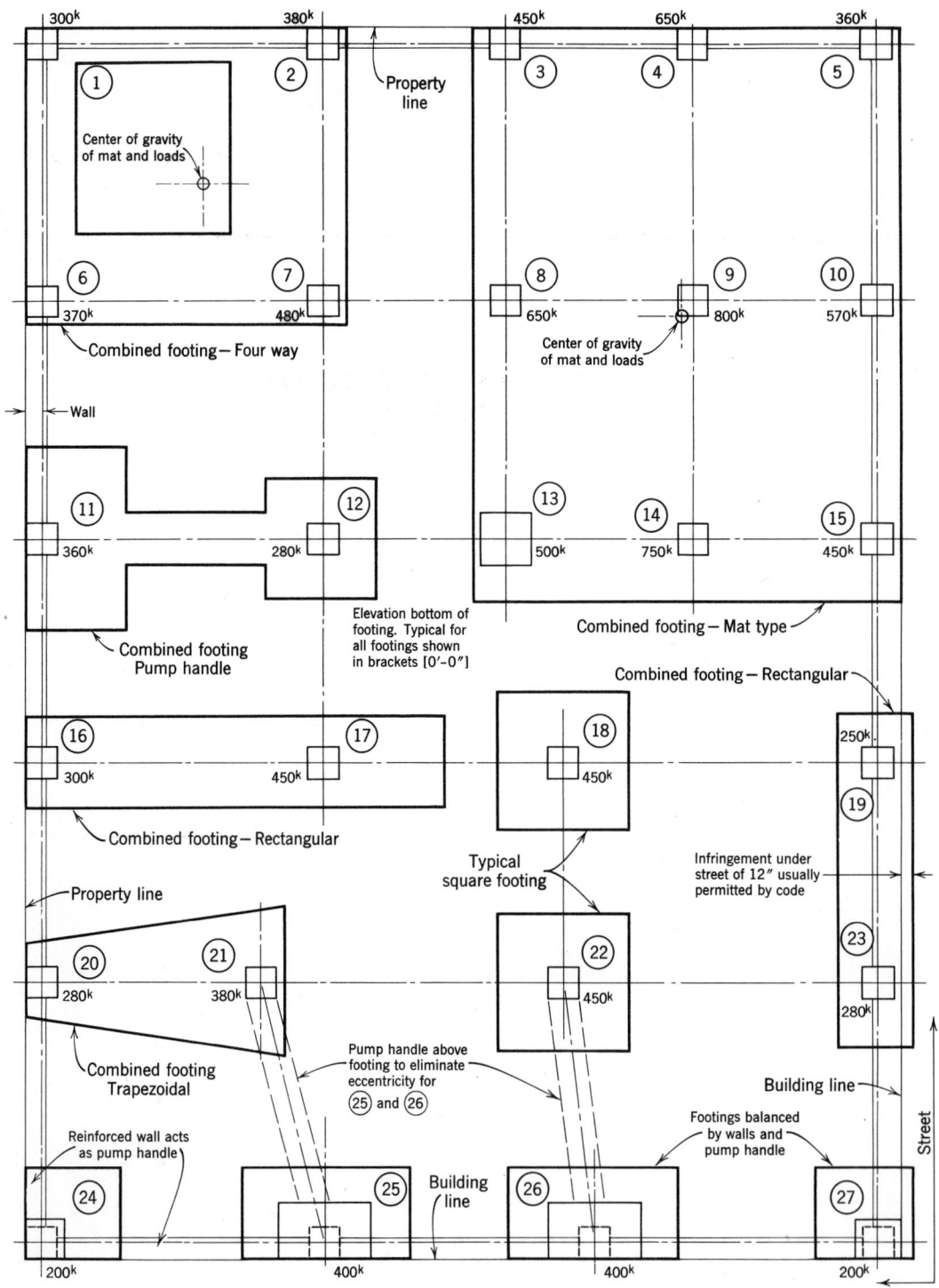

FIG. 1.   TYPICAL FOUNDATION PLAN.

BILLET

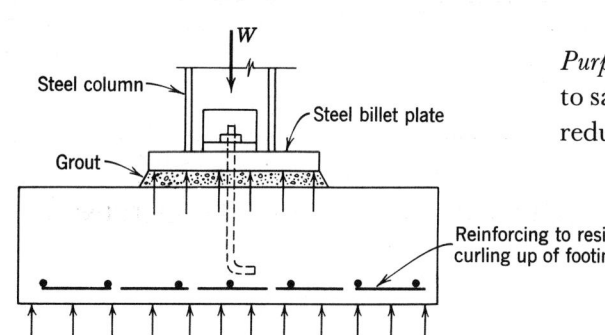

Purpose: Billet plate reduces unit pressures in column to safe unit pressure in bearing on footing. Footing reduces unit pressure to safe unit pressure on soil.

STEEL GRILLAGE

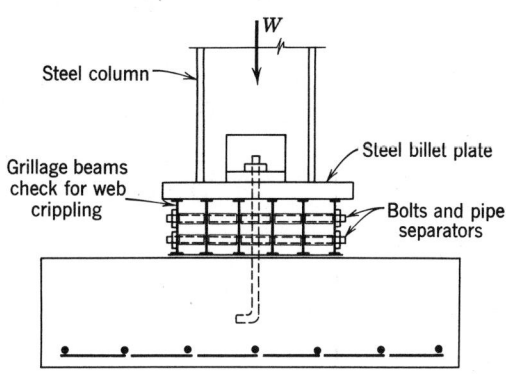

Note: Grillage may also be used on other types of foundations, such as pile caps.

FIG. 2. SPREAD FOOTINGS.

CONCRETE COLUMN

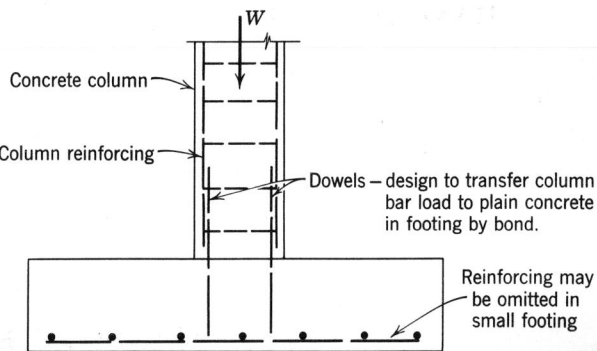

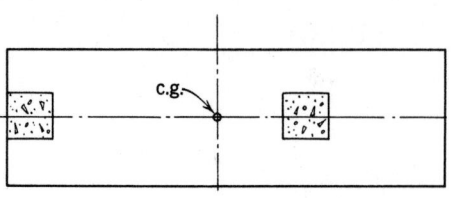

PLAN
RECTANGULAR COMBINED FOOTING

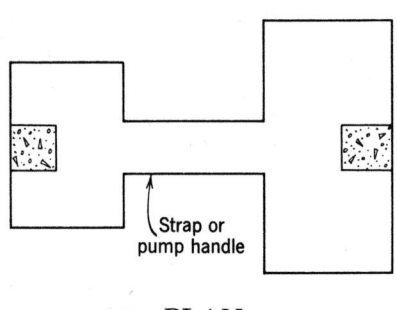

PLAN

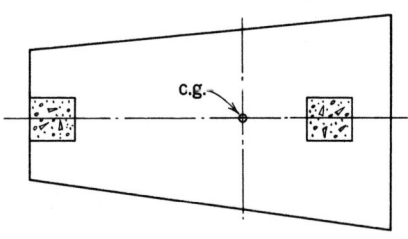

PLAN
TRAPEZOIDAL COMBINED FOOTING

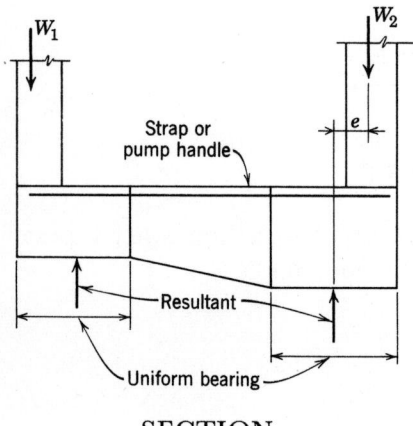

SECTION

CANTILEVER OR PUMP
HANDLE FOOTING

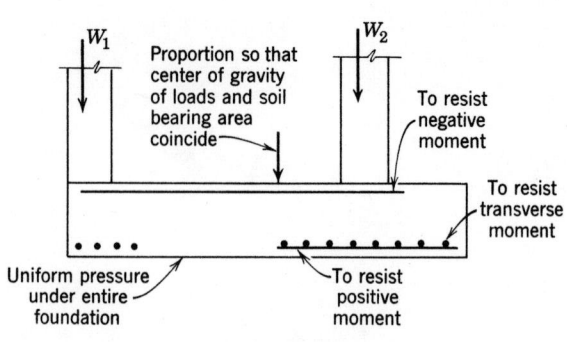

SECTION

COMBINED FOOTING

FIG. 3.   BALANCING ECCENTRIC FOOTING.

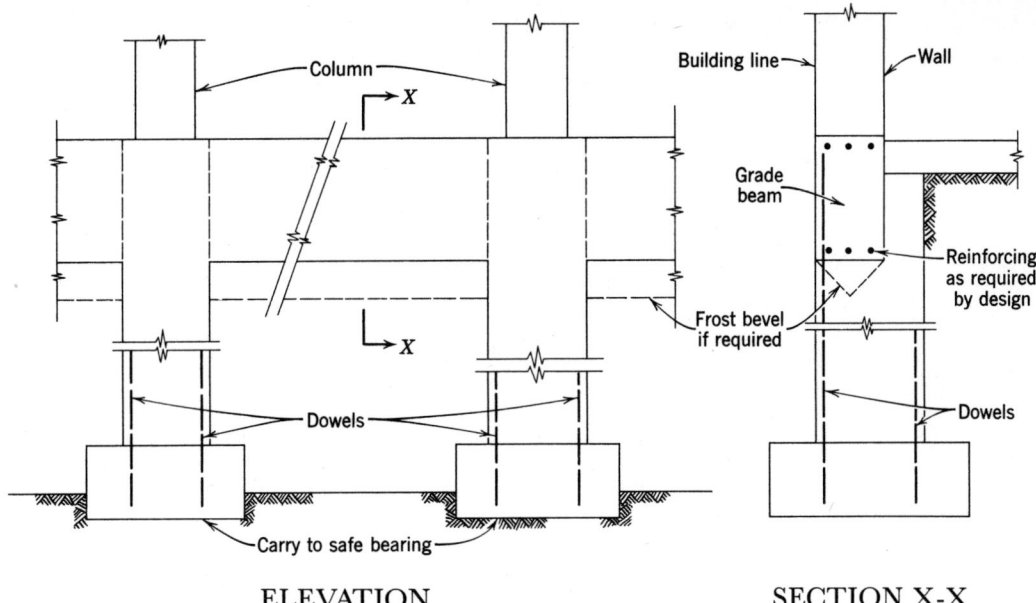

ELEVATION   SECTION X-X

Purpose: To avoid deep foundation walls.

FIG. 4.   GRADE BEAMS AND FOOTINGS.

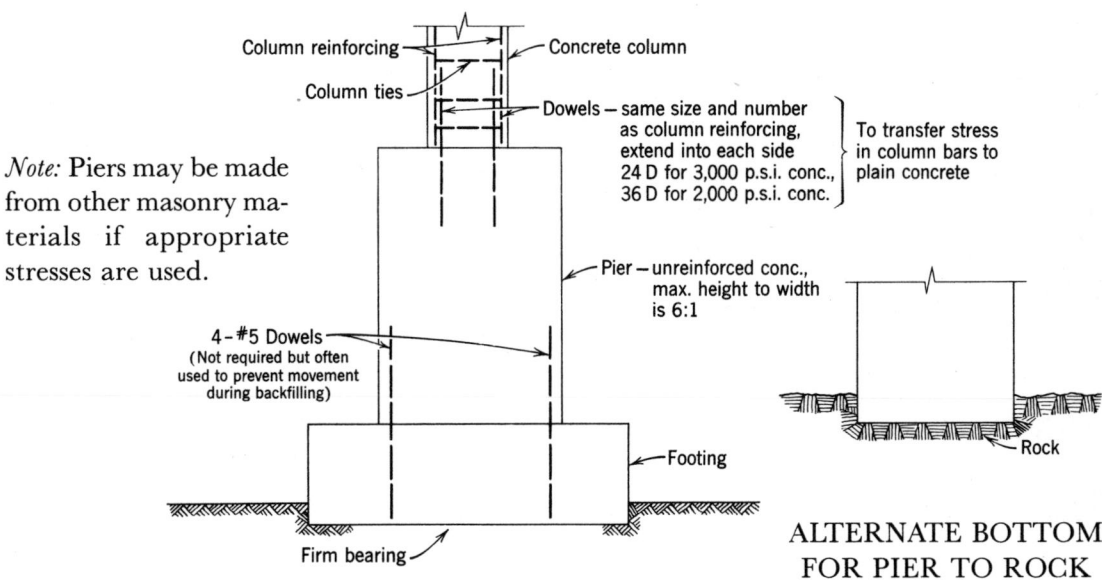

ALTERNATE BOTTOM
FOR PIER TO ROCK

Purpose: To save reinforced concrete.

FIG. 5.   TYPICAL PIER DETAIL.

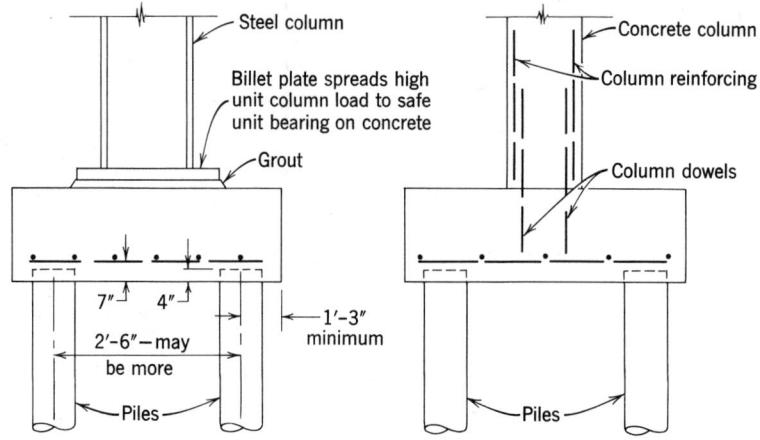

Purpose: To spread the load over a group of piles.

Note: Wall, combined, and pump handle pile caps may be used similar to spread footings.

FIG. 6.   PILE CAPS.

DETAIL *A*
METHODS OF WATERPROOFING

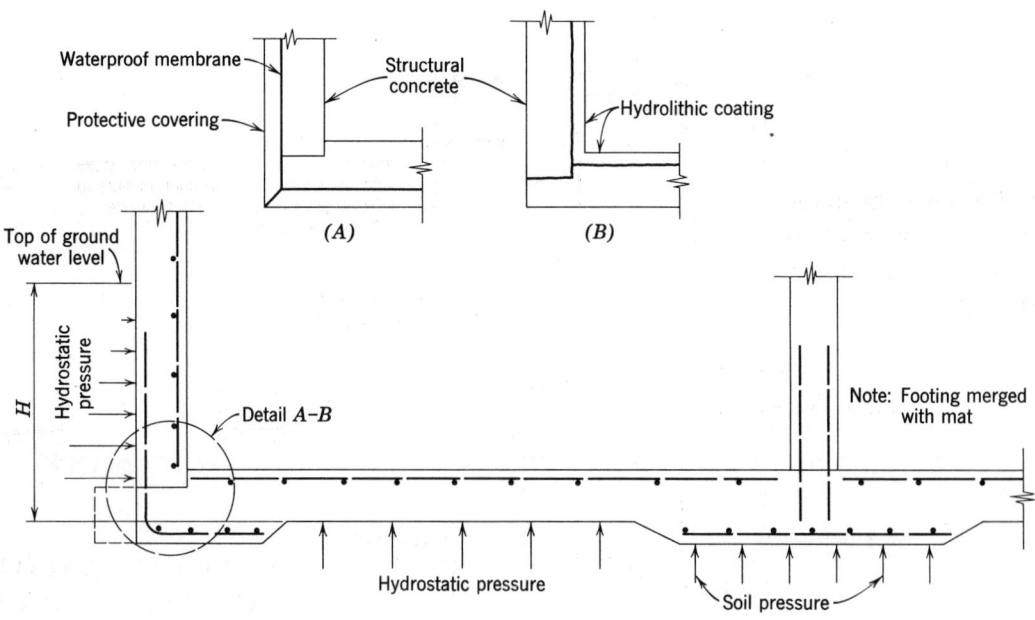

FIG. 7.   MAT FOR HYDRAULIC UPLIFT.

See Chapter 9 for waterproofing details.

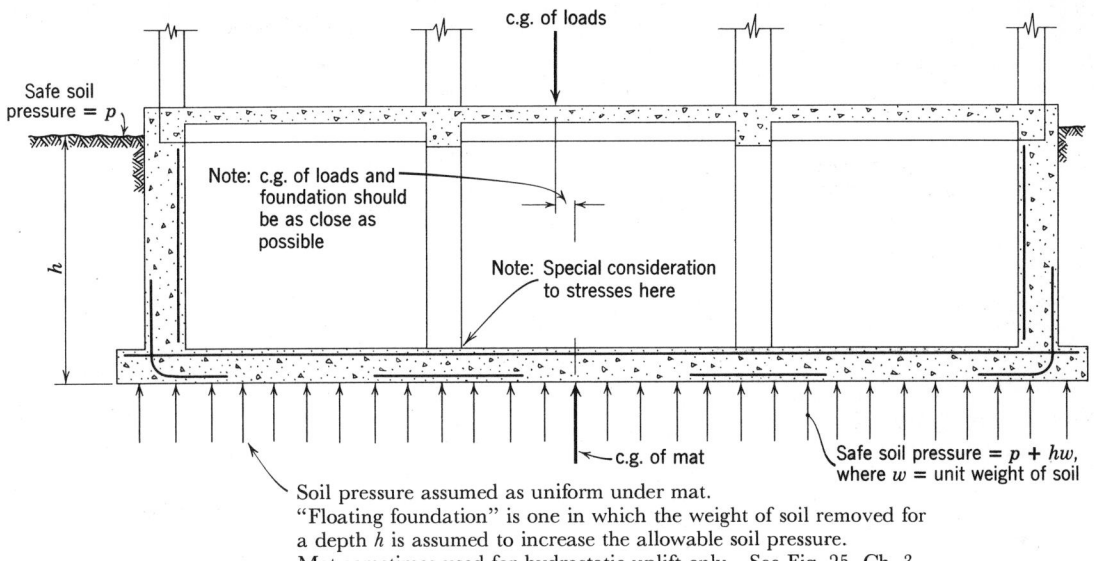

Soil pressure assumed as uniform under mat.
"Floating foundation" is one in which the weight of soil removed for
a depth *h* is assumed to increase the allowable soil pressure.
Mat sometimes used for hydrostatic uplift only. See Fig. 25, Ch. 3.

FIG. 8. MAT FOUNDATION, SOLID SLAB.

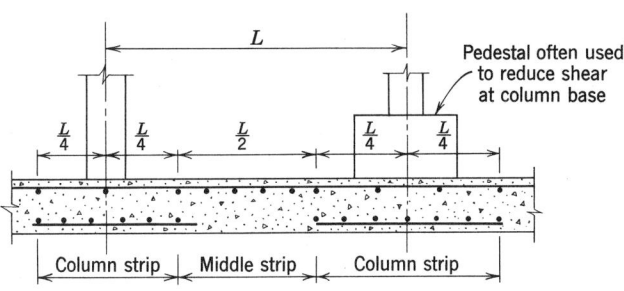

FLAT SLAB

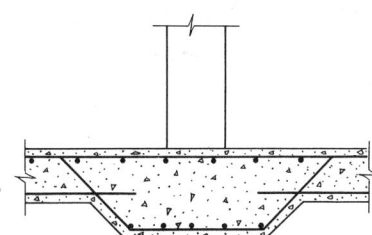

Increased depth may occur at column
base or be a band continuous between
columns.

ALTERNATIVE COLUMN BASE

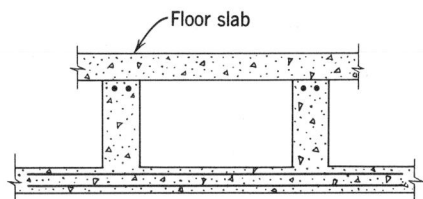

RIBBED SLAB RIBS ABOVE

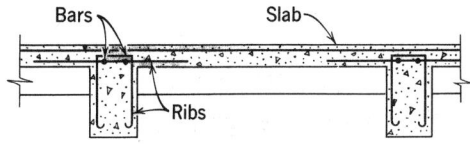

RIBBED SLAB RIBS BELOW

Used on long spans to reduce mat thickness

FIG. 9. TYPES OF MAT CONSTRUCTION.

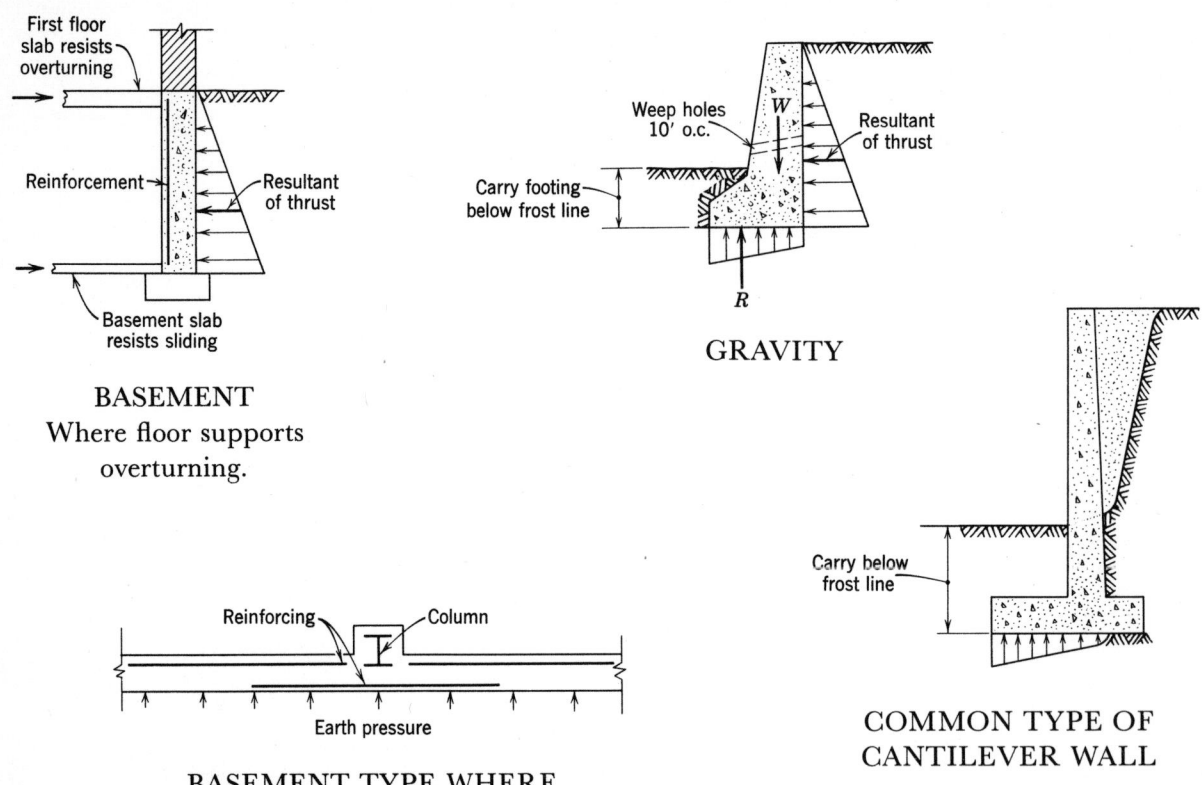

BASENT
Where floor supports
overturning.

GRAVITY

BASEMENT TYPE WHERE
COLUMNS SUPPORT WALL
(Horizontal Section)

COMMON TYPE OF
CANTILEVER WALL

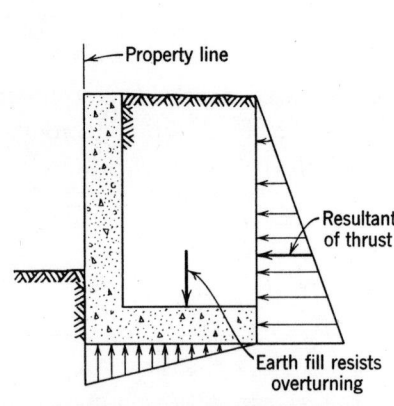

CANTILEVER
Type not to cross property line.

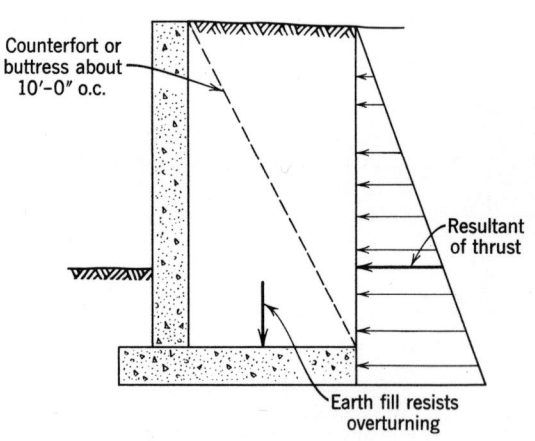

COUNTERFORT
For high walls.

FIG. 10.   TYPES OF RETAINING WALLS.

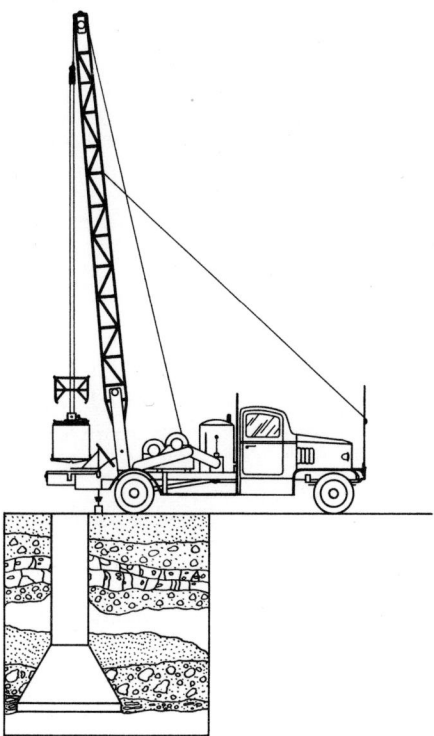

FIG. 11. DRILLED IN FOOTING.

Hole is drilled by earth auger with bell attachment on bottom. Hole shaft up to 2′ 8″ diameter bell to 12′ 0″ diameter. Hole is inspected and filled with concrete. Can be used only where soil will hold shape of hole.

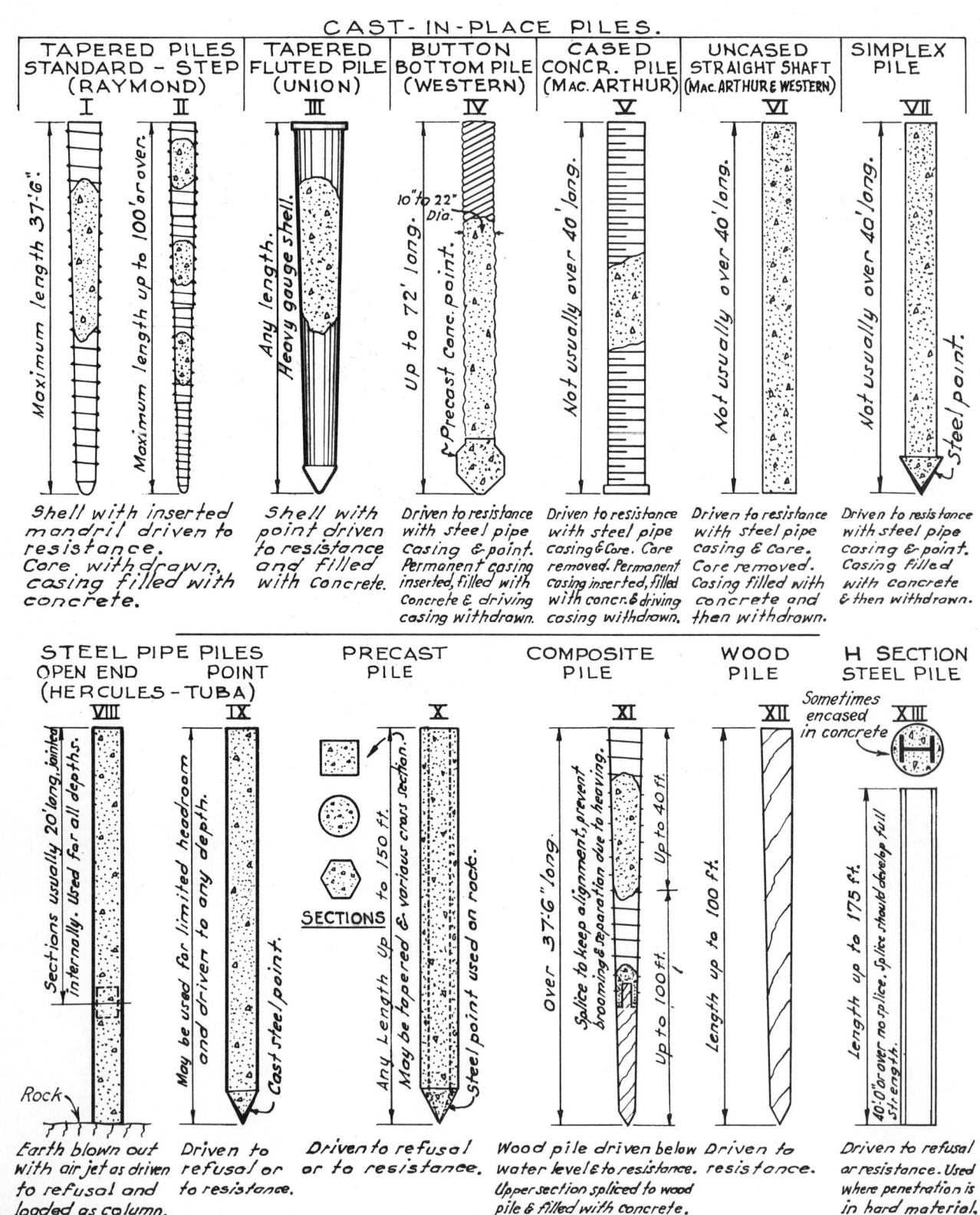

FIG. 12. TYPES OF PILES.

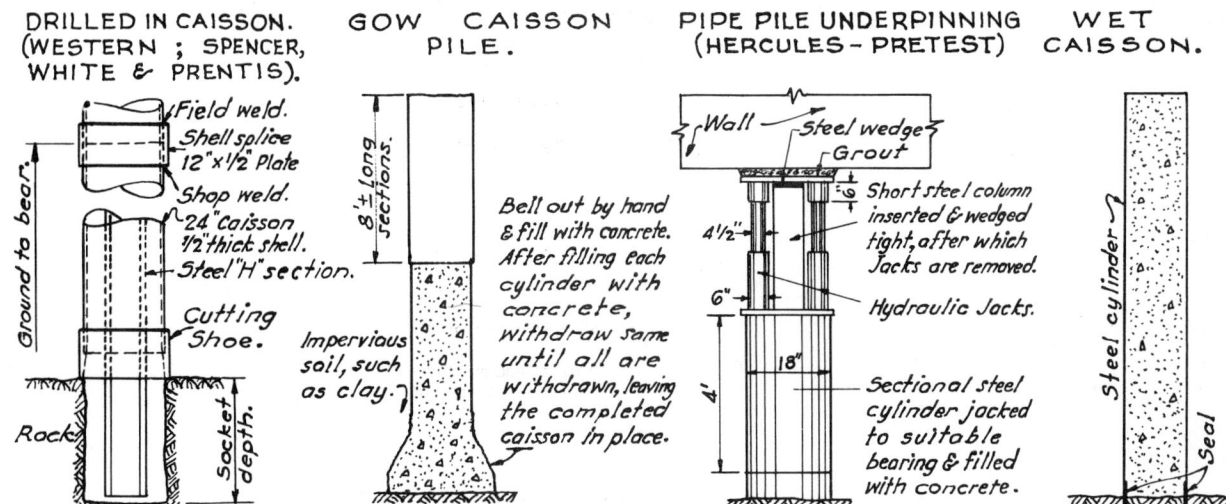

DRILLED IN CAISSON.
(WESTERN ; SPENCER,
WHITE & PRENTIS).

Field weld.
Shell splice
12" x 1/2 Plate
Shop weld.
24" Caisson
1/2" thick shell.
Steel "H" section.
Cutting Shoe.
Ground to bear.
Rock.
Socket depth.

GOW CAISSON
PILE.

8'± Long sections.
Bell out by hand & fill with concrete. After filling each cylinder with concrete, withdraw same until all are withdrawn, leaving the completed caisson in place.
Impervious soil, such as clay.

PIPE PILE UNDERPINNING
(HERCULES – PRETEST)

Wall
Steel wedge
Grout
Short steel column inserted & wedged tight, after which jacks are removed.
Hydraulic Jacks.
Sectional steel cylinder jacked to suitable bearing & filled with concrete.
4 1/2"
6"
18"
4'

WET
CAISSON.

Steel cylinder
Seal

Shell driven to rock, cleaned out. Rock socket is drilled, core inserted & shell filled with concrete.

Excavate shallow pit by hand & place top cylinder in pit. Second cylinder is placed inside the first & repeat process until caisson reaches its full depth.

Cylinder is tested with jacks to an overload capacity.

Steel cylinder sunk to rock as earth is removed. Bottom sealed, water removed and filled with concrete.

PILE NO. *	NOTES
I, II, III, V, XI	Precautions are required to prevent collapsing of shell when driving adjoining piles.
VI, VII	With uncased piles, precautions should be taken to prevent damage due to driving adjoining piles because pile has no sheet casing around it.
IV, V	When shell is inserted inside driving casing and casing withdrawn, soil must be relied upon to grip pile as firmly as if it had been driven without casing.
VIII	Concrete steel pipe piles sometimes driven open ended to predetermined depth and filled with concrete. After concrete has set pile is driven to required resistance. This is done so as not to disturb adjoining wall and foundation and also when driving cast-in-place piles to prevent heaving.
X	Precast piles are used for marine structure, require heavy handling equipment.
XI, XII	Cut off untreated wood pile below permanent water level. Creosoted wood piles used with cut off above permanent water level for 50 year life. Precautions against overdriving should be taken. Vulnerable to marine borers if not treated with creosote.
I TO IX	The piles have less give under hammer than a pile of more flexible material such as wood or concrete and consequently if driven to the same resistance have a greater safety factor.
XIII	Steel H sections should not be used through cinders, ash fill or normally active rust producing material without adequate protection.
CAISSONS	These are usually used when sinking foundation to considerable depths with heavy loads. This is done by wood sheeting, steel sheeting and steel cylinders. In case of water condition, operations carried on under compressed air.

FIG. 13. TYPES OF PILES.

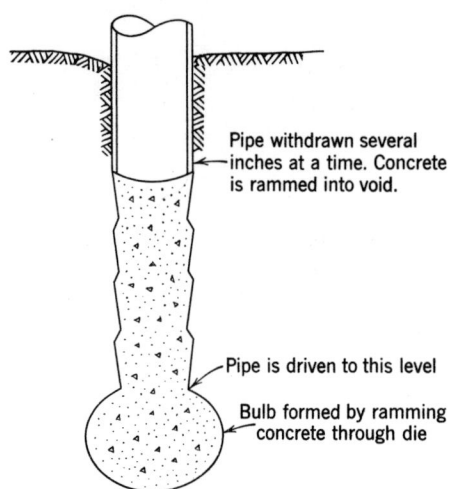

Pipe withdrawn several inches at a time. Concrete is rammed into void.

Pipe is driven to this level

Bulb formed by ramming concrete through die

FIG. 14.   FRANKI DISPLACEMENT CAISSON.

SOILS

Homogeneous Soils

Gravels. Good bearing, low compressibility. Good foundation. Will not soften under wheel action when wet. Good for stabilizing roads. Will not flow into adjoining excavation below ground water or upward from the bottom of an excavation below ground water. Not subject to mud waves, frost heaving, or to shelving of banks. Fast draining.

Fine Sands. Finer grades are called silts. Good foundations if confined so that water will not flow out when compressed. Bearing subject to squeezing out of water, permitting rapid limited settlement. Subject to capillary flow and frost heave. Will soften under wheel action when wet. Will flow into excavation below ground water and undermine adjoining foundations or will flow upward from the bottom of excavations acting like quicksand and causing boils. Not subject to mud waves or to shelving of banks. Slow draining.

Coarse and Medium Sands. Behavior properties lie between those of the gravels and those of the fine sand and silts.

Organic Silts. (Black mud and peats.) High compressibility. Completely unreliable. Will soften under wheel action when wet. Subject to mud waves, squeezing out from under a footing, shelving banks, and frost heaves. Very slow draining. Never use for building foundations.

Clays. As the finer sand grains are classified as silt, so the finer grains (submicroscopic) are classified as clays. Finer grains are more subject to water, having in their interstices free water and fixed water. Fixed water consists of molecules of water bonded to the surfaces of the particles of clay by polarization.

Shearing strength is called cohesion. If the loading conditions cause a shearing stress greater than the cohesive strength, the clays tend to flow. Since clays are very slow-draining, they are subject to long-term settlement from the squeezing out of water. They are subject to frost heave and capillary action.

Excavations can be carried below the water line as clays will not boil (become quick). Clays will soften under wheel action when wet but will resolidify rapidly. Banks will shelve if too much shearing stress is developed. Higher banks need flatter slopes.

Soil Mixtures

Hardpan. A mixture of gravel with clay as a cement. Excellent foundation material; acts like a soft rock.

Loam. A mixture of sand and clay (common dirt) which may contain some organic material. Will soften under action of wheels when wet. Subject to frost heave. An excellent binder for gravel pavements. Not recognized in codes as a foundation material but satisfactory for about 2 tons per square foot if reasonably free from organic matter. Drains well.

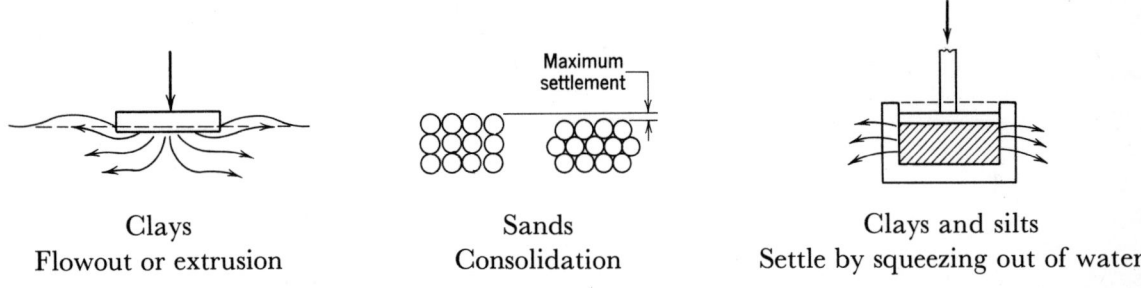

Clays
Flowout or extrusion

Sands
Consolidation

Clays and silts
Settle by squeezing out of water

FIG. 15.   CAUSES OF SETTLEMENT.

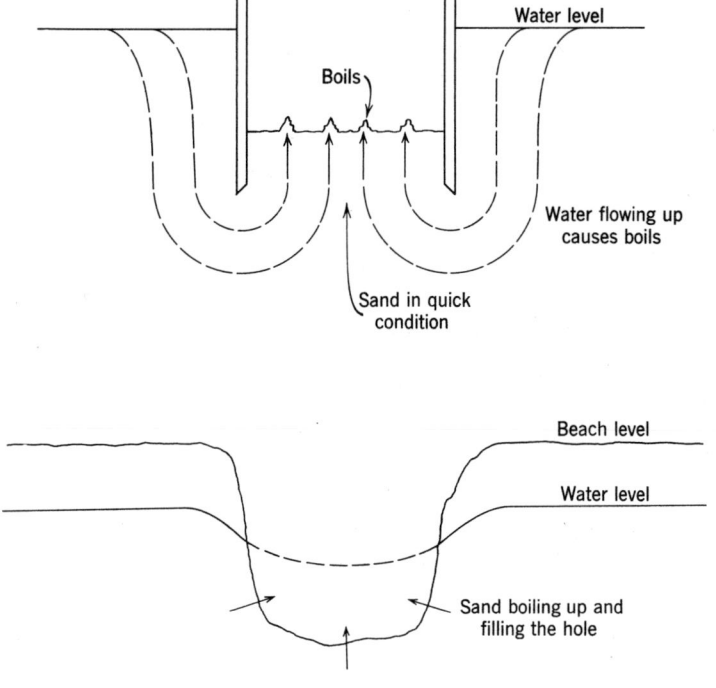

FIG. 16.   CAUSES OF QUICKSAND.

2

Push-Button Design of Spread
Footings and Pile Caps

When the designer has the following data: (*a*) column loads; (*b*) safe bearing capacity of soil or type of pile and safe load for piles, he can read off his typical square footing from the following tables.

SQUARE COLUMN FOOTINGS*

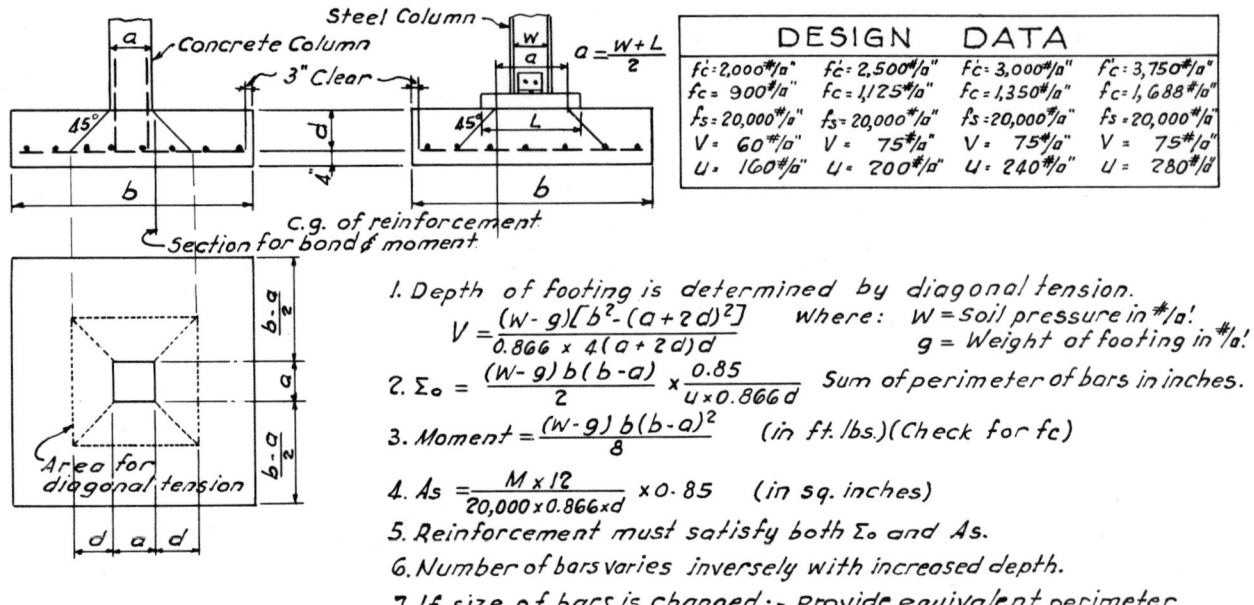

DESIGN DATA

$f'c = 2,000 \#/□''$	$f'c = 2,500 \#/□''$	$f'c = 3,000 \#/□''$	$f'c = 3,750 \#/□''$
$fc = 900 \#/□''$	$fc = 1,125 \#/□''$	$fc = 1,350 \#/□''$	$fc = 1,688 \#/□''$
$fs = 20,000 \#/□''$	$fs = 20,000 \#/□''$	$fs = 20,000 \#/□''$	$fs = 20,000 \#/□''$
$V = 60 \#/□''$	$V = 75 \#/□''$	$V = 75 \#/□''$	$V = 75 \#/□''$
$U = 160 \#/□''$	$U = 200 \#/□''$	$U = 240 \#/□''$	$U = 280 \#/□''$

1. Depth of footing is determined by diagonal tension.
$$V = \frac{(W-g)[b^2 - (a+2d)^2]}{0.866 \times 4(a+2d)d} \qquad \text{Where:} \quad \begin{array}{l} W = \text{Soil pressure in } \#/□'\\ g = \text{Weight of footing in } \#/□' \end{array}$$

2. $\Sigma_0 = \dfrac{(W-g)b(b-a)}{2} \times \dfrac{0.85}{U \times 0.866d}$ Sum of perimeter of bars in inches.

3. Moment $= \dfrac{(W-g)b(b-a)^2}{8}$ (in ft. lbs.)(Check for fc)

4. As $= \dfrac{M \times 12}{20,000 \times 0.866 \times d} \times 0.85$ (in sq. inches)

5. Reinforcement must satisfy both Σ_0 and As.

6. Number of bars varies inversely with increased depth.

7. If size of bars is changed:- Provide equivalent perimeter when larger bars are used; and equivalent area when smaller bars are used.

TABLE I - SOIL BEARING VALUE. 2,000 LB. PER SQ. FT.

COLUMN LOAD IN 1000 LB	b	d (IN.)	$f'c=2,000 \#/□''$ MIN. a (IN.)	REINF. EACH WAY	$f'c=2,500 \#/□''$ MIN. a (IN.)	REINF. EACH WAY	$f'c=3,000 \#/□''$ MIN. a (IN.)	REINF. EACH WAY	$f'c=3,750 \#/□''$ MIN. a (IN.)	REINF. EACH WAY
29	4'-0"	12	9	5-#3	9	5-#3	9	5-#3	9	5-#3
45	5'-0"	12	9	9-#3	9	6-#4	9	6-#4	9	6-#4
65	6'-0"	12	9	10-#4	9	7-#5	9	7-#5	9	7-#5
89	7'-0"	12	10	10-#5	9	10-#5	9	10-#5	9	10-#5
114	8'-0"	13	11	10-#6	10	10-#6	10	10-#6	9	10-#6
143	9'-0"	15	11	12-#6	10	12-#6	10	9-#7	10	9-#7
174	10'-0"	17	12	10-#7	11	8-#8	11	8-#8	10	8-#8
208	11'-0"	18	13	10-#8	12	8-#9	11	8-#9	11	8-#9
245	12'-0"	20	14	15-#7	13	9-#9	13	9-#9	12	9-#9
283	13'-0"	22	14	11-#9	13	11-#9	13	13-#8	13	13-#8
324	14'-0"	24	14	12-#9	14	12-#9	14	12-#9	13	12-#9
369	15'-0"	25	16	11-#10	15	11-#10	15	11-#10	14	11-#10
416	16'-0"	27	16	12-#10	15	12-#10	15	12-#10	14	12-#10

TABLE II - SOIL BEARING VALUE. 3,000 LB. PER SQ. FT.

COLUMN LOAD IN 1000 LB	b	d (IN.)	$f'c=2,000 \#/□''$ MIN. a (IN.)	REINF. EACH WAY	$f'c=2,500 \#/□''$ MIN. a (IN.)	REINF. EACH WAY	$f'c=3,000 \#/□''$ MIN. a (IN.)	REINF. EACH WAY	$f'c=3,750 \#/□''$ MIN. a (IN.)	REINF. EACH WAY
45	4'-0"	12	9	8-#3	9	5-#4	9	5-#4	9	5-#4
70	5'-0"	12	9	10-#4	9	8-#4	9	8-#4	9	8-#4
101	6'-0"	12	10	14-#4	9	10-#5	9	7-#6	9	7-#6
136	7'-0"	14	11	13-#5	10	9-#6	10	7-#7	9	7-#7
176	8'-0"	16	12	16-#5	11	9-#7	11	7-#8	10	7-#8
221	9'-0"	18	13	14-#6	12	11-#7	11	7-#9	11	7-#9
270	10'-0"	20	14	13-#7	13	10-#8	12	8-#9	11	8-#9
324	11'-0"	22	16	15-#7	15	12-#8	14	8-#10	13	8-#10
382	12'-0"	24	17	14-#8	16	11-#9	15	9-#10	13	9-#10
444	13'-0"	26	18	13-#9	16	13-#9	15	11-#10	14	11-#10
510	14'-0"	28	18	12-#10	17	10-#11	16	10-#11	15	10-#11
580	15'-0"	30	20	13-#10	19	11-#11	18	11-#11	17	11-#11
654	16'-0"	32	21	15-#10	20	12-#11	19	15-#10	17	13-#11

*Based on A.C.I. Code, 1951.
Hooks not required.

SQUARE COLUMN FOOTINGS*

TABLE III - SOIL BEARING VALUE 4,000 LB. PER SQ. FT.

COLUMN LOAD IN 1000LB.	b	d (IN.)	$f'_c=2,000$ MIN. a (IN.)	REINF. EACH WAY	$f'_c=2,500$ MIN. a (IN.)	REINF. EACH WAY	$f'_c=3,000$ MIN. a (IN.)	REINF. EACH WAY	$f'_c=3,750$ MIN. a (IN.)	REINF. EACH WAY
34.2	3'0"	12	9	6-#3	9	5-#3	9	4-#3	9	4-#3
46.5	3'6"	12	9	8-#3	9	5-#4	9	4-#4	9	4-#4
60.8	4'0"	12	9	8-#4	9	9-#3	9	6-#4	9	5-#4
77	4'6"	12	10	10-#4	9	9-#4	9	7-#4	9	5-#5
95	5'0"	12	10	13-#4	9	11-#4	9	7-#5	9	7-#5
115	5'6"	12	11	16-#4	10	10-#5	10	7-#6	9	7-#6
136	6'0"	13	11	18-#4	10	12-#5	10	8-#6	9	7-#7
159	6'6"	14	12	15-#5	11	10-#6	10	8-#7	10	7-#7
184	7'0"	16	12	15-#5	11	11-#6	11	8-#7	10	6-#8
211	7'6"	17	12	17-#5	12	12-#6	12	7-#8	11	7-#8
240	8'0"	18	14	19-#5	13	10-#7	13	8-#8	12	6-#9
268	8'6"	19	14	16-#6	13	11-#7	13	7-#9	12	7-#9
300	9'0"	20	14	17-#6	14	10-#8	14	8-#9	13	8-#9
335	9'6"	22	16	18-#6	15	10-#8	14	8-#9	13	7-#10
369	10'0"	23	16	15-#7	15	12-#8	15	9-#9	14	9-#9
405	10'6"	24	16	14-#8	15	10-#9	15	8-#10	14	8-#10
443	11'0"	25	18	18-#7	16	11-#9	15	9-#10	14	9-#10
484	11'6"	27	18	15-#8	17	12-#9	15	9-#10	15	12-#9
524	12'0"	28	18	16-#8	17	10-#10	16	10-#10	15	9-#11
610	13'0"	30	20	15-#9	18	10-#11	17	10-#11	16	10-#11
700	14'0"	32	22	17-#9	20	11-#11	19	14-#10	17	12-#11
795	15'0"	34	23	16-#10	21	13-#11	20	13-#11	18	14-#11
900	16'0"	36	25	15-#11	23	15-#11	22	15-#11	20	15-#11

TABLE IV - SOIL BEARING VALUE 5,000 LB. PER SQ. FT.

COLUMN LOAD IN 1000LB.	b	d (IN.)	$f'_c=2,000$ MIN. a (IN.)	REINF. EACH WAY	$f'_c=2,500$ MIN. a (IN.)	REINF. EACH WAY	$f'_c=3,000$ MIN. a (IN.)	REINF. EACH WAY	$f'_c=3,750$ MIN. a (IN.)	REINF. EACH WAY
43.5	3'0"	12	9	7-#3	9	6-#3	9	5-#3	9	4-#3
59	3'6"	12	9	10-#3	9	8-#3	9	5-#4	9	5-#4
77	4'0"	12	10	13-#3	9	8-#4	9	7-#4	9	5-#5
97	4'6"	12	10	17-#3	9	11-#4	9	7-#5	9	6-#5
120	5'0"	12	11	16-#4	10	13-#4	10	7-#6	9	7-#6
145	5'6"	13	11	18-#4	10	12-#5	10	8-#6	10	6-#7
172	6'0"	14	12	20-#4	11	13-#5	11	9-#6	10	7-#7
202	6'6"	16	13	21-#4	12	14-#5	11	8-#7	10	6-#8
232	7'0"	17	13	18-#5	12	12-#6	12	9-#7	11	7-#8
266	7'6"	19	14	19-#5	13	13-#6	12	10-#7	12	6-#9
301	8'0"	20	15	21-#5	14	12-#7	14	11-#7	13	7-#9
340	8'6"	21	16	23-#5	15	12-#7	14	8-#9	13	8-#9
380	9'0"	22	17	19-#6	16	14-#7	15	9-#9	14	7-#10
420	9'6"	24	17	20-#6	16	15-#7	15	9-#9	14	8-#10
464	10'0"	25	18	22-#6	17	13-#8	16	10-#9	14	11-#9
520	10'6"	26	19	19-#7	17	14-#8	16	9-#10	15	8-#11
560	11'0"	27	19	21-#7	18	13-#9	17	10-#10	16	10-#10
610	11'6"	28	21	22-#7	19	14-#9	18	9-#11	17	9-#11
661	12'0"	29	21	19-#8	20	12-#10	19	10-#11	17	10-#11
770	13'0"	31	22	22-#8	21	14-#10	20	14-#10	18	12-#11
890	14'0"	33	26	20-#9	24	13-#11	22	14-#11	20	14-#11
1015	15'0"	35	27	23-#9	25	15-#11	23	16-#11	21	16-#11
1150	16'0"	37	28	21-#10	26	18-#11	24	18-#11	22	18-#11

*Based on A.C.I. Code, 1951.
Hooks not required.

SQUARE COLUMN FOOTINGS*

TABLE V – SOIL BEARING VALUE. 6,000 LB. PER SQ. FT.

COLUMN LOAD IN 1000LB.	b (IN.)	d (IN.)	f'c=2,000#/□"		f'c=2,500#/□"		f'c=3,000#/□"		f'c=3,750#/□"	
			MIN a (IN.)	REINF. EACH WAY	MIN a (IN.)	REINF. EACH WAY	MIN a (IN.)	REINF. EACH WAY	MIN a (IN.)	REINF. EACH WAY
52	3'-0	12	9	9-#3	9	5-#4	9	6-#3	9	5-#3
71	3'-6	12	9	12-#3	9	10-#3	9	6-#4	9	6-#4
93	4'-0	12	10	12-#4	9	10-#4	9	8-#4	9	8-#4
118	4'-6	12	11	15-#4	10	13-#4	10	8-#5	9	6-#6
145	5'-0	13	11	18-#4	10	15-#4	10	10-#5	10	7-#6
175	5'-6	14	12	20-#4	11	13-#5	11	11-#5	10	7-#7
208	6'-0	15	13	18-#5	12	15-#5	11	10-#6	11	8-#7
245	6'-6	17	14	23-#4	13	16-#5	12	11-#6	11	7-#8
281	7'-0	18	15	20-#5	14	14-#6	13	10-#7	13	10-#7
322	7'-6	20	16	20-#5	15	14-#6	14	11-#7	13	7-#9
365	8'-0	21	16	24-#5	15	13-#7	14	10-#8	14	8-#9
410	8'-6	22	17	20-#6	16	14-#7	15	9-#9	14	7-#10
460	9'-0	23	18	21-#6	17	13-#8	16	12-#8	15	8-#10
510	9'-6	25	18	23-#6	17	14-#8	16	13-#8	15	7-#11
563	10'-0	26	20	25-#6	18	15-#8	17	12-#9	15	8-#11
620	10'-6	27	21	21-#7	19	16-#8	18	10-#10	17	9-#11
680	11'-0	28	21	23-#7	20	14-#9	19	10-#11	17	10-#11
740	11'-6	29	22	25-#7	20	16-#9	19	10-#11	18	11-#11
805	12'-0	30	23	22-#8	21	17-#9	20	11-#11	18	12-#11
940	13'-0	33	23	24-#8	23	16-#10	22	13-#11	20	13-#11
1080	14'-0	36	26	22-#9	24	15-#11	23	15-#11	21	15-#11
1230	15'-0	38	29	25-#9	27	20-#10	25	17-#11	23	17-#11
1400	16'-0	40	30	23-#10	28	19-#11	26	20-#11	24	20-#11

TABLE VI – SOIL BEARING VALUE. 8,000 LB. PER SQ. FT.

COLUMN LOAD IN 1000LB.	b (IN.)	d (IN.)	f'c=2,000#/□"		f'c=2,500#/□"		f'c=3,000#/□"		f'c=3,750#/□"	
			MIN a (IN.)	REINF. EACH WAY	MIN a (IN.)	REINF. EACH WAY	MIN a (IN.)	REINF. EACH WAY	MIN a (IN.)	REINF. EACH WAY
70	3'-0	12	9	9-#4	9	9-#3	9	6-#4	9	5-#4
96	3'-6	12	10	12-#4	9	13-#3	9	8-#4	9	7-#4
125	4'-0	12	11	16-#4	10	13-#4	10	11-#4	9	10-#4
158	4'-6	12	12	20-#4	11	16-#4	10	11-#5	10	10-#5
194	5'-0	14	12	22-#4	11	18-#4	11	12-#5	10	9-#6
235	5'-6	15	13	20-#5	12	16-#5	12	14-#5	11	8-#7
280	6'-0	17	14	21-#5	13	17-#5	12	12-#6	11	9-#7
327	6'-6	18	16	23-#5	15	18-#5	14	13-#6	13	10-#7
378	7'-0	19	17	25-#5	16	17-#6	15	12-#7	13	10-#8
432	7'-6	21	17	26-#5	16	18-#6	15	13-#7	14	9-#9
492	8'-0	22	18	28-#5	17	16-#7	16	12-#8	15	12-#8
553	8'-6	24	19	31-#5	18	17-#7	17	13-#8	15	11-#9
620	9'-0	25	21	26-#6	19	18-#7	18	12-#9	17	9-#10
690	9'-6	26	22	28-#6	20	21-#7	19	13-#9	18	13-#9
760	10'-0	28	22	24-#7	20	18-#8	19	14-#9	18	10-#11
835	10'-6	29	23	26-#7	21	20-#8	20	16-#9	19	10-#11
915	11'-0	30	26	27-#7	24	17-#9	23	13-#10	21	11-#11
1000	11'-6	32	27	28-#7	25	18-#9	23	12-#11	22	12-#11
1090	12'-0	33	28	31-#7	26	19-#9	24	13-#11	22	13-#11
1270	13'-0	36	29	28-#8	27	18-#10	25	15-#11	23	16-#11
1460	14'-0	39	30	27-#9	28	17-#11	26	18-#11	24	18-#11
1670	15'-0	42	32	30-#9	30	20-#11	28	20-#11	26	21-#11
1900	16'-0	44	34	27-#10	31	23-#11	29	23-#11	27	24-#11

*Based on A.C.I. Code, 1951.
Hooks not required.

SQUARE COLUMN FOOTINGS*

TABLE VII - SOIL BEARING VALUE. 12,000 LB. PER SQ. FT.

COLUMN LOAD IN 1000 LB.	b	d (IN.)	$f'_c=2,000\#/\square"$ MIN. a (IN.)	REINF. EACH WAY	$f'_c=2,500\#/\square"$ MIN. a (IN.)	REINF. EACH WAY	$f'_c=3,000\#/\square"$ MIN. a (IN.)	REINF. EACH WAY	$f'_c=3,750\#/\square"$ MIN. a (IN.)	REINF. EACH WAY
106	3'0"	12	10	13-#4	9	11-#4	9	12-#3	9	10-#3
145	3'6"	12	11	14-#5	10	14-#4	10	12-#4	10	10-#4
188	4'0"	12	12	18-#5	11	15-#5	10	16-#4	10	11-#5
240	4'6"	14	13	20-#5	12	17-#5	11	18-#4	11	12-#5
295	5'0"	15	14	23-#5	13	19-#5	13	16-#5	13	14-#5
356	5'6"	17	16	25-#5	15	20-#5	14	18-#5	13	13-#6
423	6'0"	18	17	23-#6	16	23-#5	15	16-#6	14	12-#7
495	6'6"	20	18	25-#6	17	24-#5	16	17-#6	15	13-#7
573	7'0"	21	19	27-#6	18	22-#6	17	16-#7	16	12-#8
657	7'6"	23	21	28-#6	19	23-#6	18	17-#7	17	13-#8
747	8'0"	24	22	31-#6	20	26-#6	19	16-#8	18	13-#9
840	8'6"	26	23	32-#6	21	23-#7	20	17-#8	19	14-#9
940	9'0"	27	26	34-#6	24	24-#7	23	19-#8	21	12-#10
1050	9'6"	28	27	37-#6	25	26-#7	24	17-#9	22	14-#10
1158	10'0"	30	28	38-#6	26	29-#7	24	18-#9	23	12-#11
1275	10'6"	32	29	39-#6	27	24-#8	25	16-#10	23	13-#11
1390	11'0"	33	30	36-#7	28	27-#8	26	22-#9	24	15-#11
1525	11'6"	35	31	37-#7	29	29-#8	27	16-#11	25	16-#11
1657	12'0"	36	32	34-#8	30	25-#9	28	17-#11	26	18-#11
1940	13'0"	40	33	37-#8	31	24-#10	29	20-#11	27	20-#11
2240	14'0"	42	37	42-#8	35	27-#10	33	23-#11	30	24-#11
2560	15'0"	46	39	37-#9	36	25-#11	34	26-#11	32	27-#11
2900	16'0"	48	41	44-#9	38	29-#11	36	30-#11	33	31-#11

TABLE VIII - SOIL BEARING VALUE. 16,000 LB. PER SQ. FT.

COLUMN LOAD IN 1000 LB.	b	d (IN.)	$f'_c=2,000\#/\square"$ MIN. a (IN.)	REINF. EACH WAY	$f'_c=2,500\#/\square"$ MIN. a (IN.)	REINF. EACH WAY	$f'_c=3,000\#/\square"$ MIN. a (IN.)	REINF. EACH WAY	$f'_c=3,750\#/\square"$ MIN. a (IN.)	REINF. EACH WAY
142	3'0"	12	11	13-#5	10	13-#4	10	11-#4	9	10-#4
194	3'6"	14	12	15-#5	11	13-#5	11	13-#4	10	10-#5
252	4'0"	15	14	16-#6	13	15-#5	12	16-#4	11	15-#4
319	4'6"	16	16	18-#6	15	18-#5	14	19-#4	13	14-#5
393	5'0"	18	17	20-#6	16	20-#5	15	17-#5	14	16-#5
475	5'6"	20	18	22-#6	17	22-#5	16	19-#5	15	14-#6
565	6'0"	21	20	25-#6	19	25-#5	18	21-#5	16	16-#6
662	6'6"	23	21	27-#6	20	27-#5	19	19-#6	17	14-#7
765	7'0"	25	23	25-#7	21	29-#5	19	21-#6	19	13-#8
880	7'6"	26	25	27-#7	22	26-#6	20	19-#7	20	15-#8
1000	8'0"	27	27	29-#7	24	29-#6	22	21-#7	21	14-#9
1127	8'6"	28	28	32-#7	26	32-#6	24	20-#8	22	19-#8
1260	9'0"	29	29	35-#7	27	29-#7	25	22-#8	23	18-#9
1405	9'6"	30	30	33-#8	28	31-#7	26	25-#8	24	16-#10
1555	10'0"	32	31	35-#8	29	34-#7	27	22-#9	25	15-#11
1712	10'6"	33	32	37-#8	30	31-#8	28	24-#9	26	16-#11
1880	11'0"	35	33	39-#8	31	32-#8	29	21-#10	27	18-#11
2045	11'6"	37	34	40-#8	32	35-#8	30	23-#10	28	19-#11
2230	12'0"	38	38	37-#9	35	30-#9	33	24-#10	30	21-#11
2615	13'0"	42	40	39-#9	37	34-#9	34	23-#11	32	24-#11
3020	14'0"	45	42	38-#10	39	32-#10	36	27-#11	34	28-#11
3460	15'0"	48	45	41-#10	42	30-#11	39	31-#11	35	33-#11
3930	16'0"	51	48	39-#11	45	33-#11	42	35-#11	37	37-#11

*Based on A.C.I. Code, 1951.
Hooks not required.

PILE FOOTINGS

Designed according to A.C.I. Code, 1951, for special bond bars (A.S.T.M. A305); hooks not required.

Warning: Check overloading of soil on which piles rest.

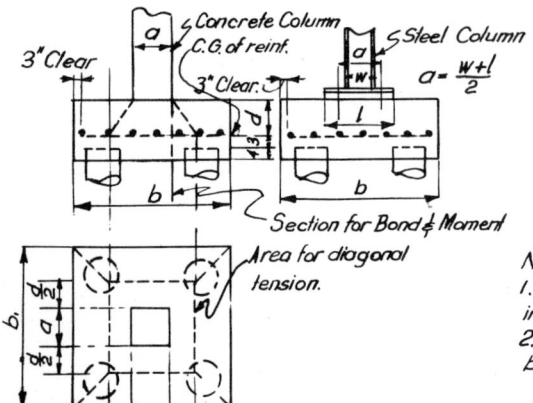

DESIGN DATA			
$f'_c = 2000\#/\square"$	$f'_c = 2500\#/\square"$	$f'_c = 3000\#/\square"$	$f'_c = 3750\#/\square"$
$f_c = 900\#/\square"$	$f_c = 1125\#/\square"$	$f_c = 1350\#/\square"$	$f_c = 1688\#/\square"$
$f_s = 20{,}000\#/\square"$	$f_s = 20{,}000\#/\square"$	$f_s = 20{,}000\#/\square"$	$f_s = 20{,}000\#/\square"$
$v = 60\#/\square"$	$v = 75\#/\square"$	$v = 75\#/\square"$	$v = 75\#/\square"$
$u = 160\#/\square"$	$u = 200\#/\square"$	$u = 240\#/\square"$	$u = 280\#/\square"$

Notes:

1. If depth of pile caps is increased steel perimeter may be decreased in proportion to depth.
2. If size of bars is changed:—Provide equivalent perimeter when larger bars are used, and equivalent area when smaller bars are used.

TABLE IX

NUMBER OF PILES	PLAN	PILE VALUE (Kips)	COLUMN LOAD (Kips)	d (IN)	a (IN)	$f'_c=2000\#/\square"$ LONG WAY	SHORT WAY	a (IN)	$f'_c=2500\#/\square"$ LONG WAY	SHORT WAY	a (IN)	$f'_c=3000\#/\square"$ LONG WAY	SHORT WAY	a (IN)	$f'_c=3750\#/\square"$ LONG WAY	SHORT WAY
1	2'-6" × 2'-6"	20	18.5	12	—	3-#5	3-#5	—	3-#5	3-#5	—	3-#5	3-#5	—	3-#5	3-#5
		30	28.5	12	—	3-#5	3-#5	—	3-#5	3-#5	—	3-#5	3-#5	—	3-#5	3-#5
		40	38.5	12	—	3-#5	3-#5	—	3-#5	3-#5	—	3-#5	3-#5	—	3-#5	3-#5
		50	48.5	12	—	3-#5	3-#5	—	3-#5	3-#5	—	3-#5	3-#5	—	3-#5	3-#5
		60	58.5	12	—	3-#5	3-#5	—	3-#5	3-#5	—	3-#5	3-#5	—	3-#5	3-#5
		80	78.5	12	8	3-#5	3-#5	8	3-#5	3-#5	7	3-#5	3-#5	7	3-#5	3-#5
		100	98.5	12	—	3-#5	3-#5	8	3-#5	3-#5	—	3-#5	3-#5	7	3-#5	3-#5
		120	118.5	12	10	3-#5	3-#5	9	3-#5	3-#5	9	3-#5	3-#5	8	3-#5	3-#5
2	5'-0" × 2'-6"	20	37	12	7	6-#4	7-#4	7	3-#6	7-#4	7	3-#6	7-#4	7	3-#6	7-#4
		30	57	15	7	7-#4	7-#4	7	5-#5	7-#4	7	3-#6	7-#4	7	3-#6	7-#4
		40	76	17	9	8-#4	7-#4	9	7-#4	7-#4	9	3-#7	7-#4	9	3-#7	7-#4
		50	96	19	9	9-#4	4-#5	9	8-#4	4-#5	9	5-#5	4-#5	9	3-#7	4-#5
		60	116	20	10	10-#4	4-#5	10	9-#4	4-#5	9	6-#5	4-#5	9	4-#6	4-#5
		80	156	21	11	8-#7	4-#5	11	9-#5	4-#5	10	10-#4	4-#5	10	9-#4	4-#5
		100	195	21	12	9-#8	4-#5	11	10-#6	4-#5	11	10-#5	4-#5	10	7-#6	4-#5
		120	235	22	14	9-#9	4-#5	13	10-#7	4-#5	12	9-#6	4-#5	12	10-#5	4-#5
3	5'-5" × 4'-8"	20	54	15	8	3 Bands of 4-#4		8	3 Bands of 3-#4		7	3 Bands of 2-#5		7	3 Bands of 2-#5	
		30	83	17	9	" " " 5-#4		9	" " " 4-#4		9	" " " 2-#6		9	" " " 2-#6	
		40	113	19	10	" " " 6-#4		10	" " " 5-#4		9	" " 3-#5		9	" " 2-#7	
		50	143	20	11	" " " 7-#4		11	" " 6-#4		10	" " 3-#6		9	" " 2-#7	
		60	172	21	12	" " 6-#5		11	" " 6-#4		10	" " 4-#5		10	" " 3-#6	
		80	234	19	13	" " 9-#6		12	" " 9-#5		11	" " 8-#5		11	" " 9-#4	
		100	293	22	14	" " 9-#6		13	" " 9-#5		12	" " 8-#5		11	" " 9-#4	
		120	353	23	16	" " 9-#6		15	" " 9-#5		14	" " 8-#5		13	" " 9-#4	
4	5'-0" × 5'-0"	20	72	14	8	10-#4	10-#4	8	9-#4	9-#4	8	7-#4	7-#4	8	5-#5	5-#5
		30	112	15	10	15-#4	15-#4	10	12-#4	12-#4	9	10-#4	10-#4	9	7-#5	7-#5
		40	152	16	12	19-#4	19-#4	11	15-#4	15-#4	10	13-#4	13-#4	9	7-#6	7-#6
		50	192	17	12	18-#5	18-#5	12	18-#4	18-#4	11	15-#4	15-#4	10	10-#5	10-#5
		60	232	18	13	16-#6	16-#6	13	17-#5	17-#5	12	17-#4	17-#4	12	12-#5	12-#5
		80	312	18	15	19-#7	19-#7	15	21-#5	21-#5	14	22-#4	22-#4	13	19-#4	19-#4
		100	392	19	17	18-#9	18-#9	15	18-#7	18-#7	15	21-#5	21-#5	14	18-#5	18-#5
		120	472	20	18	16-#11	16-#11	16	18-#8	18-#8	15	17-#7	17-#7	14	21-#5	21-#5

PILE FOOTINGS*

Plan dimensions:
- **5 piles:** 6'-2" × 6'-2"; spacing 1'-3, 1'-10, 1'-10, 1'-3
- **6 piles:** 7'-6" × 5'-0"; spacing 1'-3, 2@2'-6, 1'-3
- **7 piles:** 7'-11" × 6'-10"; spacing 1'-5½, 4@1'-3, 1'-5½
- **8 piles:** 7'-6" × 6'-10"; spacing 1'-3, 4@1'-3, 1'-3
- **9 piles:** 7'-6" × 7'-6"; spacing 1'-3, 2'-6, 2'-6, 1'-3
- **10 piles:** 10'-5" × 6'-10"; spacing 1'-5½, 6@1'-3, 1'-5½

No. of Piles	Pile Value kips	Column Load kips	d In.	a In. (2000)	Long Way (2000)	Short Way (2000)	a In. (2500)	Long Way (2500)	Short Way (2500)	a In. (3000)	Long Way (3000)	Short Way (3000)	a In. (3750)	Long Way (3750)	Short Way (3750)
5	20	90	15	10	10-#4	10-#4	10	7-#5	7-#5	9	7-#5	7-#5	9	7-#5	7-#5
	30	137	18	11	13-#4	13-#4	11	8-#5	8-#5	10	6-#6	6-#6	10	6-#6	6-#6
	40	186	21	13	14-#4	14-#4	12	9-#5	9-#5	11	7-#6	7-#6	10	5-#7	5-#7
	50	235	22	13	13-#5	13-#5	13	11-#5	11-#5	12	8-#6	8-#6	11	6-#7	6-#7
	60	284	24	14	15-#5	15-#5	14	12-#5	12-#5	14	7-#7	7-#7	12	6-#7	6-#7
	80	385	24	17	25-#4	25-#4	16	16-#5	16-#5	14	11-#6	11-#6	14	8-#7	8-#7
	100	485	25	18	20-#6	20-#6	17	19-#5	19-#5	16	14-#6	14-#6	14	10-#7	10-#7
	120	584	26	19	23-#6	23-#6	18	22-#5	22-#5	17	19-#5	19-#5	15	12-#7	12-#7
6	20	106	22	10	5-#6	10-#4	10	5-#6	8-#4	9	5-#6	7-#4	8	5-#6	6-#4
	30	164	27	12	6-#6	12-#4	11	4-#7	10-#4	10	4-#7	8-#4	10	4-#7	7-#4
	40	222	32	14	6-#6	14-#4	13	6-#6	11-#4	12	5-#7	9-#4	11	5-#7	8-#4
	50	280	35	14	7-#6	16-#4	14	5-#7	13-#4	13	5-#7	11-#4	13	4-#8	9-#4
	60	338	36	16	8-#6	15-#5	16	6-#7	15-#4	15	6-#7	13-#4	14	4-#9	11-#4
	80	459	38	18	11-#6	23-#4	16	7-#7	19-#4	15	6-#8	16-#4	14	4-#10	14-#4
	100	578	40	19	12-#6	26-#4	18	11-#6	22-#4	17	7-#8	19-#4	15	4-#11	16-#4
	120	698	39	22	19-#5	29-#4	20	13-#6	25-#4	19	10-#7	23-#4	17	7-#9	20-#4
7	20	122	21	11	10-#4	6-#5	11	9-#4	6-#5	10	6-#5	6-#5	9	5-#6	6-#5
	30	188	27	13	12-#4	7-#5	13	10-#4	7-#5	12	7-#5	7-#5	11	5-#6	7-#5
	40	255	29	14	15-#4	8-#5	14	12-#4	8-#5	14	8-#5	6-#6	13	6-#6	6-#6
	50	325	31	15	18-#4	10-#5	15	15-#4	9-#5	15	10-#5	6-#6	14	7-#6	7-#6
	60	393	32	16	16-#5	11-#5	16	17-#4	10-#5	16	11-#5	7-#6	15	8-#6	7-#6
	80	534	32	19	22-#5	20-#4	17	22-#4	10-#6	16	15-#5	7-#7	15	10-#6	7-#6
	100	674	32	21	18-#7	23-#4	20	18-#5	16-#5	19	19-#5	11-#6	17	17-#5	7-#8
	120	812	34	23	17-#8	26-#4	21	19-#6	17-#5	20	20-#5	12-#6	18	18-#5	10-#7
8	20	142	21	11	8-#5	8-#5	11	6-#6	6-#6	10	6-#6	6-#6	9	6-#6	6-#6
	30	220	24	13	11-#5	11-#5	13	8-#6	8-#6	12	6-#7	6-#7	11	6-#7	6-#7
	40	298	27	14	13-#5	13-#5	14	9-#6	9-#6	13	7-#7	7-#7	12	7-#7	7-#7
	50	375	30	16	15-#5	15-#5	16	10-#6	10-#6	15	7-#7	7-#7	14	6-#8	6-#8
	60	455	32	18	17-#5	17-#5	18	15-#5	15-#5	17	8-#7	8-#7	16	6-#8	6-#8
	80	615	32	20	27-#4	29-#4	18	18-#5	19-#5	17	13-#6	11-#7	16	11-#7	11-#7
	100	774	33	22	26-#5	34-#4	21	21-#5	22-#5	20	15-#6	16-#6	18	12-#7	10-#8
	120	934	33	26	29-#5	33-#5	24	24-#5	26-#5	22	17-#6	18-#6	21	13-#7	14-#7
9	20	160	21	12	7-#6	7-#6	11	7-#6	7-#6	10	6-#7	6-#7	9	6-#7	6-#7
	30	246	27	14	8-#6	8-#6	13	6-#7	6-#7	12	6-#7	6-#7	11	6-#7	6-#7
	40	333	31	16	8-#7	8-#7	15	7-#7	7-#7	14	7-#7	7-#7	13	7-#7	7-#7
	50	421	34	18	14-#5	14-#5	17	8-#7	8-#7	16	6-#8	6-#8	15	6-#8	6-#8
	60	509	36	20	15-#5	15-#5	19	11-#6	11-#6	18	8-#7	8-#7	17	7-#8	7-#8
	80	690	36	22	20-#5	20-#5	20	11-#7	11-#7	19	11-#7	11-#7	17	7-#9	7-#9
	100	868	37	23	24-#5	24-#5	21	16-#6	16-#6	20	10-#8	10-#8	19	8-#9	8-#9
	120	1049	37	27	29-#5	29-#5	25	19-#6	19-#6	23	14-#7	14-#7	22	11-#8	11-#8
10	20	174	25	12	8-#6	7-#5	12	6-#7	7-#5	12	6-#7	7-#5	11	6-#7	7-#5
	30	268	31	14	9-#6	8-#5	14	7-#7	6-#6	14	7-#7	8-#5	13	7-#7	8-#5
	40	366	34	16	11-#6	10-#5	16	8-#7	7-#6	15	6-#8	7-#6	14	8-#7	7-#6
	50	461	37	18	13-#6	12-#5	18	12-#6	8-#6	17	7-#8	8-#6	16	7-#8	8-#6
	60	559	40	20	14-#6	17-#4	20	10-#7	11-#5	19	7-#8	8-#6	18	6-#9	8-#6
	80	769	35	22	26-#5	25-#4	21	15-#7	16-#5	19	11-#8	12-#6	18	9-#9	10-#6
	100	970	35	26	31-#5	32-#4	24	22-#6	20-#5	23	14-#8	14-#6	21	11-#9	11-#7
	120	1169	36	28	26-#7	37-#4	26	24-#6	31-#4	24	18-#7	17-#6	23	12-#9	12-#7

*Based on A.C.I. Code, 1951. Hooks not required.

PILE FOOTINGS*

NUMBER OF PILES	PILE VALUE (Kips)	COLUMN LOAD (Kips)	d (IN)	a (IN)	LONG WAY (2000)	SHORT WAY (2000)	a (IN)	LONG WAY (2500)	SHORT WAY (2500)	a (IN)	LONG WAY (3000)	SHORT WAY (3000)	a (IN)	LONG WAY (3750)	SHORT WAY (3750)
11	20	191	27	12	7-#7	9-#5	12	7-#7	9-#5	11	7-#7	9-#5	10	7-#7	9-#5
	30	296	33	14	11-#6	10-#5	14	8-#7	10-#5	13	8-#7	10-#5	12	8-#7	10-#5
	40	402	37	16	13-#6	12-#5	16	9-#7	9-#6	15	7-#8	8-#6	14	7-#8	9-#6
	50	509	40	18	19-#5	20-#4	18	11-#7	10-#6	17	10-#7	9-#6	16	6-#9	9-#6
	60	617	43	20	20-#5	21-#4	20	12-#7	14-#5	19	11-#7	8-#7	18	7-#9	8-#7
	80	836	45	23	25-#5	26-#4	21	14-#7	17-#5	20	11-#8	12-#6	18	9-#9	9-#7
	100	1054	47	27	27-#5	31-#4	25	16-#7	20-#5	23	12-#8	14-#6	22	8-#10	11-#7
	120	1270	51	29	29-#5	35-#4	27	21-#6	28-#4	25	13-#8	20-#5	23	10-#9	12-#7
12	20	209	26	14	11-#6	10-#5	13	8-#7	10-#5	12	6-#8	10-#5	11	8-#7	8-#6
	30	322	33	15	13-#6	9-#6	15	9-#7	9-#6	14	7-#8	9-#6	13	6-#9	9-#6
	40	436	39	17	19-#5	10-#6	17	11-#7	9-#6	16	10-#7	10-#6	15	7-#9	10-#6
	50	552	43	19	16-#6	14-#5	19	12-#7	8-#7	18	11-#7	8-#7	17	7-#9	8-#7
	60	669	47	21	22-#5	15-#5	21	16-#6	11-#6	20	11-#7	8-#7	19	7-#9	8-#7
	80	902	55	24	23-#5	17-#5	22	13-#7	10-#7	21	10-#8	9-#7	19	8-#9	7-#8
	100	1141	56	27	26-#5	27-#4	25	15-#7	14-#6	24	12-#8	10-#7	22	8-#10	8-#8
	120	1379	58	30	28-#5	30-#4	27	17-#7	20-#5	26	13-#8	12-#7	24	11-#9	9-#8
13	20	221	24	14	8-#7	8-#7	13	8-#7	8-#7	12	8-#7	8-#7	11	11-#6	11-#6
	30	348	29	16	11-#7	11-#7	16	10-#7	10-#7	15	10-#7	10-#7	14	10-#7	10-#7
	40	475	32	18	16-#6	16-#6	18	12-#7	12-#7	17	9-#8	9-#8	16	8-#9	8-#9
	50	602	34	20	18-#6	18-#6	20	11-#8	11-#8	19	9-#9	9-#9	18	9-#9	9-#9
	60	729	37	22	20-#6	20-#6	22	15-#7	15-#7	21	9-#9	9-#9	19	9-#9	9-#9
	80	983	42	26	28-#5	28-#5	24	16-#7	16-#7	23	13-#8	13-#8	21	7-#11	7-#11
	100	1240	44	29	34-#5	34-#5	26	19-#7	19-#7	25	15-#8	15-#8	23	10-#10	10-#10
	120	1496	48	30	37-#5	37-#5	28	21-#7	21-#7	26	16-#8	16-#8	24	13-#9	13-#9
14	20	242	26	14	10-#6	15-#5	14	8-#7	10-#6	13	8-#7	8-#7	12	8-#7	8-#7
	30	375	32	16	13-#6	18-#5	16	12-#6	13-#6	16	7-#8	9-#7	14	10-#7	10-#7
	40	508	38	18	19-#5	21-#5	18	13-#6	18-#5	18	10-#7	10-#7	17	10-#7	10-#7
	50	643	42	22	20-#5	22-#5	21	14-#6	19-#5	20	11-#7	11-#7	19	7-#9	9-#8
	60	779	46	24	21-#5	23-#5	23	15-#6	20-#5	22	11-#7	12-#7	20	7-#9	11-#7
	80	1056	48	27	26-#5	34-#4	25	18-#6	24-#5	23	12-#8	18-#6	22	10-#8	11-#8
	100	1335	49	29	30-#5	38-#4	27	22-#6	28-#5	26	16-#7	20-#6	24	11-#9	13-#8
	120	1613	50	31	35-#5	34-#5	29	24-#6	30-#5	27	19-#7	22-#6	25	12-#9	18-#7
15	20	254	30	14	8-#7	13-#5	14	11-#6	9-#6	13	9-#7	9-#6	12	9-#7	9-#6
	30	400	34	16	11-#7	17-#5	16	11-#7	12-#6	16	11-#7	11-#6	15	11-#7	9-#7
	40	546	36	20	14-#7	21-#5	19	10-#8	18-#5	18	8-#9	13-#6	17	8-#9	10-#7
	50	693	38	22	16-#7	24-#5	21	12-#8	20-#5	20	8-#10	12-#7	19	8-#10	12-#7
	60	841	40	24	22-#6	26-#5	23	17-#7	22-#5	22	10-#9	16-#6	20	11-#9	13-#7
	80	1139	44	27	26-#6	36-#4	25	19-#7	25-#5	24	12-#9	18-#6	22	8-#11	14-#7
	100	1439	44	30	33-#6	34-#5	28	24-#7	29-#5	26	15-#9	21-#6	24	10-#11	17-#7
	120	1732	49	32	36-#6	34-#5	30	25-#7	30-#5	28	16-#9	22-#6	26	11-#11	17-#7
16	20	279	26	14	14-#6	14-#6	14	10-#7	10-#7	14	10-#7	10-#7	13	8-#8	8-#8
	30	431	32	18	18-#6	18-#6	17	16-#6	16-#6	16	12-#7	12-#7	15	8-#9	8-#9
	40	585	37	20	25-#5	25-#5	19	14-#7	14-#7	18	10-#9	10-#9	17	9-#9	9-#9
	50	739	42	22	21-#6	21-#6	21	15-#7	15-#7	20	11-#8	11-#8	19	9-#9	9-#9
	60	894	46	25	21-#6	21-#6	24	19-#6	19-#6	22	15-#7	15-#7	21	8-#10	8-#10
	80	1205	53	28	29-#5	29-#5	26	17-#7	17-#7	25	13-#8	13-#8	23	13-#8	13-#8
	100	1524	54	31	33-#5	33-#5	28	20-#7	20-#7	27	15-#8	15-#8	25	12-#9	12-#9
	120	1842	55	33	29-#6	29-#6	31	22-#7	22-#7	29	17-#8	17-#8	27	14-#9	14-#9

Table header spanning note: FOR ALL FOOTINGS (PILE VALUE, COLUMN LOAD, d, a); f'c = 2000 #/□" (REINFORCEMENT — LONG WAY, SHORT WAY); f'c = 2500 #/□" (a, REINFORCEMENT — LONG WAY, SHORT WAY); f'c = 3000 #/□" (a, REINFORCEMENT — LONG WAY, SHORT WAY); f'c = 3750 #/□" (a, REINFORCEMENT — LONG WAY, SHORT WAY).

* Based on A.C.I. Code, 1951.

PILE FOOTINGS*

PLAN diagrams (dimensions shown):
- **17 piles:** 11'-2" × 10'-0"; 8 @ 1'-3"; 1'-3", 4 @ 2'-2", 1'-3" (octagonal)
- **18 piles:** 11'-10" × 10'-0"; 8 @ 1'-3"; 1'-3", 2'-2", 2 @ 2'-6", 2'-2", 1'-3" (octagonal)
- **19 piles:** 12'-11"; 6'-5"; 6'-1", 4 @ 2'-2", 11'-2", 1'-3" (hexagonal)
- **20 piles:** 12'-6" × 10'-0"; 6'-1", 3 @ 2'-6", 1'-3"; 1'-3", 4 @ 2'-6", 1'-3", 1'-3"

NUMBER OF PILES	PILE VALUE (KIPS)	COLUMN LOAD (kips)	d (IN)	a (IN)	f'c=2000 #/□" LONG WAY	SHORT WAY	f'c=2500 #/□" a (IN)	LONG WAY	SHORT WAY	f'c=3000 #/□" a (IN)	LONG WAY	SHORT WAY	f'c=3750 #/□" a (IN)	LONG WAY	SHORT WAY
17	20	290	32	14	9-#7	10-#6	14	9-#7	9-#6	14	9-#7	9-#6	13	10-#7	8-#7
	30	454	36	18	12-#7	14-#6	18	9-#8	10-#7	17	9-#8	9-#7	16	8-#9	10-#7
	40	620	40	20	14-#7	20-#5	20	9-#9	14-#6	19	9-#9	11-#7	18	9-#9	11-#7
	50	786	42	24	17-#7	22-#5	23	16-#7	16-#6	21	8-#10	12-#7	20	8-#10	8-#9
	60	952	45	26	23-#6	24-#5	25	14-#8	17-#6	23	11-#9	13-#7	21	9-#10	8-#9
	80	1291	48	29	28-#6	30-#5	27	17-#8	20-#6	25	13-#9	16-#7	23	9-#11	13-#8
	100	1628	51	32	34-#6	34-#5	29	24-#7	23-#6	27	15-#9	18-#7	25	11-#11	14-#8
	120	1965	53	34	39-#6	38-#5	31	27-#7	26-#6	29	21-#8	20-#7	27	14-#10	16-#8
18	20	307	34	14	10-#7	9-#7	15	9-#7	9-#7	14	10-#7	10-#6	13	10-#7	11-#6
	30	481	39	18	16-#6	12-#7	18	12-#7	9-#8	18	8-#9	10-#7	17	8-#9	10-#7
	40	652	43	22	18-#6	14-#7	21	14-#7	11-#8	20	9-#9	11-#7	19	8-#10	9-#8
	50	828	46	26	21-#6	20-#6	24	15-#7	16-#7	22	13-#8	10-#8	20	11-#9	10-#8
	60	1009	48	27	23-#6	23-#6	26	17-#7	14-#8	24	9-#10	11-#8	22	8-#11	9-#9
	80	1360	52	30	22-#7	29-#5	27	14-#9	21-#6	26	11-#10	13-#8	24	10-#11	13-#8
	100	1719	53	32	28-#7	34-#5	30	17-#9	24-#6	28	13-#10	19-#7	26	11-#11	15-#8
	120	2075	56	35	37-#6	38-#5	32	23-#8	27-#6	30	15-#10	20-#7	27	13-#11	14-#9
19	20	327	32	16	10-#7	9-#7	15	9-#7	9-#7	14	10-#7	10-#7	13	10-#7	10-#7
	30	512	37	18	16-#6	12-#7	18	12-#7	9-#8	18	9-#8	9-#8	17	9-#8	9-#8
	40	694	41	22	18-#6	14-#7	21	14-#7	11-#8	20	9-#9	9-#9	19	9-#9	9-#9
	50	883	43	26	21-#6	20-#6	24	15-#7	16-#7	22	12-#8	12-#8	21	10-#9	10-#9
	60	1071	45	27	23-#6	23-#6	26	17-#7	14-#8	24	11-#9	11-#9	23	11-#9	11-#9
	80	1441	51	30	27-#6	27-#6	28	19-#7	20-#7	26	15-#8	20-#7	24	10-#10	10-#11
	100	1823	52	33	40-#5	33-#6	30	23-#7	21-#8	29	12-#10	15-#9	26	12-#10	10-#11
	120	2194	56	36	34-#6	37-#6	33	25-#7	26-#7	31	19-#8	19-#8	29	13-#10	13-#10
20	20	332	36	16	11-#7	12-#6	16	9-#8	9-#7	15	9-#8	9-#7	14	9-#8	9-#7
	30	523	42	18	9-#9	16-#6	18	9-#9	14-#6	18	9-#9	11-#7	17	9-#9	11-#7
	40	719	45	22	11-#9	24-#5	21	11-#9	17-#6	20	11-#9	10-#8	19	11-#9	10-#8
	50	914	48	26	15-#8	26-#5	24	10-#10	19-#6	22	8-#11	15-#7	21	10-#10	9-#9
	60	1104	52	28	21-#7	27-#5	26	11-#10	16-#7	24	9-#11	12-#8	22	10-#11	10-#9
	80	1506	53	31	22-#8	27-#6	28	14-#10	20-#7	26	11-#11	15-#8	25	14-#10	12-#9
	100	1902	55	34	31-#7	38-#5	31	20-#9	22-#7	29	13-#11	17-#8	27	14-#11	14-#9
	120	2297	59	37	34-#7	30-#6	34	21-#9	23-#7	32	15-#11	18-#8	29	15-#11	15-#9

*Based on A.C.I. Code, 1951.

TABLE X
CANTILEVER AND GRAVITY TYPE RETAINING WALLS

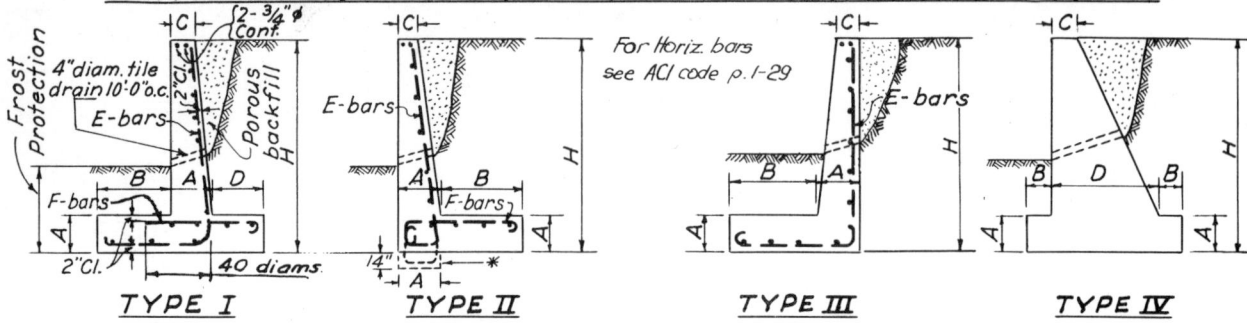

TYPE I   TYPE II   TYPE III   TYPE IV

TYPE I

H	A	B	D	C	TOE PRESSURE	E-BARS	F-BARS
5'-0"	8"	1'-2"	6"	8"	765 #/☐'	3/8"∅ – 12" O.C.	3/8"∅ – 18" O.C.
6'-0"	8"	1'-5"	8"	8"	865 "	3/8"∅ – 12" O.C.	3/8"∅ – 18" O.C.
7'-0"	8"	1'-8"	10"	8"	930 "	3/8"∅ – 9" O.C.	3/8"∅ – 18" O.C.
8'-0"	12"	1'-11"	9"	8"	1125 "	3/8"∅ – 11½"O.C.	3/8"∅ – 18" O.C.
9'-0"	12"	2'-2"	1'-0"	8"	1230 "	3/8"∅ – 7½"O.C.	3/8"∅ – 18" O.C.
10'-0"	12"	2'-5"	1'-2"	8"	1315 "	1/2"∅ – 10" O.C.	3/8"∅ – 12" O.C.
11'-0"	12"	2'-8"	1'-5"	8"	1420 "	5/8"∅ – 10½"O.C.	3/8"∅ – 12" O.C.
12'-0"	12"	2'-11"	1'-8"	8"	1515 "	3/4"∅ – 12" O.C.	1/2"∅ – 14" O.C.
13'-0"	12"	3'-2"	1'-11"	10"	1630 "	7/8"∅ – 12" O.C.	1/2"∅ – 14" O.C.
14'-0"	12"	3'-5"	2'-2"	10"	1735 "	1"∅ – 12½"O.C.	1/2"∅ – 10" O.C.
15'-0"	14"	3'-8"	2'-3"	12"	1895 "	1"∅ – 12½"O.C.	1/2"∅ – 12" O.C.
16'-0"	15"	3'-11"	2'-4"	12"	2010 "	1"∅ – 11½"O.C.	1/2"∅ – 10" O.C.
17'-0"	16"	4'-2"	2'-6"	12"	2130 "	1"☐ – 13" O.C.	1/2"∅ – 9½"O.C.
18'-0"	17"	4'-4"	2'-7"	12"	2260 "	1"☐ – 11½"O.C.	1/2"∅ – 9½"O.C.
20'-0"	19"	4'-10"	2'-11"	12"	2510 "	1"☐ – 10" O.C.	5/8"∅ – 10½"O.C.
22'-0"	21"	5'-4"	3'-3"	12"	2750 "	1"☐ – 8" O.C.	3/4"∅ – 11½"O.C.
24'-0"	24"	5'-10"	3'-5"	12"	3020 "	1"☐ – 7½"O.C.	3/4"∅ – 11½"O.C.
26'-0"	26"	6'-4"	3'-8"	12"	3240 "	1"☐ – 6" O.C.	3/4"∅ – 11" O.C.
28'-0"	28"	6'-10"	4'-0"	12"	3500 "	1"☐ – 5½"O.C.	3/4"∅ – 9" O.C.
30'-0"	31"	7'-3"	4'-2"	12"	3780 "	1"☐ – 5" O.C.	3/4"∅ – 9" O.C.

TYPE II

H	A	B	C	TOE PRESSURE	E-BARS	F-BARS
5'-0"	8"	2'-1"	8"	1170 #/☐'	3/8"∅ – 12" O.C.	3/8"∅ – 12" O.C.
6'-0"	8"	2'-7"	8"	1380 "	3/8"∅ – 12" O.C.	3/8"∅ – 12" O.C.
7'-0"	8"	3'-2"	8"	1610 "	3/8"∅ – 9" O.C.	3/8"∅ – 8" O.C.
8'-0"	12"	3'-7"	8"	1825 "	3/8"∅ – 11½"O.C.	3/8"∅ – 8" O.C.
9'-0"	12"	4'-0"	8"	2030 "	1/2"∅ – 14" O.C.	1/2"∅ – 10½"O.C.
10'-0"	12"	4'-7"	8"	2230 "	1/2"∅ – 10" O.C.	5/8"∅ – 11" O.C.
*11'-0"	12"	5'-2"	8"	2440 "	5/8"∅ – 10½"O.C.	3/4"∅ – 12" O.C.
*12'-0"	12"	5'-9"	8"	2640 "	3/4"∅ – 12" O.C.	7/8"∅ – 12" O.C.
*13'-0"	12"	6'-4"	10"	2850 "	7/8"∅ – 12" O.C.	7/8"∅ – 9½"O.C.
*14'-0"	12"	6'-11"	10"	3050 "	7/8"∅ – 9½"O.C.	1"∅ – 10" O.C.
*15'-0"	14"	7'-3"	12"	3290 "	1"∅ – 12½"O.C.	1"∅ – 10½"O.C.
*16'-0"	15"	7'-8"	12"	3510 "	1"∅ – 11½"O.C.	1"☐ – 12" O.C.
*17'-0"	16"	8'-3"	12"	3730 "	1"☐ – 13" O.C.	1"☐ – 10" O.C.
*18'-0"	18"	8'-6"	12"	3950 "	1"☐ – 12½"O.C.	1"☐ – 10" O.C.
20'-0"	20"	9'-6"	12"	4390 "	1"☐ – 10" O.C.	1"☐ – 8" O.C.
22'-0"	22"	10'-5"	12"	4820 "	1"☐ – 8½"O.C.	1"☐ – 7" O.C.
24'-0"	25"	11'-3"	12"	5270 "	1"☐ – 7½"O.C.	1"☐ – 6" O.C.
26'-0"	28"	12'-2"	12"	5690 "	1"☐ – 7" O.C.	1"☐ – 5½"O.C.
28'-0"	30"	13'-1"	12"	6160 "	1"☐ – 6" O.C.	1"☐ – 4½"O.C.
30'-0"	33"	13'-10"	12"	6580 "	1"☐ – 5½"O.C.	1"☐ – 4" O.C.

TYPE III

H	A	B	C	TOE PRESSURE	E-BARS
5'-0"	8"	1'-8"	8"	572 #/☐'	3/8"∅ – 12" O.C.
6'-0"	8"	2'-5"	8"	545 "	3/8"∅ – 12" O.C.
7'-0"	8"	3'-3"	8"	525 "	1/2"∅ – 14" O.C.
8'-0"	12"	3'-2"	8"	720 "	3/8"∅ – 10" O.C.
9'-0"	12"	4'-1"	8"	694 "	1/2"∅ – 12" O.C.
10'-0"	12"	5'-0"	8"	675 "	5/8"∅ – 12½"O.C.
11'-0"	12"	6'-0"	8"	657 "	3/4"∅ – 13" O.C.
12'-0"	12"	7'-1"	8"	640 "	3/4"∅ – 10" O.C.
13'-0"	12"	7'-9"	10"	677 "	7/8"∅ – 11" O.C.
14'-0"	12"	9'-0"	10"	657 "	1"∅ – 11" O.C.
15'-0"	14"	8'-10"	12"	800 "	1"∅ – 11" O.C.
16'-0"	15"	9'-6"	12"	838 "	1"☐ – 12" O.C.
17'-0"	16"	10'-3"	12"	875 "	1"☐ – 11" O.C.
18'-0"	18"	10'-9"	12"	955 "	1"☐ – 10½"O.C.
20'-0"	20"	12'-2"	12"	1030 "	1"☐ – 9" O.C.
22'-0"	22"	13'-8"	12"	1104 "	1"☐ – 7½"O.C.
24'-0"	25"	14'-10"	12"	1225 "	1"☐ – 6½"O.C.
26'-0"	28"	16'-2"	12"	1328 "	1"☐ – 6" O.C.
28'-0"	30"	17'-5"	12"	1425 "	1"☐ – 5" O.C.
30'-0"	33"	18'-7"	12"	1545 "	1"☐ – 4½"O.C.

TYPE IV

H	A	B	D	C	TOE PRESSURE
5'-0"	1'-0"	6"	1'-4"	8"	1046 #/☐'
6'-0"	1'-0"	6"	1'-8"	8"	1360 "
7'-0"	1'-0"	6"	2'-4"	8"	1540 "
8'-0"	1'-0"	6"	2'-10"	8"	1760 "
9'-0"	1'-0"	6"	3'-4"	8"	2040 "
10'-0"	1'-0"	6"	3'-10"	12"	2300 "
11'-0"	1'-0"	6"	4'-4"	12"	2560 "
12'-0"	1'-0"	6"	4'-10"	12"	2800 "
13'-0"	1'-0"	6"	5'-5"	12"	3040 "
14'-0"	1'-0"	6"	5'-11"	12"	3140 "
15'-0"	1'-0"	6"	6'-6"	12"	3500 "
16'-0"	1'-0"	6"	7'-0"	16"	3780 "
17'-0"	1'-0"	6"	7'-6"	16"	4040 "
18'-0"	1'-0"	6"	8'-0"	16"	4340 "
20'-0"	1'-0"	6"	9'-4"	16"	4750 "

Design based on weight of earth 100 lb. per cu. ft. and angle of repose assumed 33° and no surcharge. Designed for 2000 lb. controlled concrete. A low water-cement ratio recommended for permanency. Will pass for New York City Class B concrete. The resultant pressure on walls above is at the outer edge of middle third. Alternate vertical E-bars in types I, II, and III walls may be cut at ½ H. Expansion joints in walls should not be over 75'-0" o.c.; construction joints 30'-0" o.c. For additional data on retaining walls, see p. 2–12.

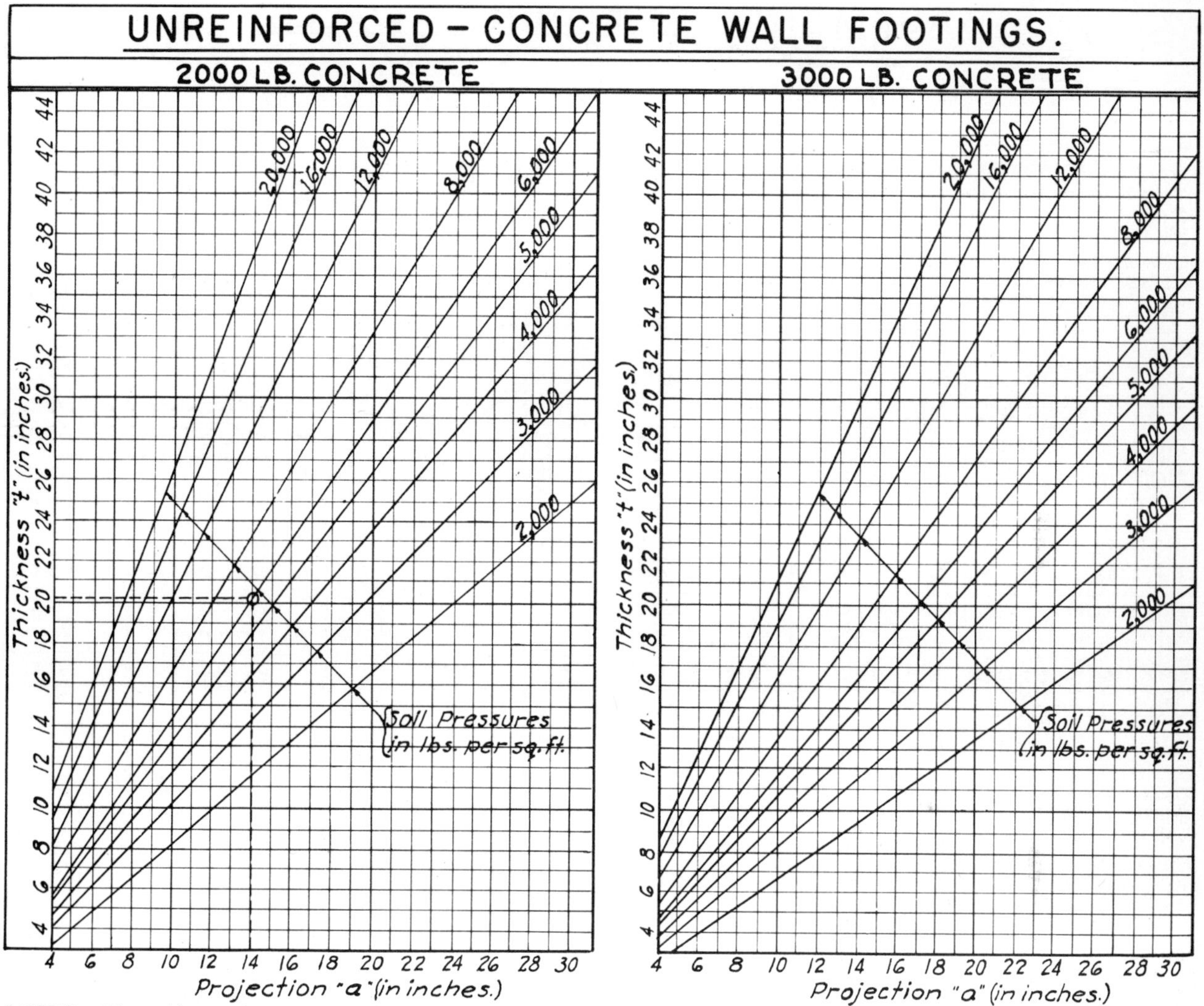

UNREINFORCED — CONCRETE WALL FOOTINGS.

2000 LB. CONCRETE

3000 LB. CONCRETE

Thickness "t" (in inches.)

Soil Pressures in lbs. per sq. ft.

Projection "a" (in inches.)

Thickness "t" (in inches.)

Soil Pressures in lbs. per sq. ft.

Projection "a" (in inches.)

NOTE: *The diagrams are in accordance with the requirements of the A.C.I. Code-1947.*
For Joint Committee requirements add 2 inches to the thickness "t" from the diagrams above.
For New York City Code requirements add 4 inches to the thickness "t" from the diagrams above.

Formula for unreinforced concrete wall footings:

$$t = a\sqrt{\frac{S}{48\,f_c}}$$

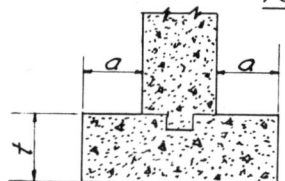

In Which: t = *Total depth of footing in inches.*
a = *Projection in inches.*
S = *Soil pressure in lb. per sq. ft.*
$f_c = 0.03\,f_c'$. *e.g. 0.03 x 3,000 = 90 lb. per sq. in. for 3,000 lb. concrete.*

EXAMPLE:- *Given:- Wall thickness = 12 inches ; Soil pressure = 6,000 lb. per sq. ft. ; and Wall load = 20,000 lb. per linear ft. of wall; 2000 lb. concrete.*

Solution:- $2a = \dfrac{20,000}{6,000} - 1.0 = 2.33 \text{ ft.} = 28 \text{ in.}$ $a = 14 \text{ in.}$

From diagram above for 2,000 lb. concrete, with a = 14 in. and 6,000 lb. soil
$t = 20.2$ in. *or* 21 in. *for A.C.I. requirements.*
$t = 23''$ *for Joint Committee requirements.*
$t = 25''$ *for New York City Code requirements.*

BASEMENT RETAINING WALLS.
$f_c' = 2,000 \#/\square''$ — $f_s = 20,000 \#/\square''$

TABLE XI – REINFORCEMENT FOR EARTH PRESSURE (DRY).

Angle of repose $\phi = 33°$
Earth W = 100 lbs. per cu.ft.
$\frac{3}{8}''\phi$ 18" o.c. Horizontal
(See A.C.I. requirements,
pg. 1-29, for exposed walls.)
Vertical steel in Table.

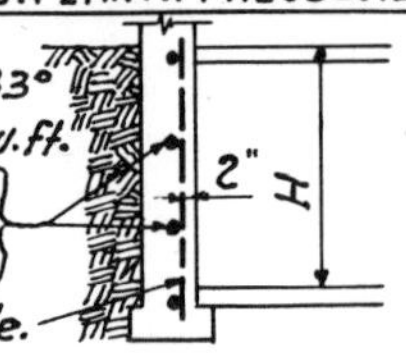

H	12" WALL	16" WALL	20" WALL
8'-0"	$\frac{3}{8}''\phi$ - 12" O.C.	$\frac{3}{8}''\phi$ - 12" O.C.	$\frac{3}{8}''\phi$ - 12" O.C.
9'-0"	$\frac{3}{8}''\phi$ - 12" O.C.	$\frac{3}{8}''\phi$ - 12" O.C.	$\frac{3}{8}''\phi$ - 12" O.C.
10'-0"	$\frac{3}{8}''\phi$ - 10" O.C.	$\frac{3}{8}''\phi$ - 12" O.C.	$\frac{3}{8}''\phi$ - 12" O.C.
11'-0"	$\frac{3}{8}''\phi$ - 7½" O.C.	$\frac{3}{8}''\phi$ - 11" O.C.	$\frac{3}{8}''\phi$ - 12" O.C.
12'-0"	$\frac{1}{2}''\phi$ - 10½" O.C.	$\frac{3}{8}''\phi$ - 8" O.C.	$\frac{3}{8}''\phi$ - 10½" O.C.
13'-0"	$\frac{1}{2}''\phi$ - 8" O.C.	$\frac{1}{2}''\phi$ - 12" O.C.	$\frac{3}{8}''\phi$ - 8½" O.C.
14'-0"	$\frac{5}{8}''\phi$ - 10" O.C.	$\frac{1}{2}''\phi$ - 9" O.C.	$\frac{1}{2}''\phi$ - 12" O.C.
15'-0"	$\frac{5}{8}''\phi$ - 8" O.C.	$\frac{5}{8}''\phi$ - 11" O.C.	$\frac{1}{2}''\phi$ - 9½" O.C.
16'-0"	$\frac{3}{4}''\phi$ - 10" O.C.	$\frac{5}{8}''\phi$ - 9½" O.C.	$\frac{1}{2}''\phi$ - 7½" O.C.
17'-0"	$\frac{7}{8}''\phi$ - 11" O.C.	$\frac{3}{4}''\phi$ - 11½" O.C.	$\frac{5}{8}''\phi$ - 10" O.C.
18'-0"	$\frac{7}{8}''\phi$ - 9½" O.C.	$\frac{3}{4}''\phi$ - 9½" O.C.	$\frac{5}{8}''\phi$ - 8½" O.C.
19'-0"	$1''\phi$ - 10½" O.C.	$\frac{7}{8}''\phi$ - 11" O.C.	$\frac{3}{4}''\phi$ - 10½" O.C.
20'-0"	$1''\square$ - 11½" O.C.	$\frac{7}{8}''\phi$ - 9½" O.C.	$\frac{3}{4}''\phi$ - 9" O.C.
21'-0"		$1''\phi$ - 11" O.C.	$\frac{7}{8}''\phi$ - 10½" O.C.

TABLE XII – REINFORCEMENT FOR SATURATED EARTH PRESS.

Saturated Earth,
Assumed equivalent
fluid weight W' = 75 lbs. per cu.ft.
Horiz. bars - same as Table A.
Vertical steel in Table.

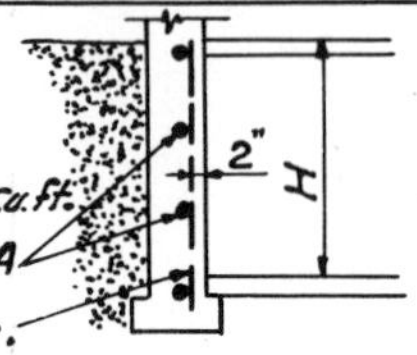

H	12" WALL	16" WALL	20" WALL
8'-0"	$\frac{3}{8}''\phi$ - 7½" O.C.	$\frac{3}{8}''\phi$ - 11" O.C.	$\frac{3}{8}''\phi$ - 12" O.C.
9'-0"	$\frac{1}{2}''\phi$ - 10" O.C.	$\frac{3}{8}''\phi$ - 7½" O.C.	$\frac{3}{8}''\phi$ - 9½" O.C.
10'-0"	$\frac{5}{8}''\phi$ - 11" O.C.	$\frac{1}{2}''\phi$ - 10" O.C.	$\frac{3}{8}''\phi$ - 7" O.C.
11'-0"	$\frac{3}{4}''\phi$ - 12" O.C.	$\frac{5}{8}''\phi$ - 11½" O.C.	$\frac{1}{2}''\phi$ - 9½" O.C.
12'-0"	$\frac{7}{8}''\phi$ - 12" O.C.	$\frac{5}{8}''\phi$ - 9" O.C.	$\frac{5}{8}''\phi$ - 11½" O.C.
13'-0"	$\frac{7}{8}''\phi$ - 10" O.C.	$\frac{3}{4}''\phi$ - 10" O.C.	$\frac{5}{8}''\phi$ - 9" O.C.
14'-0"	$1''\phi$ - 10½" O.C.	$\frac{7}{8}''\phi$ - 11" O.C.	$\frac{3}{4}''\phi$ - 10" O.C.
15'-0"		$1''\phi$ - 12" O.C.	$\frac{7}{8}''\phi$ - 11½" O.C.
16'-0"		$1''\square$ - 12" O.C.	$\frac{7}{8}''\phi$ - 9½" O.C.
17'-0"		$1''\square$ - 10" O.C.	$1''\phi$ - 10½" O.C.
18'-0"		$1''\square$ - 8½" O.C.	$1''\square$ - 11" O.C.
19'-0"			$1''\square$ - 9½" O.C.
20'-0"			$1\frac{1}{8}''\square$ - 10" O.C.
21'-0"			$1\frac{1}{4}''\square$ - 11" O.C.

Table XI is computed without surcharge: Mom. = .128 HP (See table XIII)
With surcharge, increase Mom. by ratio $\frac{H+2S}{H}$
w = weight of soil, S = height of surcharge in feet.

TABLE XIII – EARTH PRESSURES.

Angle of repose $\phi = 33°$
W = 100 lbs. per cu. ft.
$$P = \frac{1}{2} W H^2 \frac{1 - \sin \phi}{1 + \sin \phi}$$
per foot length of wall.
(Rankine)

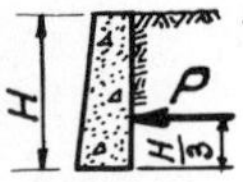

H FEET	P LBS.	P/SQ.FT. MAX.	H FEET	P LBS.	P/SQ.FT MAX.
5	370	147	14	2890	413
6	530	177	16	3770	472
7	720	206	18	4780	531
8	940	236	20	5900	590
9	1200	266	22	7130	649
10	1470	295	24	8490	708
11	1780	324	26	9960	766
12	2120	354	28	11560	825
13	2490	383	30	13260	885

TABLE XIV – SATURATED EARTH PRESS.

W' = 75 lbs. per cu. ft.
$$P = \frac{1}{2} w' H^2$$
per foot length of wall.

H FEET	P LBS.	P/SQ.FT. MAX.	H FEET	P LBS.	P/SQ.FT. MAX.
1	38	75	12	5400	900
2	150	150	13	6330	975
3	338	225	14	7350	1050
4	600	300	15	8440	1125
5	940	375	16	9600	1200
6	1350	450	17	10800	1275
7	1840	525	18	12150	1350
8	2400	600	19	13500	1425
9	3040	675	20	15000	1500
10	3750	750	21	16600	1575
11	4530	825	22	18100	1650

TABLE XV – COAL PRESSURES.

Total Pressure for
Depth H for Bituminous
Coal on Vertical Walls.
Weight per cu. ft. 50 lbs. $\phi = 35°$

H FEET	P LBS.	P/SQ.FT. MAX.	H FEET	P LBS.	P/SQ.FT. MAX.
5	170	68	11	820	149
6	240	81	12	980	163
7	330	95	14	1330	190
8	430	108	16	1730	217
9	550	122	18	2190	244
10	680	135	20	2710	271

NOTE: Use Table XI for
permanent dry earth only.
Interpolate between Tables
XI and XII for seasonal
rains resulting in saturated
earth against walls.

For additional data on retaining walls see p. 2–12.

BEARING PLATES FOR STEEL BEAMS

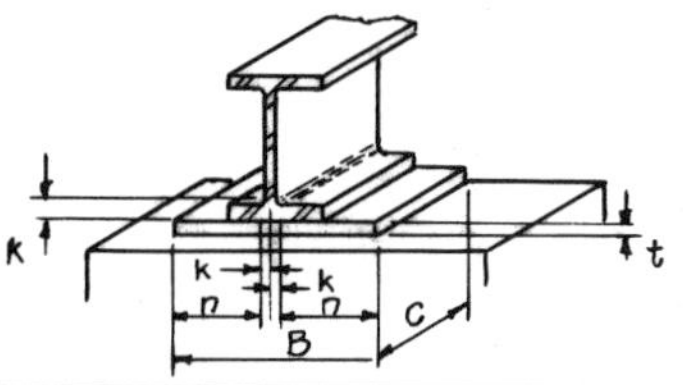
k
k
n
k
n
B
C
t

EXAMPLE: Given- 18WF 85; Load 40,000#; safe bearing pressure=200#/□" C=10"; k=1½" (from table B); To find size and thickness of plate.

$B = \frac{40{,}000}{10 \times 200} = 20"$ $n = \frac{B}{2} - k = \frac{20}{2} - 1\frac{1}{2} = 8\frac{1}{2}$

∴ From table—— $t = 1\frac{1}{2}"$

Bearing Plate = 10"×20"×1½"

Unit steel stress = 20,000#/□" (A.I.S.C.)
p = Safe pressure on masonry #/□"
t = Thickness of plate in inches as computed by

$$t = n\sqrt{\frac{.15p}{1000}}$$

TABLE XVI - VALUES OF "n"

t \ P	70	100	110	125	150	200	250	300	325	350	400	450	500	550	600	625	750	875
3/8	3.7	3.1	2.9	2.7	2.5	2.2	1.94	1.77	1.70	1.64	1.54	1.45	1.37	1.31	1.26	1.23	1.12	1.04
1/2	4.9	4.1	3.9	3.7	3.3	2.9	2.6	2.36	2.27	2.19	2.05	1.92	1.83	1.74	1.67	1.64	1.49	1.38
5/8	6.1	5.1	4.9	4.6	4.2	3.6	3.2	2.9	2.84	2.73	2.55	2.40	2.29	2.17	2.08	2.04	1.87	1.73
3/4	7.3	6.1	5.9	5.5	5.0	4.3	3.9	3.5	3.4	3.28	3.06	2.89	2.74	2.62	2.50	2.45	2.24	2.07
7/8	8.5	7.2	6.8	6.4	5.8	5.1	4.5	4.1	3.97	3.83	3.58	3.37	3.20	3.05	2.92	2.87	2.61	2.41
1	9.8	8.2	7.8	7.3	6.7	5.8	5.2	4.7	4.53	4.37	4.08	3.86	3.66	3.49	3.34	3.27	2.98	2.76
1¼	12.2	10.2	9.8	9.1	8.4	7.2	6.5	5.9	5.68	5.46	5.14	4.82	4.56	4.38	4.17	4.08	3.74	3.45
1½	14.7	12.2	11.7	11.1	10.0	8.7	7.8	7.1	6.81	6.57	6.13	5.80	5.48	5.23	5.00	4.91	4.48	4.14
2	19.6	16.3	15.6	14.6	13.4	11.6	10.4	9.4	9.06	8.75	8.18	7.70	7.33	6.98	6.68	6.55	5.99	5.53
2½	24.4	20.5	19.5	18.3	16.7	14.5	12.9	11.8	11.4	10.9	10.2	9.65	9.15	8.72	8.35	8.18	7.45	6.92
3	29.3	24.5	23.4	21.9	20.0	17.3	15.5	14.2	13.6	13.1	12.3	11.6	11.0	10.5	10.0	9.8	9.0	8.3
3½	34.2	28.6	27.3	25.7	23.4	20.2	18.1	16.5	15.9	15.3	14.3	13.5	12.8	12.2	11.7	11.5	10.5	9.7
4	39.1	32.7	31.2	29.3	26.7	23.2	20.7	18.9	18.1	17.5	16.4	15.4	14.6	13.9	13.4	13.1	12.0	11.1

TABLE XVII - VALUES OF "k" FOR BEARING PLATE DESIGN

SIZE	k	SIZE	k	SIZE	k	SIZE	k	SIZE	k	SIZE	k	SIZE	k	SIZE	k
36WF300	2 13/16	30WF132	1 11/16	24WF76	1¼	18WF60	1 3/16	14WF74	1⅜	12WF22	¾	8WF15	⅝	18I70	1⅜
36WF230	2⅜	30WF108	1½	21WF142	1⅞	18WF50	1 1/16	14WF61	1¼	10WF66	1¼	6WF25	¾	15I50	1¼
36WF194	2⅛	27WF177	2⅛	21WF112	1⅝	16WF96	1⅝	14WF53	1¼	10WF49	1 1/16	6WF16	11/16	12I50	1 5/16
36WF150	1 13/16	27WF145	1 15/16	21WF96	1 9/16	16WF78	1½	14WF38	1	10WF39	1 1/16	5WF18.5	¾	12I35	1⅛
33WF240	2 7/16	27WF114	1⅝	21WF73	1 5/16	16WF58	1¼	14WF30	⅞	10WF29	⅞	4WF13	⅝	10I35	1
33WF200	2 3/16	27WF94	1 7/16	21WF62	1 3/16	16WF50	1⅛	12WF85	1⅜	10WF21	11/16			8I23	⅞
33WF152	1⅞	24WF160	2	18WF114	1 11/16	16WF36	15/16	12WF58	1¼	10WF19	11/16	24I120	1 15/16	7I20	13/16
33WF130	1 11/16	24WF130	1¾	18WF96	1½	14WF136	1 11/16	12WF50	1¼	8WF35	⅞	24I100	1⅝	6I17.25	¾
30WF210	2 5/16	24WF100	1 9/16	18WF85	1½	14WF87	1 5/16	12WF36	15/16	8WF28	13/16	20I95	1¾	5I14.75	11/16
30WF172	2 1/16	24WF94	1 7/16	18WF64	1¼	14WF84	1⅜	12WF27	13/16	8WF20	11/16	20I75	1 9/16	4I9.5	⅝

COLUMN BASE PLATES

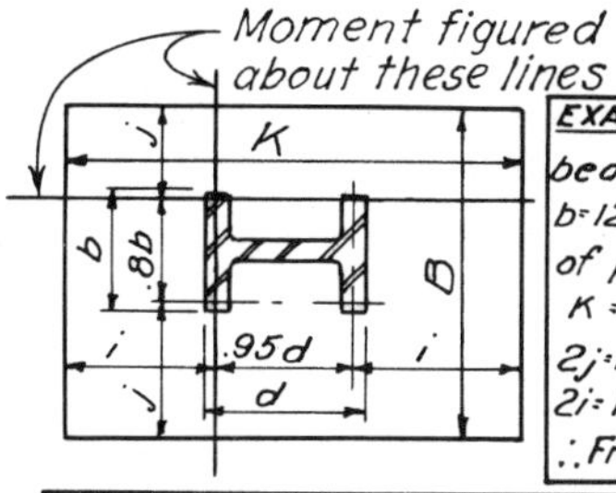
Moment figured
about these lines
K
j
b
.8b
B
i
.95d
i
d
j

EXAMPLE:- Given: Load = 400,000#; safe bearing pressure p = 875#/□"; B = 20"; b = 12"; d = 12". To find size and thickness of plate. Area required = $\frac{400{,}000}{875} = 457$□"

$K = \frac{457}{20} = 23"$

$2j = B - .8b \therefore j = \frac{20 - 9.6}{2} = 5.2$ Use larger

$2i = K - .95d \therefore i = \frac{23 - 11.4}{2} = 5.8$ one $i = 5.8$

∴ From table $t = 2\frac{1}{4}"$ —— B.P. = 20"×23"×2¼"

f = Unit steel stress 20,000#/□" (A.I.S.C.)
p = Safe pressure on masonry #/□"
t = Thickness of plate in inches as computed by $t = i \text{ or } j \sqrt{\frac{0.15P}{1000}}$
(Use i or j whichever is greater)

TABLE XVIII - VALUES OF i OR j FOR VARIOUS THICKNESSES OF PLATES

t \ P	110	200	250	500	625	750	875	t \ P	110	200	250	500	625	750	875
1	7.78	5.77	5.17	3.65	3.26	2.98	2.76	3½	27.2	20.2	18.1	12.8	11.4	10.4	9.65
1¼	9.73	7.22	6.45	4.57	4.07	3.73	3.45	4	31.1	23.1	20.6	14.6	13.0	11.9	11.0
1½	11.6	8.66	7.75	5.48	4.88	4.47	4.14	4½	35.0	25.9	23.2	16.4	14.7	13.4	12.4
1¾	13.6	10.1	9.04	6.38	5.71	5.22	4.83	5	38.9	28.8	25.8	18.2	16.3	14.9	13.8
2	15.5	11.5	10.3	7.30	6.52	5.96	5.52	5½	42.7	31.7	28.4	20.1	17.9	16.4	15.2
2¼	17.5	13.0	11.6	8.22	7.33	6.71	6.27	6	46.6	34.6	31.0	21.9	19.6	17.9	16.5
2½	19.4	14.4	12.9	9.13	8.15	7.45	6.90	6½	50.6	37.5	33.6	23.7	21.2	19.4	17.9
2¾	21.4	15.9	14.2	10.0	8.97	8.20	7.58	7	54.4	40.3	36.2	25.6	22.8	20.8	19.3
3	23.3	17.3	15.5	11.0	9.77	8.94	8.28	8	62.2	46.2	41.3	29.2	26.1	23.8	22.0

TABLE XIX. STANDARD FOUNDATION BOLTS

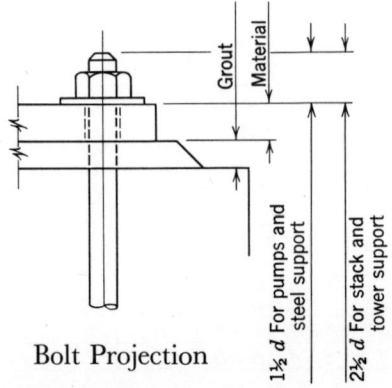

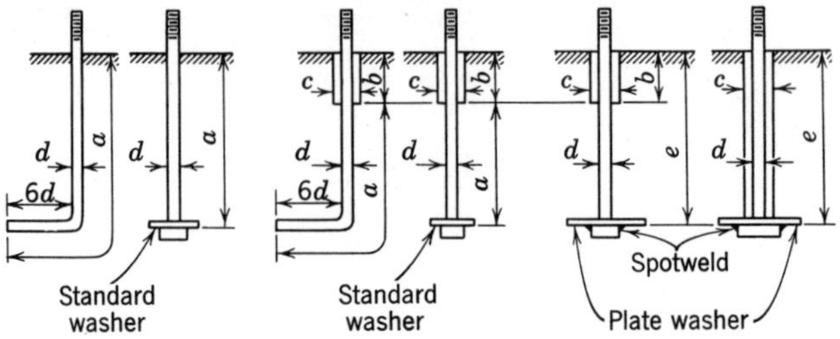

Diameter of Bolt	Tensile Strength, lb. $fs = 12,000$ p.s.i.					
d, In.	Based upon 80 p.s.i. Bond	Anchoring of Bolt in Concrete, In. $a = \sim 30d$	Length of Pipe Sleeve, In. $b = \sim 10d$	Size of Pipe Sleeve, In. $e = \sim d + 2''$	Length of Bolt in Concrete, In. e	Size of Plate Washer, In
½	1,500	1′–3	6	1½	9	4 x 4 x ½
⅝	2,425	1′–6	6	2	1′–0	4 x 4 x ½
¾	3,600	1′–10	9	2	1′–3	4 x 4 x ½
⅞	5,040	2′–2	9	2½	1′–6	6 x 6 x ¾
1	6,600	2′–6	10	3	1′–9	6 x 6 x ¾
1⅛	8,320	2′–10	12	3	2′–0	6 x 6 x ¾
1¼	10,680	3′–2	13	3	2′–2	7 x 7 x 1
1⅜	12,660	3′–6	14	3	2′–4	7 x 7 x 1
1½	15,500	3′–9	15	3	2′–6	8 x 8 x 1¼
1⅝	18,360	4′–1	16	4	2′–8	8 x 8 x 1¼
1¾	20,950	4′–5	18	4	2′–9	9 x 9 x 1½
1⅞	24,600	4′–9	19	4	2′–10	9 x 9 x 1½
2	27,600	5′–0	20	4	3′–0	11 x 11 x 1¾
2¼	36,300	5′–8	22	4	3′–3	11 x 11 x 1¾
2½	44,600	6′–3	2′–1	4	3′–6	11 x 11 x 1¾
2¾	55,400	6′–10	2′–4	6	3′–9	12 x 12 x 2
3	65,280	7′ 6	2′–6	6	4′–0	12 x 12 x 2

Bolt Projection

ANCHOR BOLTS

Anchor bolts are generally formed from plain rods. Since they are subject to corrosion, the tensile strength is figured at 12,000 p.s.i. on the root area and the bond at 80 p.s.i. For tabulated values see Table XIX. Pipe sleeves are used to permit field adjustment. They also can be set true by templates. Common practice seems to be to use them on machine but not on structural foundations.

Sometimes it is necessary to set anchor bolts into rock or existing masonry. These are generally grouted in with portland cement grout. The grout should be put in before the bolt. Some engineers fear that the grout will shrink and therefore specify lead or sulfur. Experience seems to indicate that the portland cement grout is satisfactory. Water acting on the sulfur can turn it into acid, thu corroding the steel.

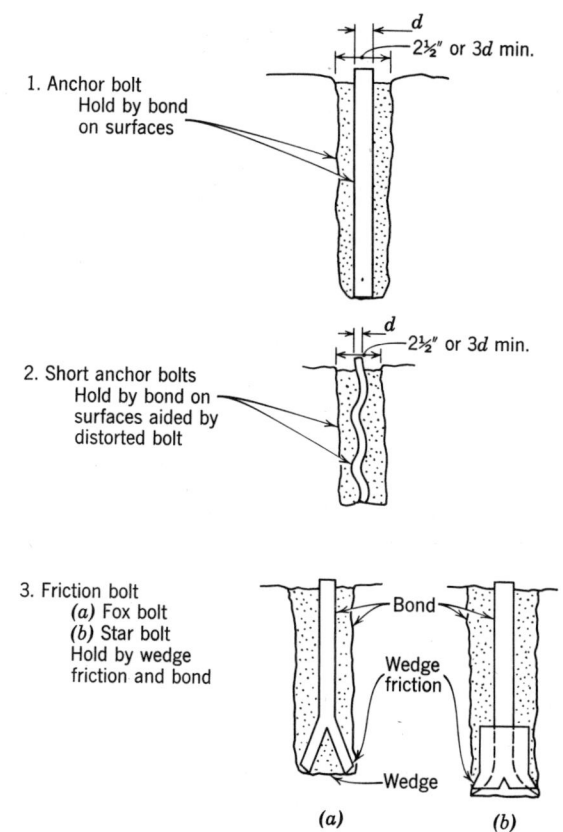

Note: Grout is recommended to reinforce all friction bolts.
Caution: Anchorage is no better than the rock.

FIG. 1.   ANCHOR BOLTS IN ROCK OR EXISTING MASONRY.

3

Detail Foundation Design

The designer's objective is a design drawing adequate to form a part of the contract and also to serve as a basis for reinforced-concrete working drawings and bar schedules.

Following this drawing is a set of notes to supplement the drawing.

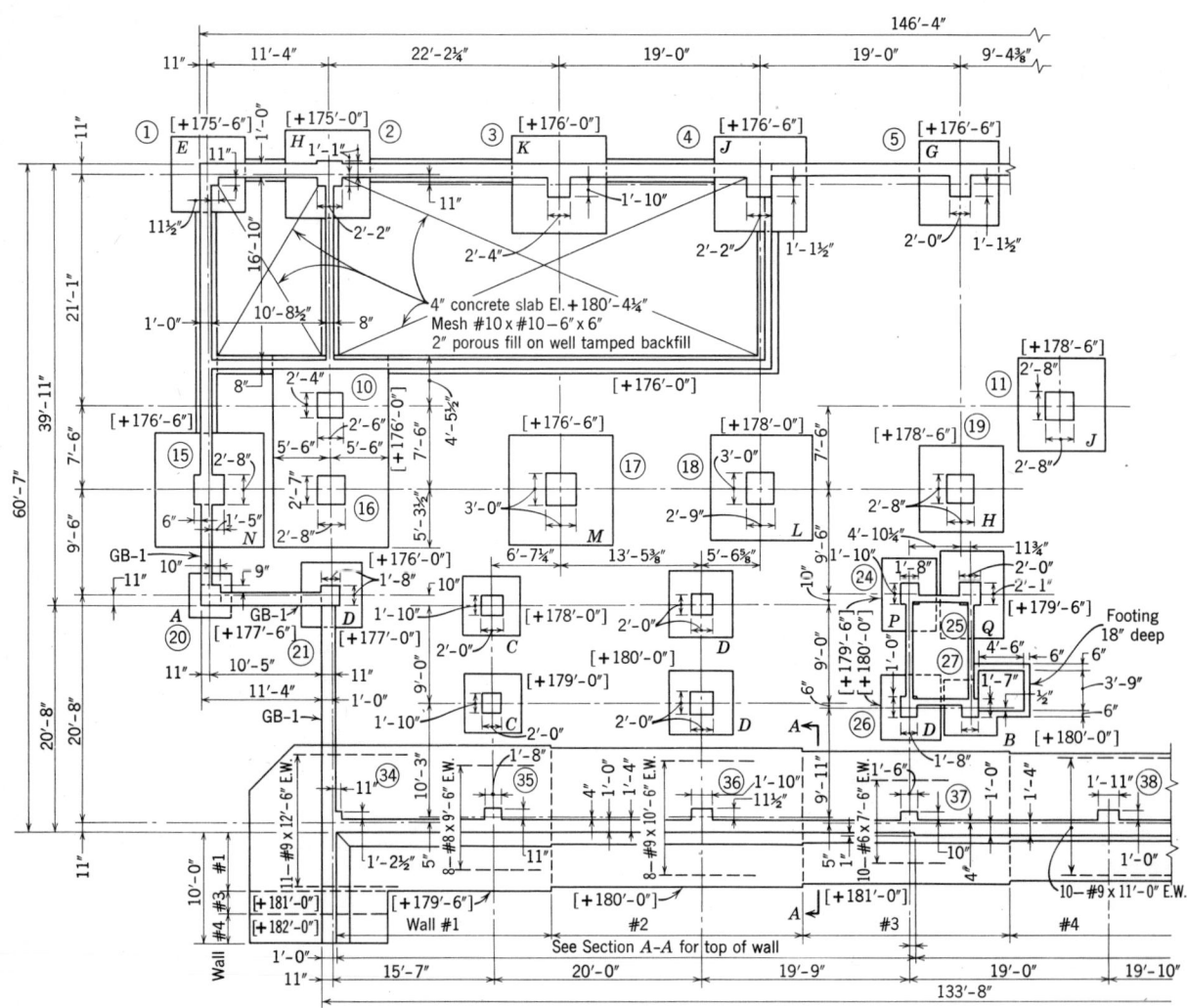

FOOTING SCHEDULE

Mark	Size	Reinforcing Each Way
A	4'-0" × 4'-0" × 16"	10– #4
B	5'-0" × 5'-0" × 17"	15– #4
C	5'-6" × 5'-6" × 18"	13– #5
D	6'-0" × 6'-0" × 19"	15– #5
E	7'-0" × 7'-0" × 22"	14– #6
F	7'-4" × 7'-4" × 24"	14– #6
G	7'-6" × 7'-6" × 24"	14– #6
H	8'-0" × 8'-0" × 25"	13– #7
J	8'-6" × 8'-6" × 26"	14– #7

PART FOUNDATION PLAN
Scale ⅛" = 1' 0"

Notes
1. Elevations of bottom of footing shown thus [+   ].
2. Basement slab to be 4" thick with mesh #10 x #10/ 6" x 6" unless otherwise noted.
3. Top of basement slab at El. +184' 0" unless otherwise noted.
4. Concrete shall develop a strength of 2500 p.s.i. at 28 days.   Reinforcement shall be intermediate grade deformed bars.
5. Foundations designed for a bearing pressure of 3 tons per square foot.   (Check in field.)

FIG. 1.   TYPICAL FOUNDATION PLAN.
From this plan working drawings and bar schedules are prepared.

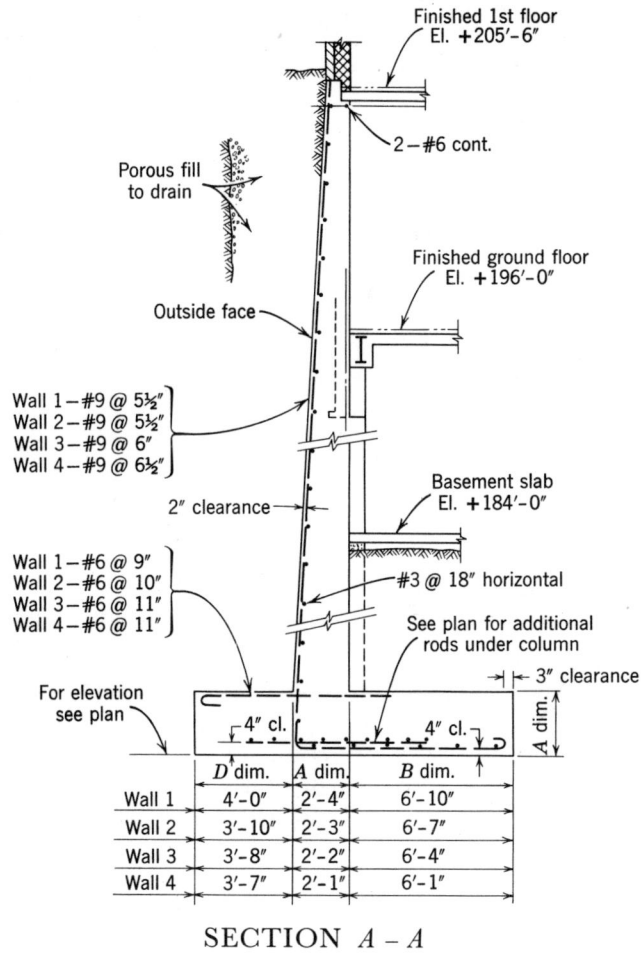

Finished 1st floor
El. +205'–6"

2 – #6 cont.

Porous fill
to drain

Finished ground floor
El. +196'–0"

Outside face

Wall 1 – #9 @ 5½"
Wall 2 – #9 @ 5½"
Wall 3 – #9 @ 6"
Wall 4 – #9 @ 6½"

2" clearance

Basement slab
El. +184'–0"

Wall 1 – #6 @ 9"
Wall 2 – #6 @ 10"
Wall 3 – #6 @ 11"
Wall 4 – #6 @ 11"

#3 @ 18" horizontal

See plan for additional
rods under column

3" clearance

For elevation
see plan

4" cl.   4" cl.

A dim.

	D dim.	A dim.	B dim.
Wall 1	4'–0"	2'–4"	6'–10"
Wall 2	3'–10"	2'–3"	6'–7"
Wall 3	3'–8"	2'–2"	6'–4"
Wall 4	3'–7"	2'–1"	6'–1"

SECTION *A – A*
TYPICAL RETAINING WALL

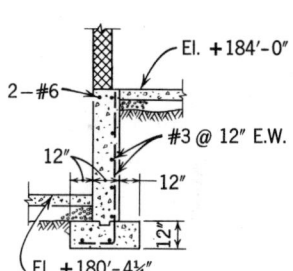

Finished ground floor
El. +196'–0"

#3 @ 12
6 – #4 cont. top.
#4 @ 12" E.W.

Varies

1" clearance for
inside face of wall

Basement slab
El. +180'–0"

2 – #6 cont.

Footing = 6" projection x 12" deep

TYPICAL EXT. WALL

El. +184'–0"

2 – #6

#3 @ 12" E.W.

12"   12"

12"

El. +180'–4¼"

TYPICAL INTERIOR
RETAINING WALL

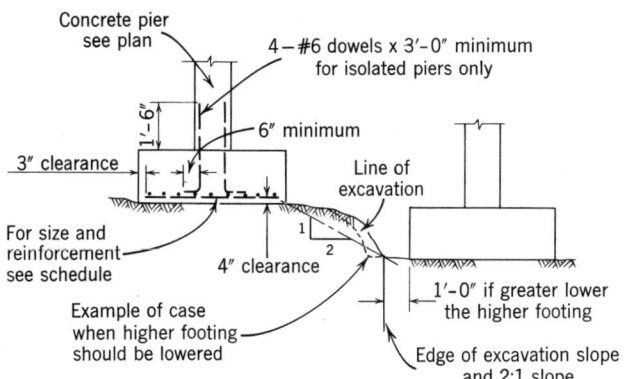

Concrete pier
see plan

4 – #6 dowels x 3'–0" minimum
for isolated piers only

1'–6"

6" minimum

3" clearance

Line of
excavation

For size and
reinforcement
see schedule

4" clearance

Example of case
when higher footing
should be lowered

1   2

1'–0" if greater lower
the higher footing

Edge of excavation slope
and 2:1 slope

TYPICAL FOOTING DETAIL

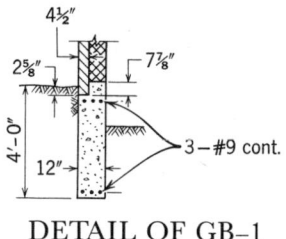

4½"

2⅝"   7⅞"

4'–0"

12"

3 – #9 cont.

DETAIL OF GB–1

Note: Where footings are at different elevations lower footing shall be placed first.

TYPICAL NOTES FOR FOUNDATION DRAWINGS

Foundation drawings should have notes to guide detailer, designer, and builder, as follows:

Design Drawings:

1. Foundations designed for _____ tons per square foot. (Check soil in field.) Engineer (or _____) will check the assumption.
2. Concrete shall develop a strength of _____ p.s.i. at 28 days.
3. No backfilling against foundation walls to be done until after superstructure is in place.
4. Where reinforced mat slabs are erected and ground-water pressure is likely to occur, relief holes should be left to relieve water pressure until approved by Engineer.
5. Extreme high water level at any time has been assumed to be not higher than elevation _____. This assumption must be checked in the field. Engineer (or _____) will check the assumption.
6. See specifications for instructions to detailers.

Working Drawings: (include in specification).

7. Concrete shall develop a strength of _____ p.s.i. at 28 days.*
8. Wall footings to be stepped where elevation changes 1 vertical to 2 horizontal, except where otherwise shown.
9. †All bars in footings to be hooked. Size of hook to be in accordance with A.C.I. requirements.
10. Provide six No. 4 round rods continuous in top and two No. 6 round continuous in bottom of all exterior walls, except as otherwise shown. Lap 45 diameters, and bend around corners.
11. Provide two No. 4 in. round rods continuous in top and bottom of all interior concrete walls, except as otherwise shown.
12. All wall, pier, and stack footings shall be 12 in. thick and project 6 in. beyond all faces of walls, piers, and stacks except as otherwise shown.
13. Provide two No. 6 round rods, all sides, for all openings in concrete walls unless otherwise noted. Extend 2 ft. beyond openings or hook ends.
14. Provide pockets in walls for all concrete beams and slabs at first floor.
15. Construction joints in foundation walls, interior and exterior, shall be placed not more than 30 ft. apart and shall be V-chamfered unless otherwise shown. Location of joints shall be as shown on the drawings or approved by the Engineer. Sections of walls shall be poured alternately.

CHECK LIST OF LOADS

Loads to Be Considered in the Design of Foundations

Dead load of structure.
Live load on structure.
Weight of foundation.
Weight of soil and live load thereon above foundation in excess of original ground level.
Uplift caused by hydrostatic pressure.
Horizontal reactions caused by earth and hydrostatic pressure.
Thrusts from arches and rigid frames.

---

* This note to be placed on Working Drawings.
† Does not apply where high bond bars (A.S.T.M. A–305) are used.

Overturning caused by unbalanced load on footing.
Uplift and overturning from wind.
Uplift caused by pump handles. Check for unbalanced loading.
Impact and vibration from machinery.

Other Loads

Reactions from pressure piping.
Overturning caused by bending in column.
Earthquake.

DESIGN DATA

TABLE I.   PRESUMPTIVE SAFE BEARING CAPACITY OF SUPPORTING SOILS *

Class	Material	Maximum Allowable Presumptive Bearing Values, tons per sq. ft.
1	Hard sound rock	60
2	Medium hard rock	40
3	Hardpan overlaying rock	12
4	Compact gravel and boulder-gravel formations; very compact sandy gravel	10
5	Soft rock	8
6	Loose gravel and sandy gravel; compact sand and gravelly sand; very compact sand-inorganic silt soils	6
7	Hard dry consolidated clay	5
8	Loose coarse to medium sand; medium compact fine sand	4
9	Compact sand-clay soils	3
10	Loose fine sand; medium compact sand-inorganic silt soils	2
11	Firm or stiff clay	1.5
12	Loose saturated sand-clay soils; medium soft clay	1

*Adapted from N.Y.C. Building Code, 1951.

TABLE II.   COMPACTION RELATED TO SPOON BLOWS WITH 2-IN. SPOONS *
FOR MEDIUM SAND

Approximate Blows per Foot

Descriptive Term	148-Lb. Hammer † 30-In. Fall	300-Lb. Hammer 18-In. Fall	150-Lb. Hammer 18-In. Fall
Loose	15 or less	10 or less	25 or less
Medium compact	16 to 30	11 to 25	25 to 45
Compact	30 to 50	26 to 45	45 to 65
Very compact	50 or more	45 or more	65 or more

* Table II was prepared by the Department of Housing and Buildings of the City of New York supplmenting Section C–26–3770,   Presumptive Bearing Capacities of Soils.
† Most common practice.

FOR CLAY

Very soft	Push to 3	Push to 2	Push to 5
Soft	4 to 12	3 to 10	5 to 15
Stiff	12 to 35	10 to 25	15 to 40
Hard	35 or more	25 or more	40 or more

Coarser soils require more blows; finer material, fewer blows. A variation of 10% in the weight of the hammer will not materially affect the values in tables.

The use of any specific size of spoon or any specific weight and fall of hammer is not mandatory in the Code. However, spoon of any other size or hammer of any weight exceeding the 10% variation from weight of hammer specified in Table II shall not be accepted until sufficient data have been submitted for investigation and approval.

TABLE III.   PRESUMPTIVE SAFE BEARING CAPACITY OF ROCKS

Type of Rock	Bearing-* Capacity	Remarks
Igneous † such as trap, granite, basalt, lava	20–60	Usually *hard*.‡ Does not erode or dissolve readily. Subject to cleavage planes and bed planes at all angles.
Sedimentary § such as		
Limestone	10–20	*Medium hard* ‡ as in limestone to *soft* ‡ as in chalks and
Shale	8–10	shales. Subject to dissolving erosion, forming of caves.
Chalk	8	Soft layers and seams, soft overburden. Bed planes gen-
Coral	8	erally horizontal.
Sandstone	10–20	
Metamorphic ¶ such as		
Gneiss	20–40	Gneiss and schist have igneous characteristics; slate and
Schist	20–40	marble have sedimentary.
Marble	10–20	
Slate	8	

* Bearing capacity of rocks suggested by author.
† *Igneous*. Derived from the interior of the earth in a molten condition by heat, pressure, and volcanic action.
‡ Approximate correlation to the *hard, medium hard,* and *soft* classification given before.
§ *Sedimentary*. Deposited in layers by water and cemented by the pressure of overburden.
¶ *Metamorphic*. Heat, pressure, and chemically active fluids have acted to impart new characteristics to the rocks.

TABLE IV. PILE SPACING AND LOADS *

Type of Pile	Friction or Bearing	Loads† Limiting Loads	Remarks	Spacing Min. c. to c.	Remarks
Wood	Friction	20 tons 6″ Point / 25 tons 8″ Point or >	15 & 20 ton piles in many codes	2′ 6″	1. Piles bearing on rock or penetrating into rock shall have a minimum spacing center to center of twice the average diameter or 1.75 times the diagonal of the pile, but not less than 24 in. 2. All other piles shall have a minimum spacing center to center of twice the average diameter or 1.75 times the diagonal of the pile but not less than 30 in., except that all piles located in groups or abutting groups that receive their principal support in materials such as clay, sand clay, or uncompacted sand shall have their spacing increased above the minimum values by 10% for each interior pile up to a maximum of 40%
Composite	Friction	Load of weaker section	—	2′ 6″	
Cast in place conc.	Friction	Max. 60 tons	Maximum axial load = $f_c \times A_c$	2′ 6″	
Pre-cast Concrete	Friction	Max. 60 tons	Maximum axial load = $f_c \times (A_c + nA_s)$, $P = 2\%$ min. 4% max.	2′ 6″	
Concrete filled steel pipe	Friction–driven with shoe	Max. 60 tons	$A_s \times 9{,}000 + A_c \times f_c$	2′ 6″	
	Bearing–driven open-ended to rock and cleaned out	Max. 200 tons or ½ jacking pressure	See p. 3–8 for sizes and loads	2′ 0″	
Steel H piles	Friction	Max. 60 tons	$A_s \times 9{,}000$	2′ 6″	
	Bearing-hard rock	120 tons max. on rock. 80 tons on hardpan or gravel boulders overlying rock (over 40 tons requires load test)	See p. 3–8 for sizes and loads	2′ 0″	
	Bearing-encased in concrete and steel shell	200 tons max. on hard-rock (over 100 tons requires load test)	See p. 3–8 for sizes and loads	2′ 0″	
Drilled in caissons	Bearing	—	Generally from 200 to 2500 tons	—	Generally one under each column

* Based on N.Y.C. Building Code, 1950.
† Load test required for friction piles over 30 tons. Use *Engineering News* formula. If piles are driven into soft clays, silts, or mud without reaching hard stratum, formula should be checked by load test.

STEEL PIPE AND STRUCTURAL STEEL PILES ON ROCK

TABLE V – STEEL PIPE PILES ON ROCKS*

DIAMETER	WALL THICKNESS	LOAD IN TONS
$8\frac{3}{4}$	$\frac{5}{16}$	40
$10\frac{3}{4}$	$\frac{5}{16}$	53
	$\frac{3}{8}$	59
	$\frac{7}{16}$	66
$12\frac{3}{4}$	$\frac{5}{16}$	67
	$\frac{3}{8}$	75
	$\frac{7}{16}$	83
	$\frac{1}{2}$	91
14	$\frac{3}{8}$	85
	$\frac{7}{16}$	94
	$\frac{1}{2}$	103
	$\frac{5}{8}$	120
15	$\frac{3}{8}$	93
	$\frac{7}{16}$	103
	$\frac{1}{2}$	113
	$\frac{5}{8}$	131
16	$\frac{3}{8}$	103
	$\frac{7}{16}$	113
	$\frac{1}{2}$	123
	$\frac{5}{8}$	143
18	$\frac{3}{8}$	122
	$\frac{7}{16}$	133
	$\frac{1}{2}$	144
	$\frac{5}{8}$	167
20	$\frac{3}{8}$	142
	$\frac{7}{16}$	154
	$\frac{1}{2}$	167
	$\frac{5}{8}$	192

TABLE VI – STRUCTURAL STEEL PILES ON ROCK*

SIZE	NOT ENCAS'D LOAD IN TONS	ENCASED LOAD IN TONS	ENCASED DIA. OF ENCAS.
8 BP 36	47	86	$15\frac{1}{2}$
10 BP 42	55	107	18
10 BP 57	75	129	$18\frac{1}{4}$
12 BP 53	70	140	21
12 BP 74	98	171	$21\frac{1}{4}$
14 BP 73	96	189	24
14 BP 89	118	200	$24\frac{1}{4}$
14 BP 102	120	200	$24\frac{1}{2}$
14 BP 117	120	200	$24\frac{3}{4}$
8 WF 31	41	78	$15\frac{1}{4}$
8 WF 58	76	118	16
8 WF 67	88	133	$16\frac{1}{2}$
10 WF 49	64	118	$18\frac{1}{4}$
10 WF 60	79	133	$18\frac{1}{4}$
10 WF 77	102	156	$18\frac{1}{4}$
12 WF 85	112	187	$21\frac{1}{2}$
14 WF 84	111	195	$22\frac{3}{4}$

TABLE VII – PILE DIMENSIONS (USE WITH FIGURE BELOW)

CENTER TO CENTER OF PILES "D" INCHES	3-PILE PIERS a INCHES	3-PILE PIERS b INCHES	5 & 13 PILE PIERS a INCHES	7,8,10,11 & 14 PILE PIERS a INCHES
24	14	7	17	21
25	15	$7\frac{1}{2}$	18	22
26	15	$7\frac{1}{2}$	$18\frac{1}{2}$	$22\frac{1}{2}$
27	16	8	19	$23\frac{1}{2}$
28	16	8	20	$24\frac{1}{2}$
29	17	$8\frac{1}{2}$	$20\frac{1}{2}$	25
30	17	$8\frac{1}{2}$	$21\frac{1}{2}$	26
31	18	9	22	27
32	19	$9\frac{1}{2}$	$22\frac{1}{2}$	28
33	19	$9\frac{1}{2}$	$23\frac{1}{2}$	$28\frac{1}{2}$
34	20	10	24	$29\frac{1}{2}$
35	21	$10\frac{1}{2}$	25	$30\frac{1}{2}$
36	21	$10\frac{1}{2}$	$25\frac{1}{2}$	31
37	22	11	$26\frac{1}{2}$	32
38	22	11	27	33
40	23	$11\frac{1}{2}$	$28\frac{1}{2}$	35
42	24	12	30	$36\frac{1}{2}$
44	26	13	$31\frac{1}{2}$	$38\frac{1}{2}$
46	27	$13\frac{1}{2}$	$32\frac{1}{2}$	40
48	28	14	34	$41\frac{1}{2}$
50	29	$14\frac{1}{2}$	$35\frac{1}{2}$	$43\frac{1}{2}$
52	30	15	37	45
54	31	$15\frac{1}{2}$	$38\frac{1}{2}$	$46\frac{1}{2}$
56	33	$16\frac{1}{2}$	40	$48\frac{1}{2}$

PILE GROUP SPACING FOR TABLE VII

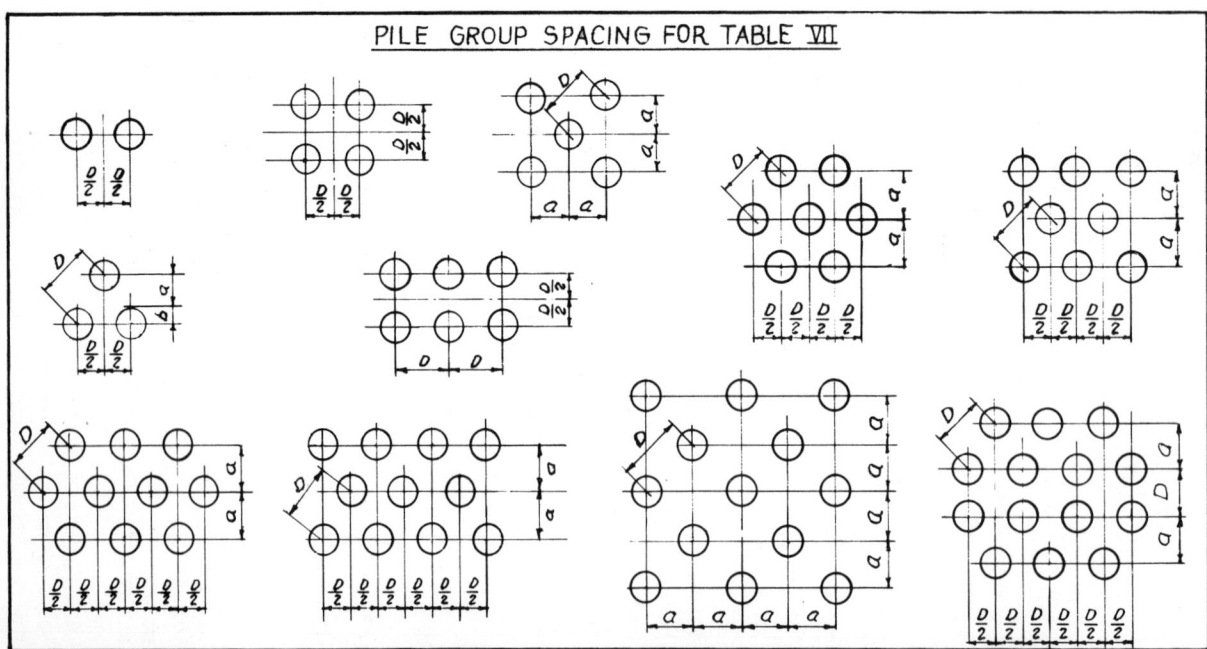

*Based on New York City Building Code, 1950. 500 p.s.i. concrete and piles not load-tested.

TABLE VIII.   PROBABLE PENETRATION EXPECTANCY FOR FRICTION PILES *

Material	Penetration	Remarks
Clean compact sand	Slight	Usually jetted.
Other sands	20 ft.	———
Sandy clay	30 ft.	———
Pure clay	35 ft.	———
Clay and silt	45 ft.	———
Silt and mud	50 to 100 ft.	———
Glacial till	Slight	Piles cannot be driven.

* Penetration can be best determined by test piles or test rods. This table is to be used only for a rough indication from borings.

SAFE UPLIFT STRENGTH OF PILES

Friction piles, in sand, clay or gravel.   Use one-half the safe bearing load.

Point Bearing Piles (piles driven to hard stratum).   Compute by contact surface area x shearing strength of material penetrated.   See p. 4–8 for soil shearing values.   Note: for sand 250 lb. per sq. ft. suggested.

Full size tests are desirable on account of the difficulty of establishing data for computation.

Batter Piles.   Maximum batter 3 on 1; many rigs can drive maximum of only 4 on 1.

Lateral force at top of piles = 1 kip allowable without test. Also 1 kip allowed on batter piles in addition to horizontal component.

LATERAL BRACING OF STRUCTURES
PACIFIC COAST UNIFORM BUILDING CODE - 1952
SUPERSTRUCTURE:

Design structure as a whole and every portion of same to resist lateral forces applied at each floor or roof level above foundations. Horizontal Force, $F = CW$ in lbs. Where: C = Force factor; factor from Table IX. W = total D.L. at and above point under consideration except for warehouses and tanks where: W = Total D.L. + Total L.L.

FOUNDATIONS:

All foundations on piles or soil with less than 2000#/◻' bearing value shall have footings interconnected with ties in two directions at 90° to each other. Tie shall transmit 10% of vertical load of heavier footing connected. Concrete slab min. 6" or ⅟48 span, and not more than 12" above top of footing may be used in place of ties. Min. reinf. ⅜"∅ at 12" O.C. each way.

GENERAL DESIGN DATA:

Stresses shall not be more than 33⅓% above allowable working stresses in code except that shear in concrete walls 6" or thicker shall not exceed .05 f_c. Overturning moment shall not exceed ⅔ of moment of stability both calculated using the same loads. Calculation of shears and moments shall be in accordance with the wind design.

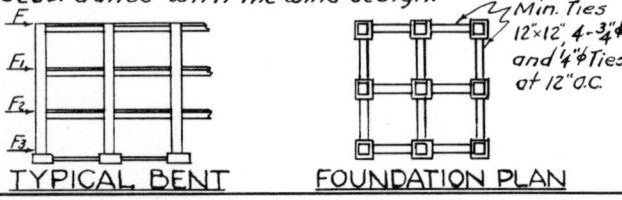

Min. Ties
12"×12", 4-¾"∅
and ¼"∅ Ties
at 12" O.C.

TYPICAL BENT   FOUNDATION PLAN

TABLE IX - HORIZONTAL FORCE FACTORS		
PART OR PORTION	VALUE OF "C" **	DIRECTION OF FORCE
Floors, roofs, columns and bracing in any story of a bldg. or the structure as a whole **	$\frac{15}{N+4\frac{1}{2}}$	Any direction horizontally
Bearing walls, non-bearing walls, partitions, free standing masonry walls over 6' in height	.05 with min. of 5%/◻'	Normal to surface of wall
Cantilever parapet and other cantilever walls, except retaining walls	.25	Normal to surface of wall
Exterior and Interior ornamentations & appendages	.25	Any direction horizontally
When connected to or a part of a building: towers, tanks, towers and tanks plus contents, chimneys, smokestacks & penthouses.	.05	Any direction horizontally
Elevated water tanks and other tower supported structures not supported by a building	.03	Any direction horizontally

* See Fig. 2 for zones. The values given "C" are minimum and should be adopted in locations not subject to frequent seismic disturbances as shown in zone 1. For location in zone 2, "C" shall be doubled. For locations in zone 3 "C" shall be multiplied by 4.
** Where wind load would produce higher stresses this load shall be used in lieu of factor shown. N is number of stories above the story under consideration, provided that for floors or horizontal bracing, N shall be only the number of stories contributing loads.

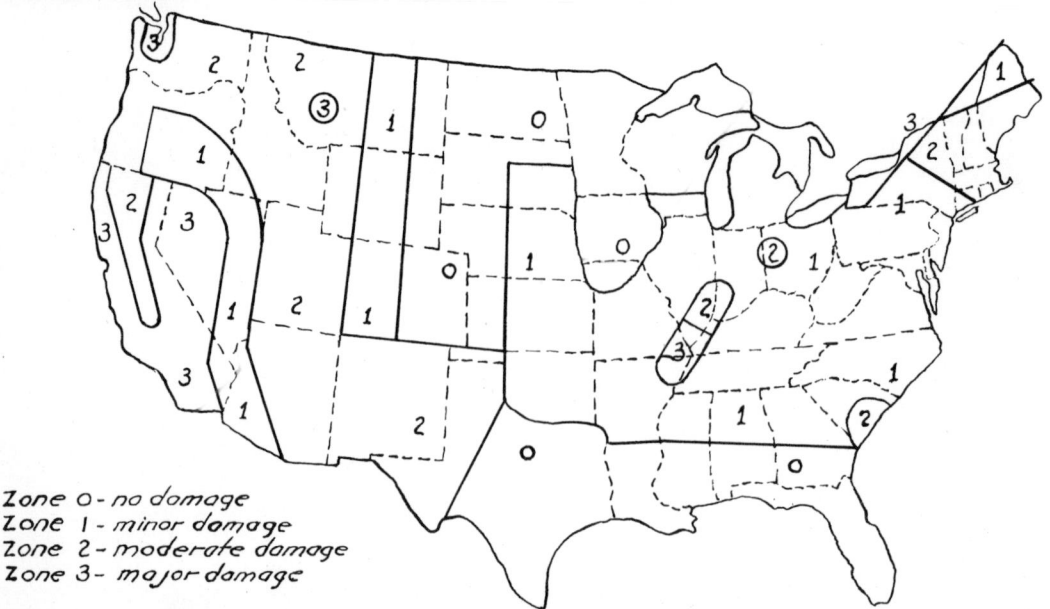

Zone 0 - no damage
Zone 1 - minor damage
Zone 2 - moderate damage
Zone 3 - major damage

FIG. 2. SEISMIC PROBABILITY MAP OF THE UNITED STATES.

DETAIL DESIGN OF ELEMENTARY FOOTINGS

As indicated in Chapter 1, the push-button square footing has many details and distortions requiring design. Certain typical problems are worked out for the aid of the user of this book.

Problem 1. Design of Square Footings

Given: Column load, 400 kips; column, 18 × 18.
   Soil bearing, 4000 p.s.f.
   Ultimate strength of concrete, 3000 p.s.i.; allowable stress, 1350 p.s.i.
   Allowable unit shear 75 p.s.i.; bond stress, 240 p.s.i.

   Column load   400
   Footing   30
                ———
                   430

To Design Footing:

   Size of footing, $430/4 = 107.5$. Use 10' 6" square. $A = 110$ sq. ft.
   For computing strength neglect weight of footing.
   Net upward pressure:

$$\frac{400,000}{110} = 3630 \text{ p.s.f.}$$

   Assume $d = 20''$. Net shear at a point 20" from column is

$$3630 \,(110 - 4.83^2) = 315,000 \text{ lb.}$$

$$\text{Unit shear} = \frac{315,000}{\tfrac{7}{8} \times 20 \times 58 \times 4} = 77.5 \text{ p.s.i.}$$

For bond:
   Shear $= 0.85 \times 4.5 \times 10.5 \times 3630$
        $= 146,000$ lb.

$$\text{Perimeter} = \frac{146,000}{\tfrac{7}{8} \times 20 \times 240} = 35 \text{ in.}$$

For moment:
   Moment $= 146 \times 2.25 = 328$ ft.-lb.

$$\text{Steel area} = \frac{328}{1.44 \times 20} = 11.4 \text{ sq. in.}$$

   Nine No. 10 bars each way. Area $= 11.4$ sq. in. Perimeter $= 35.9$ sq. in.
   Concrete Moment $= 10.5 \times 94.2 = 990$ allowable. (From Chapter 19.)

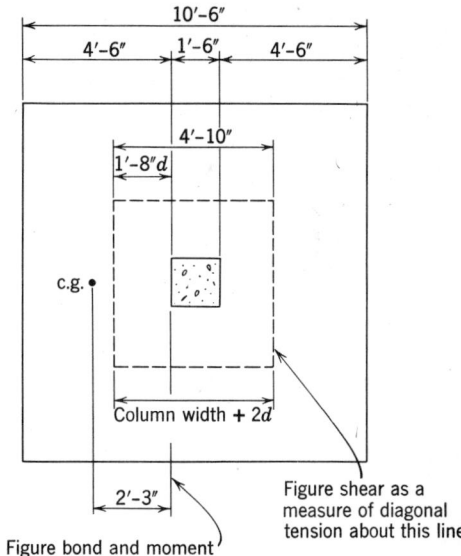

10'-6"
4'-6"   1'-6"   4'-6"
4'-10"
1'-8"d
c.g.•
Column width + 2d
2'-3"
Figure bond and moment about this line. Use 85% because of 2 way action.
Figure shear as a measure of diagonal tension about this line

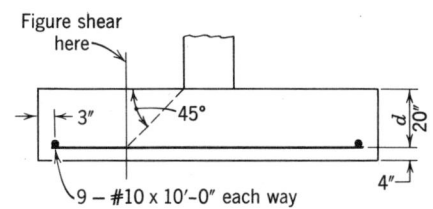

Figure shear here
3"   45°
d 20"
4"
9 — #10 x 10'-0" each way

FIG. 3.

In cases where a steel column bears on a concrete footing, the footing is designed the same way, using a column dimension of $\frac{b + c}{2}$

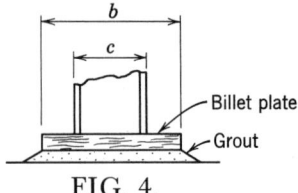

FIG. 4.

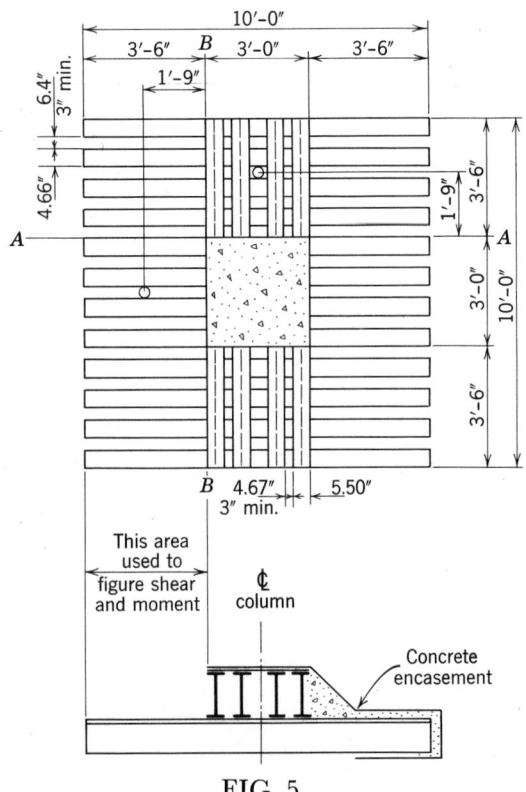

FIG. 5.

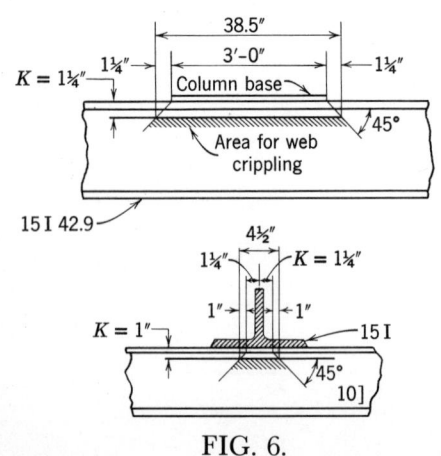

FIG. 6.

Problem 2.   Design of Column Grillage

Given: Column load 600 kips.
        Soil bearing capacity, 6000 p.s.f.
Design grillage

$$\frac{600,000}{6000} = 100 \text{ sq. ft.}   10' \times 10'$$

Top tier at line *AA*

$$\text{Shear} = \frac{3.5'}{10'} \times 600^k = 210^k   \text{Per beam} = 52^k$$

$$\text{Moment} = 210^k \times 1.75' = 368^{k'} S = 220 \text{ in.}^3$$
Per beam = 54 in.^{3}
        Use four 15 I 42.9 $S = 58.9$ in.^{3}
                Allowable $V = 80^k$.

Bottom tier at line *BB*

$$\text{Shear} = \frac{3.5'}{10'} \times 600^k = 210^k   \text{Per beam} = 17.5^k$$

$$\text{Moment} = 210^k \times 1.75' = 368^{k'}   S = 220 \text{ in.}^3$$
Per beam = 18.3 in.^{3}
12—10 I 25.4
Top tier: Check web crippling

$$\text{Per beam} = \frac{600^k}{4} = 150^k$$

$$\text{Crippling} = \frac{150,000}{38.5 \times .41} = 9,500 \text{ p.s.i.}$$

Allowable = 24,000 p.s.i.

$$\text{Bottom tier per beam} = \frac{600^k}{12} = 50^k$$

$$\text{Crippling} = \frac{50,000}{4.5 \times .31 \times 4} = 9000 \text{ p.s.i.}$$

Problem 3.   Design of Pile Cap

Given: Column load = 400 kips; 18 × 18 column.

    Pile capacity 25 tons

    Ultimate strength of concrete, 2000 p.s.i.

       Bond 160 p.s.i.   Unit shear 60 p.s.i.

    Column load 400^k

    Footing estimated $\underline{24}$

                              424

To Design Pile Cap:

    Use 9 piles.

    For strength computing neglect weight of cap.

Net pile reaction $= \dfrac{400}{9} = 44.5^k$

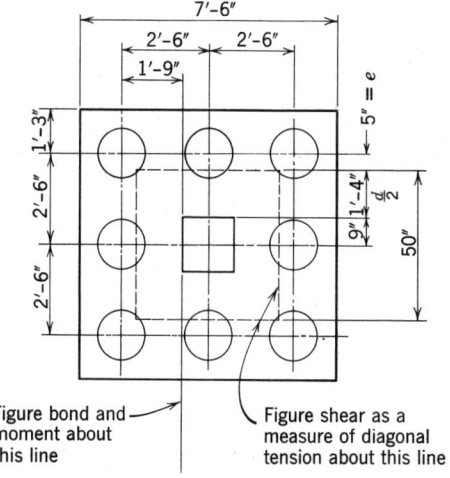

    Assume $d = 32''$.

    No. of piles producing shear = 8

          $8 \times 44.5 = 356^k$

    Since center line of pile is less than 6″ from shear plane, figure fraction of pile according to formula

$\dfrac{6 + e}{12}$, where e has an algebraic sign.   Here $e = +5$.

    Shear $= \dfrac{6 + 5}{12} \times 365 = 325$

    Unit shear $= \dfrac{325}{\frac{7}{8} \times 50 \times 4 \times 32} = 58$ p.s.i.

For bond shear $= 3 \times .85 \times 44.5 = 113^k$

    Perimeter $\dfrac{113{,}000}{160 \times \frac{7}{8} \times 32} = 25.5$

      Moment $= 113 \times 1.75 = 198$

    Steel area $= \dfrac{198}{1.44 \times 32} = 4.42$

      15— No. 5 each way.   Area = 4.65

                Perimeter = 29.4

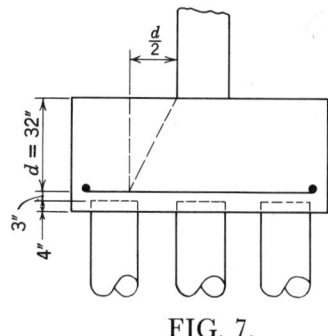

FIG. 7.

Overturning of Foundations

Problem 4.   Spread Footing

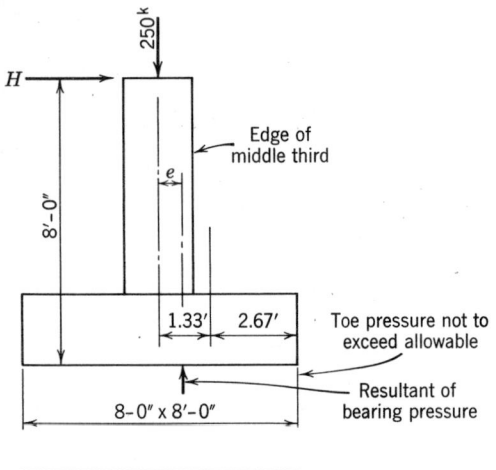

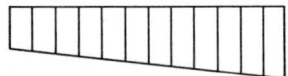

Resultant in
middle third

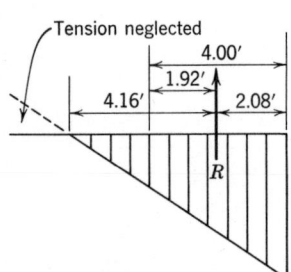

Resultant outside
middle third

FIG. 8.

General Conditions. Given: column load including footing 250 kips.

Then compute soil pressure $= \dfrac{250}{8} = 3900$ p.s.f.

Section modulus of soil contact area

$$\frac{bd^2}{6} = \frac{8 \times 8^2}{6} = 85.5$$

Case I. Given: $H = 10$ kips. Compute moment $= 10 \times 8 = 80.$

Pressure from overturning $= \dfrac{80}{85.5} = \pm 935$

Toe pressure $= 3900 + 935 = 4835$
Heel pressure $= 3900 - 935 = 2965$

Case II. $H = 60$; moment $= 8 \times 60 = 480$

$e = \dfrac{480}{250} = 1.92 \qquad 4 - 1.92 = 2.08$

Size of pressure base $= 3 \times 2.08 = 6.24$

$\dfrac{250 \times 2}{8 \times 6.24} = 10{,}000$ p.s.f. toe pressure

Problem 5. Pile Footing

Given: Column load plus cap = 250 kips Horizontal load, 65 kips.

Compute moment of inertia of pile group.

$$I = 3 \times 2.5^2 \times 2 = 37.5$$

$$S = \frac{37.5}{2.5} = 15$$

Overturning moment = $65^k \times 8' = 520^{1k}$

$$\text{Vertical load} = \frac{250}{9} = 27.8^k$$

Overturning load = $\pm \dfrac{520}{15} = \dfrac{\pm 34.6^k}{\substack{+62.4^k \text{ or} \\ -\ 6.8^k}}$
Load per pile

Note: Piles can take uplift; see p. 3–9.

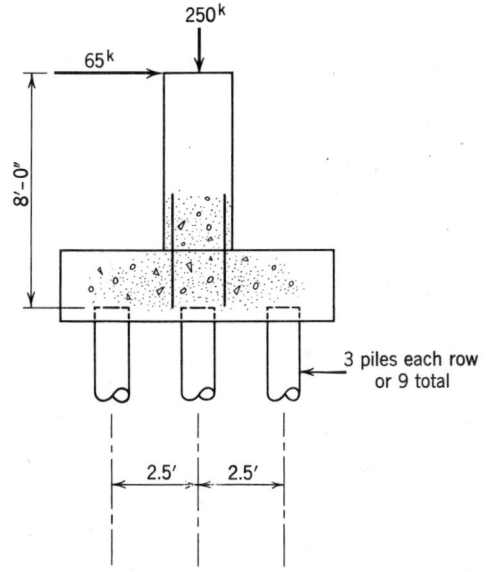

3 piles each row
or 9 total

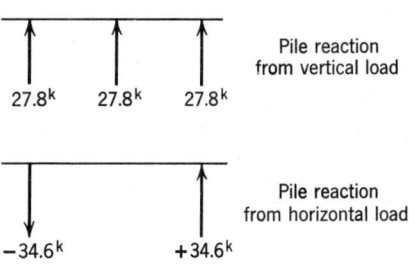

Pile reaction
from vertical load

Pile reaction
from horizontal load

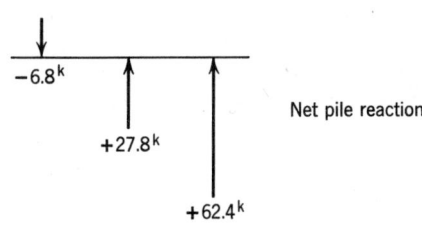

Net pile reaction

FIG. 9.

Problem 6. Design of Beam Bearing Plate

$fs = 20{,}000$ p.s.i.

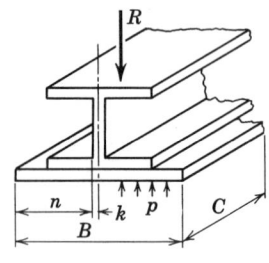

FIG. 10.

Given: $R = 40{,}000$ lb.

$p = 200$ p.s.i.

$C = 10''$ (max. bearing available)

Beam 18 WF 55 $k = 1\frac{1}{8}''$

Compute: $B = \dfrac{40{,}000}{10 \times 200} = 20''$. $n = \dfrac{B}{2} - k = \dfrac{20}{2} - 1\frac{1}{8} = 8\frac{7}{8}''$

$$t = n\sqrt{\frac{0.15\,p}{1000}} = 8.88\sqrt{\frac{0.15 \times 200}{1000}} = 1.54$$

Use $10'' \times 1\frac{1}{2}'' \times 1' - 8''$ plate, neglecting 2.7% overstress.

Problem 7. Design of Column Billet Plate

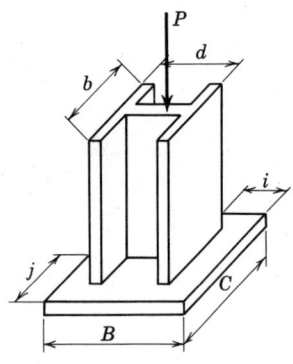

FIG. 11.

Given: $P = 400{,}000$ lb.

$p = 875$ p.s.i.

b and $d = 12$ in.

Compute $A = B \times C = \dfrac{400{,}000}{875} = 457.$

Select $20'' \times 23''$ plate, $A = 460$ sq. in., $C = 20''$.

$$j = \frac{C - 0.8b}{2} = \frac{20 - 0.8 \times 12}{2} = 5.2''$$

$$i = \frac{B - 0.95d}{2} = \frac{23 - 0.95 \times 12}{2} = 5.8''$$

Use 5.8, since it is larger than 5.2.

$$t = i\sqrt{\frac{0.15p}{1000}} = 5.8\sqrt{\frac{0.15 \times 875}{1000}} = 2.1$$

Use $20'' \times 2\frac{1}{4}'' \times 1'\text{-}11''$ plate.

Other Methods of Removing Eccentricities from Footings

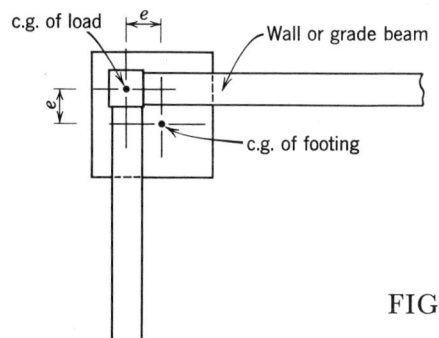

Moment caused by eccentricity (Pe) removed by walls acting as pump handles

FIG. 18.

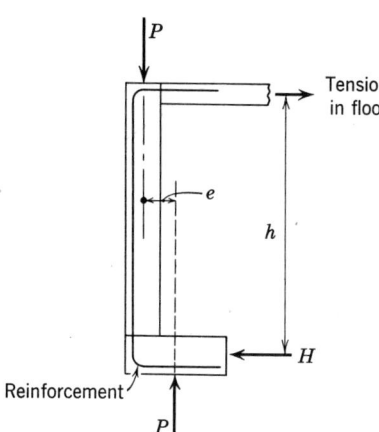

Resisting eccentric moment by horizontal forces at the floors. For equilibrium, $Pe = Hh$.

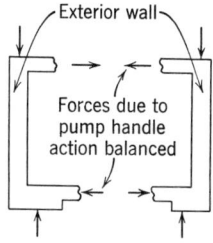

Must be balanced by similar construction on opposite side of building or by strength of floor system butressed by cross walls or portal effect of columns.

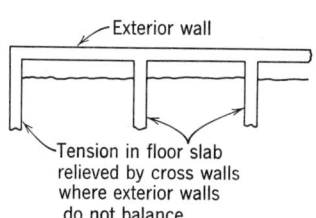

FIG. 19.

Problem 12.   Four-Way Footing

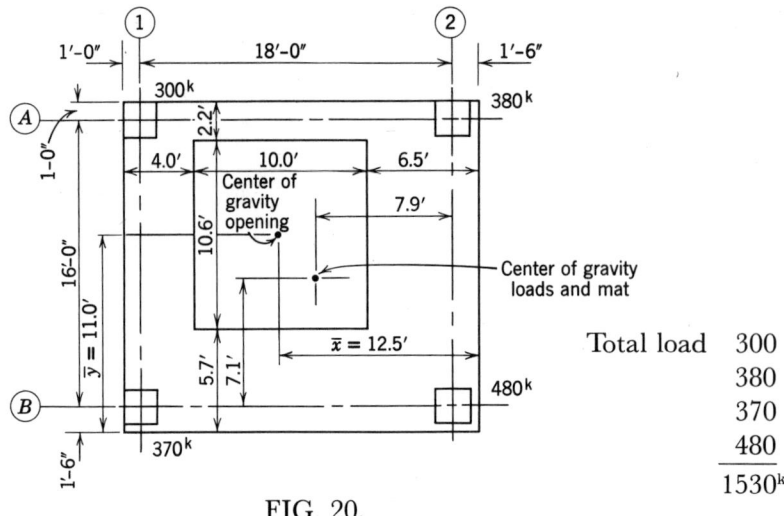

FIG. 20.

Given: Safe soil bearing = 6000 p.s.f.
Assume: Mat weighs 400 p.s.f.   Net soil bearing, 5600 p.s.f.

Compute: Required area $= \dfrac{1530}{5.6} = 273$ sq. ft.

Gross mat area $= 18.5 \times 20.5 = 379$ sq. ft.
Area of opening $= 379 - 273 = 106$ sq. ft.

Locate opening so that center of gravity of mat coincides with center of gravity of loads.
Moments about right edge of mat:

$$379 \times \frac{20.5}{2} - 106\bar{x} = 273 \times (7.9 + 1.5)$$

$$\bar{x} = 12.5$$

About bottom:

$$379 \times \frac{18.5}{2} - 106\bar{y} = 273 \times (7.1 + 1.5)$$

$$\bar{y} = 11.0$$

Select opening 10.6 × 10.0 ($A = 106$ sq. ft.), and locate as shown.

Problem 13. Design of Wall Grillage

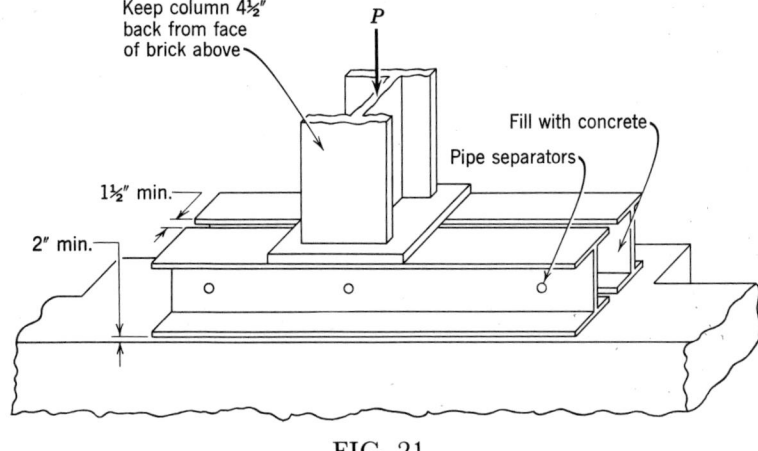

Given: $P = 225$ kips.
Column = 12 W 53
Bearing on wall, 500 p.s.i.

FIG. 21.

Compute: Bearing area $= \dfrac{225,000 \text{ lb.}}{500 \text{ p.s.i.}} = 450$ sq. in.

Assume: 2–10 I 35.0; flange 5″.

$\dfrac{450}{2 \times 5} = 45.0″$ grillage 3′–9″ long

Column flange 10″ grillage cantilever $= \dfrac{45 - 10}{2} = 17.5$

Shear $= 17.5 \times 5 \times 500 = 43.7^{\text{k}}$; unit shear $= \dfrac{43.7}{10 \times .594} = 7400$ p.s.i.

Moment $= 43.7 \times \dfrac{20}{2} = 437$ $\dfrac{437}{20} = 21.9$; S = 29.2 provided

Check bending in flange 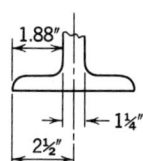 $t = 1.88\sqrt{\dfrac{500 \times .15}{1000}} = 0.54$

over 0.49 provided (O.K.)

Check for web crippling

$10 + 2\,(1) = 12$

$\dfrac{225,000}{12 \times 2 \times .59} = 15,900$ p.s.i.

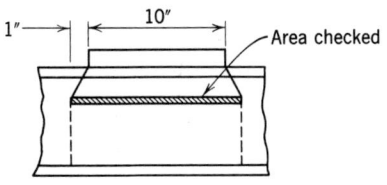

FIG. 22.

Billet Plate.   Assume 80% of column load in flanges

$$0.80 \times 225 = 180$$

Grillage beams 6″ c.c.

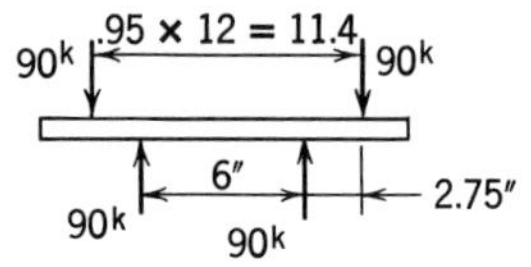

FIG. 23.

$$M = 90 \times 2.75 = 248; \frac{248}{20} = 2.4$$

$$\frac{bt^2}{6} = 2.4$$

$$t^2 = \frac{2.4 \times 6}{10} = 1.44$$

$$t = 1.2$$

Plate is 10″ × 1¼″ × 1′-2″

Note: 2–12 I 31.8 would fail by web crippling.

$$\frac{225,000}{12\frac{1}{4} \times 2 \times .35} = 26,200 \text{ p.s.i. (too high)}$$

Problem 14.   Long Billet on Wall

Given: $P = 225$ kips

Column 12 WF 53

Bearing on wall 500 p.s.i.

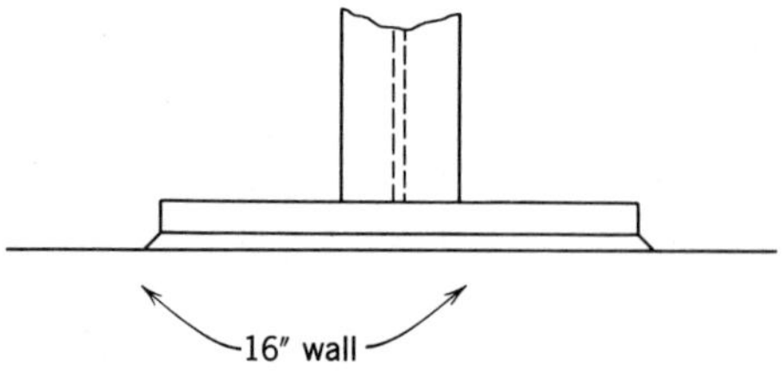

FIG. 24.

Maximum width of billet 12″ (allowing 2″ to face of wall)

Compute bearing area $\dfrac{225,000}{500 \text{ p.s.i.}} = 450$ sq. in.

Length of billet $= \dfrac{450}{12} = 37.5$; use 38″

$\dfrac{38 - 8}{2} = 15$ in. $t = 15\sqrt{\dfrac{.15 \times 500}{1000}} = 4.1$ in.

Use standard 4½ PL.   Billet is 12″ × 4½″ × 3′-2″; weight 583 lb.

DESIGN OF MAT FOUNDATIONS

Mats should be designed as continuous two-way plates strong enough to exert a continuous uniform pressure both longitudinally and transversely over the entire site. Cost limitations may limit the design to partial rather than full rigidity. On long spans, mats may be reinforced by ribs.

Mats are used:
1. To reduce concentrations of high soil pressure.
2. To resist hydrostatic head.
3. To distribute loads from the periphery of the building over the entire building area.

Uses of Mats

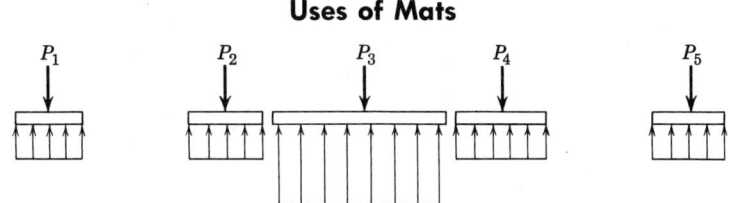

Footing under P_3 cannot be enlarged because of lack of room.

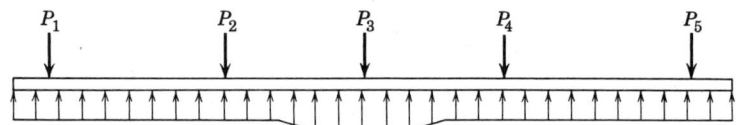

Extra load of P_3 is distributed over mat resulting in lower maximum soil pressure.

CASE I

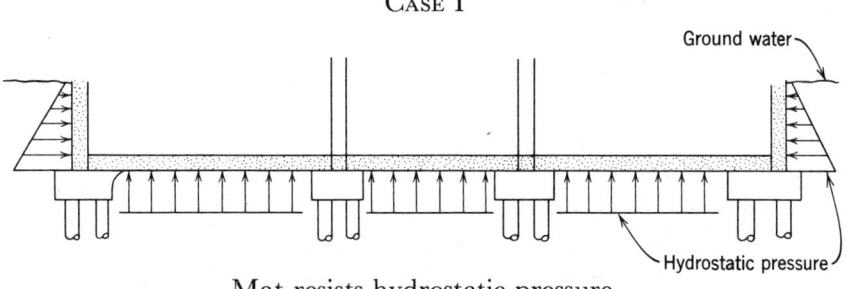

Mat resists hydrostatic pressure.

CASE II

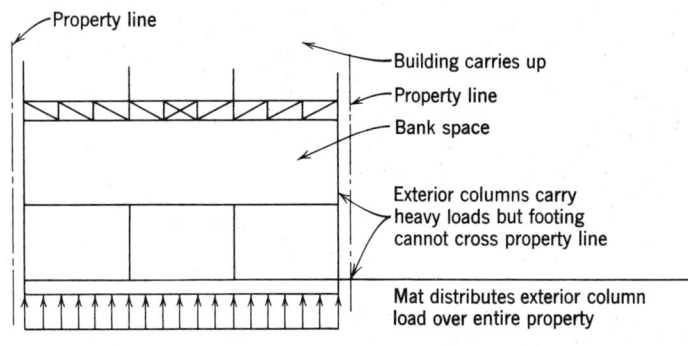

CASE III   FIG. 25.

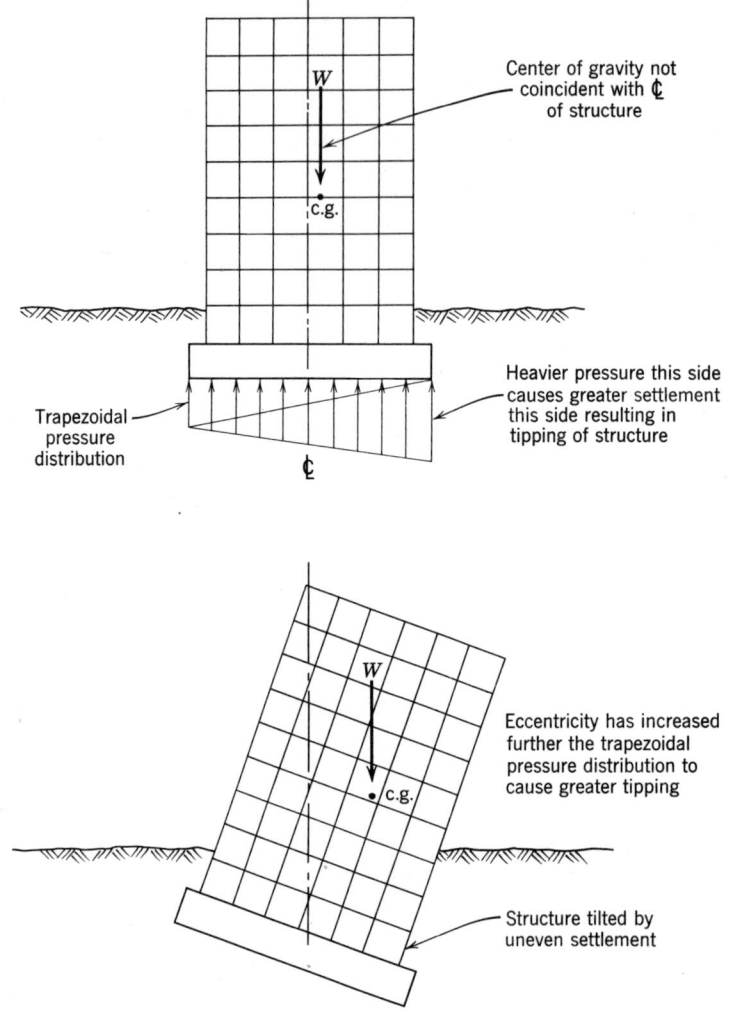

FIG. 26.   ILLUSTRATING TILTING OF WAREHOUSE.

Red Light.   Danger accompanying trapezoidal pressure distribution under mat placed on plastic soil.

Note: Granular soils are not so prone to this danger.

Problem 15.   Design of Mat

Assume mat strip 1'-0 wide as shown in Fig. 28.

$$\text{Direct soil pressure } \frac{170,000}{54} = 3150 \text{ p.s.f.}$$

Pressure from eccentricity

$$M = 170 \times 1.9 = 322$$

$$\frac{bd^2}{6} = \frac{54^2 \times 1}{6} = 485$$

$$\pm \frac{322}{485} = \pm 665 \text{ p.s.f.}$$

	Max. 3815 p.s.f.;	min. 2485 p.s.f.
Wght. of 24″ mat	300	300
Net soil pressure	4115 p.s.f.	2785 p.s.f.

Construct shear and moment diagrams as shown.   Design mat for these shears and moments. Mats with columns and two-way slabs may be designed similarly using bands.

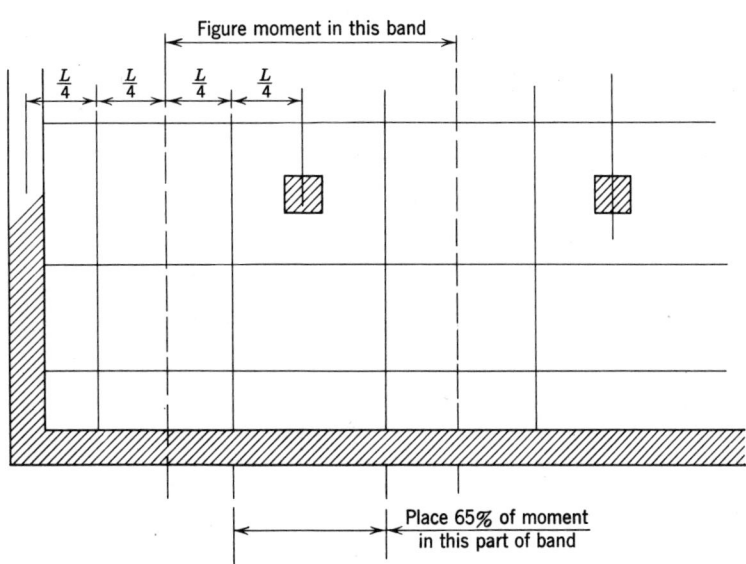

See also flat-slab design in Chapter 19.

FIG. 27.

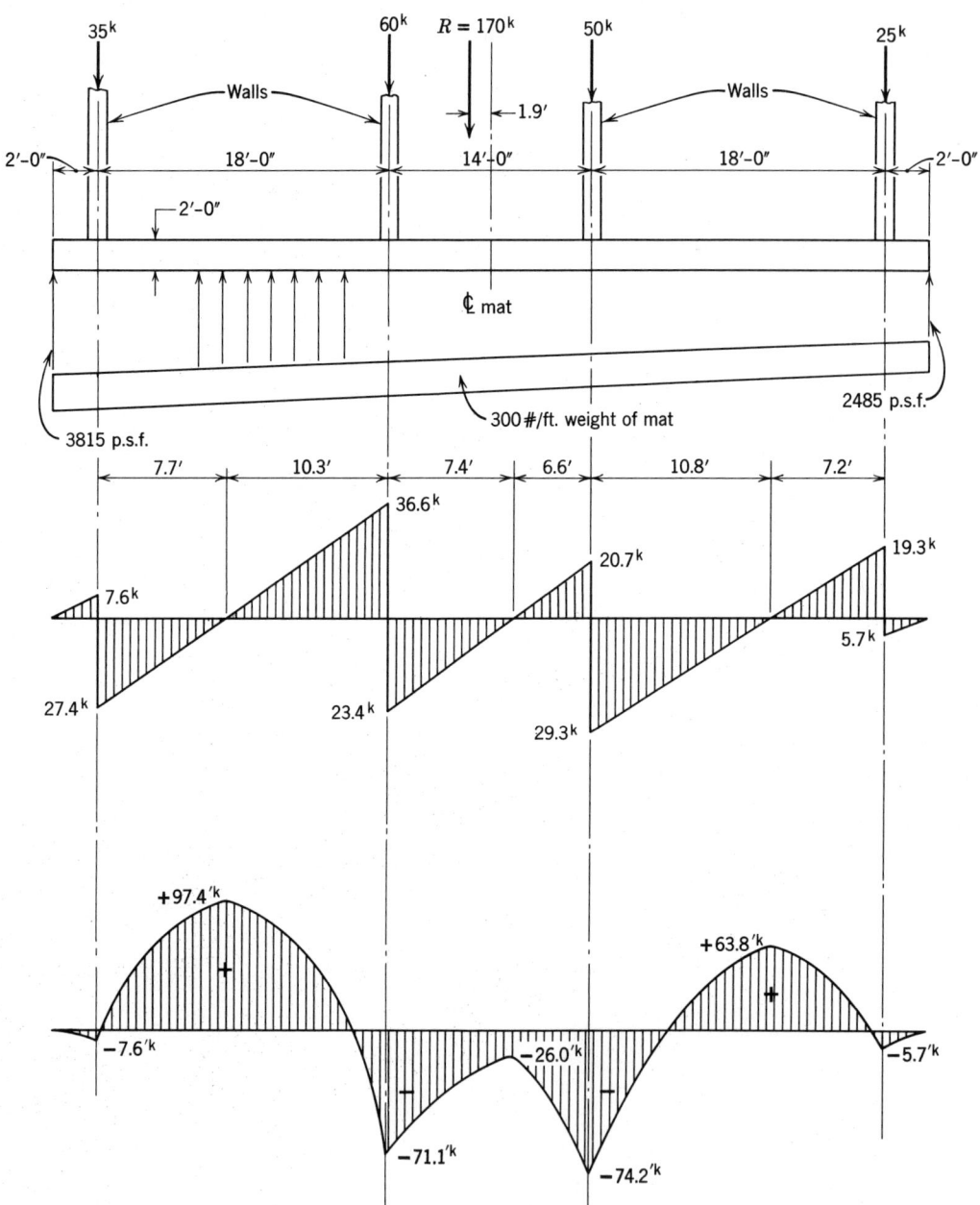

FIG. 28.

Mat for Hydrostatic Pressure Only

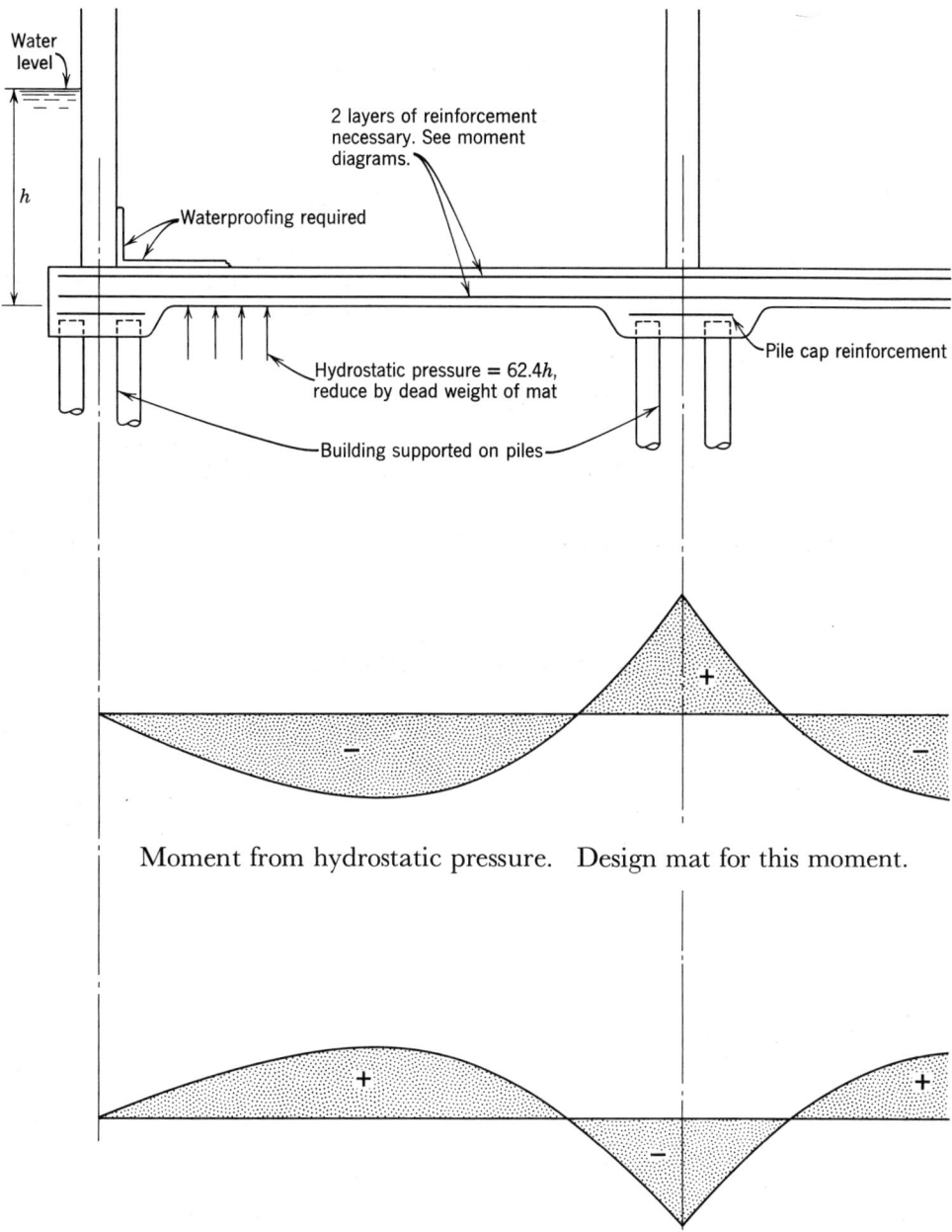

Moment from hydrostatic pressure.   Design mat for this moment.

Moment in case ground water is lowered.   Design mat for live load plus dead load using higher stresses such as 50% overstress.

FIG. 29.

DIFFERENCE IN ELEVATIONS

Difference in elevations between foundations new and/or existing pose certain problems for the designer, who must foresee them sometime in order that his design will be practicable.

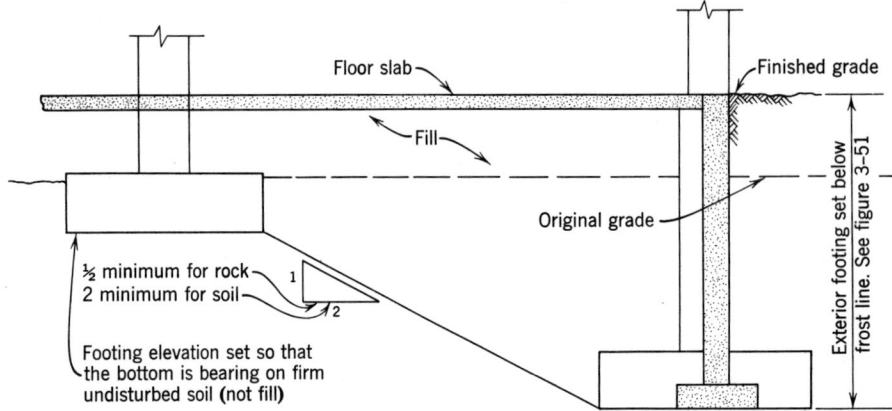

FIG. 30.   PRINCIPLES TO FOLLOW IN SETTING ELEVATIONS OF FOOTINGS.

Special Cases and Difficulties

Construction below Level of Adjacent Foundation

Work should be done by a skilled foundation contractor.

Foundation on Rock or Hardpan

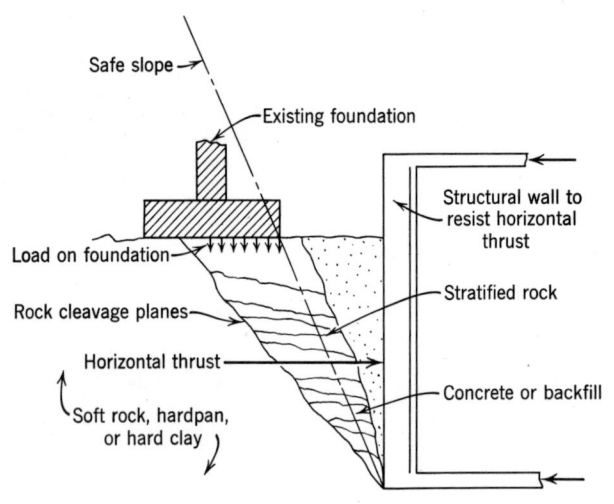

FIG. 31.

Safe slope varies with: (a) shearing strength of soil; (b) ground-water level; intensity of foundation load; (c) stratum of rock; (d) rock cleavage planes.

Suggested values are 1 on 2, clay; 0.5 on 1, hardpan; 2 on 1 to vertical, rock.

Foundation on Fine Running Sand

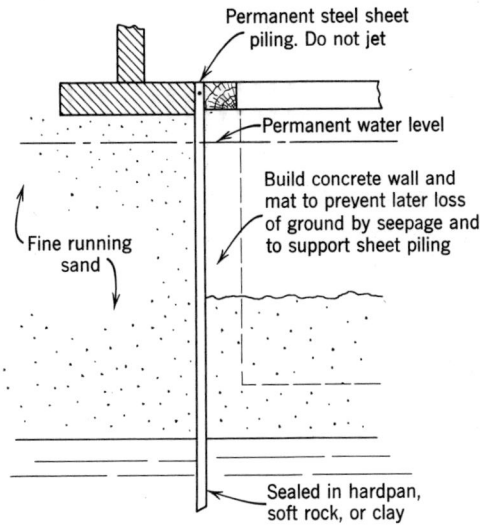

Permanent steel sheet piling. Do not jet

Permanent water level

Build concrete wall and mat to prevent later loss of ground by seepage and to support sheet piling

Fine running sand

Sealed in hardpan, soft rock, or clay

FIG. 32.

Pit construction below existing footings, below ground water, and in fine running sand.

Case I.   Lower water level with well points.

Case II.   Carry on construction under water.

Case III.   Drive down sheeting to a seal, pump by sump, and place mat.   See chapter on construction methods.

Condition to be avoided if possible.

Foundation on Soft Clay

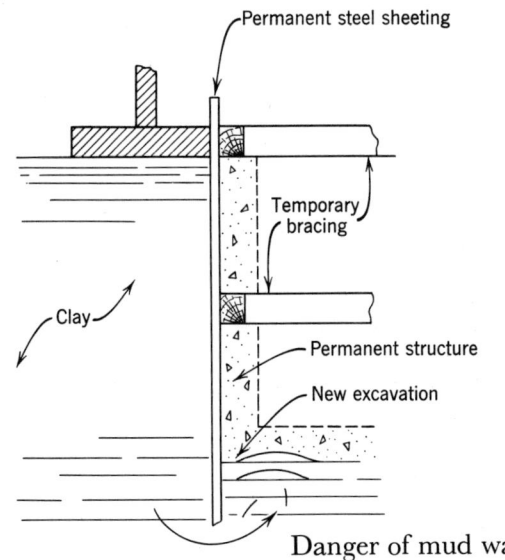

Permanent steel sheeting

Temporary bracing

Clay

Permanent structure

New excavation

Danger of mud wave.
Check soil shearing, p. 13–18.

Temporary bracing is removed as new structure is built and can take the thrust.

Warning: If sheet piling moves laterally building will settle.

Underpinning preferred except for light loads.

FIG. 33.

Footings on Gravel

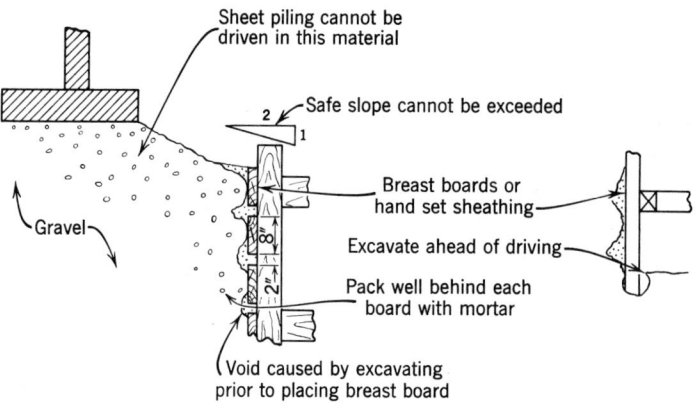

FIG. 34.

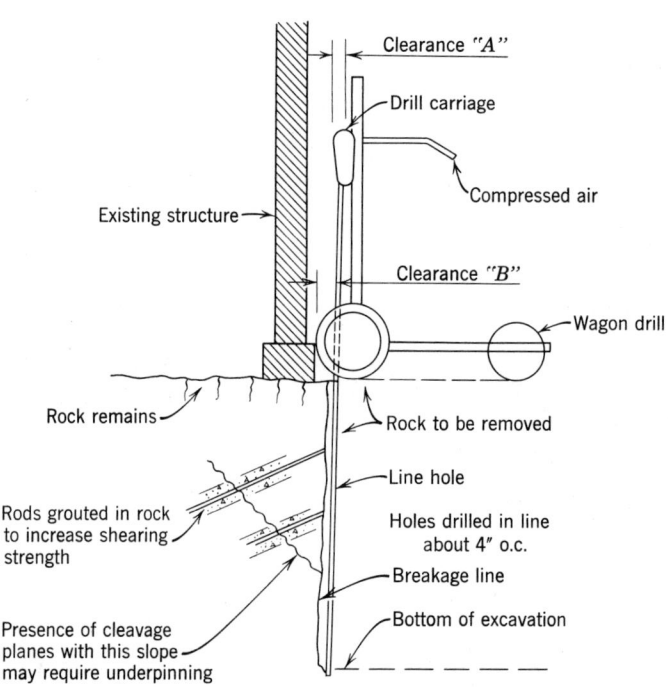

Closeness to existing structure is determined by clearance *A* or *B,* whichever is critical.   Some drills have wheels which may be rotated 90° to be parallel to wall, reducing clearance *B*.   Minimum clearance practical is 4″.

FIG. 35.   LINE DRILLING.

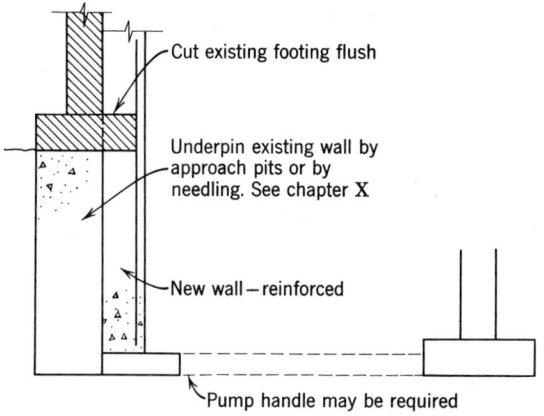

Cut existing footing flush

Underpin existing wall by approach pits or by needling. See chapter **X**

New wall—reinforced

Pump handle may be required

Warning: When soil is free running, use breast board, see Fig. 34 or pretest cylinders, see p. 1–11.

FIG. 36.   UNDERPINNING WALL.

Construction above Level of Adjacent Building

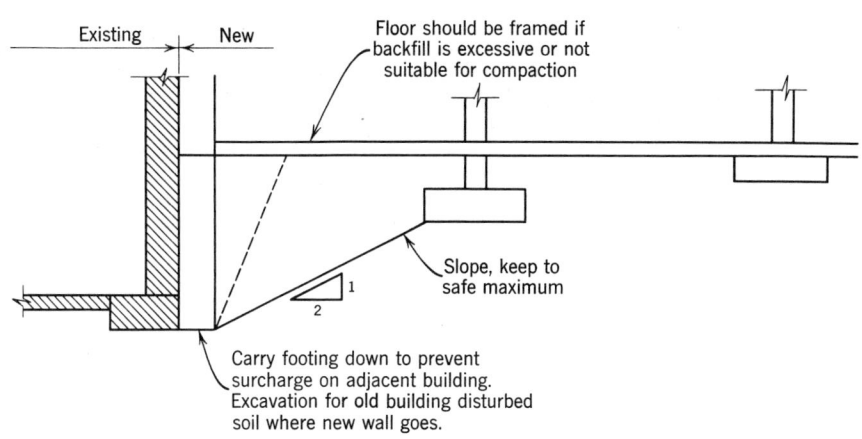

Existing

New

Floor should be framed if backfill is excessive or not suitable for compaction

Slope, keep to safe maximum

1
2

Carry footing down to prevent surcharge on adjacent building. Excavation for old building disturbed soil where new wall goes.

FIG. 37.

FOUNDATION WALLS

Foundation walls are generally supported laterally by the buildings into which they are built. Elementary types are shown in Figs. 38–40.

Case *a.*   This is the most common type of concrete wall.   Tables for "push-button" design are given in Chapter 2.   The earth pressure may be figured as shown.   *Red Light.*   Check stability of structure to resist thrust P_1.   Check adequacy of basement floor or footing to resist sliding from thrust P_2.

Case *b.*   This wall is often used when there is no way to resist thrust P_1 shown in case *a.*   It requires two faces of steel at the pilaster or cross wall.

Case *c.*   This wall is very common in house construction because of its cheapness.   It is sometimes figured for horizontal resistance as well as vertical.   Tensile stresses in masonry must be low —see Chapter 19 for values.

Red Lights

Check all foundation walls for shrinkage reinforcement and other details such as expansion joints. See discussion on p. 3–37.

Check for drainage and possibility of surcharge or hydrostatic pressure. A broken water main or a rise in ground water after a heavy rain will greatly increase the horizontal thrust. Adequate drainage will alleviate this. See Fig. 41. Provide waterproofing where necessary; see Chapter 9.

For details where slab on ground joins foundation walls, see industrial floor on ground, p. 14–34.

Problem 15

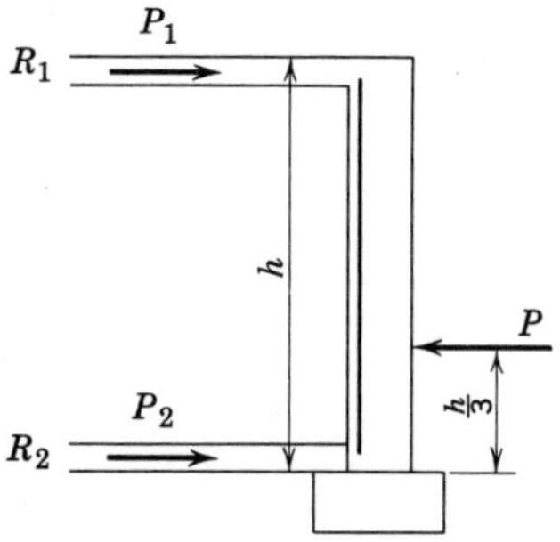

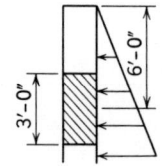

Given: Wall, Fig. 38.
Weight of earth = 100 lb. per cu. ft.
Height of wall = 10 ft.
Thickness of wall = 12 in.
Angle of repose = 33° = ϕ.
f_c = 2000.
f_s = 20,000.

> *To find: P* and *R*, and design vertical reinforced-concrete wall.

P = 1470 (see p. 2–12)
$R_1 = P/3 = 490$
$R_2 = 2P/3 = 980$
Steel required = #3 @ 10 c. to c.   See Table XI, Chapter 2.

FIG. 38.   CASE *a.*

Problem 16

Given: Same as above. Span between pilaster = 15 ft. Height of pilaster = 10 ft. To design reinforcement of wall 12 in. thick.

Compute: Moment in pilaster; thrust at floors.

FIG. 39A.   CASE *b.*

Thrust at floors and moment in pilasters = 15 times moments and thrusts computed in Fig. 38.
Compute the horizontal reinforcement as a series of bands of, say, 3′ 0″ wide.   Fig. 39A.
Then load on band 3′ 0″ = 177 × 3 × 15 = 7965 (177 is from Table XII, Chapter 2).
M = 1/10 × 7965 × 17 = 13,500
Reinforcement = 13,500/1.44 × 10 = 0.94″
∴ use 3 #5 bars in this band.

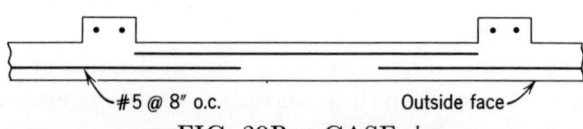

#5 @ 8″ o.c.   Outside face
FIG. 39B.   CASE *b.*

Problem 17

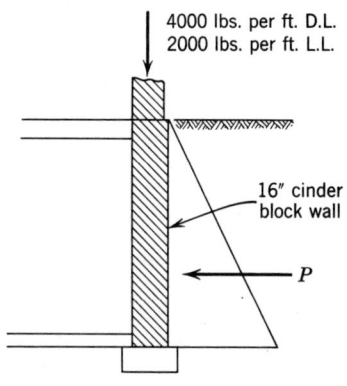

Given: Same as case *a*. $M = 1940$.

Compute:

Section modulus $= \dfrac{bd^2}{6} = \dfrac{12 \times 16^2}{6} = 512$

Bending stress $\dfrac{1940 \times 12}{512} = 45.5$ p.s.i.

Axial stress from D.L. $\dfrac{4000}{144} = 28$ p.s.i.

Axial stress from L.L. $= \dfrac{2000}{144} = 14$ p.s.i.

Net tension $45.5 - 28 = 17.5$ p.s.i.   O.K.

Max. compression $45.5 + 28 + 14 = 98$ p.s.i.   O.K.

FIG. 40A.   CASE *c.*   Plain masonry wall.   Often used for house construction.

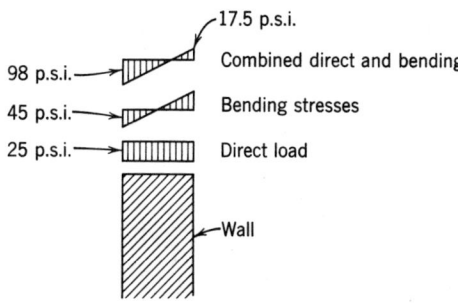

FIG. 40B.   STRESS DIAGRAMS FOR A UNIT CROSS SECTION OF WALL.

Note: For tensile of strength of masonry see Chapter 19.

Footing Drainage

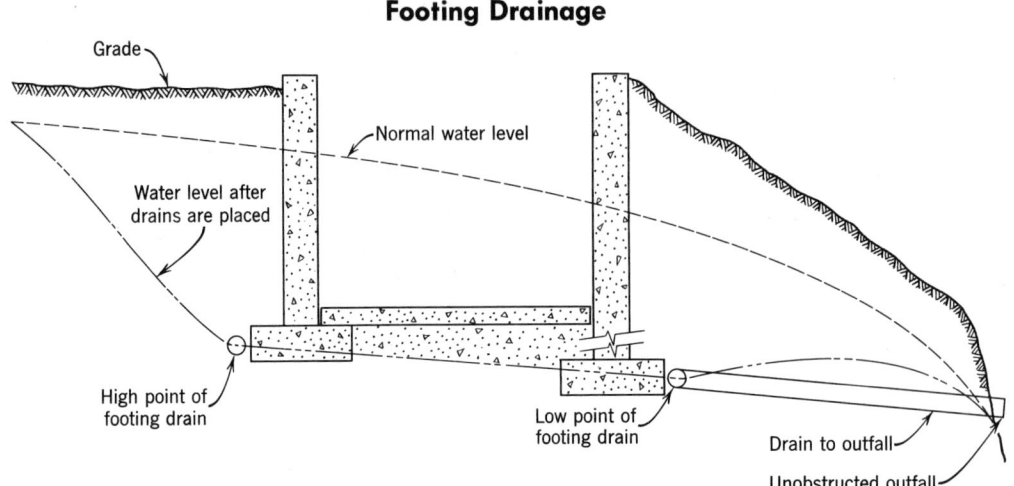

Locate invert low enough: (*a*) to drain underside of floor; (*b*) to give satisfactory slope from high point.

Lower footing bottom, if required to keep drains above bottom of footing to avoid loss of material from under footing.

FIG. 41.   ELEMENTS OF A FOOTING DRAINAGE SYSTEM.

For detail design see p. 9–2.

Reducing Shrinkage Cracks

All concrete shrinks in setting. If restrained, this causes areas of tension and often cracks; see p. 3–37. There are in general two methods of relieving this condition: (*a*) joints; (*b*) reinforcing.

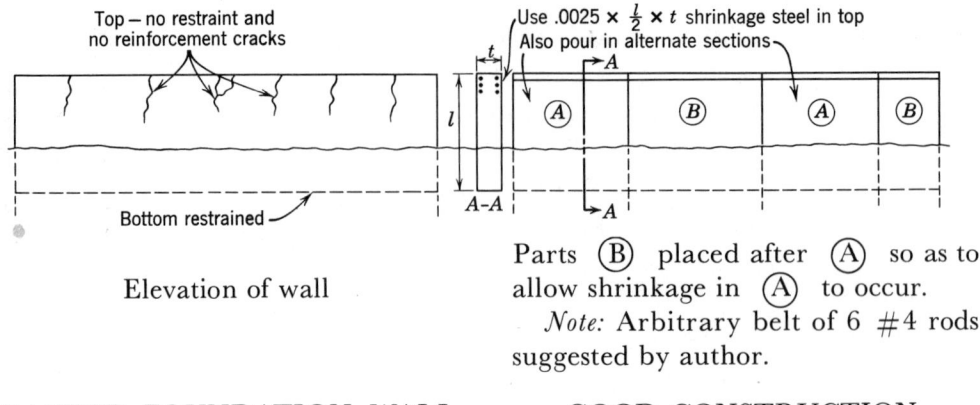

CRACKED FOUNDATION WALL   GOOD CONSTRUCTION

FIG. 42.

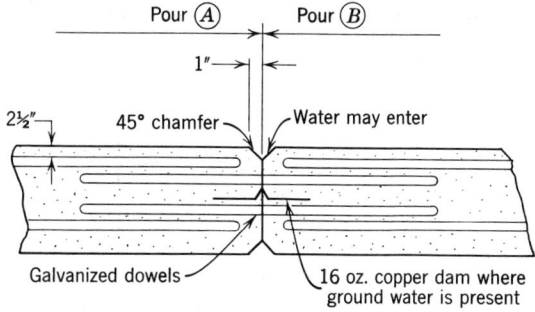

Note: On work where a tight joint is not essential, dowels may be omitted and bars made continuous.

FIG. 43. DETAIL OF CONSTRUCTION JOINT.

Preferred for exposed walls and where subject to sea water.

Note: Shrinkage coefficient of concrete is 0.0003; that is, $\dfrac{\text{Shrinkage}}{\text{Length}} = 0.0003$.

So that for unit length shrinkage = 0.0003. Modulus of elasticity of concrete for unit length = stress/strain. If modulus = 3,000,000, strain = stress ÷ 3,000,000. Since strain = shrinkage, then stress = 3,000,000 × 0.0003 or 900 p.s.i.

Problem 18. Computation of Shrinkage Reinforcement

> *Given:* Wall of 3000 p.s.i. concrete
> Ultimate tensile strength 300 p.s.i., $E = 3,000,000$
> Bond stress 210 p.s.i.
> Coefficient of shrinkage 1/30,000
> Yield point intermediate grade steel 40,000 p.s.i.
> *To find:* Reinforcement required.
> *Compute:* As above.
> Shrinkage stress 3,000,000 × 0.0003 = 900 p.s.i.

The wall would crack before this stress was reached. Therefore the wall is reinforced to reduce the crack to many small ones. The yield strength of the reinforcement should exceed the tensile stress of the wall.

$$\text{Percentage of steel is } \frac{300}{40,000} \times 100 = 0.75\%$$

Since the ground at the bottom caused the initial restraint, it will be necessary to reinforce only the top; see Fig. 42. Therefore one-half of this steel reinforcement may be used, or 0.375%.

The distance between the cracks may be figured by dividing the yield stress of the steel by the bond stresses:

$$\text{For \#4 bars } 0.20 \times \frac{40{,}000}{210 \times 1.57} = 24.2 \text{ in.}$$

$$\text{For \#5 bars } 0.31 \times \frac{40{,}000}{210 \times 1.96} = 30 \text{ in.}$$

$$\text{For \#6 bars } 0.44 \times \frac{40{,}000}{210 \times 2.36} = 35.5 \text{ in.}$$

Likewise the size of the cracks would be:

$$0.0003 \times 24.2 \text{ in.} = 0.00725 \text{ in.}$$
$$0.0003 \times 30.0 \text{ in.} = 0.00900 \text{ in.}$$
$$0.0003 \times 35.5 \text{ in.} = 0.01065 \text{ in.}$$

In all cases the crack is less than 1/64th of an inch.

Discussion

In any case the cracks are small but the use of more, smaller bars is recommended since the cracks are smaller and closer together.

Some authorities recommend reducing the yield point of the steel by the steel stress caused by a drop in temperature when figuring the shrinkage reinforcement on the theory that the temperature stress will be added to the shrinkage stress. Conservative design might justify allowing a temperature stress of 20° or 3900 p.s.i. or higher.

Distribution of Loads on Foundation Walls

(Usually Reinforced Concrete)

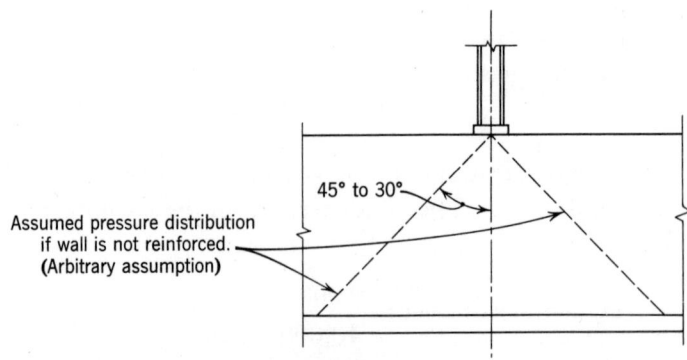

FIG. 44. LOAD DISTRIBUTION ON PLAIN WALLS.

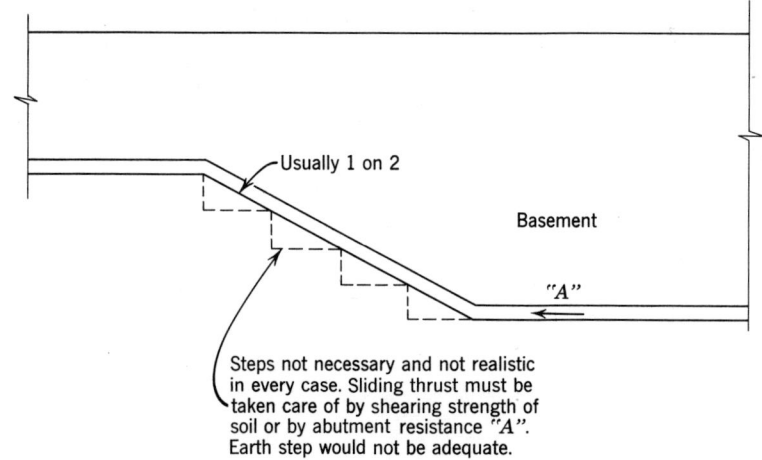

Usually 1 on 2

Basement

"A"

Steps not necessary and not realistic in every case. Sliding thrust must be taken care of by shearing strength of soil or by abutment resistance "A". Earth step would not be adequate.

FIG. 45.   STEPPING FOUNDATION WALLS.

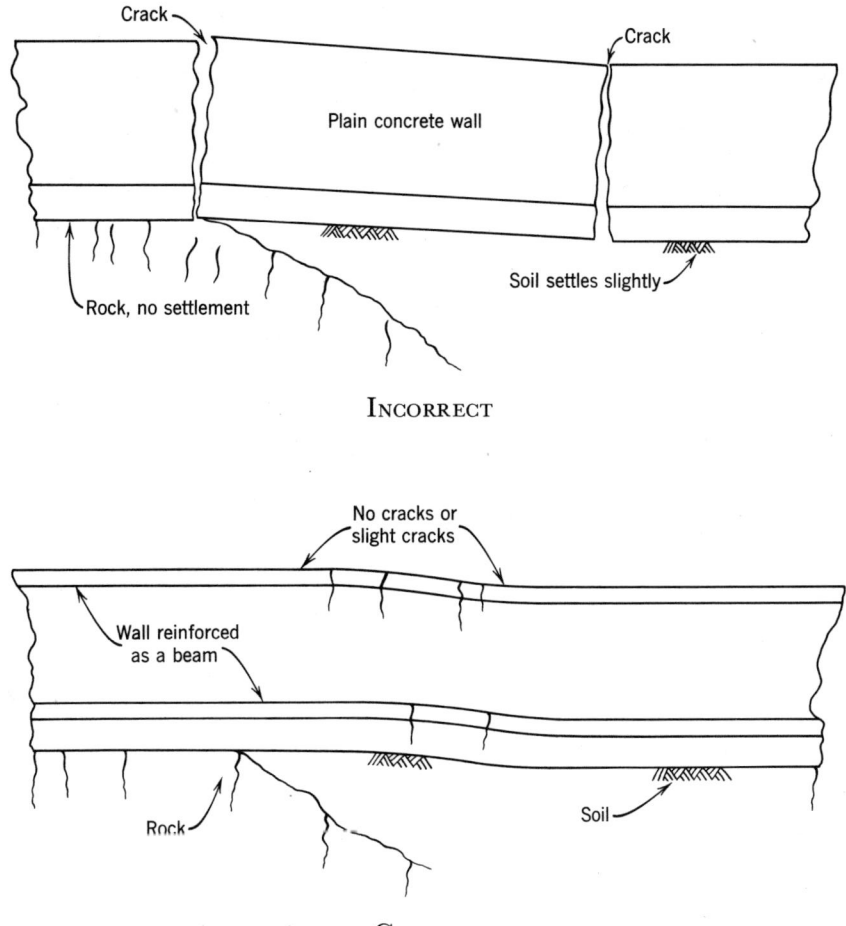

Crack

Crack

Plain concrete wall

Rock, no settlement

Soil settles slightly

INCORRECT

No cracks or slight cracks

Wall reinforced as a beam

Rock

Soil

CORRECT

FIG. 46.   CONDITION WHERE WALL PASSES FROM ROCK TO SOIL BEARING.

Legal Requirements

The following requirements apply to the N. Y. C. Building Code. They are, however, quite similar in most localities.

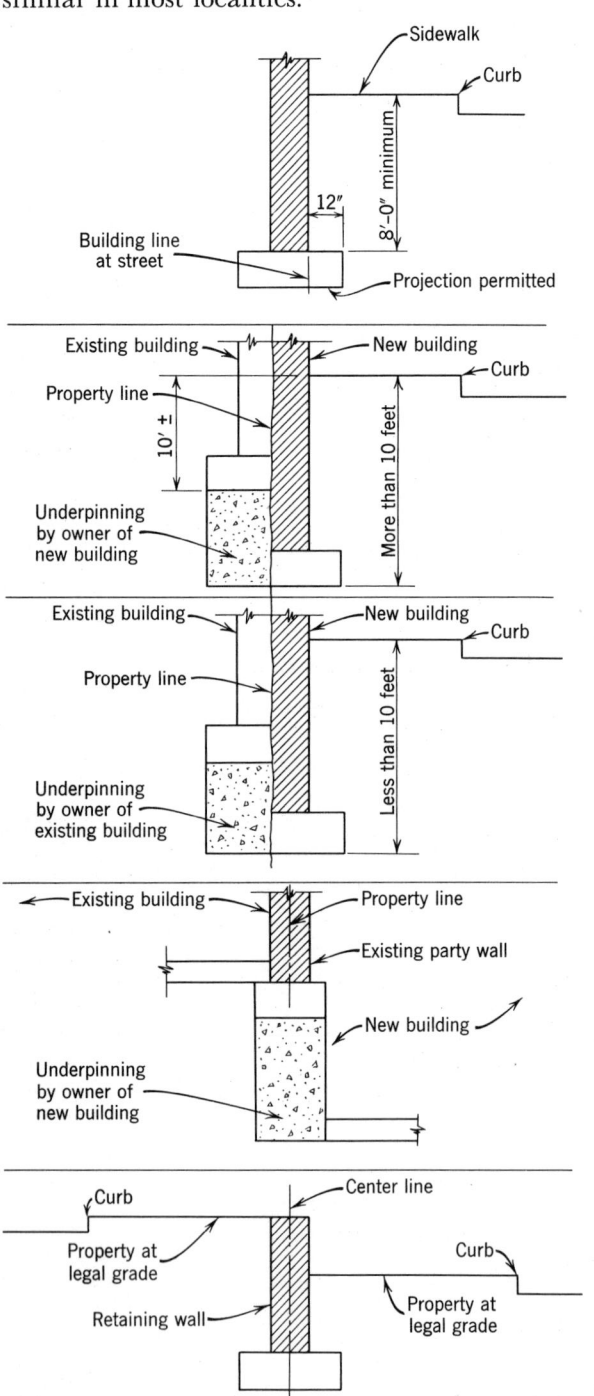

FOOTINGS

[C 26–218.0]

Footings at least eight feet below sidewalk level may project at most twelve inches beyond building line.

UNDERPINNING

[C 26–385.0 Par. a]

Owner of new building, if excavation is carried to a depth of more than 10 ft. below curb, must underpin adjoining structure.

UNDERPINNING

[C 26–385.0 Par. b]

Owner of existing building, if affected by an adjoining excavation of less than 10 ft. below curb, must underpin its own foundation.

PARTY WALLS

[C 26–385.0 Par. c]

Owner of a new building must underpin an existing party wall.

RETAINING WALLS

[C 26–563.0 Par. a]

Adjoining lots and both maintaining legal grade at curb level, any necessary retaining wall shall be made and maintained jointly by both owners and shall stand equally upon the land of each owner.

FIG. 47.

Design of Foundation Walls of Buildings

Discussion

Note: This discussion revolves around the wall standards shown in Fig. 48.

Foundation walls should be designed for two types of stresses: (1) those produced by backfill or hydrostatic pressure and the loads of the building; (2) those produced by changes in the material (shrinkage and temperature changes) and by changes in the supporting soil caused by slight differential settlement.

Stresses Caused by Changes in Volume. Concrete shrinks during the period of hydration. In a long run of concrete wall, such shrinkage will develop enough tension to crack the wall. To compensate for this the wall should be poured in alternate sections, say not over 30 ft. in length. Thus the wall is given a chance to obtain most of its initial shrinkage before being restrained by the section beyond. Such restraint may develop tension in both foundations and superstructure walls, causing cracks.

Temperature changes also cause change in volume. Since the bottom of the wall is below grade, these temperature changes are more severe at the top. The amount of reinforcement will usually be arbitrary. The ACI recommends 1/4 of 1%. The author uses six #4 bars grouped in the top.

Note: The effectiveness of the shrinkage reinforcement is proportional to the bond surface and the yield point of the steel. This indicates the use of reinforcement of small bars of high-carbon steel. In any case, there will be some shrinkage cracks, but the more effective the shrinkage reinforcement the fewer cracks. For computation of this shrinkage reinforcement, see p. 3-37. For examples of typical reinforcement see *Typical Foundation Wall* and *Typical Grade Beam,* Fig. 48.

The *Typical Basement Wall* shows the horizontal steel of 1/4 of 1% and vertical steel as required to take the tension caused by the earth pressure. When most of the outside face is exposed, 2/3 of the horizontal reinforcing should be placed on the outside face where the surface temperature changes are greatest, and 1/3 on the inside. The same procedure is followed when the outside face is covered by earth only if the law requires it. Many codes require walls over 8 in. in thickness to be reinforced on both faces. This practice is not recommended. The presence of two layers of steel makes placement of the concrete more difficult. Segregation often occurs, and the dangers of *honeycombing* are increased. The author feels that unless there is a strong compelling reason for placing reinforcing steel in two faces it should be placed in only one.

Openings further complicate walls. Their re-entrant corners act as stress concentrations, making them prone to cracks. The top must be reinforced as a lintel. The simplest opening is shown in *Case A Small Openings.* Here the opening is boxed with nominal reinforcement which is extended into the wall to prevent corner cracks.

Case B Extensive Openings shows the condition where the openings are so large that the reinforcing under the opening has become another belt. This section under the opening must be reinforced. as a horizontal beam. The piers must be designed to carry thrust from backfill along the entire wall.

Case C Predominant Openings shows openings so large that the wall really exists below the opening. The section above the opening is designed as a skeleton. The belt of six #4 bars is placed below the opening. Very often the wall is designed as a horizontal beam between columns. These columns should be given special attention in design because of the earth thrust.

For all openings, the lintel should be clearly indicated. It may be poured monolithically with the wall or with the floor, but in any case it should be clearly shown.

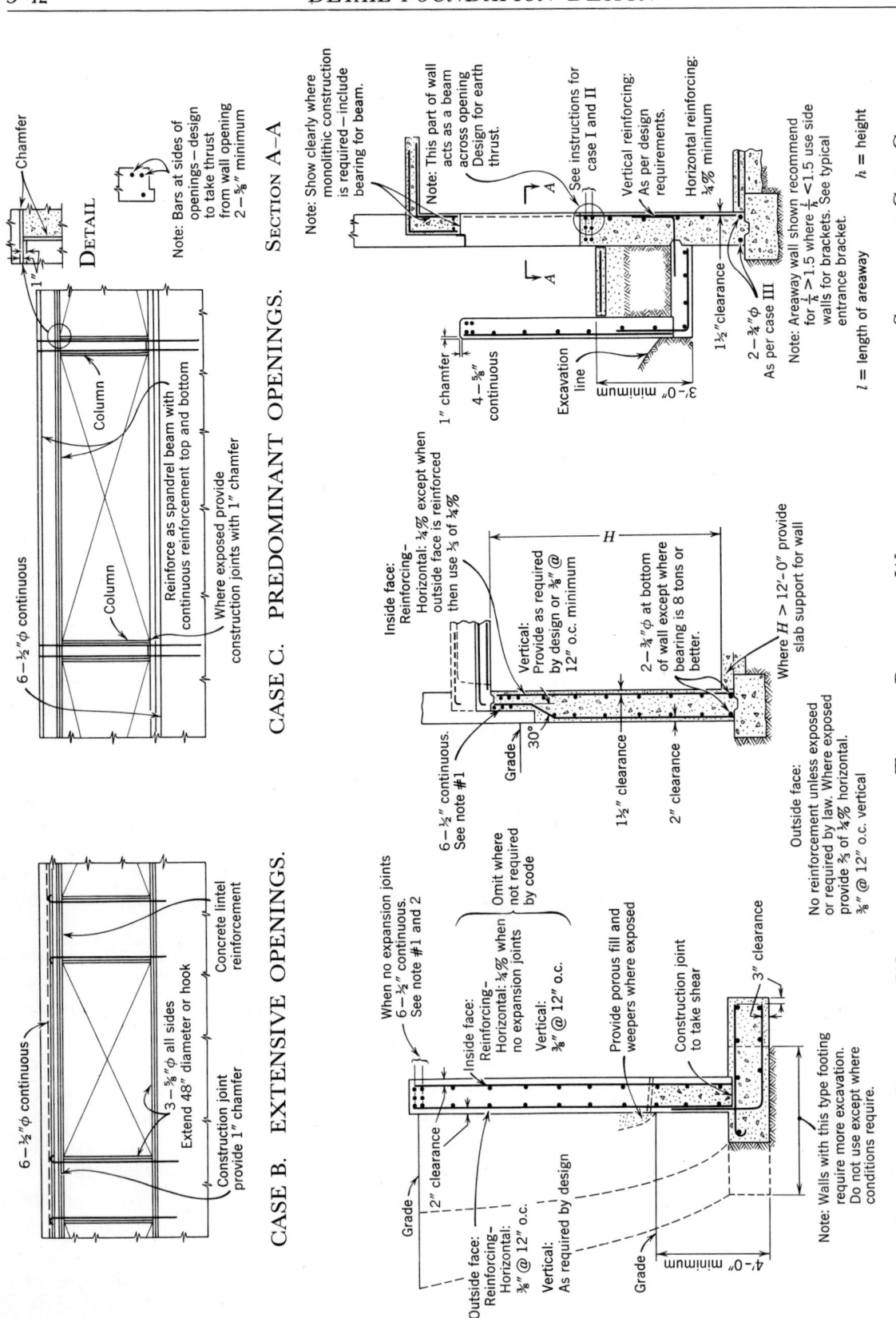

Chamfer

DETAIL

Note: Bars at sides of openings – design to take thrust from wall opening 2 – ⅝" minimum

SECTION A-A

6 – ½"φ continuous

Column

Column

Reinforce as spandrel beam with continuous reinforcement top and bottom

Where exposed provide construction joints with 1" chamfer

CASE C. PREDOMINANT OPENINGS.

Note: Show clearly where monolithic construction is required – include bearing for beam.

Note: This part of wall acts as a beam across opening Design for earth thrust.

See instructions for case I and II

Vertical reinforcing: As per design requirements.

Horizontal reinforcing: ¼% minimum

1½"clearance

Note: Areaway wall shown recommend for l/h >1.5 where l/h <1.5 use side walls for brackets. See typical entrance bracket.

2 – ¾"φ As per case III

l = length of areaway   h = height

1" chamfer

4 – ⅝" continuous

Excavation line

3'-0" minimum

SECTION OF CASE C
Showing self-supporting areaway wall

6 – ½"φ continuous

Concrete lintel reinforcement

3 – ⅝"φ all sides Extend 48" diameter or hook

Construction joint provide 1" chamfer

CASE B. EXTENSIVE OPENINGS.

Inside face:
Reinforcing–
Horizontal: ¼% except when outside face is reinforced then use ⅓ of ¼%

Vertical:
Provide as required by design or ⅜" @ 12" o.c. minimum

H

2 – ¾"φ at bottom of wall except where bearing is 8 tons or better.

Where H > 12'-0" provide slab support for wall

6 – ½" continuous.
See note #1

Grade

30°

1½" clearance

2" clearance

Outside face:
No reinforcement unless exposed or required by law. Where exposed provide ⅔ of ¼% horizontal.
⅜" @ 12" o.c. vertical

TYPICAL BASEMENT WALL

When no expansion joints
6 – ½" continuous.
See note #1 and 2

Inside face:
Reinforcing–
Horizontal: ¼% when no expansion joints

Vertical:
⅜" @ 12" o.c.

Omit where not required by code

Provide porous fill and weepers where exposed

Construction joint to take shear

3" clearance

Grade

2" clearance

Outside face:
Reinforcing–
Horizontal:
⅜" @ 12" o.c.

Vertical:
As required by design

Grade

Note: Walls with this type footing require more excavation. Do not use except where conditions require.

4'-0" minimum

CANTILEVER RETAINING WALL

*Omit horizontal reinforcing when expansion joints are less than 30'-0" on center.

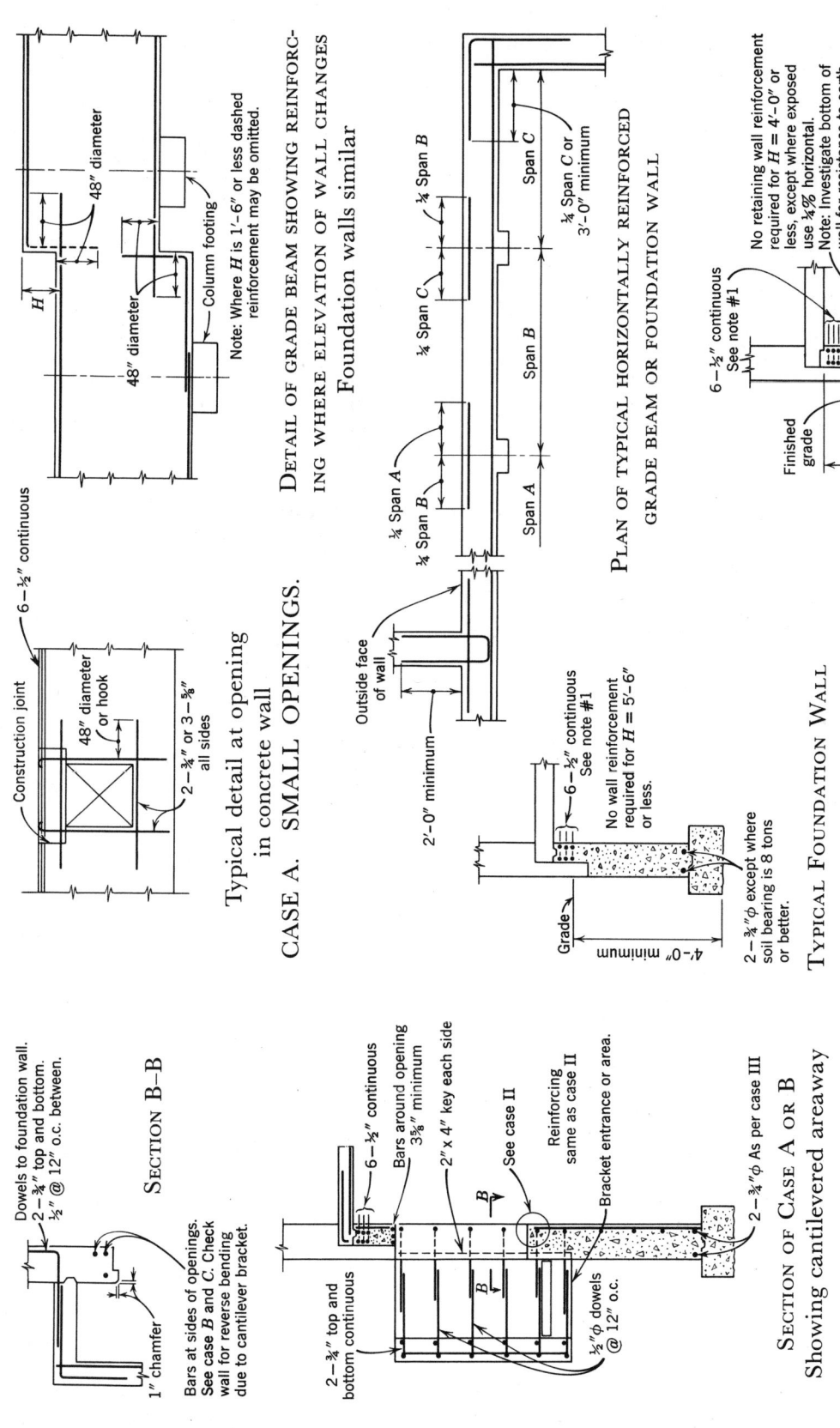

FIG. 48.

Notes:

1. Continuity bars shall be lapped 48 dia. at splices and bent around corners.
2. Limit length of all wall pours to 30'-0" ± between construction joints.
3. For basement walls depending on superstructure (1st framed slab) for support: No backfilling to be done against foundation walls until superstructure is in place.
4. Where bottom of wall depends upon a basement slab for stability, call for shoring or prohibit backfilling until slab is in place. For walls over 12'-0" high, thicken basement slab and label "Wall Support."

Areaways are of two types: bracketed or self-supporting. The bracketed is used for shallower, narrower ones. The detail is the same at the entrance except that the slab is placed on top of the wall. The self-supported areaway is used for larger types. Its foundation should be carried some distance below the area slab if subject to frost, and below soil disturbed by general excavation.

Expansion joints may be provided in foundation walls. When provided, they should have a copper water stop. The expansion joint is usually started at the top of the footings. At interior supports, double piers are provided, one on each side of joint. Wherever an expansion joint is provided in the foundation, it must be carried up through the roof. Construction joints should be finished by a V cut. See Fig. 43.

Differential settlement may cause cracks at either top or bottom because of beam action of the wall. The belt steel at the top prevents such cracks. At the bottom two #6 continuous are provided. These may be omitted on soil which is good for 8 tons or better bearing (soft rock) where there is no danger of such settlement.

Water infiltration is an ever-present danger. Corrosion of reinforcement near the surface builds up pressure from expansion which tends to explode the concrete away from the wall and reinforcing. Galvanized reinforcing is desirable. A minimum of a full 2 in. clear of concrete over the reinforcing steel should be provided; 2½ in. to 3 in. is preferred, 4 in. in case of footings. See Fig. 43.

Interior walls are not subject to the same temperature stresses as exterior ones. Shrinkage forces are still present, however, and so pouring in alternate 30-ft. sections is indicated. Usually two #4 bars are placed top and bottom as belt steel.

Earth pressure occurs against foundation walls. It is figured the same way for foundation walls as for retaining walls; see Chapter 4.

SETTLEMENT OF FOUNDATIONS

Settlement may result from the following general causes:

1. Elastic compression of the soil from the superimposed load. Amount of settlement is small usually less than 1 in. See Fig. 49.

2. Consolidation of the soil from the gradual squeezing out of water or the compaction of loose soils. Settlement may be as large as 2 or more feet, occurring slowly over a period of the order of 1 to 10 years. See Chapter 13. Settlements of loose sands are very rare but should be considered where small settlements may be important.

3. Mud waves or "poop outs" caused by the sudden flow of ground out from under foundations. Plastic soils are most susceptible.

4. Frost.

5. Erosion of the soil under footings by running water or by undermining. Such settlements are especially prevalent during construction adjacent to the structure. Fine running sands or silts are most susceptible.

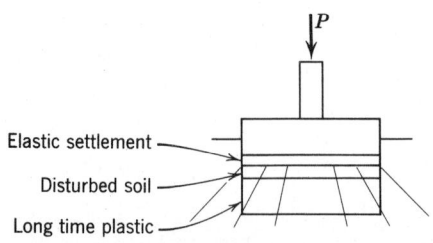

FIG. 49.

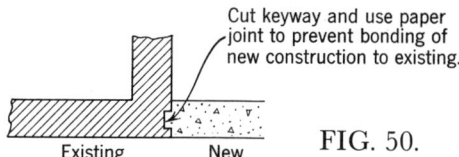

Cut keyway and use paper joint to prevent bonding of new construction to existing.

Existing   New   FIG. 50.

Differential settlement between old and new buildings is generally allowed for by vertical slip joints. See Fig. 50. Since the elastic settlement on rock is less than on soil, a special condition is required where the building rests partly on one and partly on the other. This condition is most common under foundation walls. A sand cushion between the footing and the rock is a common remedy, but a more effective solution is a reinforced-concrete distributing girder; see Fig. 46.

Frost Protection

Soils are subject to frost action weakening the supporting power furnished the footings. Therefore the exterior footings of heated buildings and all footings of unheated buildings must be placed below the level of maximum frost penetration as shown in Fig. 51.

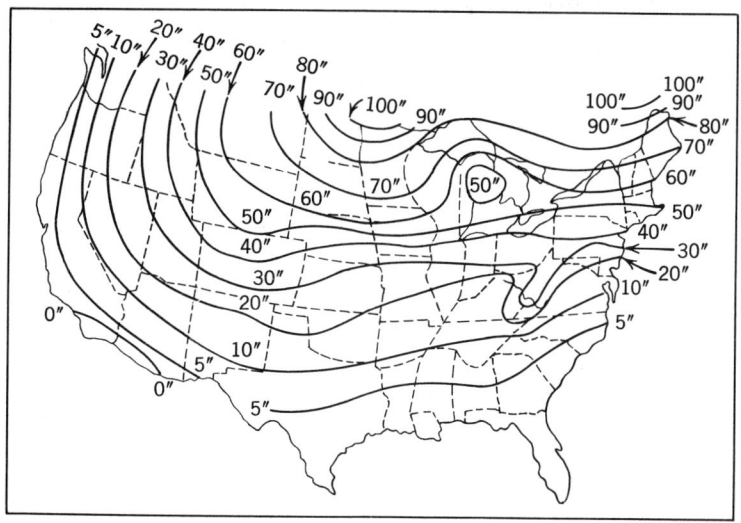

* U. S. Weather Bureau.

FIG. 51. MAXIMUM FROST PENETRATION IN INCHES.*

Use for foundations.

Red Light. Special provisions must be made in cold-storage buildings and in boiler houses having underground forced-draft intakes to prevent the freezing of ground from inside the building.

Discussion

Frost damage works in two directions. First, ice lenses form in the soil, heaving it upward. These lenses grow by absorbing additional water from below the frost line. Silts are susceptible to heaves. Well-drained sands and dense clays generally will not heave. Pavements suffer most from this action. See Chapter 14.

Second, the direction of frost action is downward. The ice lenses thaw from the top down, causing a layer of water to be trapped near the surface. This water emulsifies the soil, permitting it to flow out from under the footing.

Permafrost. In some arctic locations the ground is frozen for a great depth. The upper layer (active zone) freezes in the winter and thaws in the summer. The lower layer (inactive zone) never thaws. Unless the active layer is a well-drained granular soil, trouble may be expected from the emulsifying of the thawed ground. Foundations should be set on the inactive zone. Spread footings may be dug or piles steam jetted. For construction on permafrost see Chapter 19.

Red Light. Care must be taken to prevent the inactive zone from becoming active because the insulating overburden is removed or because of heat transmission from within the building. Power houses need special watching in this respect.

Design for Uniform Settlement

On plastic soils subject to slow, long-time settlement, the settlement caused by the dead load is greater than that caused by the occasionally present live load. Since all footings do not have the same ratio of live load to dead load, greater settlement may be expected under those footings having a greater percentage of dead load, generally the exterior ones. To compensate for this unevenness in settlement, footings are often designed for uniform soil pressure under dead load plus a part, say 1/4 to 1/3, of the live load. Such design is illustrated in Problem 19.

Problem 19. Design for Uniform Settlement

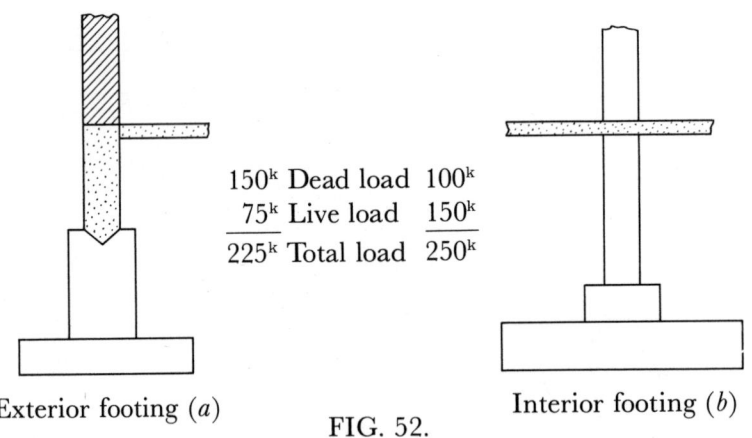

	Dead load	Live load
150^k Dead load	100^k	
75^k Live load	150^k	
225^k Total load	250^k	

Exterior footing (*a*)   FIG. 52.   Interior footing (*b*)

Given: Allowable soil pressure 2 tons per sq. ft.

Select footing with highest ratio of live to dead load, footing (*b*).

Divide total load by allowable soil pressure:

$$\frac{250}{4} = 62.5 \text{ sq. ft.}$$

Use 8'-0" × 8'-0" footing.

Divide dead load plus 1/3 live load by footing area:

$$\frac{100 + \dfrac{50}{3}}{64} = 2350 \text{ p.s.f.*}$$

---

* ⅓ L. L. is assumed to give approximately equal settlement because all of the live load does not act.

Proportion other footings for this pressure under dead load plus 1/3 live load.

For example, footing (*a*):

$$\frac{150 + \dfrac{75}{3}}{2350} = 74.5 \text{ sq. ft.}$$

Use 8'-6" × 8'-6" footing.

Design footings for shear, bond, and moment using dead load plus *full* live load.

SELECTION OF TYPES OF FOUNDATIONS

The selection of the type of foundations is a matter of judgment based upon data. The first step is the collection of data concerning the site. Often the engineer is called in after the site is acquired so that the client is denied the benefit of his experience and knowledge for the site selection. The site may be investigated by means of borings. Open pits or augers are better yet but can be used for shallow depths only. Samples may be sent to the laboratory for shear and consolidation tests. From the results of these investigations and tests, the location and capacity of the bearing stratum may be ascertained. Hence the type and cost of the foundation may be arrived at. See Chapter 8. Water level is also a factor.

Adjacent buildings offer a full-scale load test and a record of high water. The facts concerning their foundations should be carefully weighed, as many old buildings were not built according to plan.

A second step would be the development of alternative designs. Factors to be considered in the feasibility of different designs are shown in Figs. 53 and 54. The advisability of keeping concrete work and excavation out of water cannot be overemphasized. Sometimes it is better to use valuable space in the building for boilers and such than to build expensive rooms below water level.

A desirable stratum well below the water line may be reached easily in clay but with difficulty in fine running sand. In the former case piers or open caissons may be indicated, in the latter, piles may be preferred.

The third step is the economic study of the different designs. In such studies it is important to consider all aspects, including the superstructure, so that a true economic picture can be had. A very elementary problem follows.

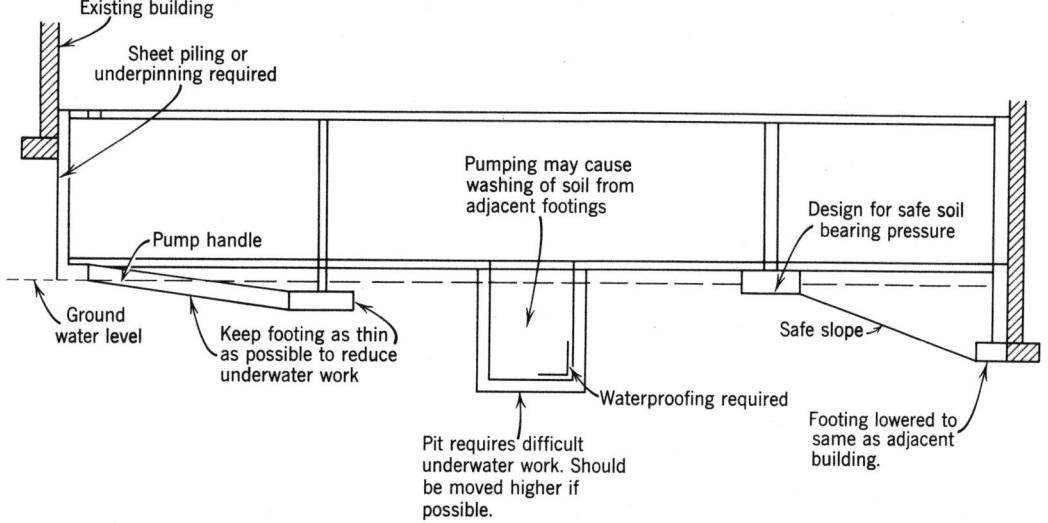

FIG. 53.   FACTORS AFFECTING SPREAD FOOTINGS.

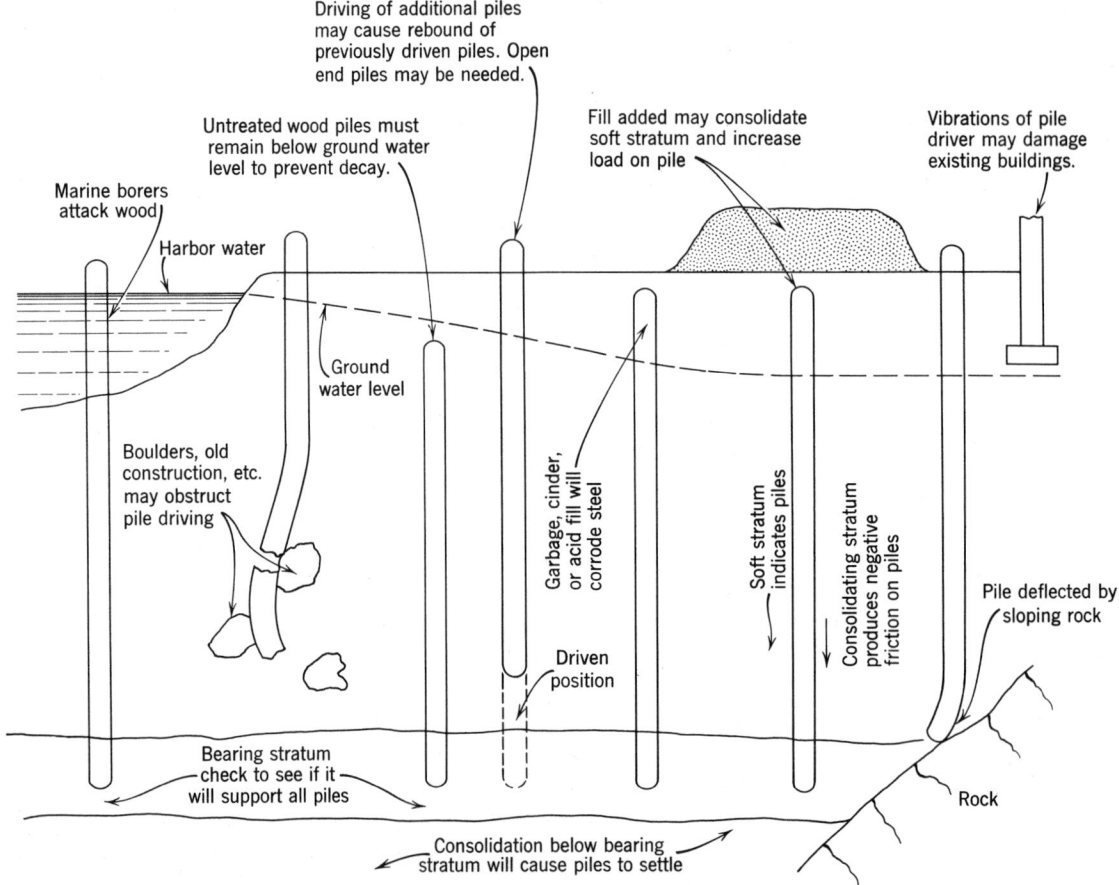

FIG. 54. FACTORS AFFECTING PILE FOOTINGS.

Selection of Economic Foundation

Given: As per Fig. 55.

Load	-	500 kips
Safe soil pressure	-	4000 lb. per sq. ft.
Rock	-	20 tons per sq. ft.
Concrete	-	3000 lb. per sq. in.

Rock 10 ft. below bottom of footing.

Case I. Steel pipe piles.

Pile foundation of five 10¾ in. piles, ⁵⁄₁₆ in. shell (p. 3–8).

Pile cap 6'2" x 6'2", 2'6".

Reinforcement twenty-eight #6 rods, 5'10" long (p. 2–7).

Case II. Wood piles, treated.

Assume 8 in. point, 10 piles at 25 tons per pile.

Hexagonal pile cap 6'10" x 10'5" x 3'8" deep (p. 2–7).

Reinforcement seven #8 rods long way and eight #6 rods short way.

Case III. Concrete pier to rock.

    Load 500^k, assume weight pier 15^k, total 515^k

    Size of pier 515 ÷ 40 = 12.9 sq. ft. = 3'8" x 3'8".

Case IV. Spread footing.

    Footing 12' x 12' x 2'8".

    Reinforcement twenty #10 rods, 11'8" long (p. 2–3).

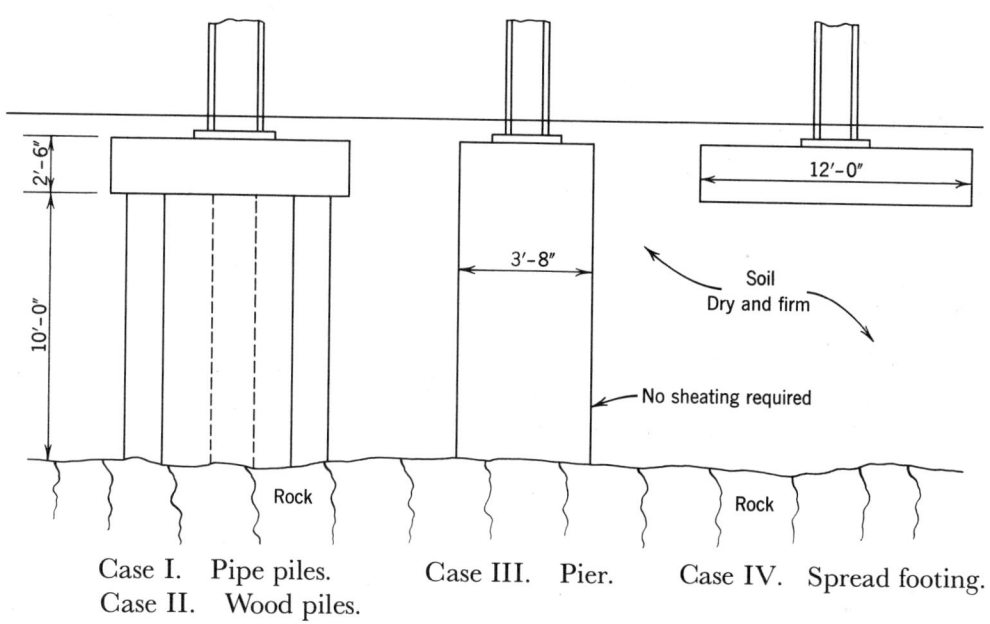

Case I. Pipe piles.   Case III. Pier.   Case IV. Spread footing.

Case II. Wood piles.

FIG. 55.

TYPES OF FOUNDATIONS UNDER CONSIDERATION IN ECONOMIC STUDY.

TABLE VII. ESTIMATE OF COST

Item	Case I			
Piles	52.5 lin. ft.	@ $ 7.50 =	$394
Concrete	3.5 cu. yd.	@ 25.00 =	88
Excavation	4 cu. yd.	@ 2.00 =	8
Reinforcing	244 lb.	@ 0.15 =	37
Forms	62 sq. ft.	@ 0.80 =	50
Total			$577

Item	Case II			
Piles	120 lin. ft.	@ $ 2.00 =	$240
Concrete	6.0 cu. yd.	@ 25.00 =	150
Excavation	7 cu. yd.	@ 2.00 =	14
Reinforcing	236 lb.	@ 0.15 =	35
Forms	125 sq. ft.	@ 0.80 =	97
Total			$536

Item	Case III		
Piles			
Concrete	6.25 cu. yd.	@ $25.00 =	$157
Excavation	21.2 cu. yd.	@ 4.00 =	86
Reinforcing			
Forms	188 sq. ft.	@ 0.80 =	150
Total			$393

Case IV			
14.4 cu. yd.	@ $25.00 =	$360
16 cu. yd.	@ 2.00 =	32
1000 lb.	@ 0.15 =	150
130 sq. ft.	@ 0.80 =	104
		$646

    For costs see Chapter 16.

36977

Discussion

From Table VII it will be seen that pier to rock is the cheapest.

Should water be present requiring excavation to be sheeted, then to the cost of the pier to rock should be added:

Sheeting 250 sq. ft. @ $2.00	$500
Pumping (1 day)	41
Reduced excavation (sides not sloped)	19 (Credit)
	$522

or a total cost of $915.   Clearly then, the presence of ground water would make the timber piles the most economical.   On large jobs it might be cheaper to dewater by well points or drainage and excavate in the dry.   See Chapter 11.   The economy of a mat should be considered in a similar manner.

Note that for an exterior column on a property line the pier to rock would have the further economic advantage of not needing a pump handle.   See Fig. 56.

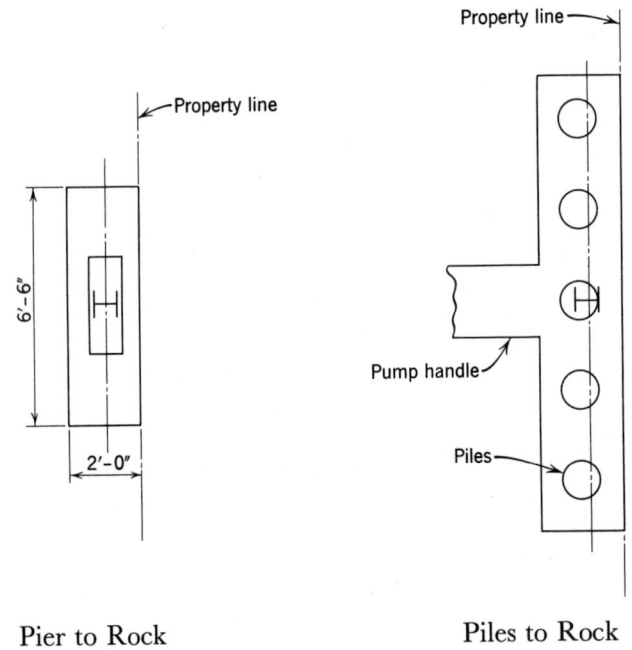

Pier to Rock   Piles to Rock

Pier requires no pump handle, whereas piles do.   A single row of piles must always be tied, regardless of amount of eccentricity.

FIG. 56.   BEARING OF EXTERIOR CONDITION ON COST STUDY.

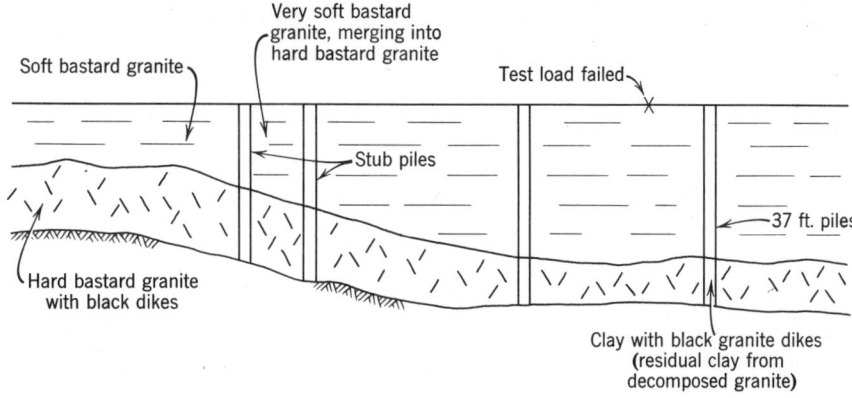

Foundation for 30-story Textile Building, Charlotte, North Carolina

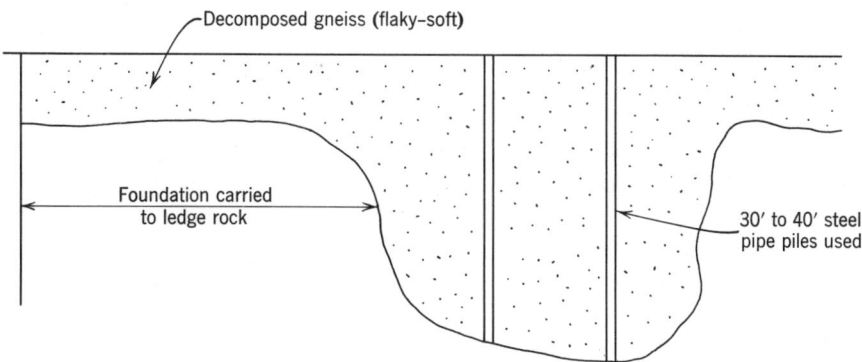

Foundations for St. Helene's Parish Convent, New York City

FIG. 57.   USE OF PILES IN DECOMPOSED ROCK.

THEORIES OF PILE SUPPORT

Discussion

Pile support is derived from two general methods: (1) end bearing of the pile on a hard stratum such as rock (end bearing piles); (2) friction between the sides of the pile and the soil (friction piles). Such friction may be developed only along part of the pile.

Piles, driven through soft material, are considered as laterally supported columns.   However, piles in water, for example, piers, must be checked also for unbraced column action.   For all pile formations, provision must be made for horizontal loads, if present, by providing ties, batter piles, or other means.   Piles in themselves are weak in resisting horizontal forces.

Not only must the pile be capable of developing its strength by bearing or friction but also the soil below must be capable of taking the load.   In cases of pile clusters it often would be a grave mistake to assume that the total safe load on the pile cluster is the same as the sum of the safe loads on each pile.   Such an assumption is valid only when the stratum in the immediate area of the cluster is capable of handling the entire load.   Some soils may be so disturbed by pile driving as to be worthless.

Skin friction acts upward and supports the pile. If, after the pile is set in place, the soil adjacent is loaded, the consolidation of this soil may produce a downward or *negative skin friction*—a dangerous condition. See Fig. 60.

In clays or silts the driving of a pile may disturb the soil and produce a film of water on its side. This film acts as a lubricant, permitting the pile to drive easily. Should pile driving cease, this film of water is dissipated and the pile "freezes up" to produce greater resistance. If pile driving is resumed, it is difficult to break the pile loose and get it moving again, but once it does move it continues very easily.

In a permeable soil the above phenomenon is not very noticeable.

Pile capacity is generally established by test (p. 15–22) or by driving resistance (p. 15–23).

The selection of pile capacity for design use depends upon the type of pile, type of soil, and location of bearing strata.

End bearing piles to rock can take heavy loads. Generally concrete-filled steel pipe piles or caissons are indicated. For this case see p. 3–8.

High permanent ground water indicates that untreated timber piles may be used as they will not decay when permanently submerged. Otherwise timber piles, if used, should be pressure-treated by creosoting.

Boulders or riprap may best be penetrated, if at all, by H piles or pointed steel pipe piles or by steel spuds for piles cast in place.

Very deep soft layers require long piles. Timber piles are often too short unless specified. Most easily driven piles are H piles. Because of the great amount of pile above the supporting layer which gives no support, the design tendency is to reduce the number of piles by increasing the capacity.

In sand, piles must generally be jetted into position. Jetting may disturb adjacent buildings.

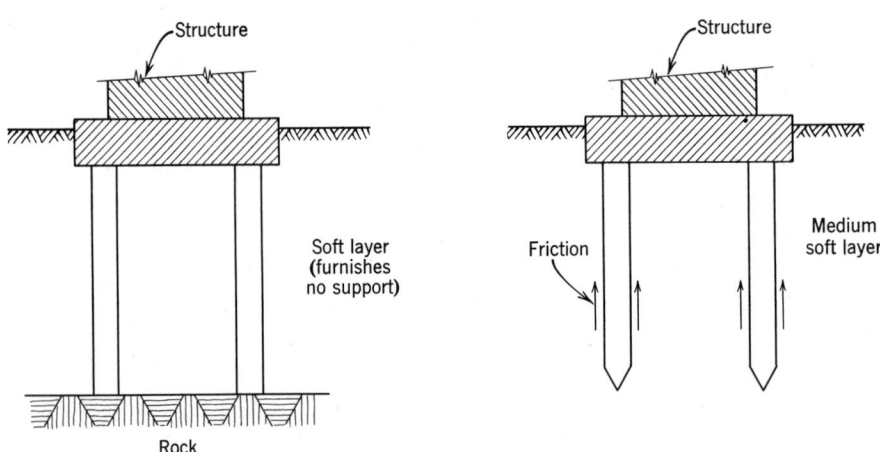

END BEARING PILE   FRICTION PILE

FIG. 58. THEORIES OF PILE SUPPORT.

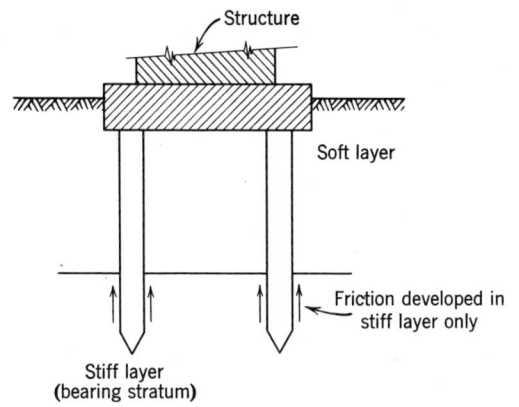

FRICTION PILES DRIVEN THROUGH SOFT LAYER TO BEARING STRATUM
Note: Affects length of penetration required.

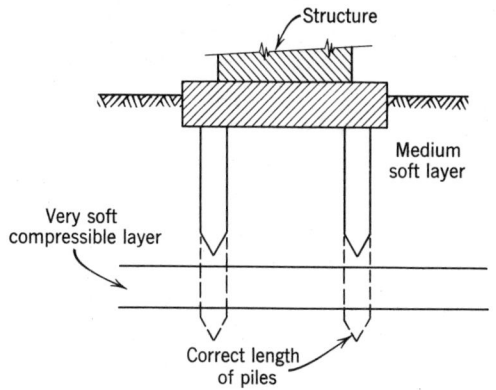

ONE EXAMPLE OF DANGEROUS PRACTICE

Red Light: Watch out for pile uplift due to batter piles.

Batter pile may have a maximum slope of 3 on 1. Many rigs can furnish only 4 on 1. Sufficient dead weight must be furnished or pile *A* will be in tension.

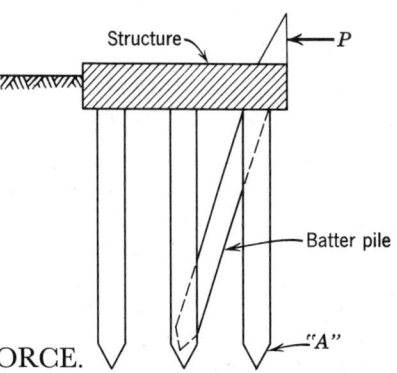

USE OF BATTER PILES TO TAKE HORIZONTAL FORCE.

FIG. 58. (CONT.) THEORIES OF PILE SUPPORT.

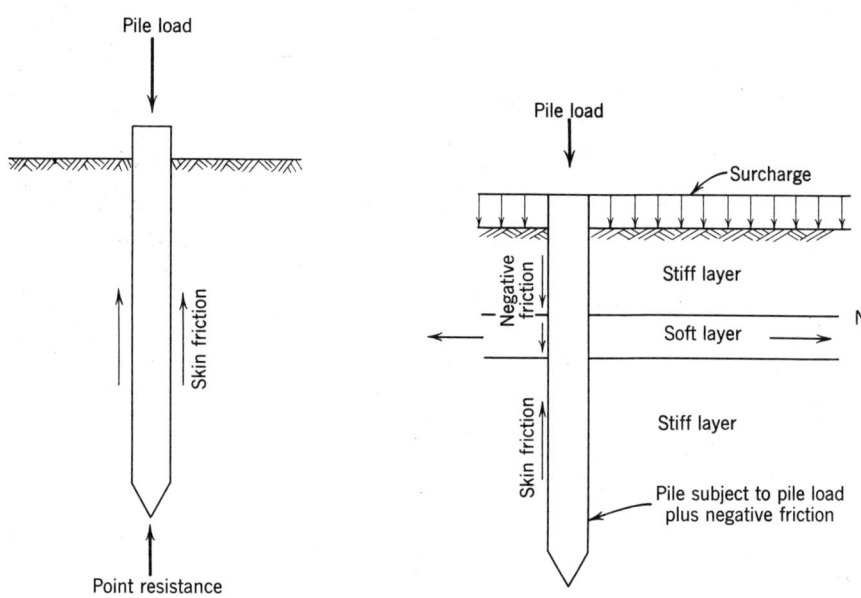

FIG. 59.
DISTRIBUTION OF STRESSES IN A PILE.

FIG. 60.
EXAMPLE OF NEGATIVE FRICTION.

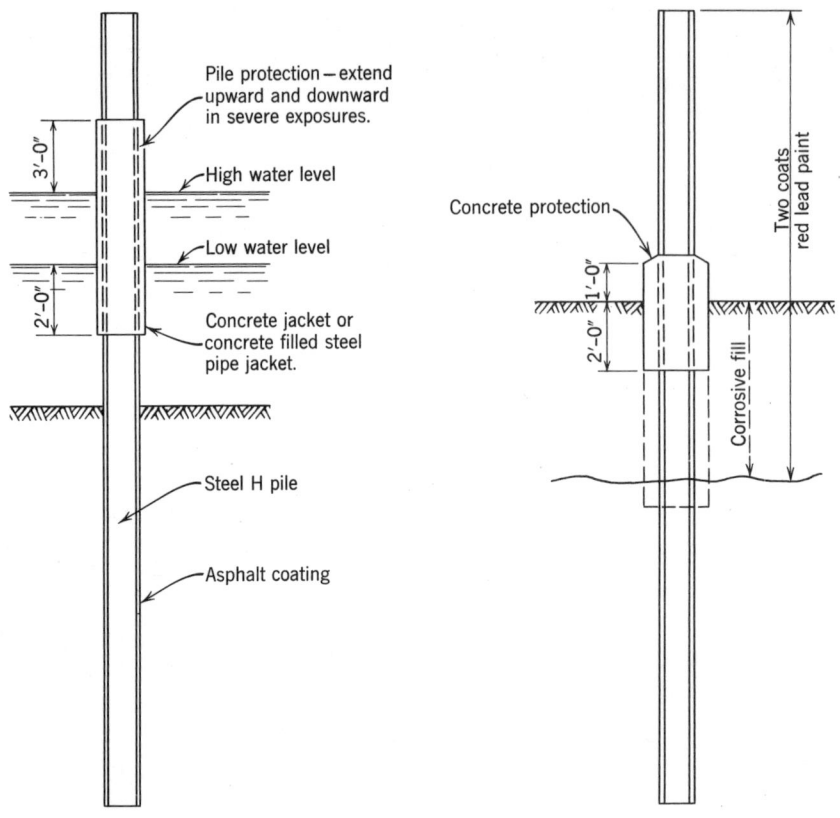

H PILE IN WATER   H PILE ON LAND

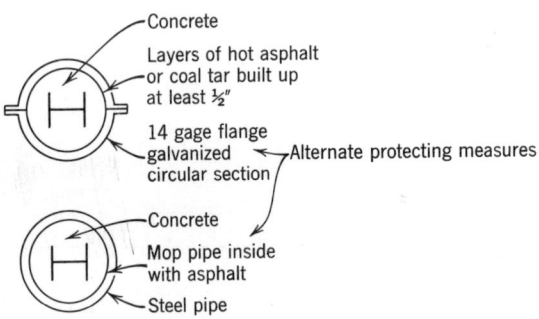

ALTERNATIVE PROTECTIVE
MEASURES

Note: For concrete protection,
use galvanized reinforcement
if reinforcement is required.

FIG. 60*A*.   STEEL H PILES, CORROSION PROTECTION.

Tidal waters usually require preservatives for timber piles to retard deterioration from marine borers, *Teredo* and *Limnoria*. Untreated timber is particularly subject to marine borers if sea water is not polluted. New York Upper Harbor, for instance, is practically free from borers. See p. 19-1.

Timber piles are limited to lower capacities because of the danger of damage from overdriving or of injury due to obstructions in an effort to reach high capacities. Many codes limit timber piles to 20 tons, although, theoretically, a well-driven timber pile is as strong as a cast-in-place pile. Some codes limit concrete piles to 30 tons.

Length of pile is determined by the location of the bearing strata. Sometimes it is necessary to drive through soil of apparently satisfactory resistance to reach a lower stratum since the upper strata are not capable of taking the entire building load. Fourteen-inch H piles have been driven up to 304 ft. in length. Ordinary practice is 90 ft. to 110 ft. limit.

Economic study is generally needed to make the final selection from the types of pile indicated. Only by such a study can the different values of capacity, length, number of piles needed, ease of driving, and other factors be properly evaluated. An example follows.

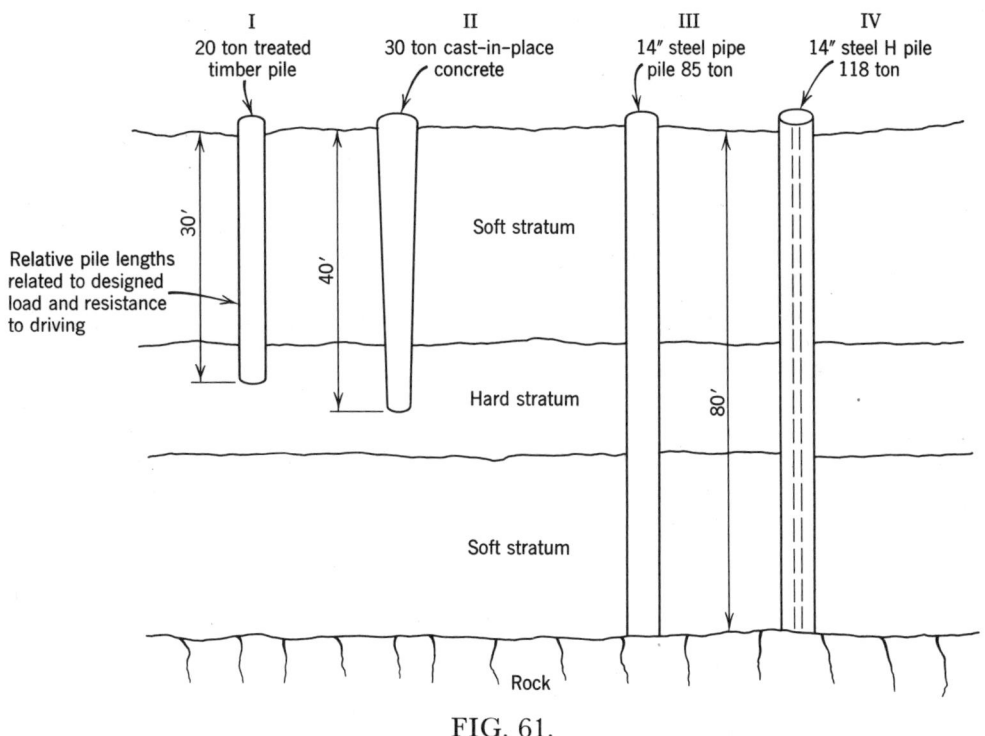

FIG. 61.

Given: Load of 1000^k.

TABLE VIII.   ECONOMIC SELECTION OF PILES

Case	Load per Pile	No. of Piles	Pile Length	Total Length of Piling	Cost per* Foot	Total Cost
I	40^k	25	30′	750′	$ 2.00	$1500
II	60^k	17	40′	680′	4.50	3060
III	170^k	6	80′	480′	10.00	4800
IV	236^k	5	80′	400′	8.10	3240

* See Chapter 16.
Timber piles are generally cheapest where feasible, cast in place the next cheapest.

Pile Red Lights

1. Setttlements of group piles may be greater than those for single piles. See Fig. 62.

2. Drive and inspect all shells in a group for a cast-in-place pile before filling with concrete to see whether driving an adjacent pile collapses one in place.

3. Untreated wood piles must be cut off below permanent water level.

4. Steel H piles must be cut off below an acid-bearing fill such as cinders, or must be protected; see p. 3–54.

5. Piles which permit inspection after driving have an advantage in soils containing boulders or other obstructions. This applies to open-ended pipe pile or cast-in-place piles.

6. Piles subject to *Limnoria* action in water should be either pressure-creosoted timber, or steel, or concrete.

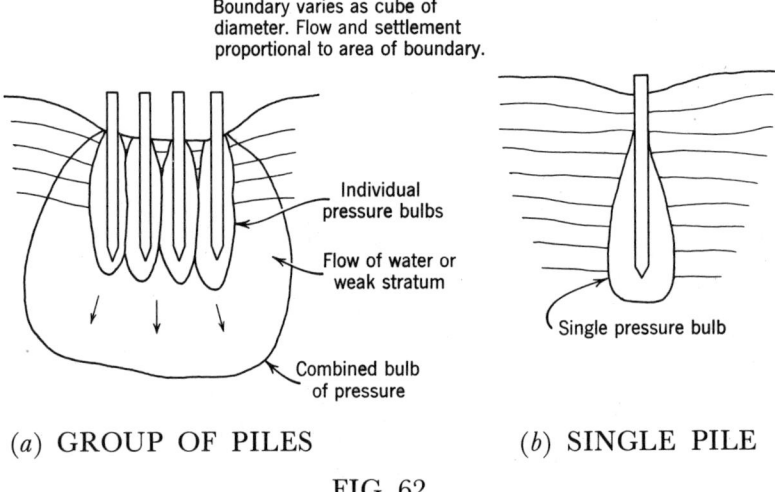

Boundary varies as cube of diameter. Flow and settlement proportional to area of boundary.

(*a*) GROUP OF PILES   (*b*) SINGLE PILE

FIG. 62.

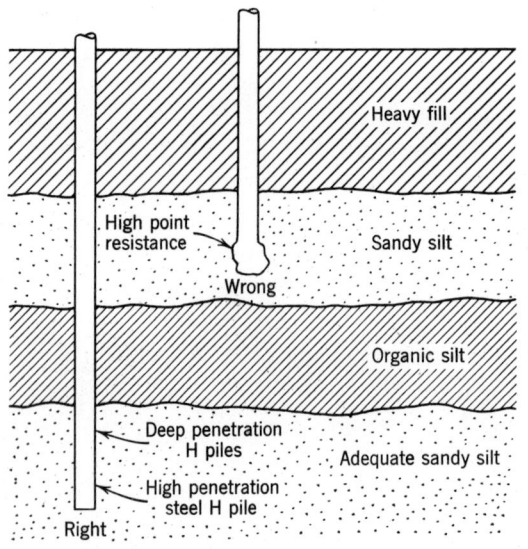

Piles not driven to adequate bearing stratum even though the resistance to driving is adequate.

Dangerous.

FIG. 63.

Do not use *Engineering News* pile formula without adequate borings in non-homogeneous soil.

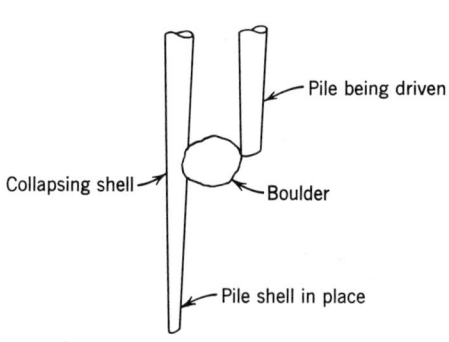

CAST-IN-PLACE PILES

Precaution: Drive all shells in cluster and inspect, before placing concrete. Damaged shells may be repaired by driving additional shells inside old ones.
FIG. 64.

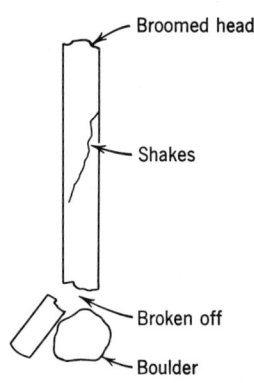

WOOD PILE

Do not overdrive if pile will not go down to expected depth.
FIG. 65.

Foundation Red Lights, General

1. "Build not your house on *fill.*"

2. Inorganic silts (very fine sand) are not necessarily a poor foundation if dense. They are, however, likely to be found in a loose state.

3. Foundations should not be constructed on peat or organic materials.

4. Foundations should go down to maximum frost penetration. See p. 3–45, and check local building codes.

5. Deep, adjoining excavation may dry out clays, causing shrinkage and settlement.

6. Settlements on clays should be studied. For important structures, time settlement relations should be studied, p. 13–24. Interior footings on clay may settle more than wall footings if same unit pressures are used; see p. 13–27. This is not always true for preloaded clay; see p. 13–25.

7. Vibrating machinery may cause settlement in some soils. Insulation may be indicated. See p. 10–20.

8. Pumping operations should not be permitted to carry away soil from under foundations. Sands and silts should be particularly watched.

9. Foundations should be below pipe and trench excavations.

10. Settlement of plastic soils at any depth will occur if the critical pressure is exceeded. Excess soil pressure can occur either directly under footing (see Mats) or at a lower level. The critical pressure is raised by preloading (see Soils in Chapter 13). Excess soil pressure directly under the footing is reduced by using larger footings. At all levels it is reduced by the removal of overburden, often accomplished by the basement excavation.

11. For soft clay upheaval under sheeting, see p. 13–23.

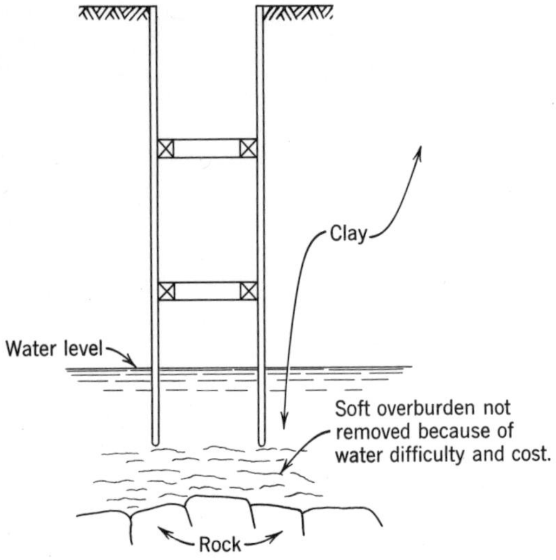

Clay

Water level

Soft overburden not
removed because of
water difficulty and cost.

Rock

FIG. 66.

DISHONEST BOTTOM FOR A COLUMN PIER DESIGNED TO BE SEATED ON HARD ROCK.

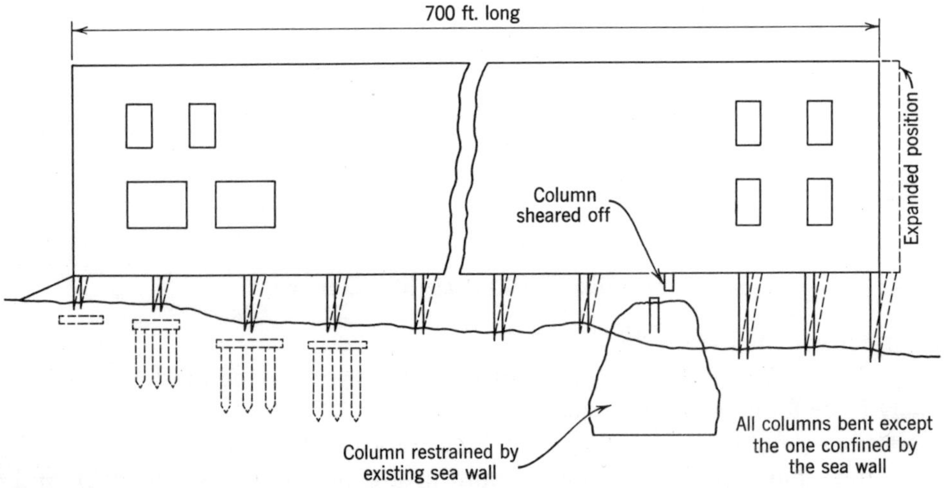

700 ft. long

Expanded position

Column
sheared off

Column restrained by
existing sea wall

All columns bent except
the one confined by
the sea wall

FIG. 67.   EXPANSION IN A LONG STRUCTURE SHEARS OFF A COLUMN.

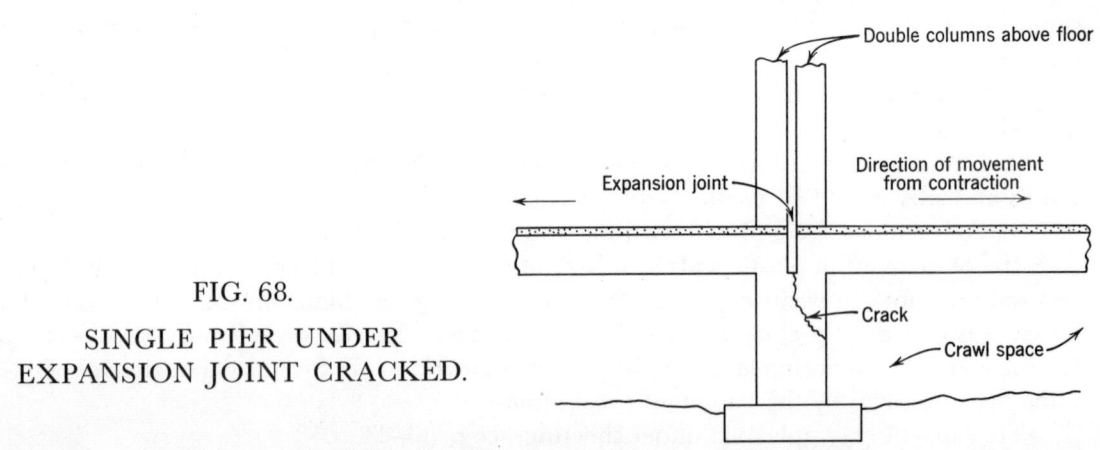

Double columns above floor

Expansion joint

Direction of movement
from contraction

Crack

Crawl space

FIG. 68.

SINGLE PIER UNDER EXPANSION JOINT CRACKED.

Errors in Mats

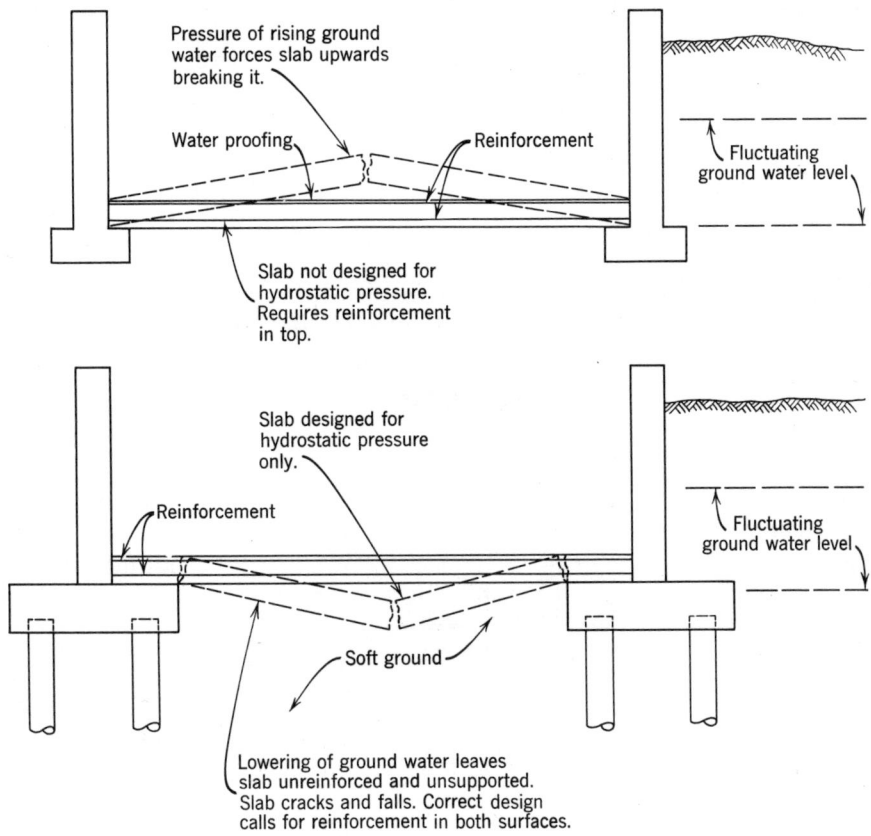

Pressure of rising ground water forces slab upwards breaking it.

Water proofing

Reinforcement

Fluctuating ground water level

Slab not designed for hydrostatic pressure. Requires reinforcement in top.

Slab designed for hydrostatic pressure only.

Reinforcement

Fluctuating ground water level

Soft ground

Lowering of ground water leaves slab unreinforced and unsupported. Slab cracks and falls. Correct design calls for reinforcement in both surfaces.

FIG. 69.

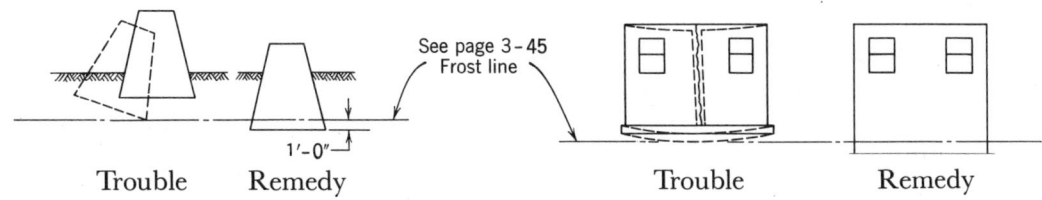

See page 3-45 Frost line

1'-0"

Trouble   Remedy

FIG. 70.   PIER CONSTRUCTION.

Trouble   Remedy

FIG. 71.   HOUSE CONSTRUCTION.

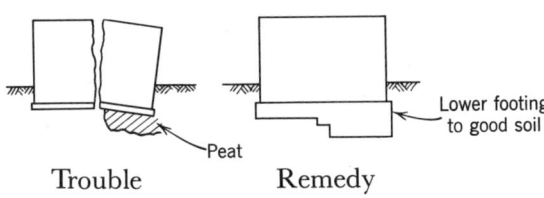

Peat

Lower footing to good soil

Trouble   Remedy

FIG. 72.   SOIL CONDITION.

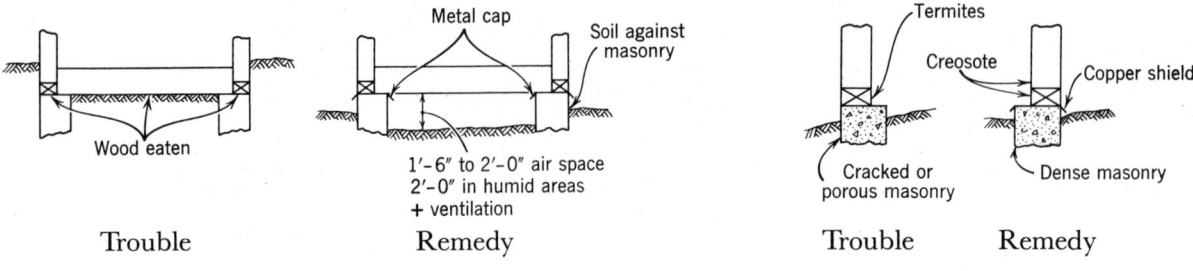

FIG. 73.   TERMITE CONTROL.

1. Clean up building and grounds of all wood trash.
2. Break all wood-to-earth contacts, and treat ground with pentachloraphenol.

Red Lights

Cause	Sketch	*Method of Avoidance*

Cause

Cracks at wall openings, a result of relief at weakest section of stresses due to settlement.

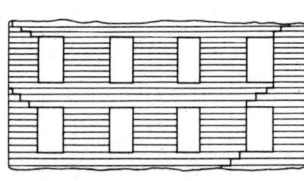

FIG. 74.

Method of Avoidance

For shrinkage control see p. 3–37.   Design adequate foundations.

Cause

Cracks due to settlement of new building in relation to old.

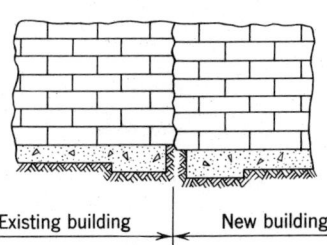

Existing building   New building

FIG. 75.

Method of Avoidance

(*a*) Joint separating wall of new building from old. (*b*) Reduce the design unit load on the footings of the new building adjoining the old.

Cause

Very dangerous bulging basement wall resulting from inadequate section to act as retaining wall. Contributing cause surcharge. Lack of drainage of base of wall causes build-up of hydrostatic pressure.

Shrinkage in concrete

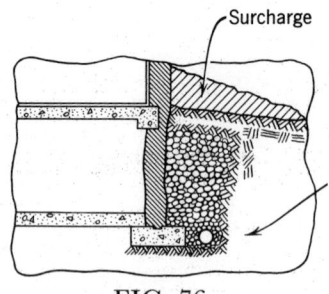

Surcharge

Provide for draining when ground does not drain away from wall naturally.

FIG. 76.

Method of Avoidance

Use adequate wall thickness to resist earth and frost thrust.

Provide adequate belt steel reinforcement. Pour concrete wall in short alternate sections to take up initial set.

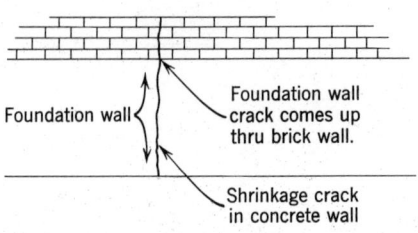

Foundation wall

Foundation wall crack comes up thru brick wall.

Shrinkage crack in concrete wall

FIG. 77.

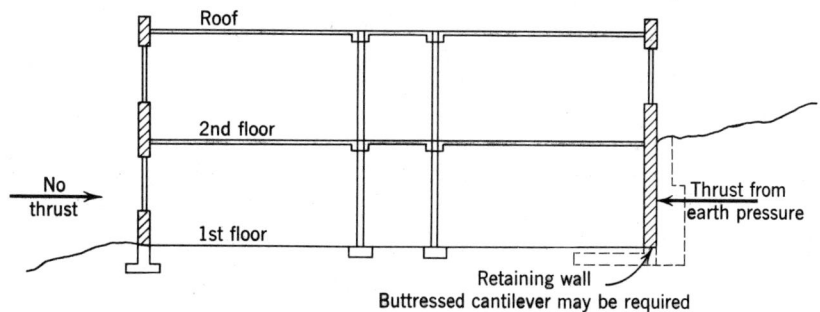

Note: Either 2nd floor must be buttressed or retaining wall must be designed as contilevered.

FIG. 78.   UNBALANCED EARTH PRESSURE RACKS BUILDING.

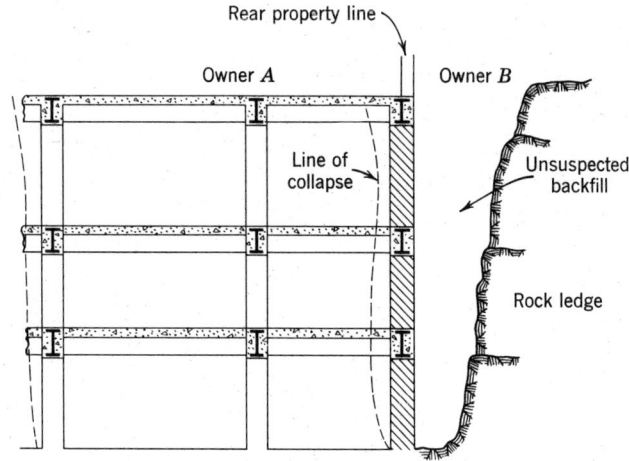

FIG. 79.   STEEL SKELETON OF BUILDING FAILED WHEN OWNER
OF REAR PROPERTY BACKFILLED.

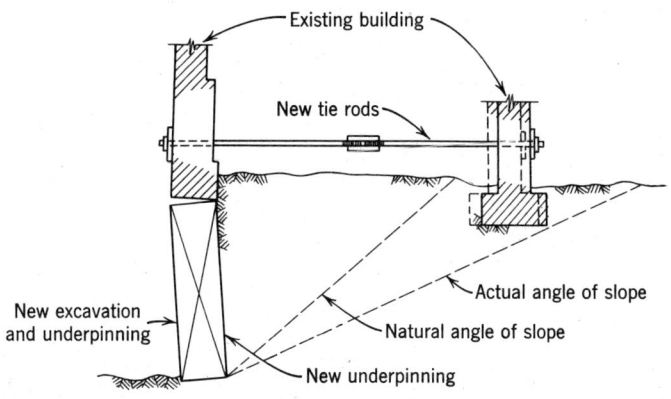

FIG. 80.   TIE ROD PULL CHANGES ANGLE OF REPOSE.

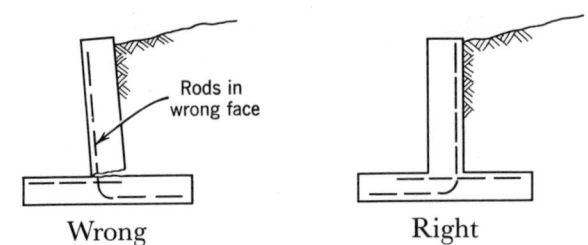

Wrong   Right

FIG. 81.   REINFORCED RETAINING WALL.

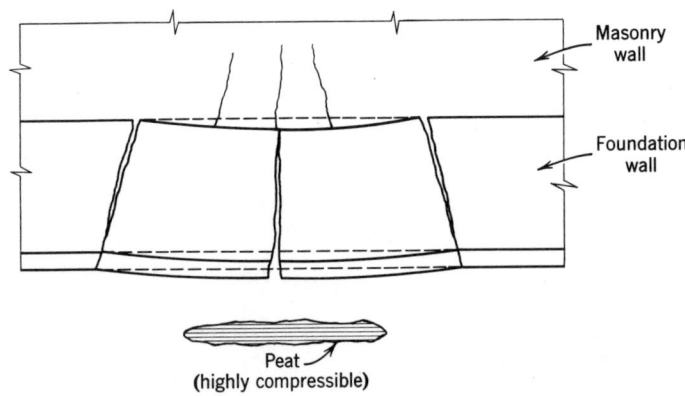

FIG. 82.   STRATUM OF ORGANIC MATERIAL.

Local foundation failure.

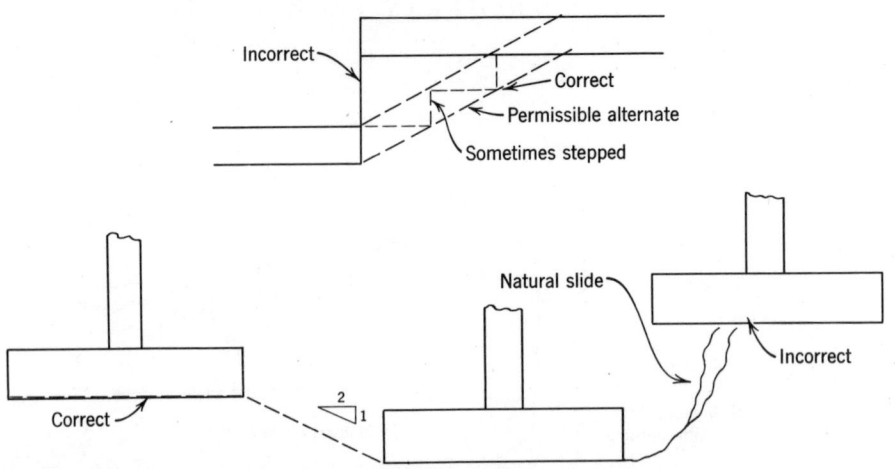

FIG. 83.   STEPPING DOWN FOOTINGS TO MAINTAIN STABILITY OF
FOUNDATION MATERIAL.

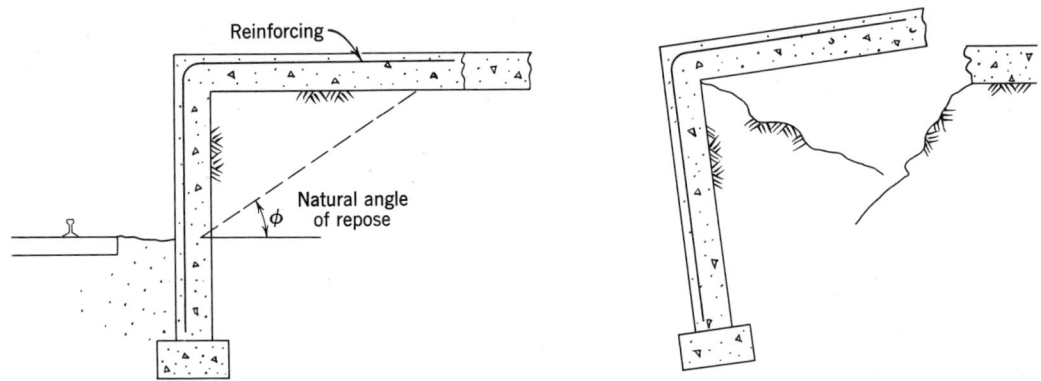

FIG. 84.   INSUFFICIENT ANCHORAGE IN A PLATFORM.
Set p. 4–13 for tie back.

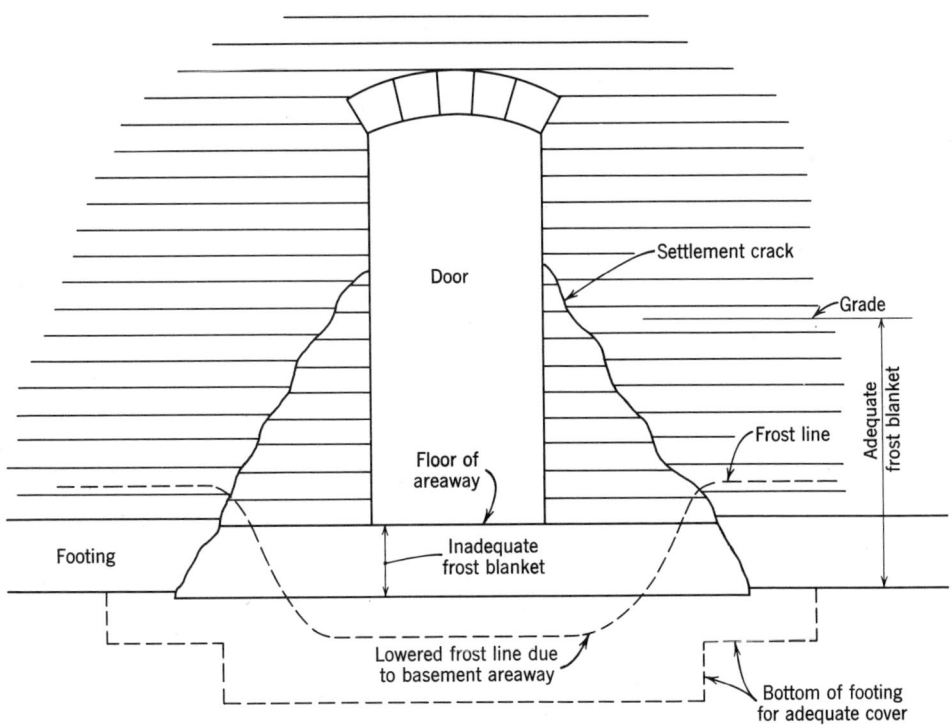

Settlement of footing due to change in frost blanket.   Note that this can occur even if the basement is heated.   The prevention is to lower the footing by steps under an areaway or wherever the cover is reduced for any reason.

FIG. 85.   EFFECT OF BASEMENT DOOR, PARTICULARLY WHEN BUILDING IS NOT HEATED.

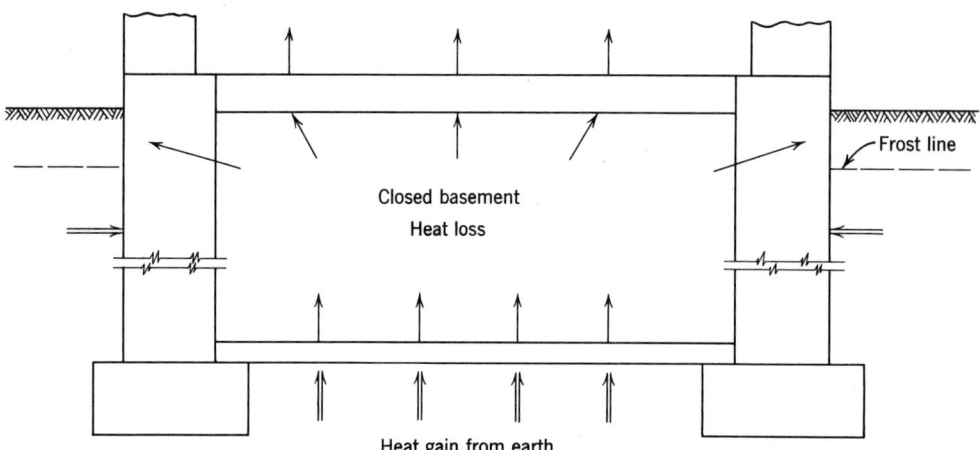

In temperate-zone climates, a closed basement may remain above freezing temperature even with frozen ground outside, because the gain in heat through walls and floor below the frost line exceeds the losses above it.

FIG. 86.   FREEZING; EFFECT ON FROST LINE OF BASEMENTS; UNHEATED BUILDING.

4

Retaining Walls

Emphasis should be placed upon such considerations as:

    Adequacy of foundations
    Shrinkage cracks
    Surface disintegration
    Mass disintegration
    Drainage
    Frost
    Expansion joints
    Backfill
    Hydrostatic uplift
    Equal foundation pressure on elastic soils

The selection of a type of wall is made with an eye to these factors and to the relative economy.

THEORETICAL DESIGN

The author believes that theories of foundation wall pressures have been "worried" and complexed by many fine engineering minds to a point far beyond any value to the designing engineer. Two theories are commonly used.

The Rankine theory is based on complex concepts but is simple in application. Soil pressures are reduced to an equivalent fluid pressure varying in weight with the angle of repose (or angle of internal friction). It has been espoused by the majority of practical engineers.

The Rankine theory is based on the assumption that sand in a state of failure acts like a liquid and produces liquid pressures on the wall.

This leads to the fundamental equations in Fig. 3.

The Coulomb theory is based on simple concepts but is not simple in application. A wedge of soil is held up by the cohesion or shearing strength of the boundary slope and resistance of the wall. See Fig. 5. The theory is valuable for checking the Rankine theory, particularly in cohesive or plastic soils.

For the meaning of angle of internal friction ϕ, angle of repose ϕ, and cohesion C, see p. 13–16, Soil Mechanics.

This theory would fit the case of plastic soils better than the Rankine, which is based on a plastic state of granular soils.

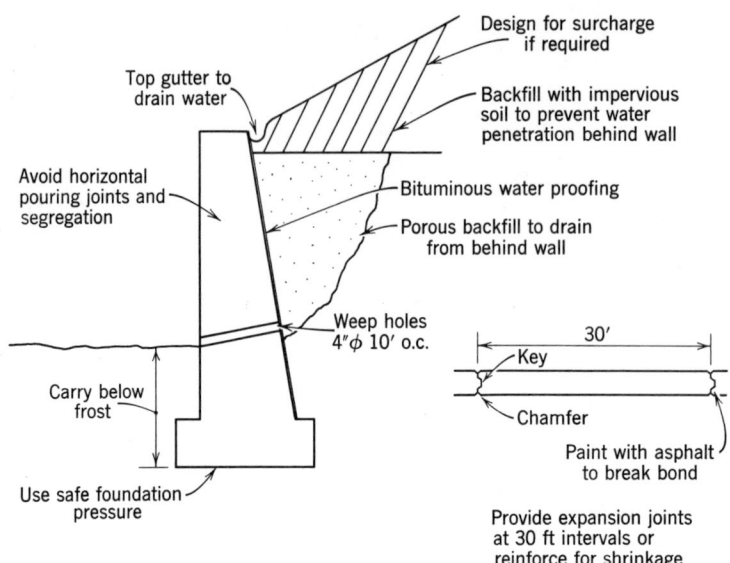

FIG. 1. ESSENTIAL ELEMENTS OF RETAINING WALLS.

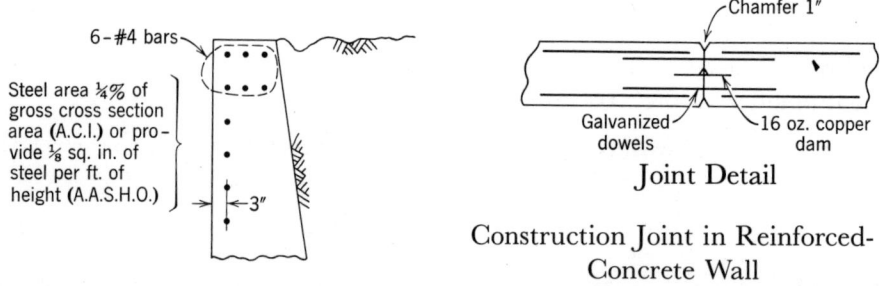

FIG. 2. SHRINKAGE REINFORCEMENT (IF USED).

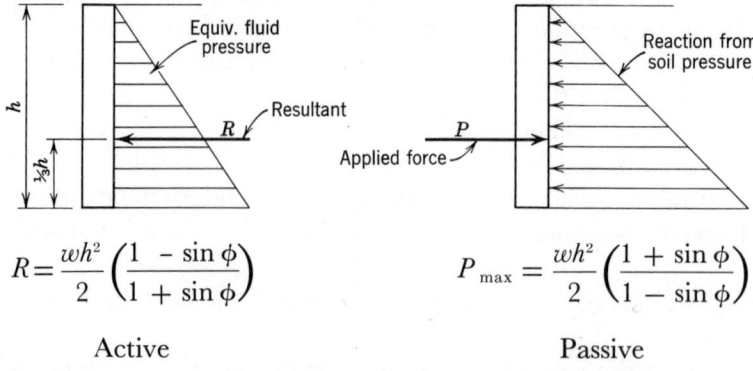

$$R = \frac{wh^2}{2}\left(\frac{1 - \sin\phi}{1 + \sin\phi}\right)$$

Active

$$P_{\max} = \frac{wh^2}{2}\left(\frac{1 + \sin\phi}{1 - \sin\phi}\right)$$

Passive

W = unit weight of soil; ϕ = angle of repose.   For values see Tables I and II.

FIG. 3. LATERAL PRESSURE UPON RETAINING WALLS, RANKINE SOLUTION.

P = equivalent fluid unit weight
W = unit weight of soil behind wall
Let $k = P/W$
l = pounds per square foot of surcharge
h = equivalent fluid head without surcharge
h' = head with surcharge

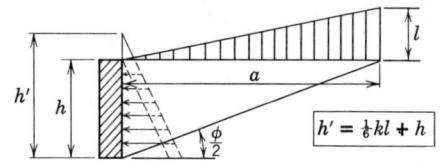

$$h' = \tfrac{1}{6}kl + h$$

Case I.   Surcharge due to sloping bank.

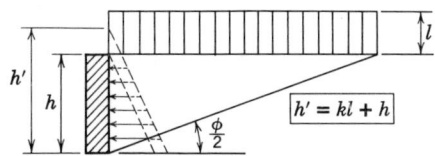

$$h' = kl + h$$

Case II.   Uniform surcharge.

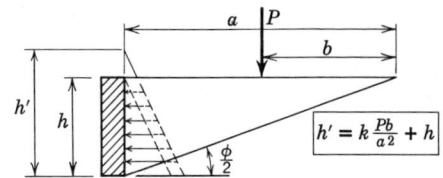

$$h' = k\frac{Pb}{a2} + h$$

Case III.   Concentrated load.

FIG. 4.   RELATION OF SURCHARGE TO EQUIVALENT FLUID PRESSURE.

Alternative Approaches to Surcharge

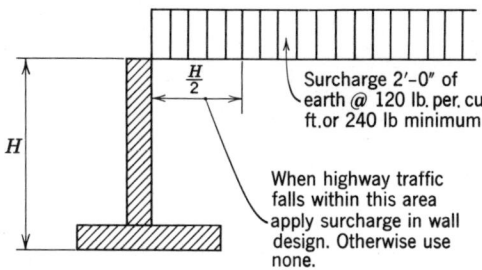

Surcharge 2'-0" of earth @ 120 lb. per. cu. ft. or 240 lb minimum

When highway traffic falls within this area apply surcharge in wall design. Otherwise use none.

FIG. 4a.   EARTH PRESSURE FROM HIGHWAY TRAFFIC.   FROM A.A.S.H.O. CODE.

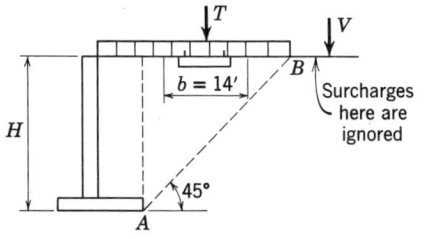

Surcharges here are ignored

Case I.   Surcharge within line AB.   Equivalent uniform surcharge $= T/b$.

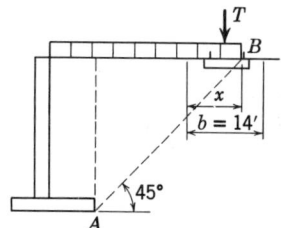

Case II.   Surcharge partly within line AB. Equivalent uniform surcharge $= \dfrac{x}{H} \times \dfrac{T}{b}$.

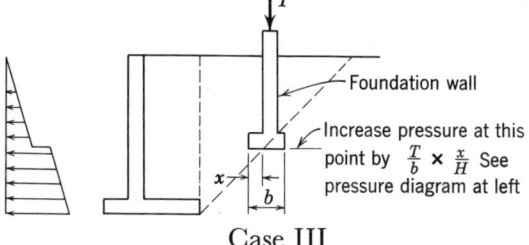

Foundation wall

Increase pressure at this point by $\dfrac{T}{b} \times \dfrac{x}{H}$ See pressure diagram at left

Case III

FIG. 4b.   EARTH PRESSURE FROM RAILROADS AND FOUNDATION WALLS,
RECOMMENDATIONS A.R.E.A.*

* T is Cooper's "E" loading divided by the axle centers.

Simple Conception of the Coulomb Approach

Note that the shaded area in Fig. 5 is a prism of plastic soil (clay) outside an arbitrary surface of slip, held up by a thrust R against the back of the wall, and by the shearing strength of the plastic soil C.

The position assumed for the arbitrary surface which would produce a maximum value of R could be found by cut and try, but the angle $\alpha = 45°$ gives a practical approximation for a purely plastic soil.

If the soil has a natural angle of friction as in a soil mixture, α may be taken $= 45 + \dfrac{\phi}{2}$.

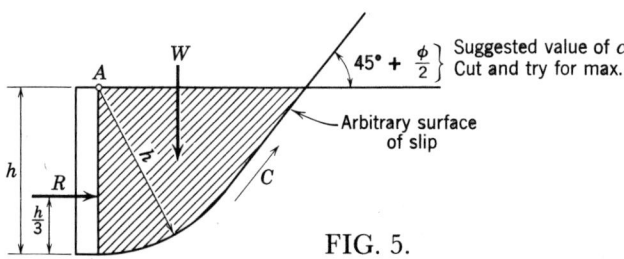

FIG. 5.

Wedge analysis of retaining wall:

W = weight of soil wedge.
C = cohesion of soil, by laboratory test. Approximate value from factual data, p. 4–8.
ϕ = angle of internal friction, factual data, p. 4–8.
R = reaction of soil on wall.

By taking moments about A, R may be evaluated. Allowance may also be made for friction on walls as shown; see Fig. 6.

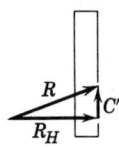

C' = cohesion, or friction, between wall and soil.
R/H = horizontal component of R.

FIG. 6.

Problem 1. Analysis of Pressure on Retaining Wall

After Coulomb

For cohesive soils having low internal friction.

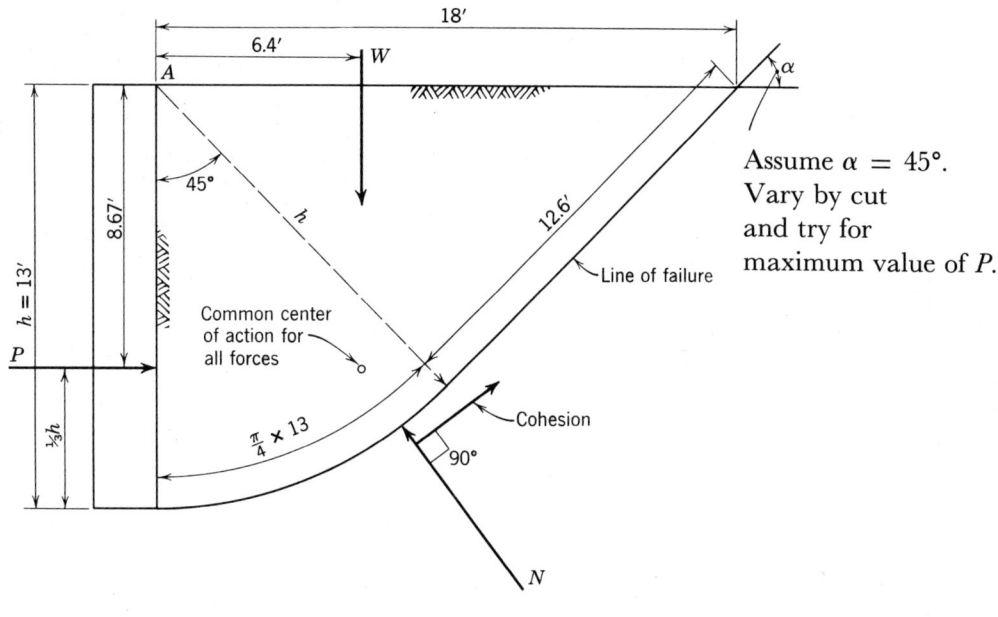

FIG. 7.

Given: $h = 13$; weight of soil $= 100$ lb./ft.^{3}; cohesion $= 100$ lb./sq. ft.
To find: Thrust on wall.
Construct figure as shown.   Area of wedge $= 148$ sq. ft. $W = 148 \times 100 = 14{,}800$ lb.

$$\text{Cohesion} = \left(\frac{\pi}{4} \times 13 + 12.6 \right) 100 = 2280 \text{ lb.}$$

Take moments about *A:*
$$14{,}800 \times 6.4 - 2280 \times 13 - 8.67\, P = 0$$
$$P = 7500$$

Problem 2.   Force Distribution about Retaining Wall

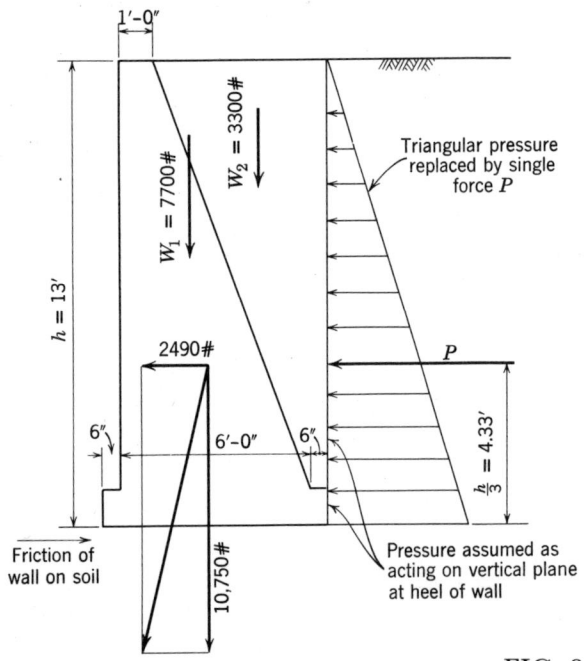

Given: $h = 13'$
$\phi = 33°$
$w = 100$ lb./ft.^{3}

$$P = \tfrac{1}{2}wh^2\left(\frac{1 - \sin\phi}{1 + \sin\phi}\right)$$

$$= \tfrac{1}{2} \times 100 \times 13^2\left(\frac{1 - \sin 33°}{1 + \sin 33°}\right)$$

$$= 2490$$

Evaluate W_1 and W_2. Resolve by graphics as shown.

FIG. 8.

Foundation Pressures

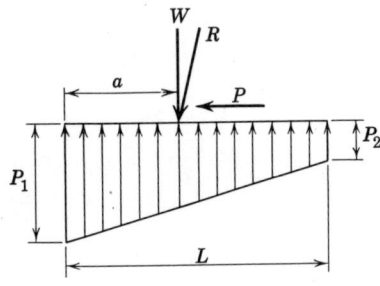

$$P_1 = (4L - 6a)\frac{W}{L^2}$$

$$P_2 = (6a - 2L)\frac{W}{L^2}$$

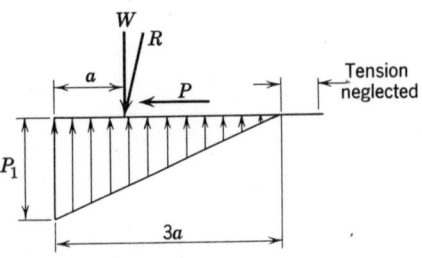

$$P_1 = \frac{2W}{3a}$$

FIG. 9.

For safe toe pressure see Table 3–I, but for plastic soils use ½ value given.

Sliding *

Coefficient of Friction

Dry clay   0.5 – 0.6
Wet clay   0.33
Sand   0.4
Gravel   0.6

Use factor of safety 1½.

It is the author's opinion that where concrete is used the shearing strength of the soil will govern.

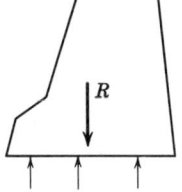

Case I

Compute number of rows of piles, and center on resultant.

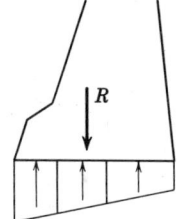

Case II

1. Draw equivalent trapezoid due to resultant.

2. Determine number of rows of piles = N.

3. Subdivide large trapezoid into N trapezoids of equal area.

4. Center piles on centroid of small trapezoids.

FIG. 10.   LOCATION OF PILES UNDER A RETAINING WALL.

* By permission from *Design of Concrete Structures*, 4th edition, by Urquhart and O'Rourke, copyright, 1940, by McGraw-Hill Book Co., Inc.

TABLE I – SLOPES OF REPOSE

KIND OF EARTH	SLOPE OF REPOSE	
	NON-SUBMERGED	SUBMERGED
Sand, clean	1 on 1.5	1 on 2
Sand and clay	1 on 1.33	1 on 3
Clay, dry	1 on 1.75	
Clay		1 on 3.5
Clay, damp, plastic	1 on 3	
Gravel, Clean	1 on 1.33	1 on 2
Gravel and clay	1 on 1.33	1 on 3
Gravel, sand, and clay	1 on 1.5	1 on 3
Soft, rotten rock	1 on 1	1 on 1
Hard rotten rock	1 on 1	
Hard rock, riprap		1 on 1
Bituminous cinders	1 on 1	
River mud		1 on 3 to 1 on 20
Anthracite Ashes	1 on 1.5 to 1 on 2	

Rule of thumb for submerged excavated slopes:
Sand– 1 on 2   Clay–1 on 1.5 to vertical
Stiff mud–1 on 1 to vertical   Sluiced Mud–1 on 10 to 1 on 20

TABLE IV – SOIL SHEAR VALUES

KIND OF EARTH	COHESION, lbs/sq.ft.	ANG. OF INT. FR.
Clay – liquid †	100	0°
" very soft	200	2°
" soft	400-500	4°
" firm	1000	6°
" stiff	2000	12°
" very stiff	2000-4000	14
Sand wet	0	10°-15°
Sand dry or unmoved	0	34°
Silt	0	±20°
Cemented Sand & Gravel - Wet	500	34°
" " " " - Dry	1000	34°

TABLE VII – WEIGHT OF SOLIDS SUBMERGED IN SEA WATER

MATERIAL	POUND PER CUBIC FOOT		
	MAXIMUM	MINIMUM	AVERAGE
Gravel and Marl		42.0	62.9
Gravel and Sand	73.0	42.0	62.4
Sand	66.0	42.0	58.3
Gravel, Sand and Clay	80.9	51.2	70.0
Stiff Clay	64.8	38.4	47.8
Stiff Clay and Gravel	70.3	44.8	52.6

* C.B.R. = California Bearing Ratio.

**Adapted from "American Civil Engineers' Handbook" by Merriman & Wiggin.

† For classification see p. 3-6 (New York City Code).

TABLE II – UNIT WEIGHT OF SOILS

KIND OF EARTH	UNIT WEIGHTS-lb/cu.ft.
Moist Soils	110
Medium or stiff clay	120
Saturated earth	110 + % voids × 62.5 = say 132
Submerged earth	132 – 62.5 = say 70
Soft clay or mud	100

TABLE III – UNIT WEIGHTS AND C.B.R. VALUES FOR COMPACTED SOILS

SOLIDS AT OPTIMUM COMPACTION	WELL GRADED		NOT GRADED	
	UNIT WT.	C.B.R.*	UNIT WT.	C.B.R.
Sand and Silt	120	–	105	8-30
Sand and Clay (Binder)	125	20-60	105	8-30
Sands	120	20-60	100	10-30
Gravel	130	>50	115	25-60
Silts inorganic	–	–	100	6-25
Organic Silts	–	–	90	3-8

TABLE V – ROUGH DATA FOR EQUIVALENT FLUID PRESSURES OF SOILS

MULTIPLY UNIT WEIGHT BY "K"

KIND OF EARTH	"K"
Granular Sand	0.33
Mixtures of Clay and Granular Soils	0.50
Soft Clays, Silts, Organic Soils	1.00
Stiff Clays	1.00

TABLE VI – EQUIVALENT FLUID PRESSURES FOR SOILS SUBMERGED IN SEA WATER**

SLOPE OF REPOSE OF EARTH	WEIGHT 'W' OF SUBMERGED EARTH LB./CU.FT.							
	40	44	48	52	56	60	64	68
1 on ½	66.2	66.4	66.7	66.9	67.1	67.3	67.6	67.8
1 on ¾	68.2	68.9	69.3	69.8	70.2	70.7	71.1	71.6
1 on 1	70.9	71.6	72.2	72.9	73.6	74.3	75.0	75.7
1 on 1¼	73.2	74.2	75.1	76.0	76.9	77.9	78.8	79.7
1 on 1½	75.4	76.6	77.7	78.9	80.0	81.2	82.3	83.5
1 on 1¾	77.5	78.8	80.2	81.5	82.9	84.2	85.6	86.9
1 on 2	79.3	80.8	82.3	83.9	85.4	86.9	88.4	90.0
1 on 2½	82.3	84.2	86.0	87.8	89.7	91.5	93.3	95.2
1 on 3	84.8	86.9	88.9	91.0	93.1	95.2	97.2	99.3
1 on 3½	86.8	89.0	91.3	93.6	95.9	98.2	100.0	102.0
1 on 4	88.4	90.8	93.3	95.7	98.1	101.0	103.0	105.0
1 on 5	90.9	93.6	96.3	99.0	102.0	104.0	107.0	109.0
1 on 6	104.0	108.0	112.0	116.0	120.0	124.0	128.0	132.0

To obtain equivalent fluid pressure for a given slope of repose, say 1¾:1, get the weight of the submerged soil from table VII, say 60, enter table VI at column marked nearest to this value. Obtain equivalent weight, 84.2 from row of given slope of repose.

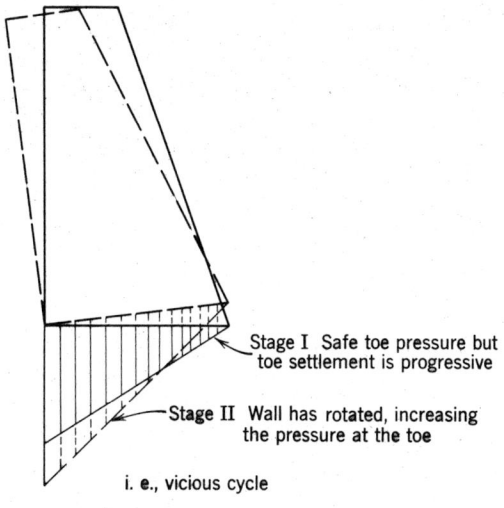

FIG. 11.

Vicious Cycle of Retaining Wall Base on Plastic Soil

1. Settlement is proportional to pressure; i.e. water is squeezed out in proportion to pressure.

2. Difference in toe and heel pressure causes differential settlement resulting in rotation of the wall.

3. Rotation of the wall moves the resultant forward. This movement increases the toe and reduces the heel pressure.

4. This change in pressure produces more differential settlement with more rotation. More rotation moves the resultant still farther forward, creating a vicious cycle.

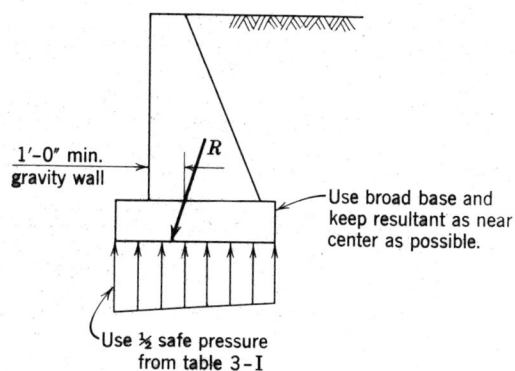

FIG. 12. AVOIDANCE OF ROTATION OF WALL ON PLASTIC SOIL.

Additional Pressures on Retaining Wall

In addition to ordinary earth pressures, retaining walls are subject to (*a*) hydrostatic pressure, (*b*) frost pressure, (*c*) surcharges.

Hydrostatic pressure should be designed for on the basis of a fluid pressure of about 75 lb. per cu. ft. (soil and water included). See Table VI, p. 4–8. It is possible for hydrostatic pressure to occur temporarily in locations where indications are against its occurrence as a result of intense rain or a broken water main.

Frost action may occur in silty backfill. The pressure of the ice lenses, p. 14–14, is more than any wall can stand. Therefore the cause of the ice lenses should be removed by preventing water from entering behind the wall and by draining away whatever water does enter; Fig. 13.

Surcharges are designed for as shown on p. 4–3. Those occurring from trucks (basement walls near loading areas are a good example) and from railroads may be evaluated as shown in Fig. 4a.

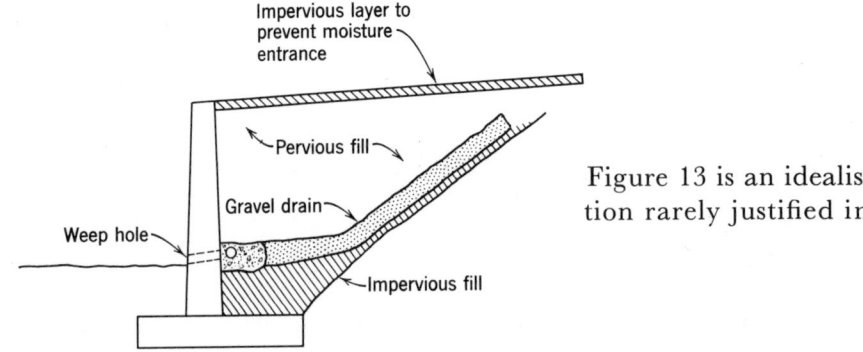

Figure 13 is an idealistic suggestion rarely justified in practice.

FIG. 13.   PREVENTIVE MEASURES AGAINST FROST ON RETAINING WALLS.

Figure 14 is the more common solution.

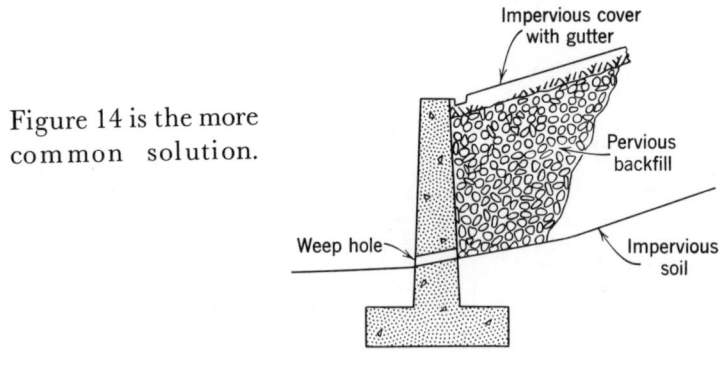

FIG. 14.

CRIB WALL

Crib walls are sometimes used for retaining wall. Originally they were constructed as rock-filled log cribs. Now several types of precast-concrete sections are on the market. They offer a cheap method of wall construction, having the advantage of good drainage. The crib should be filled before any backfill is placed. Then the filled crib acts as a gravity wall unit. An example follows.

Unlike masonry retaining walls, foundations of crib walls need not go below frost because of their flexibility and hence comparative immunity from settlement cracks.

However, sections of crib below grade should be filled with an impervious material to prevent ponding around foundation. See Fig. 15.

High crib walls should have adequate foundations carried below frost line.

Problem 3.   Design of Crib Wall

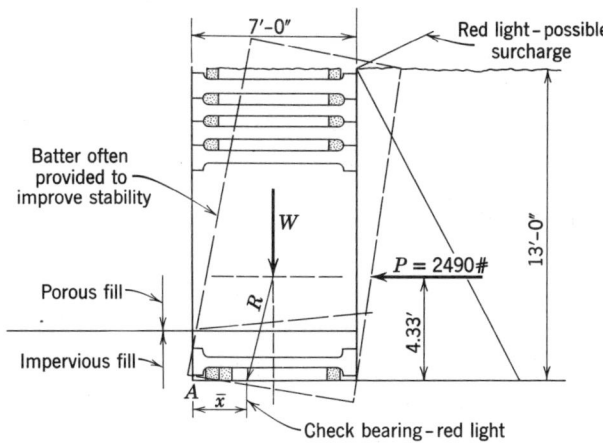

FIG. 15.

Given: Wall shown in figure.

To check: Solution of frictional sliding.

$P = 2490$ lb. $W = 7 \times 13 \times 100 = 9100$ lb.

Take M about A

$$9100 \times 3.5 = 31,800$$
$$2490 \times 4.33 = \underline{10,800}$$
$$21,000$$

$$\bar{X} = \frac{21000}{9100} = 2.32'$$

Resultant at edge of middle third.   O.K.

Check sliding friction: $\dfrac{9100}{2} = 4500$ (Coefficient of friction = 0.5.)

Factor of safety: $\dfrac{4550}{2490} = 1.83$. O.K.

Crib as a free body is all right.

Crib should be filled prior to placing backfill against it.

Then the crib pieces can be figured as silos rather than using the heavier retaining wall pressures.   Arch action occurs between the front and back crib walls, reducing the maximum thrust. The design of the pieces is as follows.

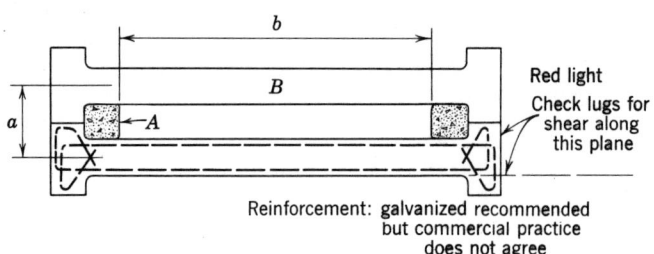

FIG. 16.

Design stretcher A

   Lateral force = 0.5 abw (w = unit weight of soil)

   Vertical force = lateral force $\times$ tan δ

           δ = friction angle of soil on wall (30°)

Design header B

   Axial force = reaction from stretcher

   Vertical force same as stretcher

Example: $a = 1'$ $b = 5'$ Headers 6'-0 o.c.   Concrete

   Stretcher

   6" x 6" x 6' 0   Lateral force = 0.5 $\times$ 1 $\times$ 5 $\times$ 100 $\times$ 6 = 1500 lb.

$$M_h = \frac{1500}{8} \times 6 = 1125 \text{ ft. lb.} \qquad A_s = 0.20$$

   Vertical force 0.58 $\times$ 1500 = 870 lb.

   Dead load   240 lb.

                                  1110 lb.

$$M_v = \frac{1110}{8} \times 6 = 830 \text{ ft. lb.} \qquad A_s = 0.14$$

   One #4 each corner

   Header

   6" x 6"   Bending $M = \dfrac{1110}{8} \times 5.5 = 760$ ft. lb. $A_s = 0.13$

   Tension = 1500 lb. $A_s = \underline{0.08}$

                                                        0.21

   One #3 each corner

BULKHEADS AND RELIEVING PLATFORMS

   Bulkheads consist of sheet piling of either steel, timber, or reinforced concrete restrained at the bottom by the soil and at the top by a wale tied back to a deadman or pile anchor.

   Extreme care must be taken to prevent a mud wave from flowing out from under the toe of the sheet piling. The passive resistance of the soil is used to hold the toe in place in the design examples that follow so that the moment in the sheet piling may be computed. In actual practice, however, the only safe procedure is to *drive the sheeting to firm resistance.*

The tie back must be anchored far enough back so that it acts independent of the bulkhead and the soil behind; Fig. 17.

The relieving platform is similar except that the top thrust is taken by batter piles. The uplift from the batter piles is taken by the weight of the fill over the platform. Very often the platform is placed just below low water. Then all the construction from platform down may be made of wood without danger of decay. The wall above may then be of concrete.

Timber used for such work is generally a minimum of 4 to 8 in. thick. Steel sheeting is designed for a bending stress of 24,000 p.s.i. It can be driven through old fill with boulders and other trash more easily than timber or concrete sheeting.

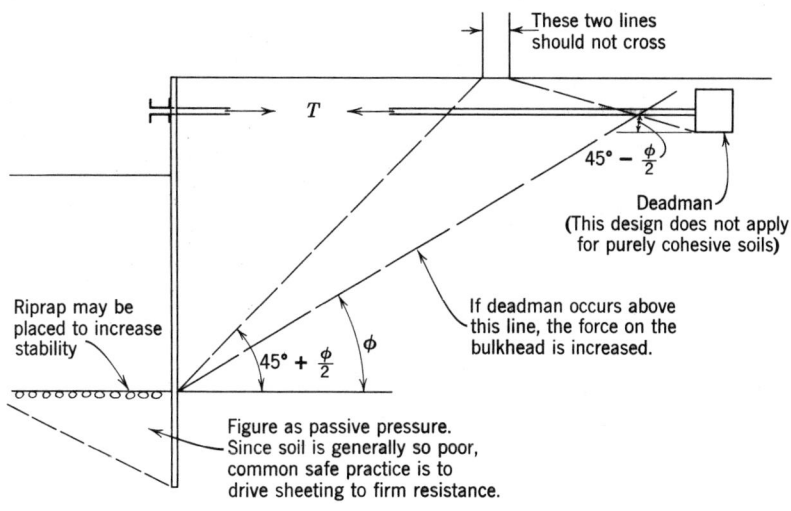

FIG. 17.   SHEET PILE BULKHEAD.

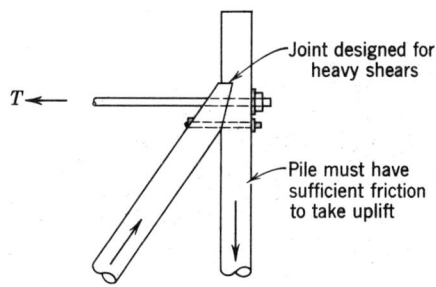

FIG. 18.   PILE ANCHORAGE USED IN PLACE OF DEADMAN ABOVE.

Problem 4.   Design of Steel Sheet Pile Wall

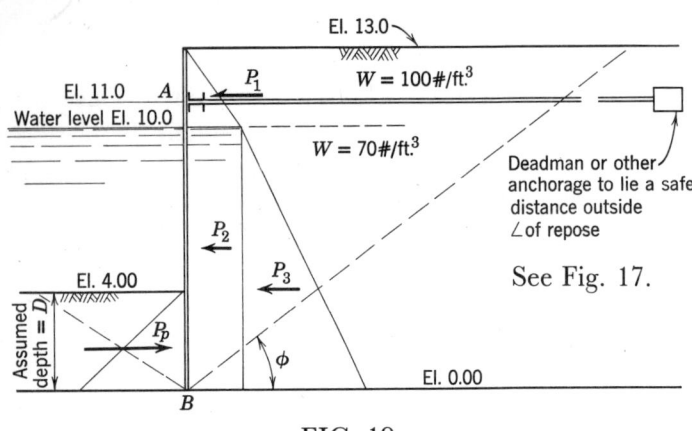

FIG. 19.

For design of deadman see p. 4–15.

$$\phi = 33°$$
$$\frac{1 - \sin \phi}{1 + \sin \phi} = 0.295$$

Given: Bulkhead shown in Fig. 19.

To find: D.

P_1	$3 \times 100 \times 0.295 = 88.5$	$88.5 \times 3 \times \frac{1}{2} =$ 133
P_2		88.5×10 $=$ 885
P_3	$10 \times 70 \times 0.295 = 206$	$206 \times 10 \times \frac{1}{2} = \underline{1030}$
		2048

Take moments about A and solve for required P_p (passive pressure).

$$885 \times 6 = 5,310$$
$$1030 \times 7.67 = \underline{7,900}$$
$$13,210$$

$$P_p = \frac{13,200}{967} = 1370$$

Minimum passive pressure possible: $\phi = 33°$.

$$= \frac{1}{2} \times 4^2 \times 70 \times \frac{1}{0.295} = 1900$$

Factor of safety $= \dfrac{1900}{1370} = 1.39$

Red Light: $\phi = 33°$. O.K. for sand. For muck and silt, see Table I. Very important, as most failures occur here.

Tie Rod Stress

Take moments about B.

$$133 \times 11 \quad = 1463$$
$$885 \times 5 \quad = 4425$$
$$1030 \times 3.33 = \underline{3430}$$
$$9318$$
$$1370 \times 1.33 = \underline{1820}$$
$$7500$$

Tie rod stress $= \dfrac{7500}{11} = 682$ lb.

$682 + 1370 = 2052.$ Checks with 2048.

Design sheet pile as a beam with these forces. P_1, P_2, P_3 and P_p.

Find point of zero shear. El. 5.75

$$
\begin{array}{lr}
682 & 133 \\
4\tfrac{1}{4} \times 88.5 = & 376 \\
(4\tfrac{1}{4})/2 \times 0.295 \times 70 = & 186 \\
\hline
682 & 695 \qquad \text{Close enough}
\end{array}
$$

Take moments about point of zero shear:

$$
\begin{array}{lr}
(682 - 133) \times 5.25 = 2880 & \\
- 376 \times 4.25/2 = & 800 \\
- 186 \times 1.42 = & 264 \\
\hline
& 1064 \quad + M = 1816
\end{array}
$$

Using $f_s = 24,000$ p.s.i., as is common for steel sheet piling:

$$ S = \frac{1816 \times 12}{24,000} = 0.91 $$

SP-9 section is chosen; see Chapter 19.

Red Light: Toe depth of sheeting should be checked for adequate resistance of soil. Sheeting should best be driven into firm soil. Many failures caused by flow of soil under toe have been recorded.

Problem 5.   Design of Deadman

Given: Continuous deadman.

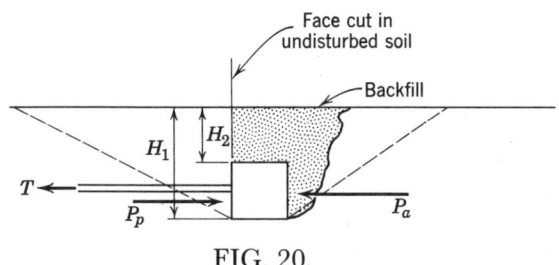

FIG. 20.

$\text{T} = \dfrac{P_p - P_a}{2}$ where 2 is factor of safety.

Given: $H_1 = 3$ ft. $H_2 = 1$ ft. $\phi = 33°$.

Compute:

$$ \frac{1 - \sin \phi}{1 + \sin \phi} = 0.294 \qquad \frac{1 + \sin \phi}{1 - \sin \phi} = 3.40 $$

To find safe load per foot:

$$
\begin{aligned}
\text{Net resisting pressure at top} &= 100 \times (3.4 - 0.29) = 311 \\
\text{at bott} &= 100 \times (3.4 - 0.29) \times 3 = 933
\end{aligned}
$$

Total resistance: $\dfrac{933 + 311}{2} \times 2 = 1244$ lb. per ft.

Safe resistance: $\dfrac{1244}{2} = 622$ lb. per ft.

End condition (often omitted as a factor of safety).

At each end an additional resistance may be allowed because the plane of resisting soil will turn out at an angle ϕ. Therefore the additional safe end resistance would be

$$622 \tan \phi = 622 \times 0.575 = 358 \text{ lb.}$$

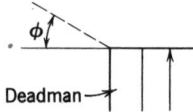

FIG. 21.　PLAN OF END OF DEADMAN.

Resistance to Overturning by Passive Pressure

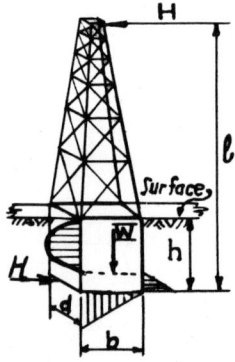

FIG. 22.　TRANSMISSION TOWER.

h　= depth in feet below surface.
H　= horizontal force.
$\overline{W}$　= total vertical force.
W　= weight of earth per cubic foot.
ϕ　= angle of repose.
d　= width of foundation.

$$\frac{3}{2} h \left(HL - \frac{wb}{6} \right) < \frac{dwh^2}{8} \left(\frac{1 + \sin \phi}{1 - \sin \phi} \right)$$

$$\frac{2\overline{W}}{db} < \text{safe bearing value of soil.}$$

Resistance to overturning by passive pressure is used for transmission towers and *low* vertical cantilever walls.

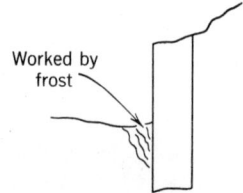

Worked by frost

Problem 6.   Design of Relieving Platform

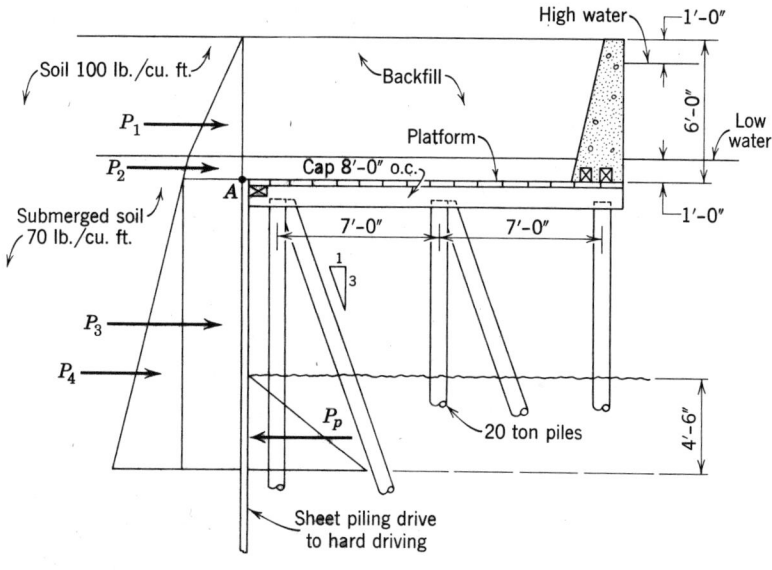

FIG. 23.

Given: Relieving platform as shown in Fig. 23. $\phi = 33°$

To check: $\dfrac{1 - \sin \phi}{1 + \sin \phi} = 0.295$

   Pressure at

0	0	$P_1 = \frac{1}{2} \times 5 \times 147 = 367$
-5	$5 \times 0.295 \times 100 = 147$	$P_2 = 147 + \dfrac{168}{2} = 158$
-6	$1 \times 0.295 \times 70 + 147 = 168$	$P_3 = 12.5 \times 168 = 2100$
-18	$12.5 \times 0.295 \times 70 + 168 = 426$	$P_4 = 258 \times \dfrac{12}{2} = 1610$

Take moments about A to find required P_{p}.

$$\begin{array}{ll} 2100 \times 6.25 = 13{,}100 & \\ \underline{1610 \times 8.33 = 13{,}400} & \dfrac{26{,}500}{11.0} = 2400 \text{ lb.} \\ 3710 \qquad\quad 26{,}500 & \end{array}$$

$$\text{Minimum } P_{\mathrm{p}} \text{ possible} = \tfrac{1}{2} \times 4.5^2 \times 70 \times \frac{1}{0.295} = 2400 \text{ lb.}$$

Horizontal force on platform $= P_3 + P_4 - P_p = 3710 - 2400 = 1310$

Force on wall $= P_1 + P_2 = 525$ lb.

Select wall from p. 2–10, using H $= 7$ ft. since the A dimension of $1'0''$ is part of the platform.

Weight of wall and soil over sloping back:

$$\frac{1.67 + 2.33}{2} \times 6 \times 150 = 1350$$

$$\frac{1.67}{2} \times 6 \times 100 = \underline{500}$$

$$1850 \text{ lb. per lin. ft.}$$

Weight of soil: $6 \times 100 = 600$

           Platform $= \underline{50}$

                 650 lb. per sq. ft.

Load per pile: $8 \times 7 \times 0.65 = 36.4^k$ O.K.

Weight of wall: $8 \times 1.850 = 14.8^k$ End pile will carry wall.

Total horizontal thrust $= 525 + 1310 = 1835$ lb. per ft.

$$8 \times 1835 = 14.7^k$$

Batter piles at 1:3 $\dfrac{36.4}{3} = 12.1^k$ max. per pile

Use 2 batter piles.

Note: If the sheet piling were omitted and the soil allowed to pass through, then only one batter pile would be required. With such construction a check of the lower stratum must be made to prevent a mud wave.

For design of sheet pile see p. 4–15.

Red Lights: 1. Timber must be protected against marine borers. See Chapter 19.
                2. Consider pile uplift due to batter piles.

SELECTION OF RETAINING WALL

Retaining walls are generally selected on the basis of economy. For low heights the gravity wall is generally cheapest, for medium heights the cantilever, and for substantial heights the buttressed or counterfort. When selecting a cantilevered wall, particular attention must be paid to the position of the wall on the footing. Placing the wall at the toe increases the excavation behind the wall but permits its placement nearer the property line, Fig. 24. Also, the toe pressure is greater, which may or may not be critical. An example of an economic study follows.

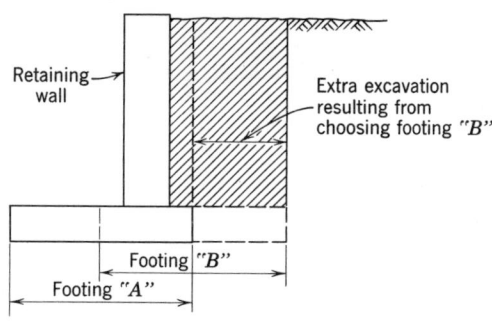

FIG. 24.

Given a retaining wall 10 ft. high with frost protection of 4' 0''. Make an economic study of T-shaped cantilever wall and gravity wall. Select type I and type IV walls from p. 2–10.

Gravity Wall

Forms	29 sq. ft. @ $ 0.80—	$23.20
Concrete	1⅔ cu. yd. @ 25.00—	41.75
Reinforcing steel	—	
Excavation (additional)*	1⅔ cu. yd. @ 2.00—	3.30
Cost per foot of wall		$68.25

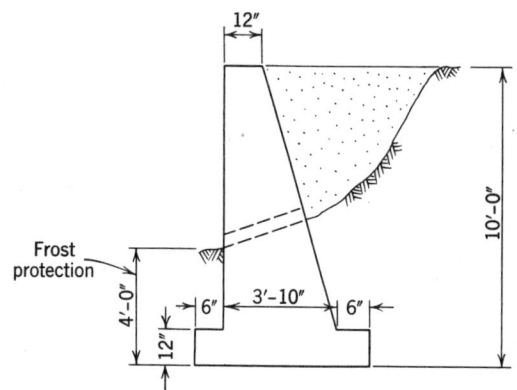

Cantilever Wall

Forms	28 sq. ft. @ $ 0.80—	$22.40
Concrete	0.73 cu. yd. @ 25.00—	18.25
Reinforcing steel	26 lb. @ 0.15—	3.90
Excavation (additional)*	—	
Cost per foot of wall		$44.55

---

* Only additional excavation included in cost.

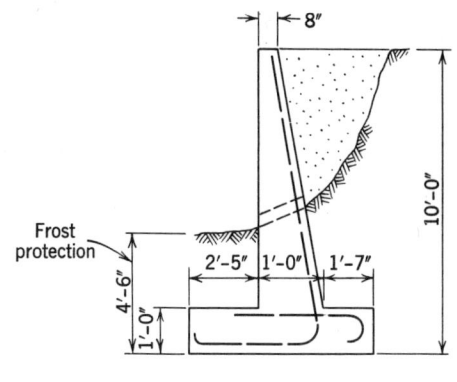

FIG. 25.

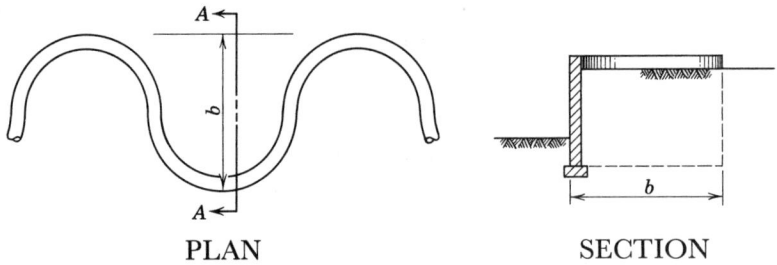

PLAN   SECTION

Serpentine garden wall.   Relies on dimension *b* for stability.
Designed by Thomas Jefferson for the University of Virginia.

FIG. 26.

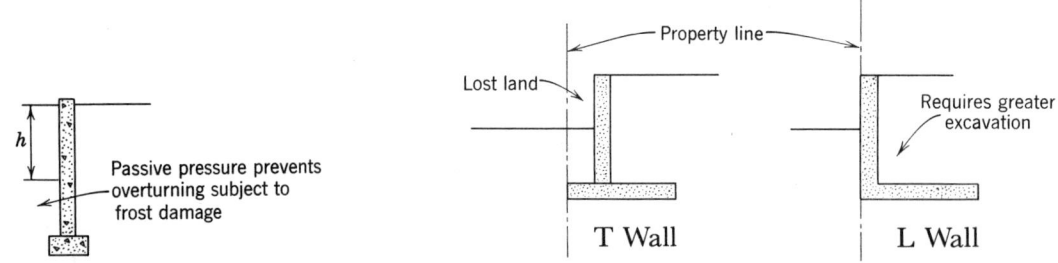

FIG. 27.   CANTILEVER GARDEN WALL
USUALLY H. LIMITED TO ABOUT 4 FT.

FIG. 28.   SELECTION OF
CANTILEVER WALL.

Red Lights

1. Use extreme caution in placing retaining walls on plastic soils to prevent vicious cycle; Fig. 11.

2. Beware of possible surcharges present or future behind retaining walls.

3. Batter piles in relieving platform must have sufficient downward force to resist uplift or the horizontal resistance cannot be developed.

4. Deadmen and anchorages must be kept far enough from bulkheads not to affect the angle of repose.

5. Drive sheeting to firm resistance to prevent "poop out" or flow of soil out from under the toe.

6. *Walls of Slip Side Wharves.*   In areas where tide range is great, water left in the ground can exert hydraulic pressure equivalent to a liquid heavier than water, for example, perhaps 100 lb. per cu. ft. during a period of tidal fall.

7. Avoid exceeding safe toe pressure.

8. Provide for shrinkage by expansion joints or reinforcement.   (Reinforced walls for shrinking, see foundation wall sheet, Fig. 3-48.)

9. Surfacing.   See specification.

10. Adequate provision against frost thrust, see p. 4–10.

11. Avoid horizontal construction joints.

12. See also red lights in Chapter 3.

5

Bridge Piers and Abutments

TYPES OF ABUTMENTS

Discussion

Types I, II, and III (Figs. 1 and 2) are standard types with abutment and wing walls and may be used as a basis of comparison with other types. They present certain disadvantages:

(a) They tend to restrict the flood prism and hence increase scour and raise the upstream flood level.

(b) The scour may require deeper foundations and/or sheet piling protection.

(c) Foundations may have to be built in the wet. Note that the angle of the wings may be governed by desirable restriction of space occupied by slopes. These types are indicated for small heights. Special attention must be paid to the junction of the wing and abutment walls to prevent cracks.

Type IV (Fig. 3), *stub or Piggyback abutment,* has advantages over waterways in: (a) presenting a maximum flood prism; (b) simpler foundation construction. Its obvious disadvantage is, of course, a longer bridge deck. This type has its greatest economy where piles are required and heights are fairly high. Piles in fill are much cheaper than massive walls of types I to III. Rock near the surface can generally be reached more economically by types I to III, or the buried abutment without using piles.

Type V (Fig. 4), *buried abutment,* is similar in idea to the stub abutment. It is generally built prior to the placing of the fill. Since it is filled on both sides, the earth pressure is low. Superstructure erection can begin before placement of fill.

Type VI (Fig. 5), *box abutment,* employs a short span of bridge built integral with columns to act as a frame and resist earth pressure of the approaches. It is most often used for overpass work where the short span may be employed for pedestrian passage.

Type VII (Fig. 6), *arch abutment,* is used where arches are employed because of their beauty of line or because of their economy in certain conditions. The high inclined skewback thrusts are difficult to handle unless the abutment can be seated in rock. Therefore they are often used for spans over gorges.

Type VIII (Fig. 7), *the rigid frame,* is a combination girder and abutment. By using the abutment as a girder with bending in it, it is possible to have the advantages of the arch with the additional advantages of wider headroom and less thrust. It has the disadvantage that slight differential settlements will cause high secondary stresses in the superstructure. To overcome this disadvantage as well as to take advantage of more economical superstructure design, attempts have been made to provide hinges between the abutment wall and footing as shown in Fig. 15.

TYPES OF PIERS

Discussion

There are many different shapes of bridge piers to be selected for economical design or for good appearance. A few are shown in Fig. 8.

The solid shaft (*A*), since it is most rugged, is used in rapidly running water or in water subject to ice or debris. It presents less friction to flow than multiple-column piers.

On ground the multiple-column or bent type (*B*) is often used. The section of wall at the bottom may or may not be used. It is needed in overpass work where traffic runs parallel close to the bent to reduce damage to the columns in case of accident. It is lighter and may be more economical than the solid shaft, but it requires more form work and material.

The pile bent (*C*) is used for low piers over unstable ground. The pile is used both for a support by driving to resistance and for a column by projecting above ground. For temporary work and for timber work, the part of the pile above ground may be long and braced with a system of longitudinal and transverse diagonal bracing, resulting in a structure called a trestle. The outside piles are usually battered.

Separate piers (*D*) are sometimes used for high bridges. These may be low piers with steel columns above or concrete piers up to the bridge level. In water, they may be combined with a solid shaft below up to floodwater level. They may have the advantage of lower cost than solid shafts.

TYPES OF ABUTMENTS

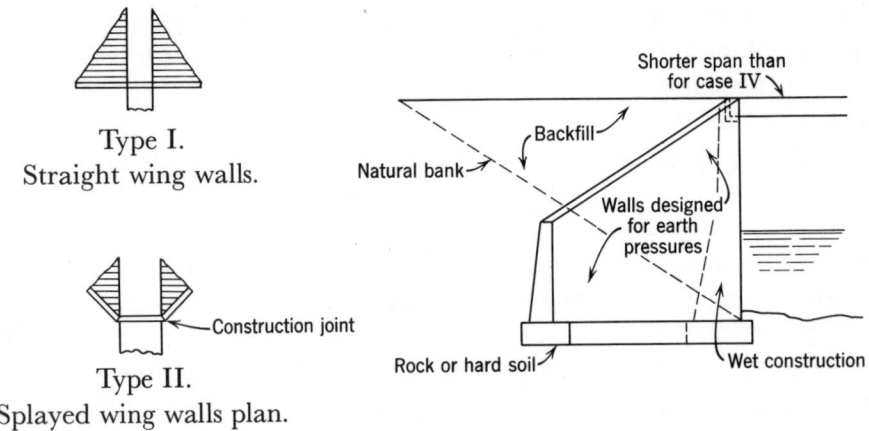

Type I.
Straight wing walls.

Type II.
Splayed wing walls plan.

FIG. 1. STANDARD GRAVITY ABUTMENT WITH WING WALLS.

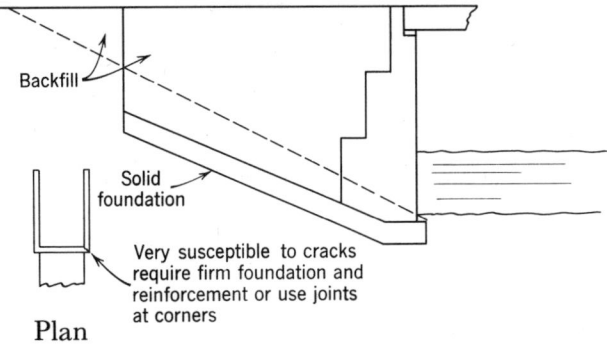

FIG. 2.   TYPE III.   U-SHAPED ABUTMENT.

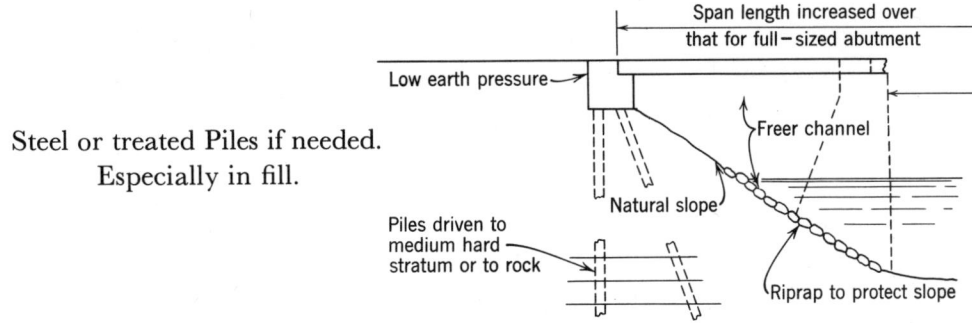

Steel or treated Piles if needed.
Especially in fill.

FIG. 3.   CASE IV.   STUB ABUTMENT.

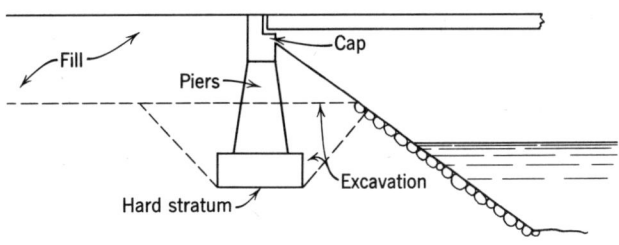

FIG. 4.   CASE V.   BURIED ABUTMENT.

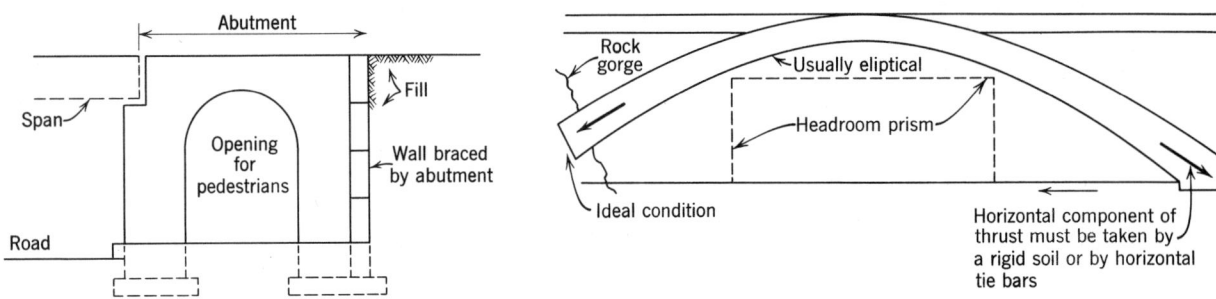

FIG. 5. CASE VI. BOX ABUTMENT.   FIG. 6. CASE VII. ARCH.

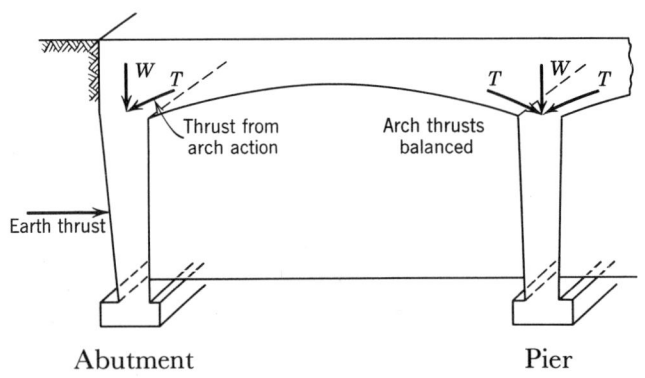

FIG. 7. CASE VIII. RIGID FRAME.

Note. Abutment footing must be secured against horizontal movement from difference between arch thrust and earth thrust, which may act in either direction. Generally, batter piles or friction on earth will suffice.

TYPES OF PIERS

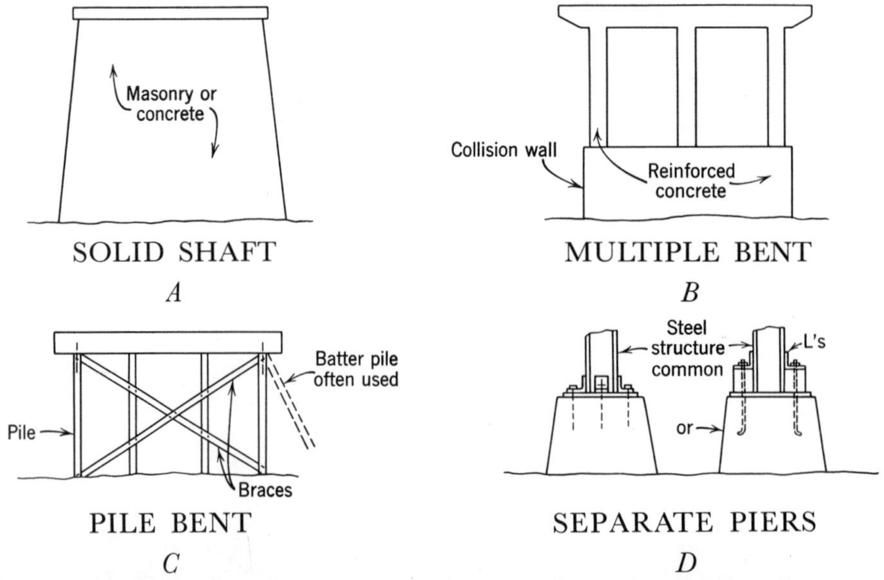

SOLID SHAFT

A

MULTIPLE BENT

B

PILE BENT

C

SEPARATE PIERS

D

FIG. 8. SOME SIMPLE TYPES OF BRIDGE PIERS.

Bridge Bearing Details

The bridge bearings carry the load from the stringers, girders, or trusses to the pier or abutment. Their shape affects the direction and magnitude of the forces transmitted to the pier. Each girder is provided with a fixed bearing at one end to take the horizontal forces of traction and braking, and a movable bearing at the other to permit expansion.

The simplest type of bearing is the steel plate, type I (Fig. 9). The fixed end is anchored to the concrete. The expansion end permits one steel plate to slide over the other. Sometimes the lower plate is faced with a phosphor bronze wear surface to prevent erosion and reduce the coefficient of friction. The surfaces of the plate should always be level even if the girder is not. It is recommended that this type be limited to spans of 70 ft. (AASHO Code).

Type II (Fig. 10) is an outgrowth of type I. The use of a curved surface directly under the girder permits it to deflect without producing an eccentricity on the bearing surface. For spans of 70 ft. or more the expansion bearing should have a rocker as shown in type III (Fig. 11).

Type III is the rocker type of expansion bearing. It allows for the deflection of the beam and also allows expansion with a reduced horizontal force. It is used in conjunction with the fixed bearing of type II. Particular attention should be paid to the red light, as failures have occurred from this error. See Fig. 13.

Type IV (Fig. 12a) is a cast-steel type of fixed bearing for use with the heaviest loads.

Type V (Fig. 12b) is the roller used for heavy loads. It has generally been superseded by type III.

In general, bearing details should be so designed that they are easy to inspect, easy to keep clean, and drain water to prevent corrosion.

In addition to the general vertical bearing there are inclined ones used for arches and suspension bridges as shown in Fig. 14.

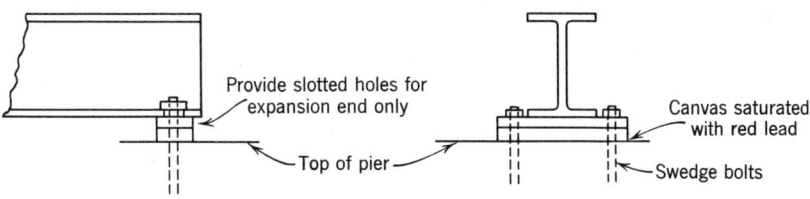

SIDE ELEVATION   END ELEVATION

FIG. 9. TYPE I. BEARINGS.

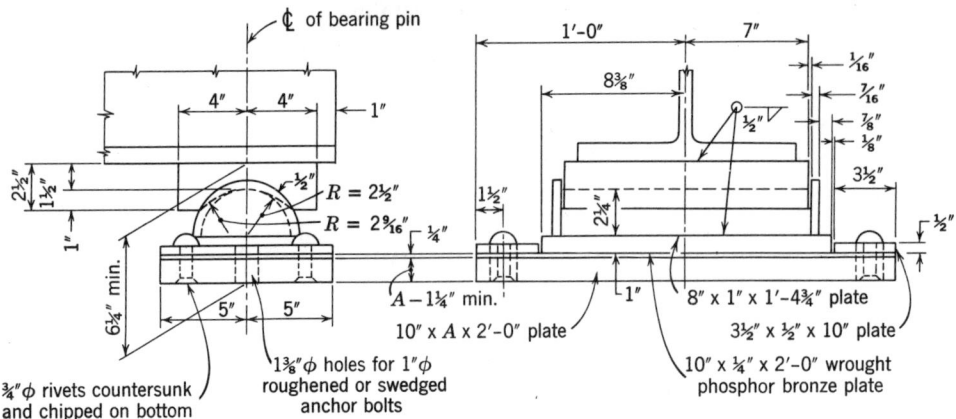

Finish both curved bearing surfaces and bottom of pin on all bearings.

SIDE ELEVATION   END ELEVATION

EXPANSION BEARINGS TYPE A

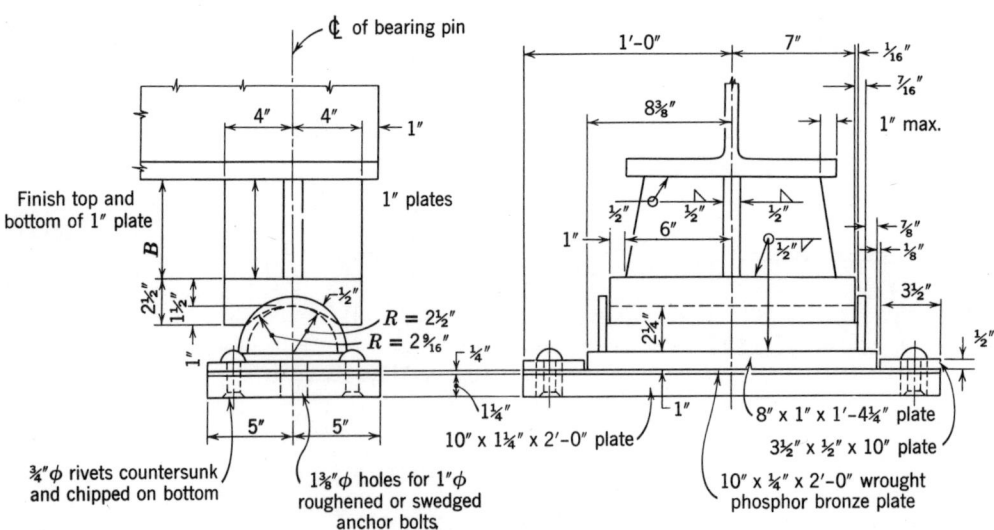

This type of bearing is to be used under the shallower stringer when depths of stringers on same pedestal differ by 3 or more inches.

SIDE ELEVATION   END ELEVATION

EXPANSION BEARINGS TYPE B

FIG. 10.   TYPE II.   BEARINGS.

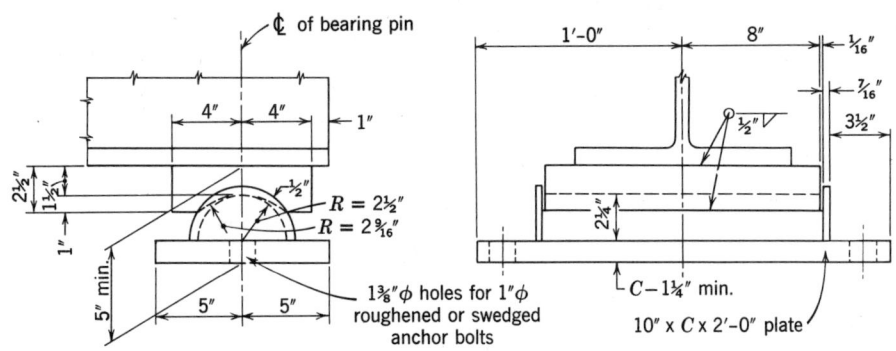

SIDE ELEVATION   END ELEVATION

FIXED BEARINGS

FIG. 10. (CONT.)   TYPE II.   BEARINGS.

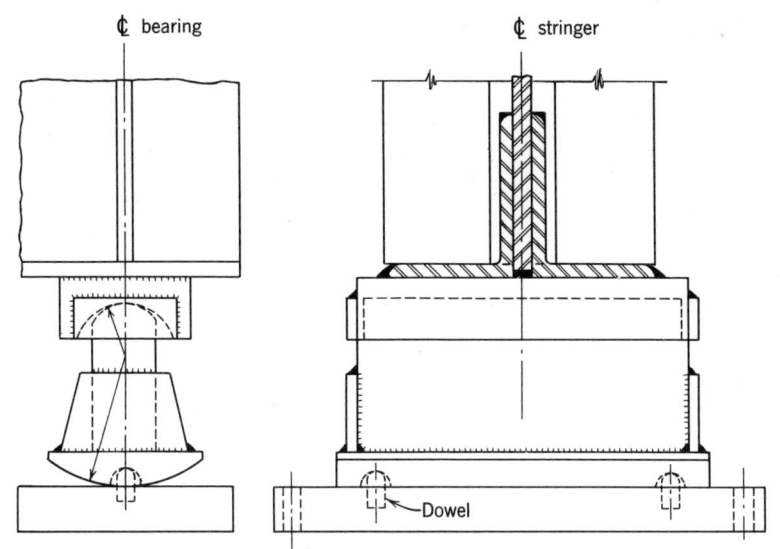

SIDE ELEVATION   END ELEVATION

FIG. 11.   TYPE III.   EXPANSION-TYPE BRIDGE BEARING.

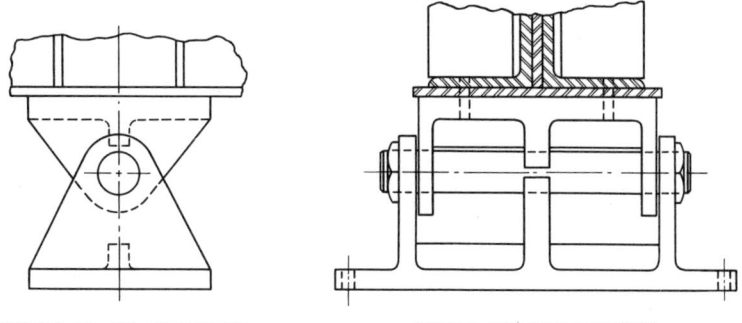

SIDE ELEVATION   END ELEVATION

FIG. 12a.   TYPE IV.   FIXED-TYPE BEARING.

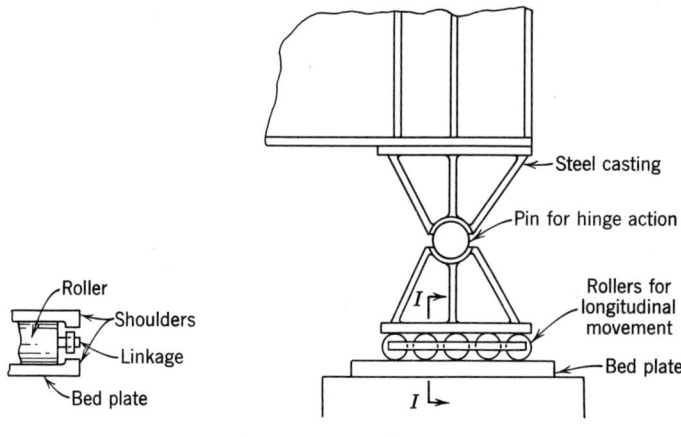

SECTION I–I   SIDE ELEVATION

FIG. 12*b*.   TYPE V.   ROLLER BEARING.

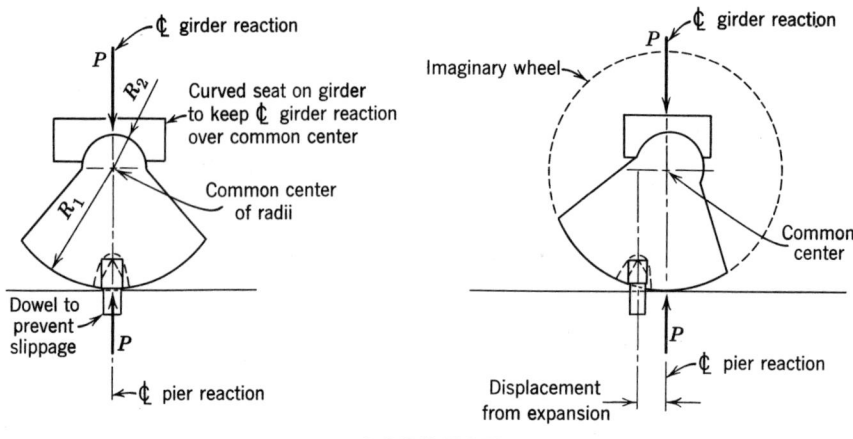

CORRECT

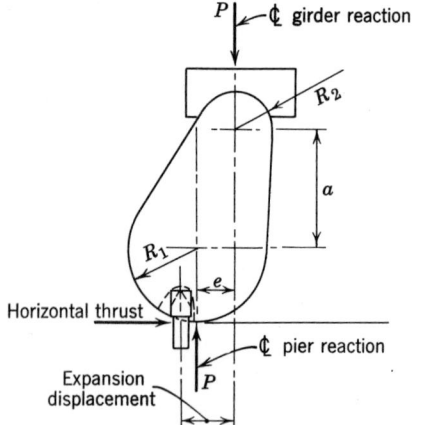

Horizontal thrust

Note: Failure to make the two radii concentric produces a horizontal thrust on the girder and pier equal to

$$\frac{Pe}{a}$$

This thrust can cause a horizontal deflection of the pier, thus increasing e and creating a vicious cycle.

INCORRECT.

FIG. 13.   RED LIGHT.   HORIZONTAL THRUST FROM ROCKER.

Method of Figuring Thrust on Pier from Expansion

Horizontal thrust from expansion T

$$T = \frac{P \times R_2}{R_1} \times F$$

where P is the vertical dead load and F is the coefficient of friction (0.25 for steel), R_1 and R_2 are the radii shown in Fig. 13.

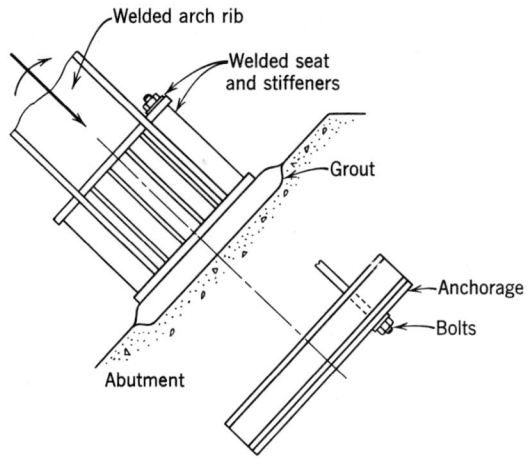

FIG. 14a. FIXED BEARING FOR
STEEL RIB ARCH BRIDGES.

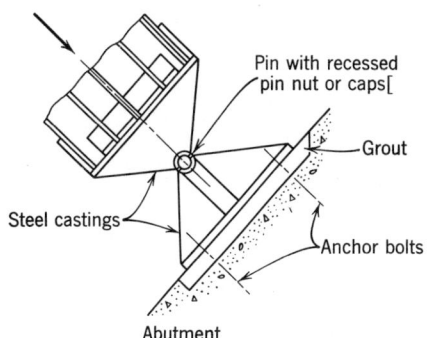

FIG. 14b. HINGED OR PINNED
BEARING FOR STEEL RIB
ARCH BRIDGES.

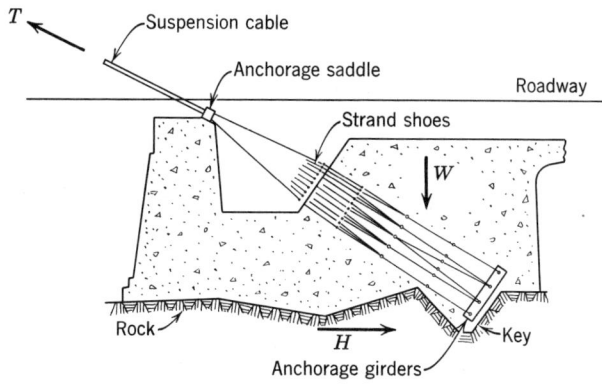

FIG. 14c. SUSPENSION BRIDGE ANCHORAGES.

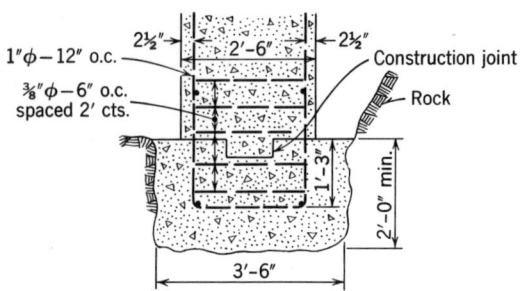

Westchester County Park Commission. Clear span 62′ 5″. A. G. Hayden, Engr.

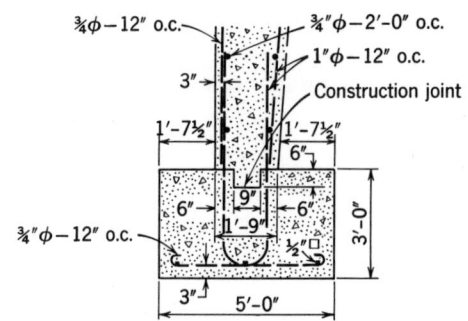

Bridge at Big Pipe Creek, Union Mills, Maryland. 2 spans at 35′ clear. State Roads Commission, Maryland. W. C. Hopkins, Bridge Engr.

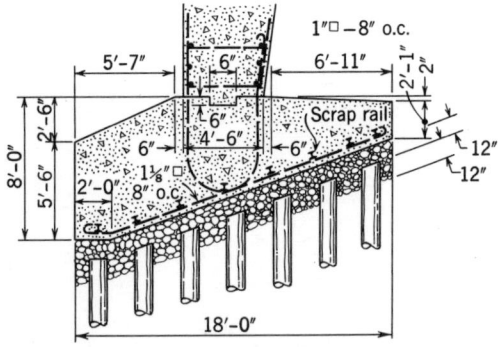

Railway Bridge Near Vaudreuil, P. Q. Clear span 72′ 6¼″. Canadian National Rys. C. P. Disney, Bridge Engr., Central Region.

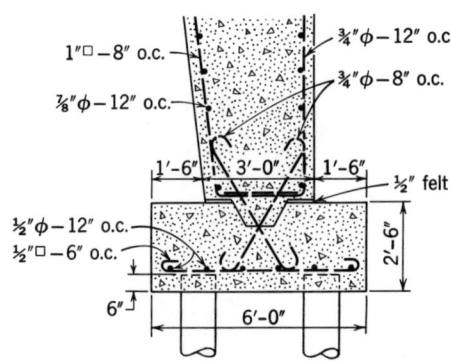

Krape Park Bridge, Freeport, Ill. Clear span 70′ 0″. Mogens Ipsen, Engr.

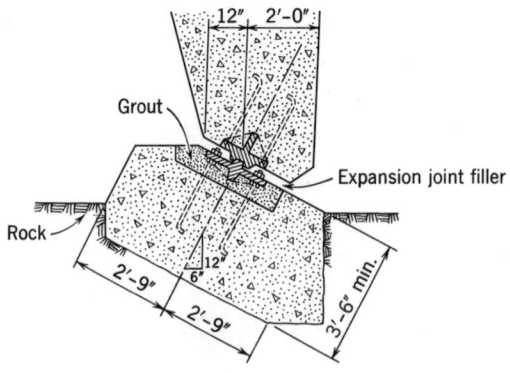

Bridge at Canton, Mo. Clear span 100′ 0″. Rock Island District Corps of Engineers, U. S. Army. A. B. Auerbach, Junior Engr.

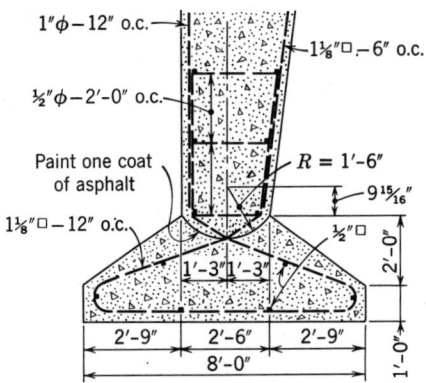

Don Gasper Street Bridge, Santa Fe, New Mexico. Clear span 50' 0". New Mexico State Highway Department. E. B. Van De Greyn, Bridge Engr.

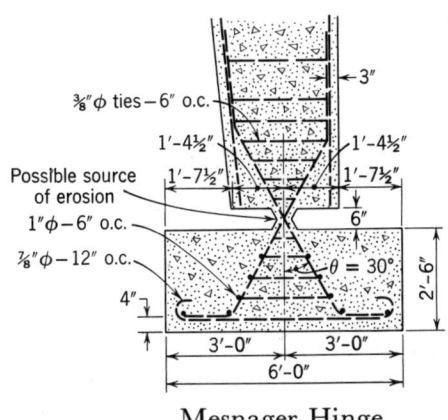

Mesnager Hinge

FIG. 15. HINGES FOR RIGID FRAME ABUTMENTS.

DESIGN OF BRIDGE PIERS AND ABUTMENTS

Piers and abutments are designed according to the principles shown in Chapters 3 and 4. The loads are highly variable and occur in several directions. The pier must be investigated for several combinations of loading to determine the most severe. Particular attention must be paid to stability and safe soil pressure.

Vertical Loads

Reactions of superstructure. These reactions will cause an eccentricity when one span only is loaded. Also some end details are so standardized as to dimensions that eccentricity may be caused by difference in span lengths. See Fig. 16.

Longitudinal Loads

Traction or deceleration, 5% of lane load with concentrated load for moment applied 4 ft. above roadway.†

Temperature expansion, longitudinal force due to friction at expansion bearings.

Expansion range:

Metal for moderate climate: 0°F. to +120°F.

Cold climate, 30°F. to +120°F.

Concrete for moderate climate: rise, 30°F.; fall, 40°F.

Cold climate rise, 35°F.; fall, 45°F.†

Add to live load on one track only at 6 ft. above rail 15% of live load without impact for braking, or 25% of load on driving wheels without impact for traction, whichever is larger. Decrease 50% where abutments will take part of load.*

---

*AREA Specifications.
†AASHO Specifications.

Lateral Loads

Wind. A transverse wind force on the structure applied as a moving horizontal load of 50 lb. per sq. ft. on 1½ times the area of the structure as seen in elevation, including the floor system and railings, and on one-half of the area of all trusses or through girders in excess of two in the span. In no case shall the total of this force be less than 300 lb. per lin. ft. of bridge. This is for bridges with dead load only.

For bridges with live and dead load, the intensity of this force may be reduced 70% (to 15 lb. per sq. ft.) when included in the combination of forces.†

Check uplift on bents by applying 400 lb. per lin. ft. on the lee side for highway bridges and 800 lb. per lin. ft. for highway bridges with trolley.†

Wind application on moving load: 300 lb. per lin. ft. on one track at 8 ft. above rail. Wind application on structure: 30 lb. per sq. ft. as follows. Girder spans: 1½ × vertical projection of span; truss spans: vertical projection of span + any portion of leeward trusses not shielded by floor system; viaduct towers and bents: vertical projections of all columns and tower bracing.

Total wind force on girder and truss spans: not less than 200 lb. per lin. ft. on loaded flange or chord (flange or chord supporting floor beams) + 150 lb. per lin. ft. on unloaded flange or chord.

Total wind force on unloaded bridge not less than 50 lb. per sq. ft. on surfaces as above.*

Centrifugal force on curves:

$$1.167 \times 10^{-5} WV^2 D$$

where W = weight of moving traffic.

  V = velocity in miles per hour.

  D = degree of curvature.

Nosing of Locomotives. A lateral force to be added: 20,000 lb. at top of rail at any point in either lateral direction (vertical effects of this force to be disregarded). Centrifugal force on curves: Apply horizontally 6 ft. above top of rail along a line perpendicular to center line of track at each axle. Percentage of axle load to apply = 1.755 $(E + 3)$, where E = superelevation in inches.*

Pressure on Piers. Force of flowing water. For square-end piers it is $1.5V^2$ lb. per sq. ft.; for round-end piers, $0.75V^2$, where V is the velocity in feet per second. In piers subject to scour this force should be figured down to the depth of scour.

Ice. Thought on proper values varies greatly. Empirical values ranging from 2500 lb. per horizontal foot of pier width for a triangular-nosed pier with zero velocity to 10,000 lb. for a square-end pier with a velocity of 5 ft. per sec. have been suggested.§ The pressure of ice can be reduced by the use of starlings and dolphins, Fig. 28. These are desirable where the possibility of ice jams exists.

Impact of live load is neglected.

Impact of floating debris is generally neglected.

Earthquake.

---

* AREA Specifications.

† AASHO Specifications.

§ Dunham, *Foundations of Structures*, McGraw-Hill Book Co.

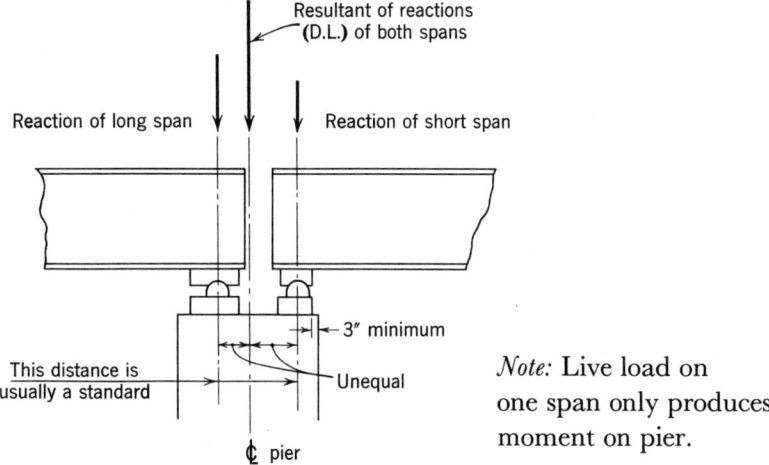

FIG. 16.   SETTING BEARINGS ECCENTRIC SO THAT CENTER OF REACTIONS COINCIDES WITH CENTER OF PIER REDUCES MOMENT.

DESIGN EXAMPLES

The principles outlined in this chapter are incorporated in the design examples that follow. The design analysis is carried only as far as analyzing the forces on the members.   The design of the reinforcing can be figured from the forces determined by means of standard reinforced-concrete design.

Abutments

The examples shown are for a standard and a stub type.   Wind has been neglected because of the extreme width, 96 ft., of the abutment.   For an economic comparison of these two examples see p. 5–18.

Pier

A simple concrete bent pier is analyzed as shown in Fig. 21.

Problem 1

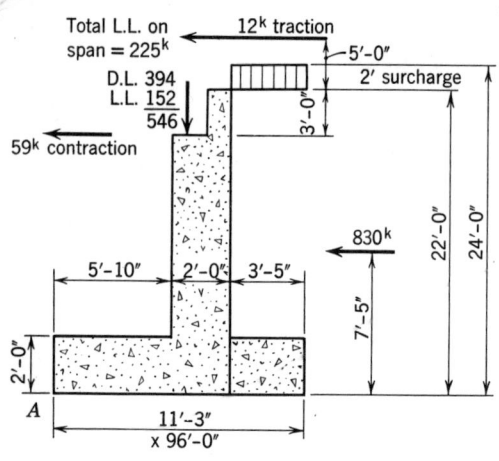

FIG. 17.

Given: Abutment with reactions shown.

D.L.	= 394
L.L.	= 152
T.L.	= 546

To design abutment:

Contraction $= 0.15 \times 394 = 59^k$ (Sliding
Traction $= 0.05 \times 225 = 12^k$ bearing)

$$\text{Earth pressure} = \frac{24^2 \times 30}{2} = 8.65^k$$

$$96 \times 8.65 = 830^k$$

Weights:

Footing	11.25×2	$\times 96 \times 0.15$	$= 324^k$
Wall	2.0×20	$\times 96 \times 0.15$	$= 575^k$
Soil	3.42×20	$\times 96 \times 0.10$	$= 655^k$
Surcharge	2.0×3.42	$\times 96 \times 0.10$	$= 66^k$

Moments about A:

	Totals	Totals		Totals
$830 \times 7.5 = 6230$			$324 \times 5.62 = 1820$	
$59 \times 19 = 1120$	7350		$575 \times 6.82 = 3920$	
$8 \times 27 = 326$	7675	1554	$655 \times 9.5 = 6230$	11,970
			$66 \times 9.5 = 620$	
		2014	$394 \times 6.5 = 2560$	15,150
		2166	$152 \times 6.5 = 990$	16,140

Location of resultant:

Without superstructure $\dfrac{11{,}970 - 6230}{1554} = 3.69'$

Dead load only $\dfrac{15{,}150 - 7350}{2014} = 3.88'$

Dead and live load $\dfrac{16{,}140 - 7675}{2166} = 3.90'$

The edge of the middle third is $\dfrac{11.25}{3} = 3.75'$

Maximum soil pressure $= \dfrac{2100}{11.25 \times 96} \times 2 \times 1000 = 3900$

Wing walls must be provided also.

Problem 2

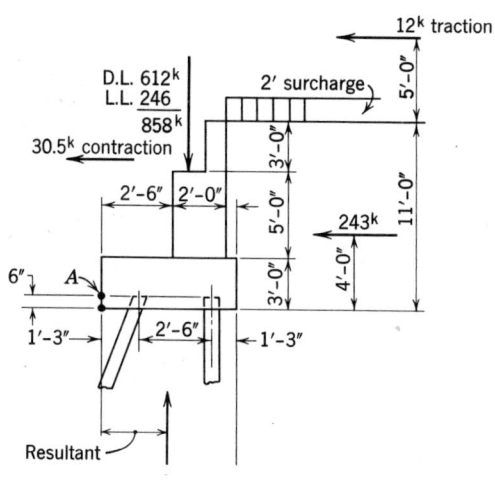

FIG. 18.

Given: Abutment with reactions shown. To design abutment.

Contraction $\quad 0.05 \times 612 = 30.5^k$ (rocker)
Traction $\qquad 0.05 \times 246 = \quad 12^k$

Earth pressure $= 13^2 \times \dfrac{30}{2} = 2.53^k$

$$96 \times 2.53 = 243^k$$

Total horizontal force $= 243 + 12 + 30 = 285$

Weights:
  Footing $3 \times 5 \times 96 \times 0.15 = 216$
  Wall $\quad 5 \times 3 \times 96 \times 0.15$
  $\qquad\qquad + 3 \times 96 \times 0.15 = 259$
  Soil $\qquad 8 \times 96 \times 0.05 = \quad 38$

Moments about A:	Totals	Totals		Totals
$243 \times \quad 3.5 = 850$		$216 \times \quad 2.5 = \quad 540$		
$30 \times \quad 7.5 = 228$	1080	$259 \times \quad 3.5 = \quad 905$		
$291 \quad 18.2 \times 15.5 = 282$	1360	$513 \quad 38 \times 4.75 = \quad 180$	1625	
		$1125 \quad 612 \times 3.17 = 1940$	3565	
		$1371 \quad 246 \times 3.17 = \quad 780$	4345	

Location of resultant:

Without superstructure $\quad \dfrac{1625 - 850}{513} = 1.51'$

Dead load only $\qquad\quad \dfrac{3565 - 1080}{1125} = 2.21'$

Dead and live load $\qquad \dfrac{4345 - 1360}{1371} = 2.18'$

Load on front piles $= \quad 1371 \times \dfrac{1.5}{2.5} = 825^k \qquad$ Back row 548^k

Use 30-ton piles
  Front row $\dfrac{825}{60} = 13.75 \qquad$ 14 piles $\qquad$ Back $\dfrac{548}{60} = 9$ piles

Batter front piles $\dfrac{825}{285} = 2.89 \qquad$ Batter 3 to 1

No wing walls.

Design of Bridge Pier

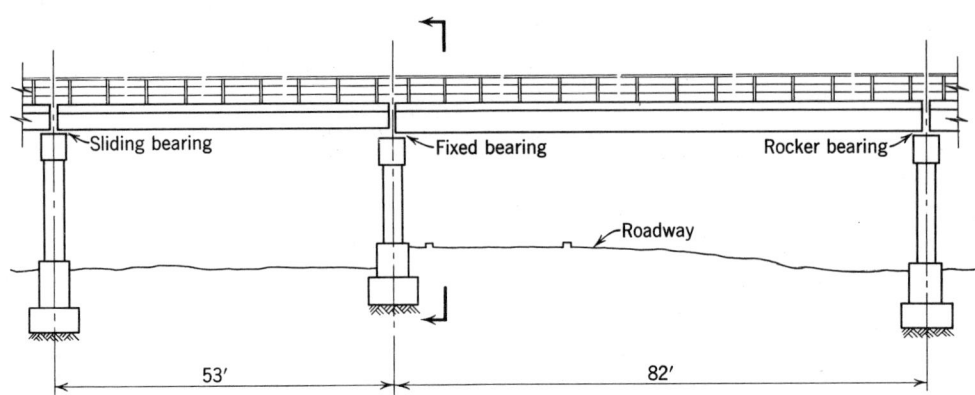

ELEVATION

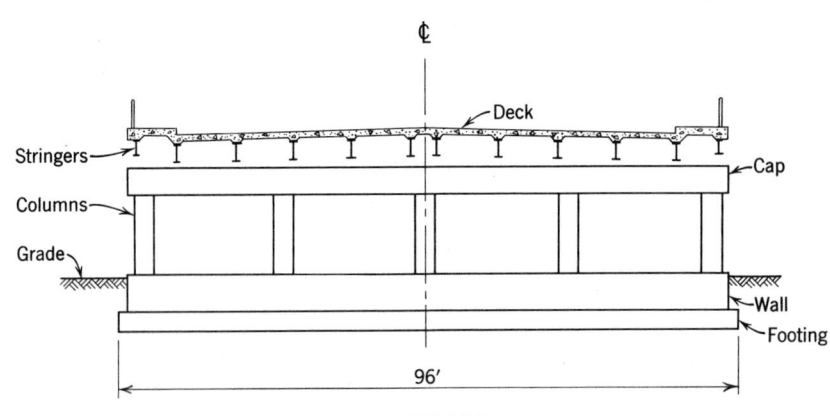

SECTION

FIG. 19.

Problem 3.   Design of Bridge Bent

See FIG. 19.

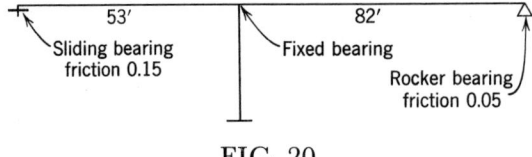

FIG. 20.

Live load $R = 388^k$

D.L. From 2 fascia: $2 \times \dfrac{53}{2} \times 1.49 =$ 79 $2 \times \dfrac{82}{2} \times 1.49 = 122$

10 stringers: $10 \times \dfrac{53}{2} \times 1.19 = \underline{315}$ $10 \times \dfrac{82}{2} \times 1.19 = \underline{490}$

Total D.L.   394   612

Temperature thrust:

$$0.15 \times 394 = 59^k \qquad\qquad 0.05 \times 612 = 30.5^k$$

$$\text{Net } 59 - 30.6 = 28.4$$

Force from traction = 5% of L.L. = $0.05 \times 776 = 38.8^k$. Acting 5′ above center line of road (by code)

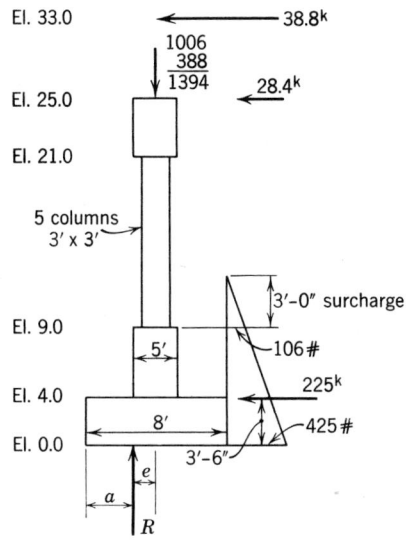

FIG. 21.

Earth pressure $= 120 \times \dfrac{1 - \sin 33°}{1 + \sin 33°} = 35.4$

$$106 + \frac{425}{2} \times 9 = 2.39^k \text{ per ft.}$$

Bent 94′ wide $94 \times 2.39 = 225^k$

Dead weight of bent

$$
\begin{aligned}
8 \times 4 \times 96 \times .15 &= 460 \\
9 \times 5 \times 94 \times .15 &= 650 \\
5 \times \pi \times 9/4 \times 12 \times 0.15 &= 64 \\
\hline
&1174
\end{aligned}
$$

Total vertical load: Bent   1174
Deck D.L. 1006
L.L.   388
                        2568

Overturning moment:

$$
\begin{array}{ll}
38.8 \times 33 & = 1280 \\
28.4 \times 25 & = 710 \\
225 \times 3.6 & = 810 \\
\hline
292.2 & 2800
\end{array}
\qquad
e = \frac{2800}{2570} = 1.09
$$

$$a = 4 - 1.09 = 2.91$$

Maximum pressure $= (32 - 6 \times 2.91) \times \dfrac{2570}{8^2 \times 96} = 6050$ lb. per. sq. ft.

The resultant lies in the middle third

Sliding $\dfrac{292}{2570} = .113$ O.K. as it is less than safe coefficient of friction, p. 4–7.

Forces other direction:

Wind 50 lb. per. sq. ft. on 1½ elevation + ½ stringers in excess of 2

Elevation 8′ $50 \times 8 \times 1.5 = 600$
             $\underline{10 \times 50 \times 3 \times 0.5 = 750}$
                           1350 lb. ft.

Wind force $= 1.35 \times \dfrac{53 + 82}{2} = 91^k$

This force will be negligible on foundation though the pier must be designed for it.

ECONOMIC COMPARISON OF ABUTMENTS

See Fig. 22.

TYPE I

Concrete	276 cu. yd. @	$ 25.00 =	$ 6,900
Reinforcement	8832 lbs. @	0.15 =	1,325
Forms	5280 sq. ft. @	0.80 =	4,200
Excavation (wet) *	500 cu. yd. @	3.00 =	1,500
Additional backfill	1050 cu. yd. @	0.90 =	945
Cofferdaming	960 sq. ft. @	2.50 =	2,400
Pumping	30 days @	130.00 =	3,900
			$21,170

TYPE IV

Concrete	115 cu. yd. @	$25.00 =	$2,900
Reinforcement	3680 lbs. @	0.15 =	552
Forms	2110 sq. ft. @	0.80 =	1,700
Piles	960 lin. ft. @	4.50 =	4,320
Excavation *			$9,472

The saving of type IV over type I is $11,698. Against this saving must be figured the cost of the additional span of bridge. (*Note:* On a single-span bridge, the use of type IV abutments might necessitate a two-span bridge with a pier in the center.)

---

* Only additional excavation included in cost.

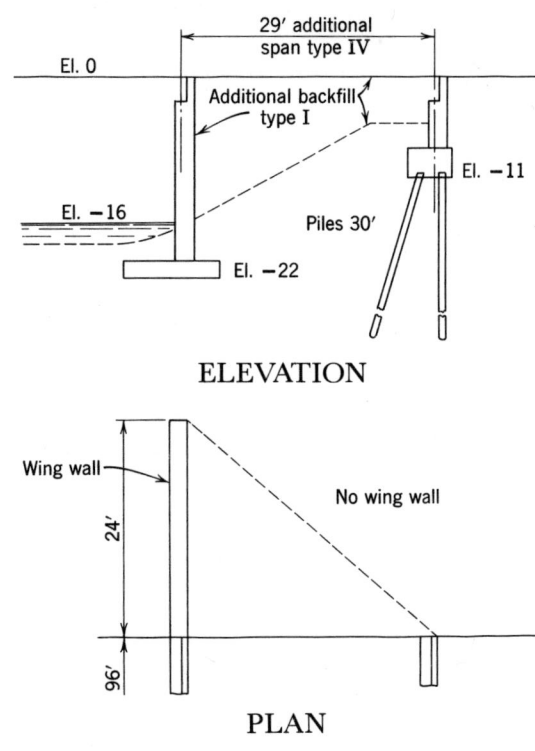

ELEVATION

PLAN

TYPE I   TYPE IV

FIG. 22.   ECONOMIC COMPARISON BETWEEN TYPE I AND TYPE IV ABUTMENTS.

SCOUR PROTECTION

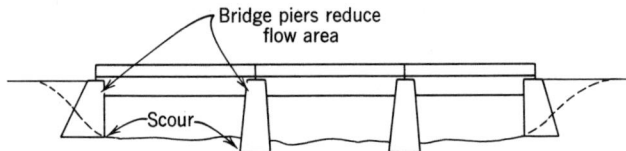

Reduced flow area increases velocity.   Increased velocity permits water to carry more soil. Soil is picked up from river bottom, producing scour.

FIG. 23.   SCOUR.

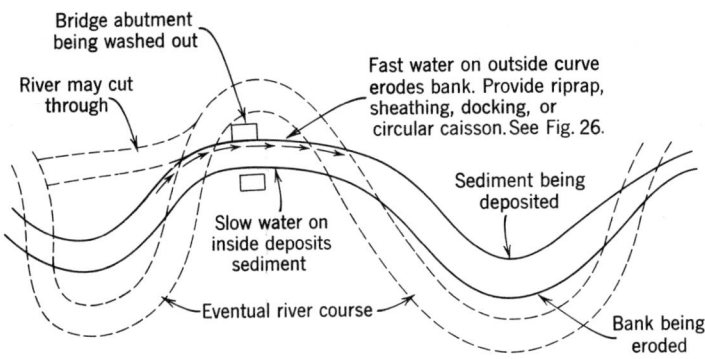

Serpentine meanders are common to flat valley rivers.   They may also be caused by man-made obstructions.   Once started, they form an increasing sinusoidal course, leading to cutoffs.

FIG. 24.   MEANDERS.

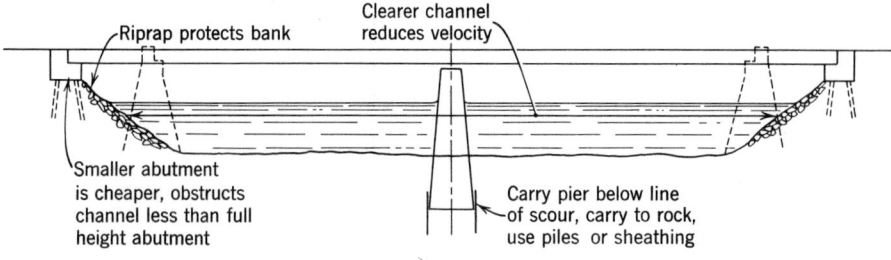

FIG. 25.   AVOIDANCE OF SCOUR.

Pier increases velocity, increasing scour; see Fig. 23.

Riprap and Revetments

Riprap as distinguished from manually placed slope paving is rough stone of various sizes deposited usually by mechanical means for slope protection to prevent erosion or undermining.   Unless such stone is obtainable as spoil from mass rock excavations, it would ordinarily be ordered from a commercial crushed-stone quarry.   In this case stone which passes the initial crusher and is screened thereafter through a grizzly should be well graded from a minimum of 2½ in. to a maximum of 18 in.   The next larger size stone would vary from zero to 1-ton pieces.   The largest stone would be 2- to 8-ton pieces on the quarry floor.

Riprap for flood erosion and especially ocean-wave erosion should be large.   It should have a foundation below the bed of the stream.   Docking is often used to prevent erosion.   It may consist of timber or concrete cribbing sunk well below the bed of the stream.

Circular sheet pile caissons are used for heavy-duty protection, particularly around abutments.

Protection of Banks from Erosion

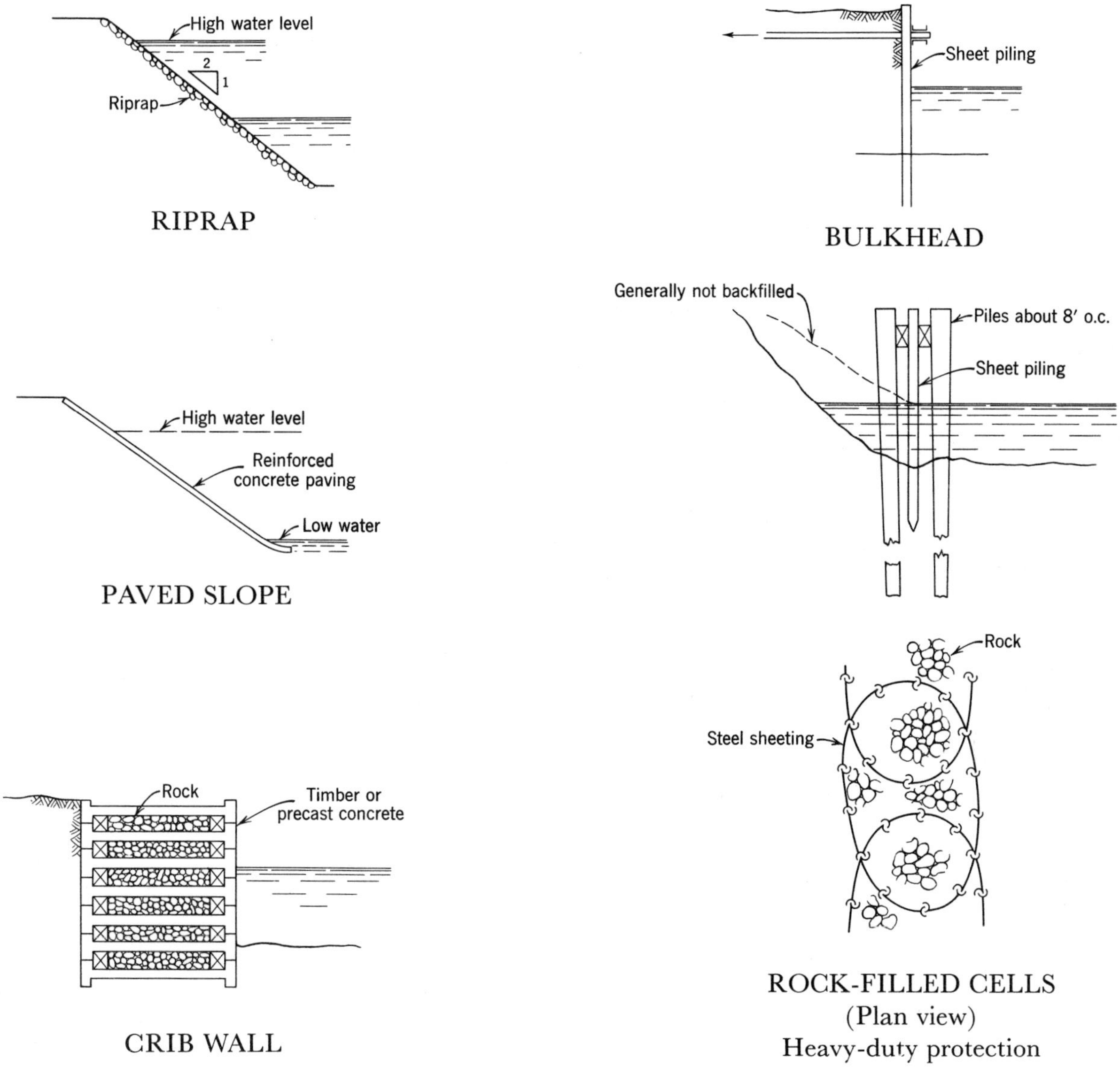

RIPRAP

High water level

2 / 1

Riprap

PAVED SLOPE

High water level

Reinforced concrete paving

Low water

CRIB WALL

Rock

Timber or precast concrete

BULKHEAD

Sheet piling

Generally not backfilled

Piles about 8' o.c.

Sheet piling

ROCK-FILLED CELLS
(Plan view)
Heavy-duty protection

Rock

Steel sheeting

FIG. 26.

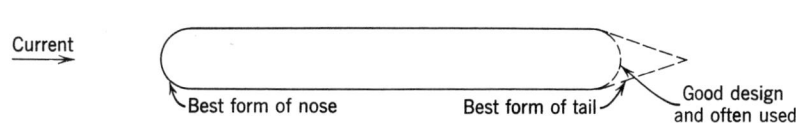

Current

Best form of nose   Best form of tail   Good design and often used

FIG. 27.   SHAPE OF PIER TO CAUSE LEAST INTERFERENCE WITH FLOW OF WATER

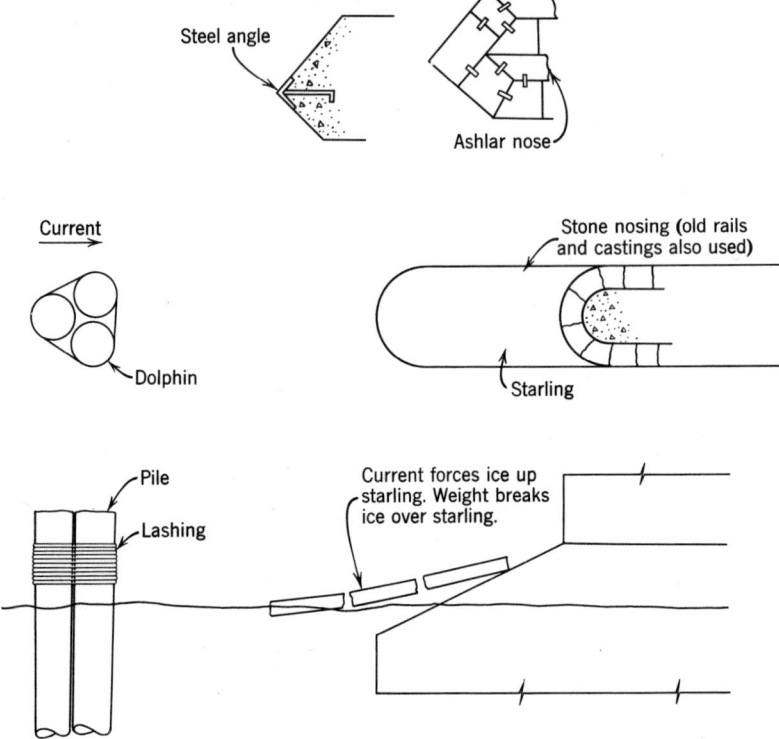

PROTECTION OF PIERS FROM ICE

Starlings used more than dolphins

FIG. 28.   DETAILS OF ICE PROTECTION.

RED LIGHTS

1. Types I, II, and III. See p. 5–1. Tendency of wings to crack off main abutments owing to varying tilts causing a warping of surface.

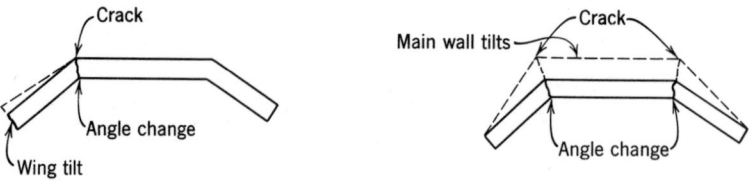

FIG. 29.

Remedy:
- (*a*) Joint at angle.
- (*b*) Reinforcement.
- (*c*) Rigid foundation.

2. Settlement of fill and forward movement during settlement may cause displacement of IV. See p. 5–1. Drive piles through fill after settlement has ceased. Note pressure on pile and abutment.

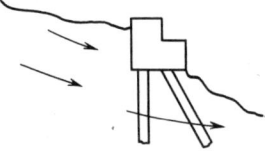

FIG. 30.

3. Type V. See p. 5–1. Tendency to displacement during settlement is great. Remedy:
   (*a*) Excavate through fill for abutment.
   (*b*) Omit fill adjacent to abutment.
   (*c*) Use battered piles.

4. Abutments fail by scour. Remedy:
   (*a*) Prevent excessive velocity due to flow restriction.
   (*b*) Carry down foundations to rock or below probability of scour undercut.
   (*c*) Use steel sheet piling.
   (*d*) Use riprap.

5. Abutments fail by erosion. Remedy:
   (*a*) Prevent disintegration of mass concrete. See *Field Practice.*
   (*b*) Protect upstream surface against ice and water erosion by sheathing, and nosing. See p. 5–22.
   (*c*) Protect against collision by dolphins. See p. 5–22.
   (*d*) Avoid construction joints wherever possible.

6. Meanders cause serious changes in banks at structures. Remedy: revetments; see Meanders, Fig. 24.

7. Bridge may fail from flood overtopping. That is, if water crosses road behind the abutment it may cut a ditch or channel. Or if water reaches bridge floors it may cause a dam up and bridge failure due to lateral pressure.

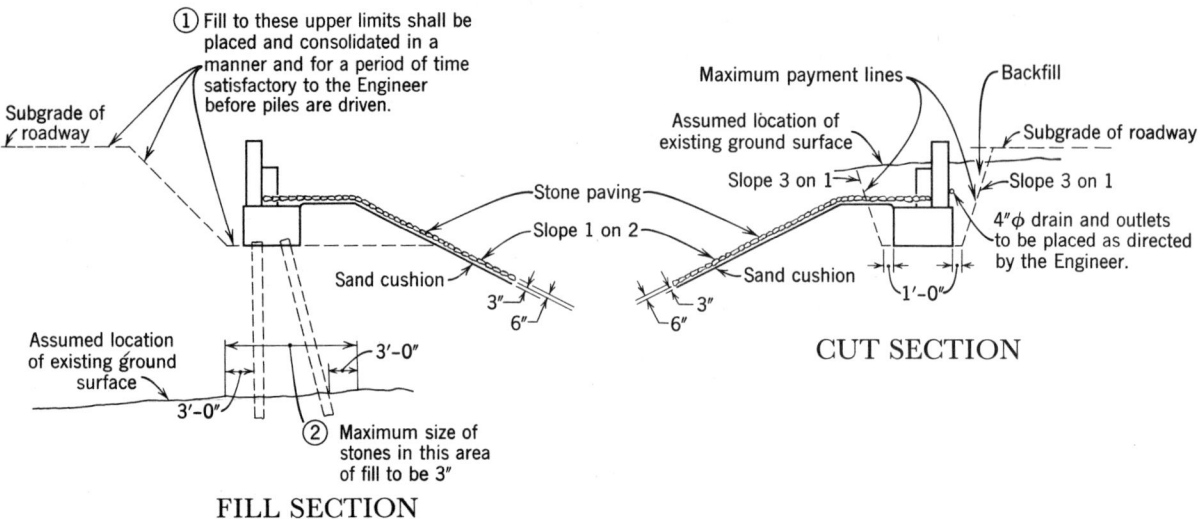

FIG. 31. EMBANKMENT DETAILS AT ABUTMENTS

(1) Very important; otherwise consolidation of the fill will produce negative friction and thrust on piles—a dangerous condition.

(2) To permit easy pile driving.

New York State Throughway standards shown. New Jersey practice often does not provide a berm on the span side.

RED LIGHTS

Allowance for flood conditions inadequate.
- (*a*) Erosion due to inadequate channel.
- (*b*) Erosion due to not carrying foundation to solid rock.
- (*c*) Erosion due to not carrying sheet pile cutoff wall low enough.
- (*d*) Failure to allow sufficient flood waterway resulting in overtopping of structure.
- (*e*) Too low a superstructure, resulting in overtopping.
- (*f*) Inadequate riprap.
- (*g*) Natural shifting of stream meanders not foreseen in the design.
- (*h*) Poor concrete, resulting in surface disintegration.
- (*i*) Construction joints resulting in disintegration. (See p. 3–37.)
- (*j*) Exposure of reinforcing steel and fittings. (See p. 3–37.) Avoid reinforcement when possible, as it is subject to corrosion and destruction of concrete. All fittings such as bolts should be galvanized or of non-ferrous metal.
- (*k*) Special precautions for sea water. (See p. 3–37.)
- (*l*) Mechanical protection. (See p. 3–54.)
- (*m*) Horizontal joint poor bond.

Large Box Culvert in Slide

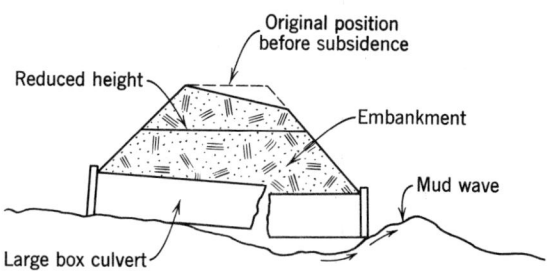

Correction after construction: Reduce height.   Original design should have foreseen this.

FIG. 32.

Abutment Shifting

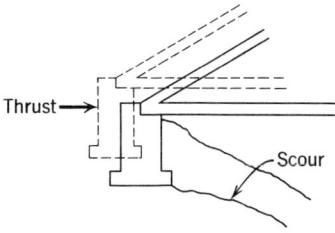

Earth thrust or scour caused left end of span to drop.   Correction: Provide for horizontal thrust; prevent scour by deepening abutment base to hard soil or by sheet-piling its toe.

FIG. 33.

6

Foundations for Pipes, Conduits, and Culverts

Note: For practical section and considerations see p. 15–1.

To design a pipe foundation we must know:

The type of trench.

The type of backfill.

The load upon the pipe.

The type of bedding and pipe.

The type of trench is classified as either trench condition, imperfect trench condition, or projection condition; see Fig. 4. The condition is generally given or assumed.

The load upon the pipe may be either backfill, concentrated load upon the backfill (such as a wheel), or uniform surcharge over the backfill, or a combination of any of these. The value of the backfill load varies with the type of trench.

Backfill

Load per lineal foot is equal to CwB^2, where C is a coefficient from Fig. 3, w the unit weight of backfill, and B the width of trench (Fig. 4).

Example 1

Given: $B = 3.67$ ft. Trench condition $= H = 20$ ft. deep. Backfill is sand weighing 100 lb. per cu. ft.

Compute $H/B = 20/3.67 = 5.45$. Enter Fig. 3 at $H/B = 5.45$, and cross over to sand. Turn down and read $C = 2.3$. Load on pipe $= 2.3 \times 100 \times 3.67^2 = 3100$ lb. per lin. foot.

Example 2

Given: 30-in. culvert pipe projecting 21 in. above existing ground. Backfill to be sand (120 lb. per cu. ft.) to a depth of 15 ft.

Compute $H/B = 15/2.5 = 6$; $p = 21/30 = 0.7$. Enter Fig. 3 at H/B equal to 6. Cross over to line marked $p = 0.7$. Turn down and read $C = 11.0$. Load on pipe $= 11 \times 120 \times 2.5^2 = 8250$ lb. per lin. ft.

Concentrated Load

Load is expressed as a percentage of the total load as per coefficient from Fig. 5. Increase moving loads 50% for impact. Load is assumed as acting on 3 lin. ft. of pipe.

Example 3

Given: Wheel load of 12,000 lb. crossing over a 36-in. culvert with 4 ft. of cover (trench condition). Enter Fig. 5 at 4 ft. Go up to line marked 3 ft. Go left and read $C = 22\%$. Wheel load on pipe $= 12,000/3 \times 0.22 \times 1.5 = 1320$ lb. per lin. ft.

Uniform Surcharge Load

Load per lineal foot is equal to *CwB,* where C is a coefficient from Table II.

Example 4

Given: Trench condition 4 ft. wide and 16 ft. deep. Sand backfill. A surface surcharge of 1000 lb. per sq. ft. to be added all over.

Compute $H/B = 16/4 = 4.00$. Enter Table II at $H/B = 4.00$, and read $C = 0.27$ in col. 1. Surcharge load on pipe $= .27 \times 1000 = 270$ lbs. per lin. ft.

The load per lineal foot is divided by the load factor (Table I) for the bedding used (Fig. 2). This resulting load is checked against the ultimate strength of the pipe (Tables IV and V).

Example 5

Given a 24-in. pipe with a total load of 4480 lb. per lin. ft.

Assume a reinforced standard-strength concrete pipe and first-class bedding. From Table I the load factor $= 1.9$; $4480/1.9 = 2360$.

From Table IV the ultimate load of the pipe is 3000.

Factor of safety is 3000/2360.

Note: The factor of safety is generally assumed as 1.0, although the U. S. Army uses 1.5. Impermissible and ordinary bedding is not recommended but is occasionally encountered. The type of pipe is often set by hydraulic considerations so that only the type of bedding may be varied to meet the changing load conditions.

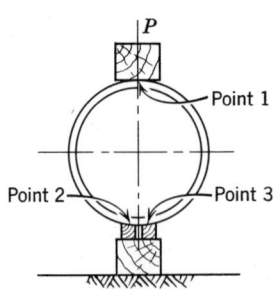

FIG. 1. THREE-EDGE BEARING METHOD FOR LABORATORY TESTS OF PIPES

This test represents a loading condition very closely approaching the most unfavorable one and is likely to produce greater stresses than any of the four bedding types illustrated below.

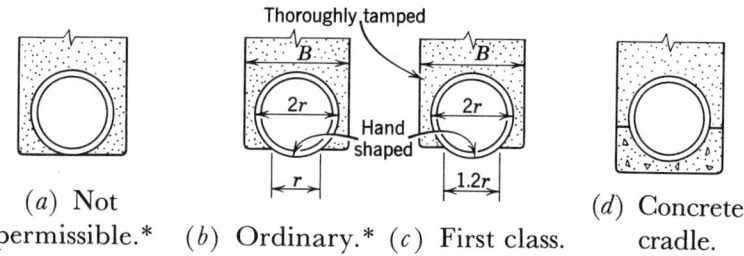

(a) Not permissible.*   (b) Ordinary.*   (c) First class.   (d) Concrete cradle.

FIG. 2. TYPES OF BEDDING FOR SEWERS AND OTHER DITCH CONDUITS

TABLE I

LOAD FACTORS†

Bedding Type	Ratio Ultimate (Failure) to Three-Edge Bearing Load
Not permissible	1.1
Ordinary	1.5
First class	1.9
Concrete cradle	2.2-3.4

LOADS ON SEWER PIPES

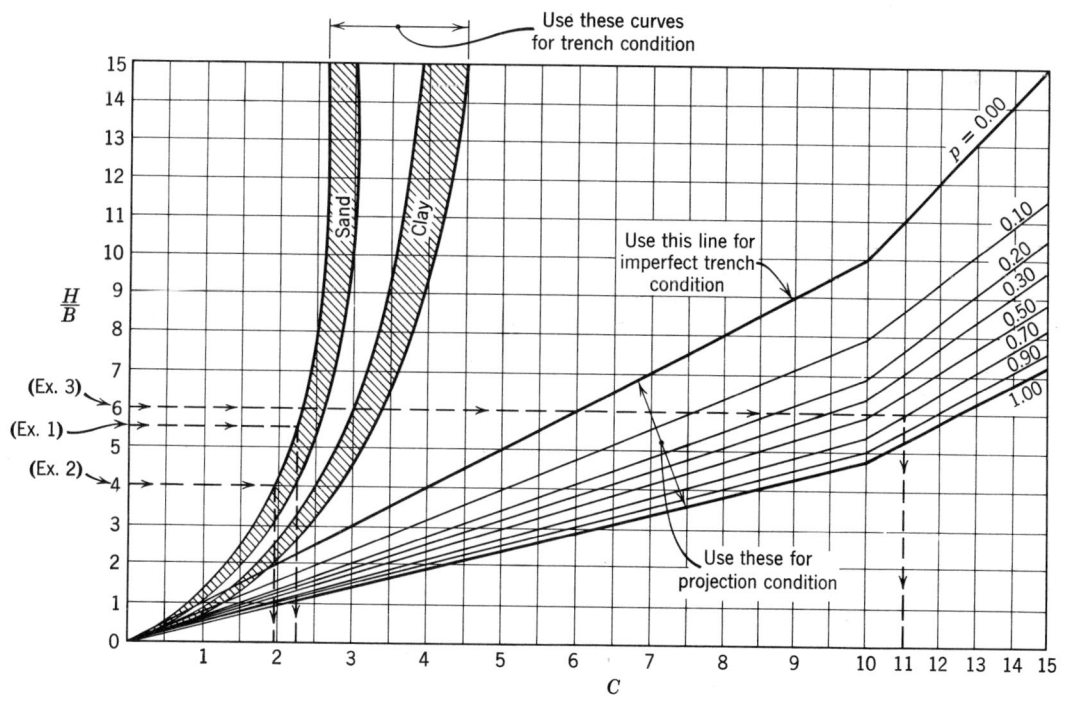

FIG. 3. C VALUES TO BE USED WITH BACKFILL LOAD FORMULA.

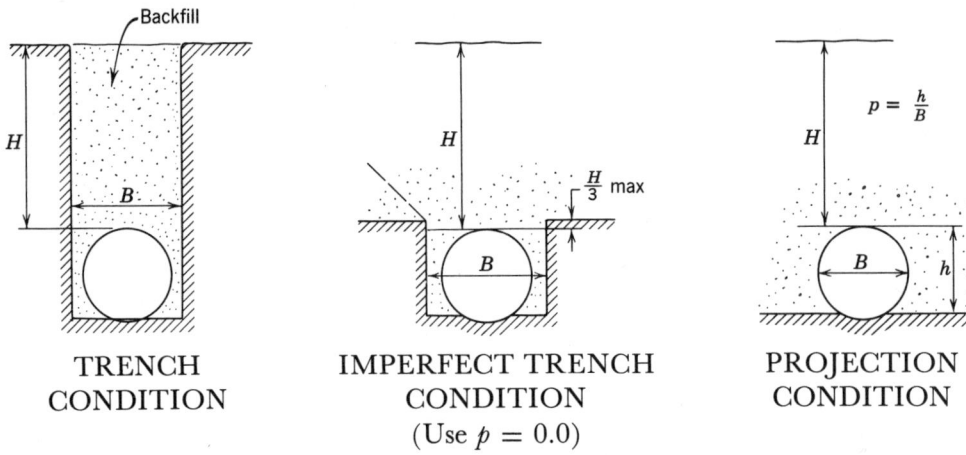

FIG. 4. TRENCH CONDITION.

Vertical load $= CwB^2$, where C is the coefficient from Fig. 3 and w is unit weight of soil.

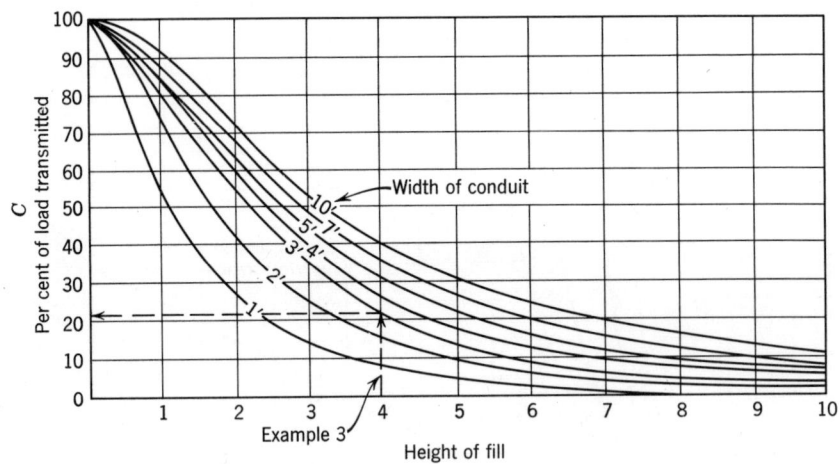

FIG. 5. CONCENTRATED SURFACE LOAD COEFFICIENTS C.

Load per foot $W = \frac{1}{3} \times 1.5^* \times C \times$ Total Load

* Impact. Use 1 for static loads.

TABLE II

SAFE VALUES OF *C* FOR SUPERIMPOSED UNIFORM LOAD

Bulletin 96, Iowa Engineering Experiment Station

$\frac{H}{B}$	Sand and Damp Top Soil	Saturated Top Soil	Damp Yellow Clay	Saturated Yellow Clay
0.0	1.00	1.00	1.00	1.00
0.5	0.85	0.86	0.88	0.89
1.0	0.72	0.75	0.77	0.80
1.5	0.61	0.64	0.67	0.72
2.0	0.52	0.55	0.59	0.64
2.5	0.44	0.48	0.52	0.57
3.0	0.37	0.41	0.45	0.51
4.0	0.27	0.31	0.35	0.41
5.0	0.19	0.23	0.27	0.33
6.0	0.14	0.17	0.20	0.26
8.0	0.07	0.09	0.12	0.17
10.0	0.04	0.05	0.07	0.11

Ex. 2

Load per foot $= W = C \times B \times$ Load per square foot.

TABLE III

MINIMUM RECOMMENDED WIDTHS OF TRENCHES FOR STANDARD VITRIFIED-CLAY PIPE

Diameter of pipe, in.	6	8	10	12	15	18
Width of trench, ft. and in.	2–0	2–2	2–4	2–6	2–10	3–1
Diameter of pipe, in.	21	24	27	30	33	36
Width of trench, ft. and in.	3–5	3–8	4–0	4–3	4–6	4–10

TABLE IV

PIPE CLASSES & PROPERTIES

Column groups:
- **CONCRETE SEWER PIPE** — PLAIN (A.S.T.M. SPEC. C-14-41); REINFORCED (A.S.T.M. SPEC. C-75-41)
- **CONCRETE CULVERT PIPE** — REINFD. STAND. STRENGTH (A.S.T.M. SPEC. C-76-41); REINFD. EXTRA STRENGTH (A.S.T.M. SPEC. C-76-41)
- **CORRUGATED METAL PIPE** — WT. PER LIN. FT. (lbs.) for 16, 14, 12, 10 and 8 GAUGE

For each concrete group: Shell Thickness (inches) · Wt. per Lin. Ft. (lbs.) · Design Strength 3-Edge Bearing (lbs. per lin. ft.)

INSIDE PIPE DIA. (IN.)	PLAIN Shell Thk.	PLAIN Wt/ft	PLAIN Design	REINF. Shell Thk.	REINF. Wt/ft	REINF. Design	STAND. Shell Thk.	STAND. Wt/ft	STAND. Design	EXTRA Shell Thk.	EXTRA Wt/ft	EXTRA Design	16 Ga.	14 Ga.	12 Ga.	10 Ga.	8 Ga.
4	9/16		1000														
6	1"	25	1100														
8	1"	35	1300										7.6	9.3			
10	1 1/8	48	1400										9.3	11.4			
12	1 3/4*	60	1500	1 3/4*	100	1800	1 3/4†	100	2250				10.8	13.3	18.5		
15	2*	90	1750	2*	125	2000	2†	125	2625				13.3	16.4	22.7		
18	2 1/4*	120	2000	2 1/4*	160	2200	2 1/4†	160	3000				15.8	19.5	27.0		
21	2 3/8*	190	2200	2 3/8*	205	2400	2 3/8†	205		2 3/4	255		18.3	22.5	31.2	39.7	
24	2 5/8*	225	2400	2 5/8*	260	2400	3*	260	3000			4000	21.0	26.0	35.9	45.7	
30	3*			3*	315	2700	3 1/2*	370	3375			5000	21.0	31.7	43.9	55.9	
36	3 1/2*			3 1/2*	450	3000	4*	520	4050			6000		37.9	52.4	66.7	81.1
42	3 3/4*			3 3/4*	560	3200	4 1/2*	680	4725			7000		44.4	61.5	78.3	95.1
48	4 1/4*			4 1/4*	720	3400	5*	850	5400			8000		50.5	70.0	89.1	108.3
54	4 5/8*			4 5/8*	880	3700	5 1/2*	1050	5850			9000		57.8	80.1	102.0	123.9
60	5*			5*	1060	4000	6*	1280	6000			9000			88.2	112.3	136.4
66	6 1/2§			6 1/2§	1480	4250	6 1/2*	1480	6300			9500			96.6	123.1	149.5
72	7§			7§	1835	4500	7*	1835	6600			9900			105.1	133.9	162.6
84	8§			8§	2300		8*	2300								156.6	190.3

*Conc. 3500 p.s.i. ‡Conc. 3000 p.s.i. †Conc. 4500 p.s.i. "first crack" strength.

§Design Strength given for reinf. conc. pipe is for -4 ft.

Standard laying length -4 ft.
Weights per lin. ft. furnished by Universal Concrete Pipe Co.
Weights shown are for Bell & Spigot to 21" diam.
Weights shown are for Tongue & Groove Jts., 21" diam. and larger.

Furnished in any length in multiples of 2 ft. Data furnished by Armco Drainage & Metal Products, Inc.

TABLE V

PIPE CLASSES AND PROPERTIES

	VITRIFIED CLAY SALT GLAZED						ASBESTOS-CEMENT SEWER PIPE (TRANSITE)								
	Standard Strength ASTM Spec. C13–44T			Extra Strength ASTM Spec. C200–44T			Building Sewer Pipe			Class 1			Class 2		
Inside Pipe Diam. (Inches)	* Shell Thickness (Inches)	Wt. per Lin. Ft. (Lbs.)	Average Strength 3 Edge Bearing Lbs. per Lin. Ft.	* Shell Thickness (Inches)	Wt. per Lin. Ft. (Lbs.)	Average Strength 3 Edge Bearing Lbs. per Lin. Ft.	* Shell Thickness (Inches)	Wt. per Lin. Ft. (Lbs.)	Average Strength 3 Edge Bearing Lbs. per Lin. Ft.	* Shell Thickness (Inches)	Wt. per Lin. Ft. (Lbs.)	Average Strength 3 Edge Bearing Lbs. per Lin. Ft.	* Shell Thickness (Inches)	Wt. per Lin. Ft. (Lbs.)	Average Strength 3 Edge Bearing Lbs. per Lin. Ft.
4	½	8	1000				0.32	4.4	1740						
5							0.35	5.8	1680						
6	⅝	14.5	1000	11/16	15.5	2000	0.35	6.9	1420	0.425	9.1	2600			
8	¾	23.0	1000	⅞	24.0	2000				0.480	13.2	2500			
10	⅞	31.5	1100	1	36.5	2000				0.525	18.4	2400	0.590	18.2	3000
12	1	43.5	1200	1 3/16	55.5	2250				0.560	24.0	2300	0.640	26.2	3000
14										0.590	29.6	2200	0.740	34.8	3400
15	1¼	67.5	1400	1½	89.5	2750									
16										0.630	35.9	2200	0.825	44.2	3700
18	1½	96.0	1700	1⅞	116.0	3300				0.670	42.4	2200	0.910	53.5	4000
20										0.700	49.0	2200	0.960	63.5	4000
21	1¾	37.0	2000	2¼	180.0	3850									
24	2	171.5	2400	2½	218.0	4400				0.810	67.6	2400	1.110	82.4	4500
30	2½	270.0	3200	3	344.0	5000				1.040	105.8	3200	1.330	130.6	5200
36	2¾	390.0	3900	3½	505.0	6000				1.270	154.0	4000	1.570	184.0	6000

Laying lengths:
Standard strength—2, 2½ or 3 ft.
Standard and extra strength—2, 2½, 3 or 4 ft.
Weights per lin. ft. from *Handbook of Vitrified Clay Sewer Pipe,* Clay Sewer Pipe Assoc., Inc.

Standard laying length of 13 ft. for sewer pipe.
Standard laying length of 10 ft. for building sewer pipe.
Furnished only in straight lengths.
Asbestos-cement fittings recommended for branch connections.
Ultimate strengths determined by tests made in accordance with procedure of A.S.T.M.
All data furnished by Johns-Manville Corp.

* Subject to manufacturers tolerances.

TABLE VI

CONCRETE CRADLE FOR CONCRETE PIPE DIMENSIONS, CRADLE AREAS AND TRENCH WIDTHS

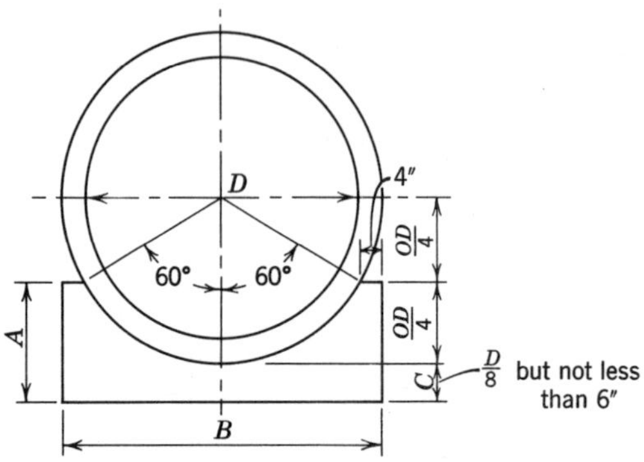

Pipe I.D., in.	Pipe O.D., in.	Cradle Dimensions, in. A	B	C	Cradle Area, sq. ft.	Maximum Trench Width = O.D. + 3′0″ ft.	in.
12	16	10	21⅞	6.00	1.25	4	4
15	19½	10⅞	24⅞	6.00	1.47	4	7½
18	23	11¾	27⅞	6.00	1.71	4	11
21	26½	12⅝	31	6.00	1.97	5	2½
24	30	13½	33	6.00	2.23	5	6
27	33½	14⅜	37	6.00	2.50	5	9½
30	37	15¼	40	6.00	2.78	6	1
36	44	17	46⅛	6.00	3.38	6	8
42	51	18¾	52½	6.00	4.02	7	3
48	58	20½	58¼	6.00	4.70	7	10
54	65	23	64⁵⁄₁₆	6.75	5.77	8	5
60	72	25½	70⅜	7.50	6.94	9	0
66	79	28	76⁷⁄₁₆	8.25	8.20	9	7
72	86	30½	82½	9.00	9.58	10	2
78	93	33	88½	9.75	11.07	10	9
84	100	35½	94⅝	10.50	12.66	11	4
90	107	38	100⅝	11.25	14.36	11	11
96	114	40½	106¾	12.00	16.16	12	6
102	121	43	112¹³⁄₁₆	12.75	18.07	13	1
108	128	45½	118⅞	13.50	20.08	13	8
114	135	48	124⅞	14.25	22.21	14	3
120	142	50½	131	15.00	24.43	14	10

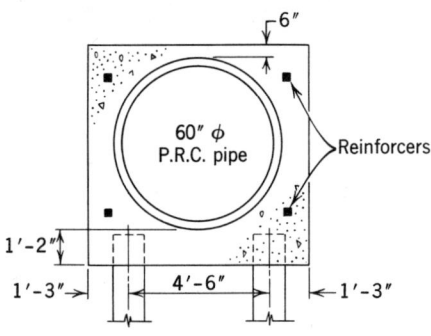

Pile spacing, 4'-0" c. to c.

REINFORCED-CONCRETE SUPPORT
(At Rockaway, N.Y., Outfall.)

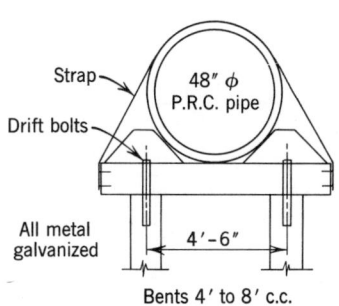

TIMBER FRAME (ON WATER)
(Crossing of Westchester Creek, Hunts Point, N.Y.)

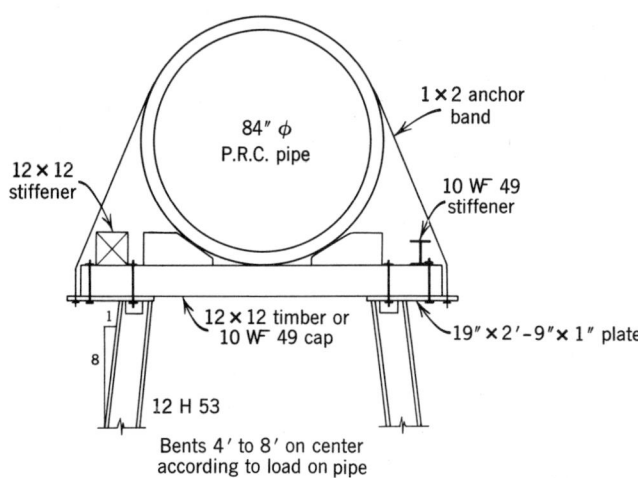

P.R.C. = Precast reinforced concrete

STEEL OR TIMBER FRAME
(At Hunts Point, N.Y., Bronx River Crossing.)

FIG. 6. MARINE TYPE SEWER PIPES * (SUPPORT DETAILS)

* All above pipes are under backfill.

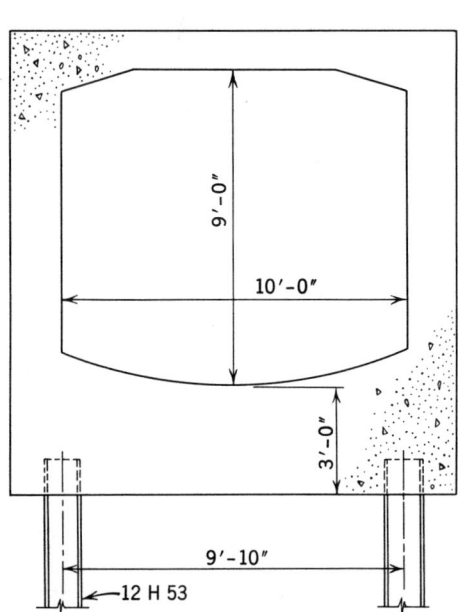

FIG. 7.   SEWER ON PILES.
(At Hunts Point)

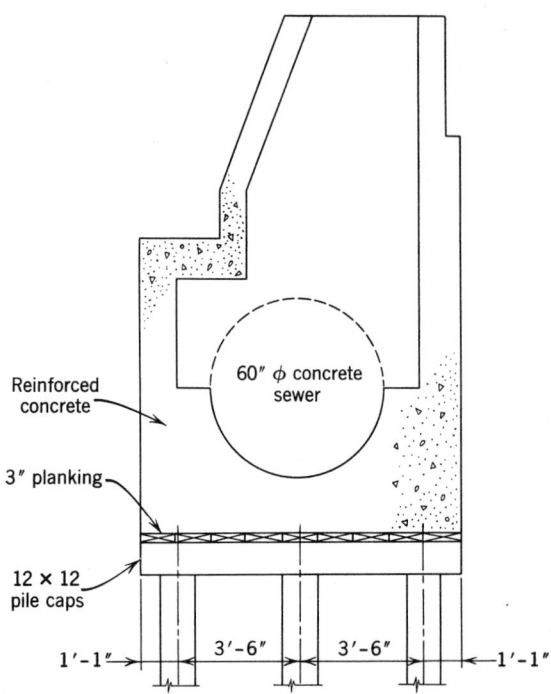

FIG. 8.   TIMBER PLATFORM SUPPORT
FOR A MANHOLE.
Tallman Island outfall and manhole

RED LIGHT

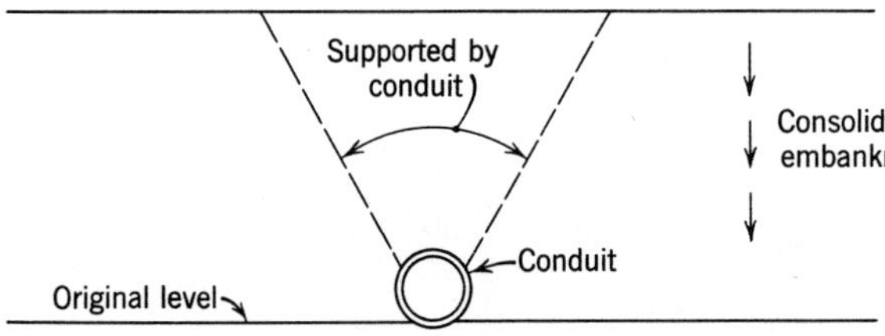

Wrong.   Conduit takes heavy load.

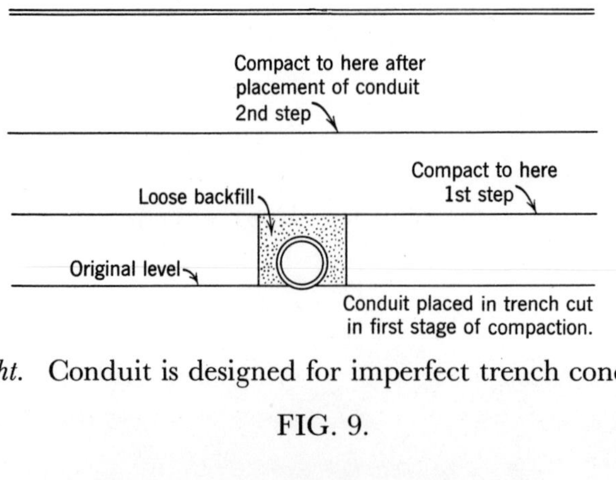

Right.   Conduit is designed for imperfect trench condition.

FIG. 9.

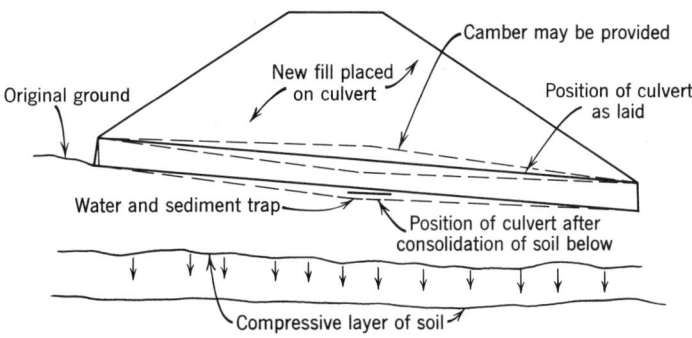

Wrong. Settlement of culvert from weight of new surcharge.

FIG. 10.

Preventive Measures

Where compressible layers occur, place entire backfill to consolidate them. Then excavate, place culvert, and backfill. Make temporary provision for drainage.

DESIGN OF SEWERS AND CULVERTS

Discussion

The design charts on sewers and culverts are empirical, based upon the experimental work of Professor Marston at the Iowa State Experimental Engineering Station.

The difference in load caused by trench conditions is the result of arching of the backfill between the walls of the trench; i.e., narrow trenches will develop the arch better. Efforts should therefore be made to keep the trench narrow. Increasing the width of the trench increases the load up to the point where it is the same as figured for a projection condition on the bottom of the trench. This width is often called the transition width.

It should be kept in mind that sewers also behave like other structures as regards settlement. They should be placed on undisturbed soil. In case of rock, a sand cushion of at least 8 in. or a concrete cradle should be provided so as to prevent concentrated reactions. The addition of a large fill over a consolidating soil will cause a settlement of a sewer pipe placed under it; Fig. 10.

For poor soils, and, more especially, for under-water outfalls, piles are often used either in the form of bents or in connection with concrete cradles; Figs. 6, 7, and 8.

See points made in Field Practice, Chapter 15, to avoid impractical locations and details.

RED LIGHTS

Pipes which require movement should be erected in pipe tunnels or in the open.

Specify flexible glands for pipes that pass through rigid masonry such as walls or footings.

If pipes occur under floors on ground or in fill, do not permit point support, such as a rock ledge, under pipe, which might cause it to break its back when the fill settles.

Pipe Guides, Anchors, and Expansion Joints.

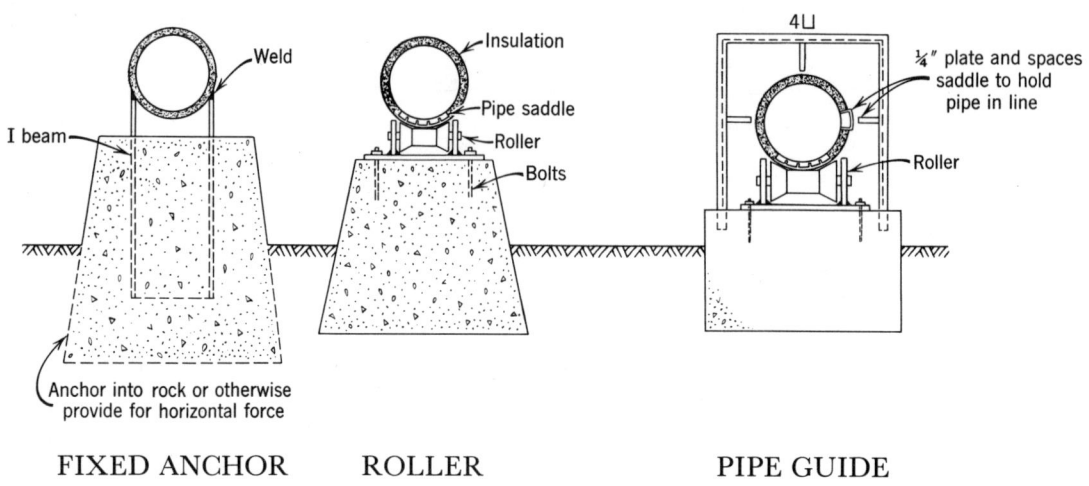

FIXED ANCHOR   ROLLER   PIPE GUIDE

FIG. 11.

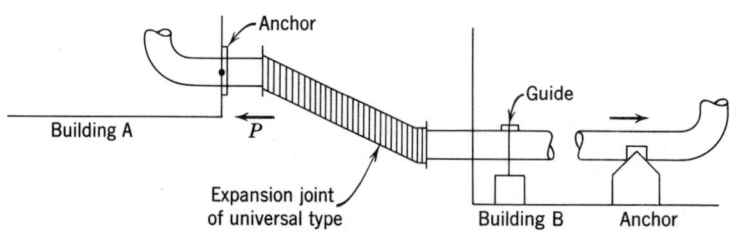

FIG. 12.   USE OF A UNIVERSAL JOINT BETWEEN BUILDINGS WHERE
DIFFERENTIAL SETTLEMENT IS EXPECTED.

Notes to Figs. 11 and 12.   Thrusts and expansion to be furnished by pipe designer.   These details apply to pipes laid free, not in backfill.

* Courtesy Zallea & Co.

THRUST BLOCKS FOR UNDERGROUND PIPES AND FITTINGS *

Since most pipe joints will not take tensile forces readily, thrust blocks are installed whenever the pipe line (*a*) changes direction, as at tees and bends; (*b*) changes size, as at reducers (also some crosses and tees); or (*c*) stops as at a dead end.

Anchorage of Pipe on Slopes

Pipes have to be anchored on slopes only in the event that there is a possibility of the backfill around the pipe slipping down and carrying the pipe with it. To prevent such slippage, anchors, keyed or tied into undisturbed soil, can be used at every third length of pipe.

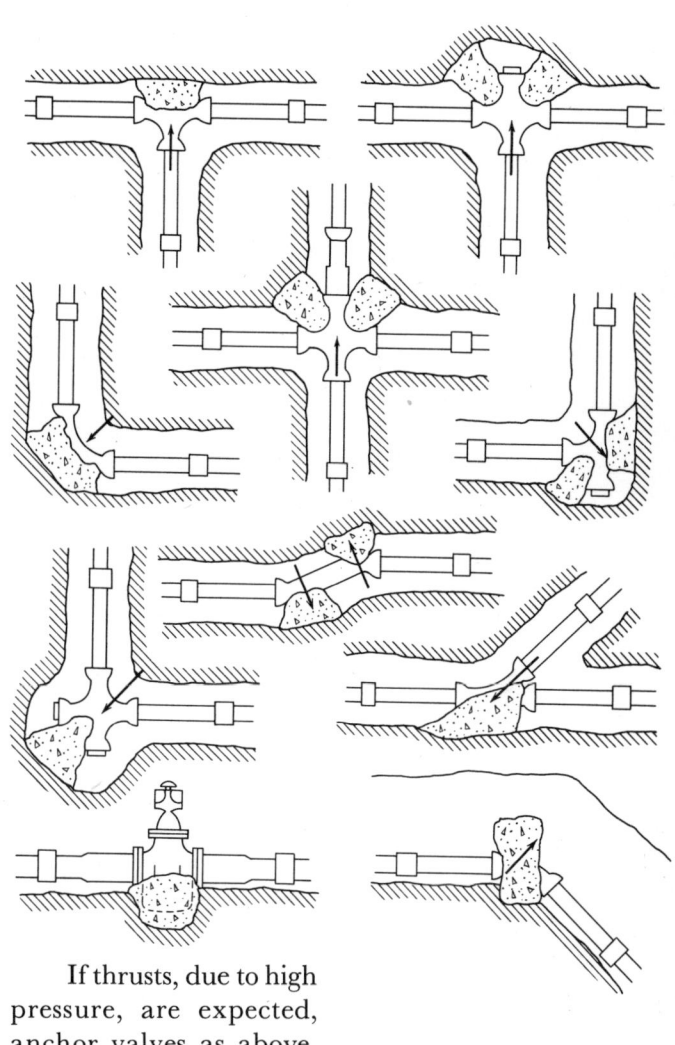

If thrusts, due to high pressure, are expected, anchor valves as above.

FIG. 13. LOCATION OF THRUST BLOCKS.

Red Light. These details indicate points of rigid support for pipe which might crack owing to settlement between these points and are risky. This points to the advantage of using pipe tunnels or using steel or wrought iron.

---

* Courtesy Johns-Manville Co.

7

Dams and Reservoirs

The foundations for dams and reservoirs cannot be considered without considering the entire section. Both dams and reservoirs serve to impound water. Therefore the problem of design becomes twofold:

1. Design of a structure strong enough to resist the hydrostatic and other forces introduced upon it.

2. Prevention of loss of water over, under, through, or around the structure.

Dams must be designed not only for hydrostatic pressure but also for:

    Ice

    Wave action

    Uplift caused by flow of water under dam

    Earthquake.

MASONRY DAMS

Plates I, II, and III give data and methods of design of masonry dams.

Plate I. Discussion

Explanation of Zones, Fig. C

Zone I: Governed by freeboard requirements. If ice occurs at top of water level, zone I will be governed by resistance to ice pressure. Generally the width is set by requirements of a roadway on top of dam.

Zone II: That section lying between zone I and zone III. Convenience rather than stress dictates design.

Zone III: Downstream face starts to batter so that the resultant with the reservoir full remains at the edge of the middle third.

Zone IV: Upstream face starts to batter so that resultant with the reservoir empty lies at upstream edge of middle third. Zone IV may extend downward until the inclined stress reaches the maximum for the material used. For higher dams, redesign is indicated.

Regardless of the governing design rule, the design should be checked for position of resultant, resistance to sliding, and inclined compressive stress for all zones.

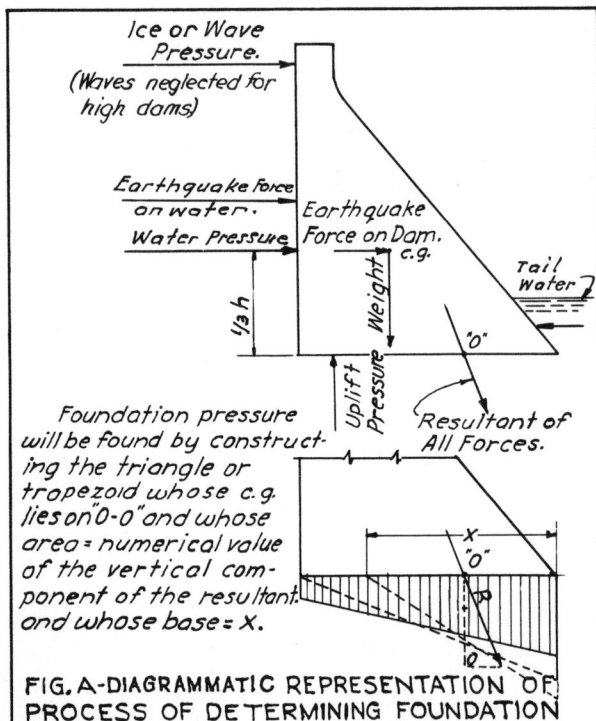

Ice or Wave Pressure.
(Waves neglected for high dams)

Earthquake force on water.
Water Pressure

Earthquake Force on Dam. c.g.

1/3 h

Uplift Pressure
Weight

Tail Water

Resultant of All Forces.

"0"

Foundation pressure will be found by constructing the triangle or trapezoid whose c.g. lies on "0-0" and whose area = numerical value of the vertical component of the resultant and whose base = x.

x
"0"
"0"

FIG. A—DIAGRAMMATIC REPRESENTATION OF PROCESS OF DETERMINING FOUNDATION PRESSURES ON A MASONRY DAM.

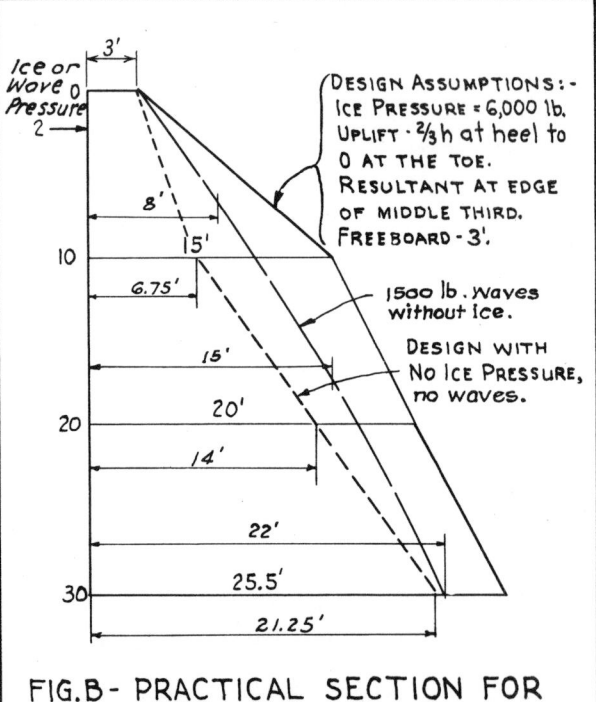

Ice or Wave Pressure
0
2

3'

8'
15'
6.75'

15'
20'
14'

22'
25.5'
21.25'

10

20

30

DESIGN ASSUMPTIONS:-
ICE PRESSURE = 6,000 lb.
UPLIFT - 2/3 h at heel to 0 AT THE TOE.
RESULTANT AT EDGE OF MIDDLE THIRD.
FREEBOARD - 3'.

1500 lb. waves without ice.

DESIGN WITH NO ICE PRESSURE, no waves.

FIG. B— PRACTICAL SECTION FOR CONCRETE DAMS TO 30' HIGH.

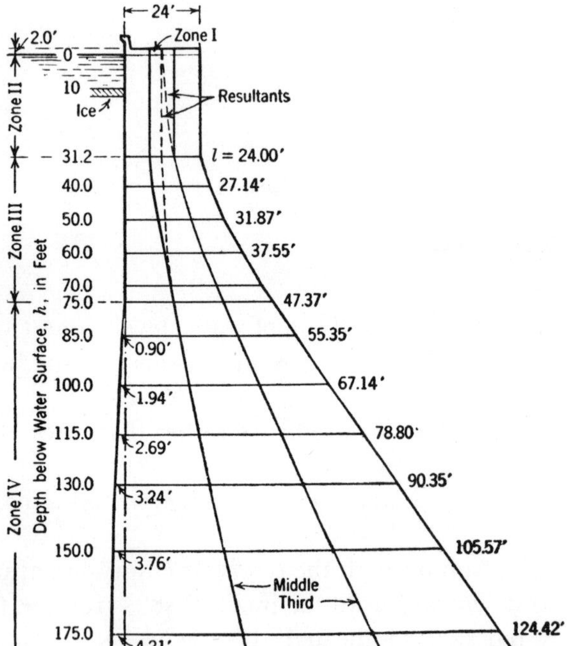

24'
Zone I
2.0'
0
10
Zone II
Ice
Resultants

31.2
40.0
50.0
60.0
70.0
75.0
85.0
100.0
115.0
130.0
150.0
175.0
200.0

Zone III
Zone IV
Depth below Water Surface, h, in Feet

l = 24.00'
27.14'
31.87'
37.55'
47.37'
55.35'
0.90'
1.94'
67.14'
2.69'
78.80'
3.24'
90.35'
3.76'
105.57'
Middle Third
4.21'
124.42'
4.49'
143.10'

DESIGN ASSUMPTIONS:
Maximum Inclined Compressive Stress is 60,000 lb./sq. ft.
Maximum Friction Factor = 0.75
Maximum Uplift Pressure = 0.5 height of water.
Uplift Area - Across full base width.
Wind Velocity = 80 miles per hour.
Ice Pressure = 9,000 lb./lin. ft.
Fetch = 4 miles.

FIG. C— PRACTICAL CONCRETE DAM SECTION.*

*Adopted from Engineering for Dams by Creager, Justin & Hinds.

PLATE I.

These data represent average practice and should only be used to supplement scientific analysis based on tests and on models.

PRESSURE DUE TO ICE: *Commonly assumed of 5,000# to 20,000#(Maine) per linear foot*

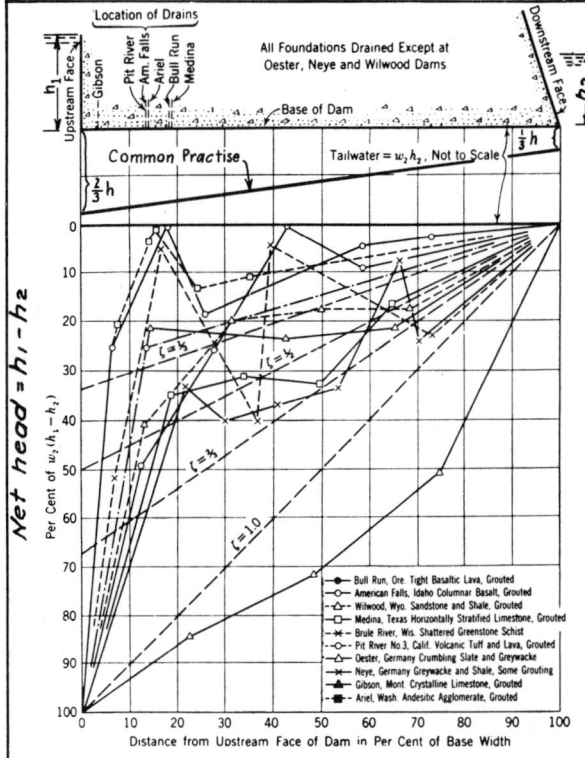

FIG. A - UPLIFT PRESSURE ACROSS BASE OF MASONRY DAM ON ROCK FOUNDATION.*

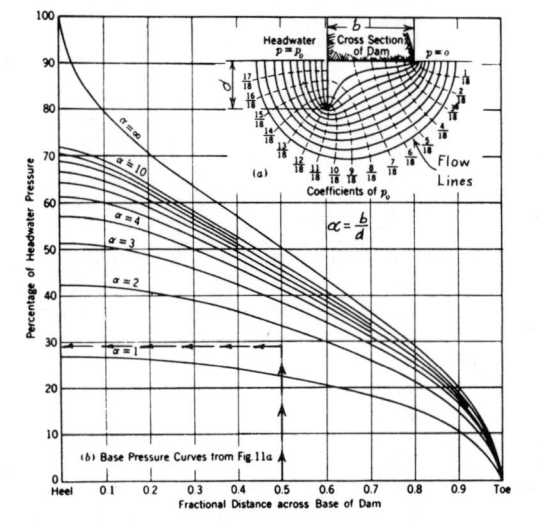

EXAMPLE:

Given: Dam with: 10' base; 6' cut off; and 12' net head.

Required: To find uplift pressure at mid-point of base.

Solution: $\frac{b}{d} = \frac{10}{6} = 1.67$; from chart = 29%

$0.29 \times 12'$ head = 3.5' head.

FIG. B - UPLIFT PRESSURE ACROSS BASE OF MASONRY DAM ON EARTH FOUNDATION.**

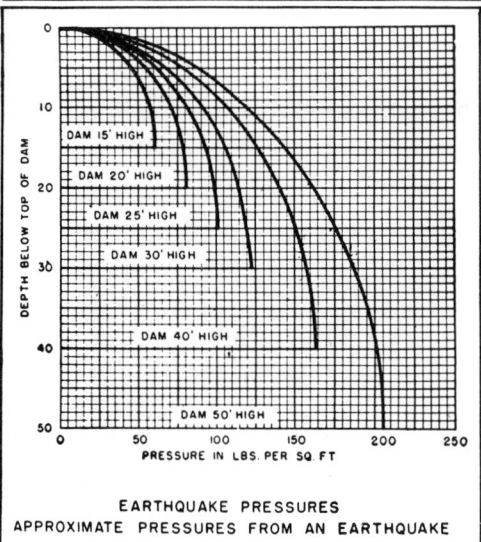

EARTHQUAKE PRESSURES
APPROXIMATE PRESSURES FROM AN EARTHQUAKE
OF AMPLITUDE = 0.1G. AND PERIOD = 1 SEC.

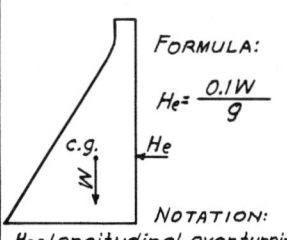

FORMULA:

$$He = \frac{0.1W}{g}$$

NOTATION:

He = Longitudinal overturning force applied at c.g.

W = Weight of dam.

g = 32.2.

NOTE: Avoid location across a fault line.

Other factors are: Water pressure due to shock, relations between period of vibration of the foundation and of the structure. As these approach each other, there is danger of resonance.

FIG. C - FORCES CAUSED BY EARTHQUAKES.***

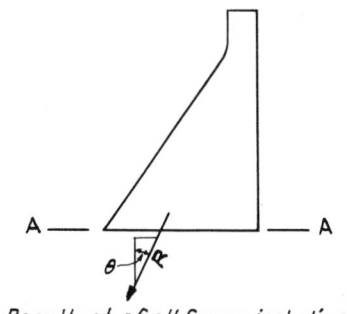

R = Resultant of all forces including uplift acting above plane A-A.

Keep "R" within middle third of base in all cases.

Keep $\tan \theta < 0.75$

Maximum inclined pressure 60,000 lb. per sq. ft. or less depending on nature of rock.

FIG. D - RESISTANCE TO SLIDING - FOR ROCK.

*Ivan E. Hoak, Civil Eng. 1932. **L. F. Harza, Trans. A.S.C.E. 1935 *** From Low Dams by National Resources Comm.

PLATE II.

SEEPAGE DATA: *The flow of water from the upstream side of dam to the downstream side, through the embankment of earth dams and along the line of creep, must be kept within safe limits in respect to volume and velocity to prevent piping & boiling.*
Creep = Path of water along contact surface between structure and foundation.

TABLE A – RECOMMENDED CREEP RATIOS,* R (After Lane).

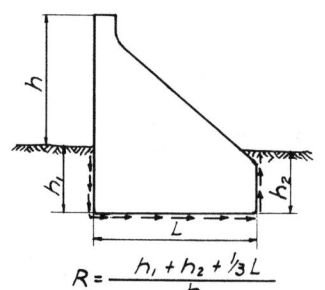

MATERIAL	R	MATERIAL	R
Very Fine Sand & Silt.	8.5	Boulders with some Cobbles and Gravel.	2.5
Fine Sand	7.0		
Medium Sand	6.0	Soft Clay	3.0
Coarse Sand	5.0	Medium Clay	2.0
Fine Gravel	4.0	Hard Clay	1.8
Medium Gravel	3.5	Very Hard Clay or Hardpan.	1.6
Coarse Gravel including some Cobbles.	3.0		

$$R = \frac{h_1 + h_2 + \frac{1}{3}L}{h}$$

R = Creep Ratio.
(A check against piping)

NOTE: If "R" for a critical section is less than the tabular value, additional flow resistance should be inserted in design section.
Limitations: Does not take into account –
  1. Importance of shape - see Fig. C & D p. 7-17
  2. Line of creep may not be most direct path of seepage.

TABLE B – SEEPAGE LOSSES FROM COFFERDAMS.**

Ratio of Areas a/A	0.1	0.2	0.3	0.4	0.5	0.6	0.7	0.8	0.9
ϕ	0.49	0.62	0.74	0.86	1.00	1.16	1.35	1.62	2.06

MATERIAL	K
Clean Gravel	$0.2662 \ - 0.02778$
Clean Sand	$5787 \times 10^{-7} - 5787 \times 10^{-9}$
Fine Sand or Silt	$2778 \times 10^{-9} - 2778 \times 10^{-12}$
Clay.	Less than -2778×10^{-12}

SCHOKLITSCH FORMULA.

$$Q = 100 \, K \phi \frac{h}{2}$$

Where: Q = Quantity of flow in cu.ft./sec.
  K = Coefficient of permeability in cu.ft./sec.-See Table B, but a soil analysis is indicated.
  ϕ = Value in Table B above.

Alternate Formula:†

$$Q_1 = C L h$$

Where:-
  Q_1 = Flow in gal. per min.
  C = 1.25 × effective (or 10%) grain size of sand.
    See p. 8-03 for visual determination of grain size.
  h = Head loss in feet.
  L = Length of dam in feet.

NOTE: On dams over 15' high, seepage losses through embankments should be determined by experiments on scale models.

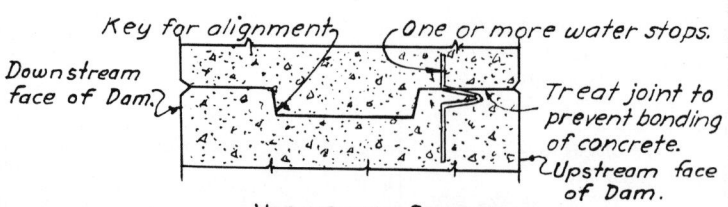

Key for alignment.
One or more water stops.
Downstream face of Dam.
Treat joint to prevent bonding of concrete.
Upstream face of Dam.

HORIZONTAL SECTION.
Allow lapse of time between concreting adjoining sections to reduce shrinkage. See also p. 7-05

FIG. C – CONSTRUCTION JOINT ESSENTIALS.

FLOTATION GRADIENT.†
Hydraulic Gradient at which boils or piping occur.
Flotation Gradient = F_c
$$F_c = \frac{H}{L} = (1-P)(S-1)$$
F_c = 1 approximately.
P = Proportion of voids.
S = Specific gravity of sand grains.
H = Hydraulic head.
L = Thickness of bed.

*Adapted from Transactions of A.S.C.E. - 1935, pg.1235 by E.W. Lane. **from Low Dams by National Resources Comm. † Adapted from White & Prentis, Cofferdams, by permission of Columbia University Press.

PLATE III.

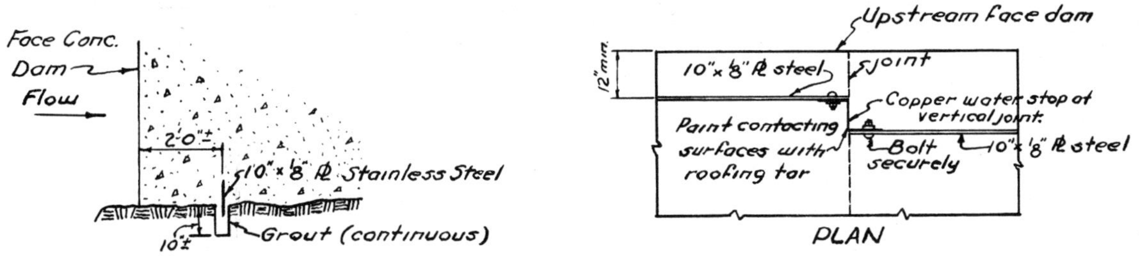

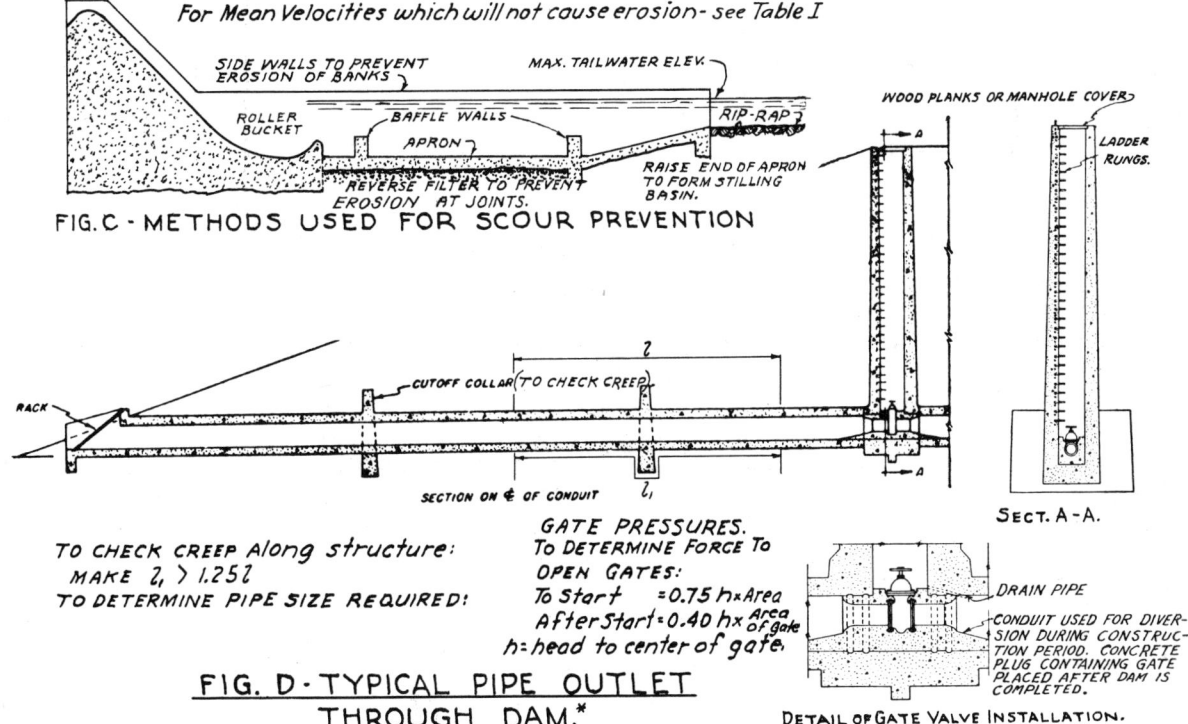

Face Conc. Dam
Flow
2'-0"±
10"×8" ℞ Stainless Steel
Grout (continuous)
10±

CONTINUOUS LEDGE WATER STOP

12 min.
Upstream face dam
10"×8" ℞ steel — Joint
Paint contacting surfaces with roofing tar
Copper water stop at vertical joint.
Bolt securely
10"×8" ℞ steel

PLAN

HORIZONTAL STEEL WATER STOP

FIG. A - WATERSTOPS

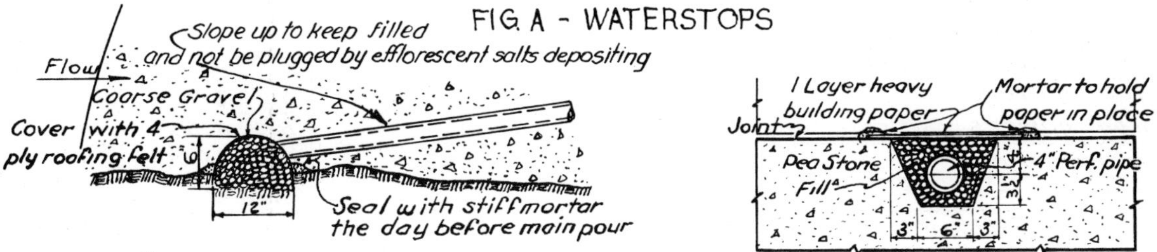

Flow
Slope up to keep filled and not be plugged by efflorescent salts depositing
Coarse Gravel
Cover with 4 ply roofing felt
12"
Seal with stiff mortar the day before main pour

CONTINUOUS GRAVEL LEDGE DRAIN

Joint
I Layer heavy building paper
Mortar to hold paper in place
Pea Stone Fill
4" Perf. pipe
3" 6" 3"

HORIZONTAL DRAIN

Note: If felt is punctured, cover hole with stiff mortar. Cover all joints so there is no leakage from wet concrete to gravel drain.

FIG. B - DRAINS

For Mean Velocities which will not cause erosion- see Table I

SIDE WALLS TO PREVENT EROSION OF BANKS
MAX. TAILWATER ELEV.
ROLLER BUCKET
BAFFLE WALLS
APRON
RIP-RAP
REVERSE FILTER TO PREVENT EROSION AT JOINTS.
RAISE END OF APRON TO FORM STILLING BASIN.

FIG. C - METHODS USED FOR SCOUR PREVENTION

WOOD PLANKS OR MANHOLE COVER
LADDER RUNGS.

RACK
CUTOFF COLLAR (TO CHECK CREEP)
l
l_1
SECTION ON ℄ OF CONDUIT

SECT. A-A.

TO CHECK CREEP ALONG STRUCTURE:
MAKE $l_1 > 1.25 l$
TO DETERMINE PIPE SIZE REQUIRED:

GATE PRESSURES.
To DETERMINE FORCE TO OPEN GATES:
To Start = 0.75 h×Area
After Start = 0.40 h × Area of gate
h = head to center of gate.

FIG. D - TYPICAL PIPE OUTLET THROUGH DAM.*

DRAIN PIPE
CONDUIT USED FOR DIVERSION DURING CONSTRUCTION PERIOD. CONCRETE PLUG CONTAINING GATE PLACED AFTER DAM IS COMPLETED.

DETAIL OF GATE VALVE INSTALLATION.

*From Low Dams by National Resources Comm.

PLATE IV.

TABLE I - MEAN VELOCITIES WHICH WILL NOT ERODE CHANNELS AFTER AGING.		
MATERIAL OF CHANNEL BED	**VELOCITY IN FEET PER SEC.**	
	SHALLOW DITCH	DEEP CANAL $*$
Fine sand or silt, non-colloidal	0.50-1.50	1.50-2.50
Coarse sand or sandy loam, non-colloidal	1.00-1.50	1.75-2.50
Silty or sand loam " "	1.00-1.75	2.00-3.00
Clayey loam or sandy clay " "	1.50-2.00	2.25-3.50
Fine gravel	2.00-2.50	2.50-5.00
Colloidal clay or non-colloidal gravelly loam	2.00-3.00	3.00-5.00
Colloidal, well-graded gravel	2.25-3.50	4.00-6.00
Pebbles, broken stone, shales or hardpan	2.50-4.00	5.00-6.50
Sodded gutters	3.00-5.00	—
Cobbled gutters, not grouted, or bituminous paving	5.00-7.50	—
Stone masonry	7.50-15.00	—
Solid rock or concrete	15.00-25.00	—

AGING OF CHANNELS increases resistance to erosion as density and stability of channel bed improve due to deposit of silt in interstices and as cohesion increases due to cementation of soil by colloids. New channels may be safely operated at less than maximum design velocities by use of temporary check structures.

VELOCITIES are to be reduced for depths of flow under 6 inches and for water which may transport abrasive materials.

$*$ Based on Report of Special Committee on Irrigation Research A.S.C.E., 1926.

STEVENSON FORMULA :

For "F" greater than 20 miles :

$$h = 0.17 \sqrt{VF}$$

For "F" less than 20 miles :

$$h = 0.17 \sqrt{VF} + 25 - F^{\frac{1}{4}}$$

Where: h = Height of wave in feet.
V = Wind velocity in miles per hour.
F = Unobstructed length of lake in statute miles (fetch).

Wave Pressure, P = 125h² in pounds per linear foot.

Maximum height of waves: On a vertical surface = 1.33h.
On an inclined surface = 1.5h.

Minimum Freeboard on lakes less than 2 miles long = 2 feet.

FIG. A - HEIGHT OF FREEBOARD WAVE ACTION.*

NOTE: Waves exert scouring action as they travel up and down slopes. Embankment should be protected by paving, rip-rap, etc.; provision for drainage, in case of rapid drawdown of reservoir, should be made.

ZUIDER ZEE FORMULA :

$$S = \frac{V^2 F}{1400 d} \times \cos A$$

Where: S = Rise of water level above normal in feet.
V = Wind velocity in miles per hour.
F = Unobstructed length of lake in miles (fetch).
d = Average depth of water in feet.
A = Angle between fetch and direction of wind.

FIG. B - RISE IN WATER LEVEL DUE TO WIND.

*Adapted from *Trans.* A.S.C.E., p. 984, by D. A. Miller.

PLATE V.

Uplift on Masonry Dams

Discussion

The hydrostatic pressure of the impounded water forces water into the foundation and masonry of the dam. No rock foundation is entirely free of fissures into which water may be forced.

Figure A, Plate II, shows observations of upward pressure made on certain dams.

One reason for requiring the resultant to be within the middle third is that a tensile crack on the upstream face would greatly increase the uplift factor.

Figure B, Plate II, shows a flow net under a masonry dam resting on soil together with uplift pressure.

EARTH DAMS

Essentials

Figure I shows the essential elements of an earth-dam cross section. Plate VII suggests how an analysis may be made of shear and sliding stresses in a dam by the "sliding block" method.

Compaction should be made to maximum density at optimum moisture.

Impervious sections and coarse sections should be within the limits given in Fig. 2.

Spillways. Earth dams require separate overflow structures, as water overtopping the dam will destroy it.

Foundation Material. Foundations should never be on peat or vegetable loam, and the subsoil should be compacted in 6-in. layers with power equipment. Sheepsfoot rollers may be required to reduce moisture.

Riprap reinforced with fine gravel and sand should be provided on the upstream surface to protect against wave action. A reverse filter should be provided in case of sudden drawdown.

Sod or riprap protection should be provided on the downstream slope to safeguard against rain erosion.

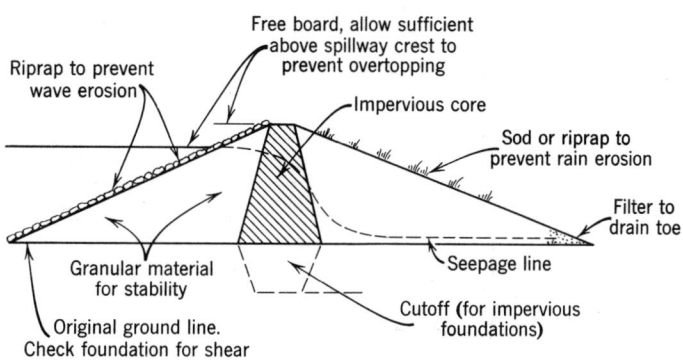

Keep seepage line well inside downstream face.

Check stability of structure.

Note: Construction varies with site and material available. See Plate VI for typical sections.

FIG. 1. ESSENTIAL ELEMENTS OF EARTH DAMS.

DAMS AND RESERVOIRS

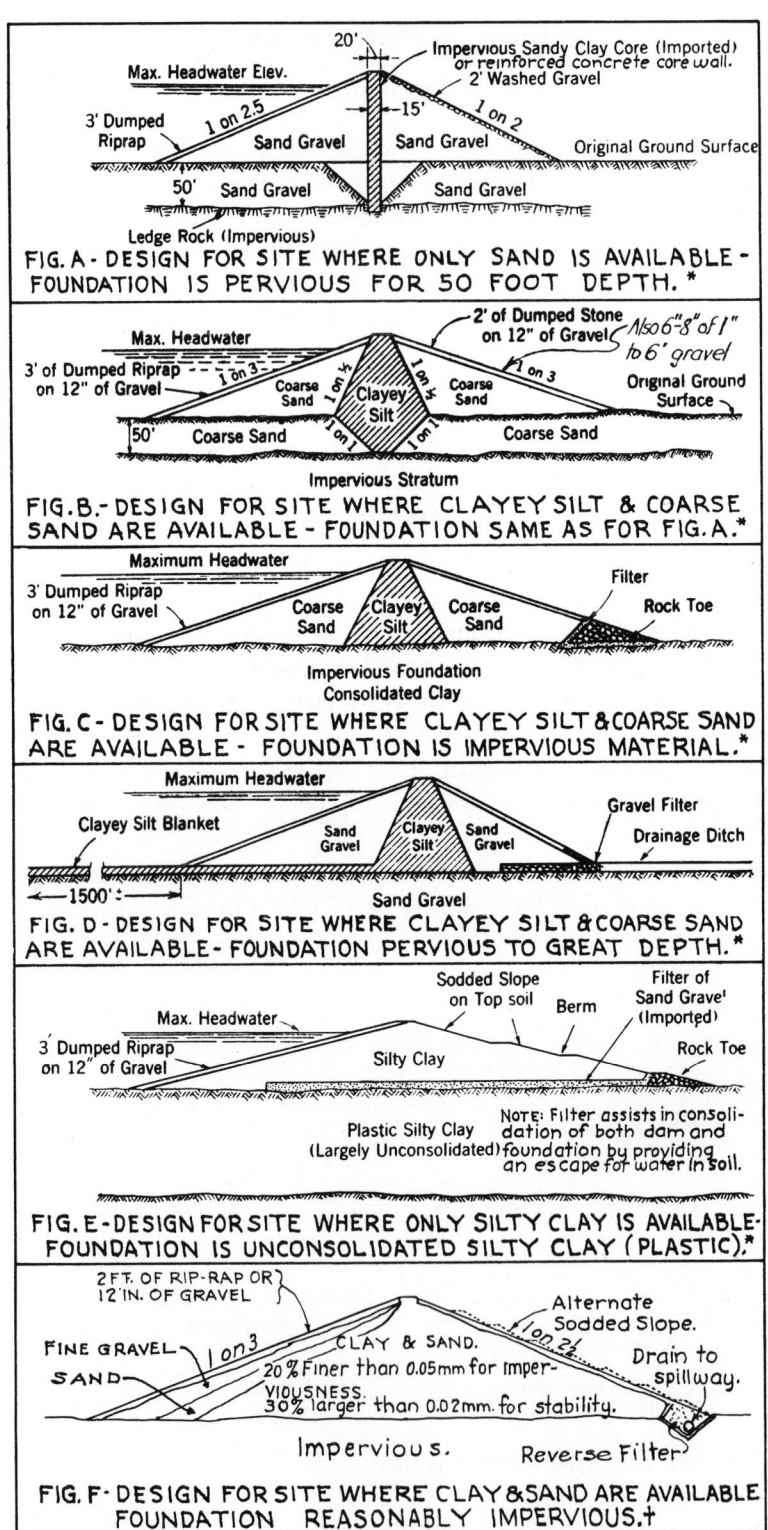

FIG. A - DESIGN FOR SITE WHERE ONLY SAND IS AVAILABLE - FOUNDATION IS PERVIOUS FOR 50 FOOT DEPTH. *

FIG. B. - DESIGN FOR SITE WHERE CLAYEY SILT & COARSE SAND ARE AVAILABLE - FOUNDATION SAME AS FOR FIG. A. *

FIG. C - DESIGN FOR SITE WHERE CLAYEY SILT & COARSE SAND ARE AVAILABLE - FOUNDATION IS IMPERVIOUS MATERIAL. *

FIG. D - DESIGN FOR SITE WHERE CLAYEY SILT & COARSE SAND ARE AVAILABLE - FOUNDATION PERVIOUS TO GREAT DEPTH. *

FIG. E - DESIGN FOR SITE WHERE ONLY SILTY CLAY IS AVAILABLE - FOUNDATION IS UNCONSOLIDATED SILTY CLAY (PLASTIC). *

FIG. F - DESIGN FOR SITE WHERE CLAY & SAND ARE AVAILABLE FOUNDATION REASONABLY IMPERVIOUS. †

*Adapted from *Engineering for Dams* by Justin, Hinds & Creager   † by Author.

PLATE VI.

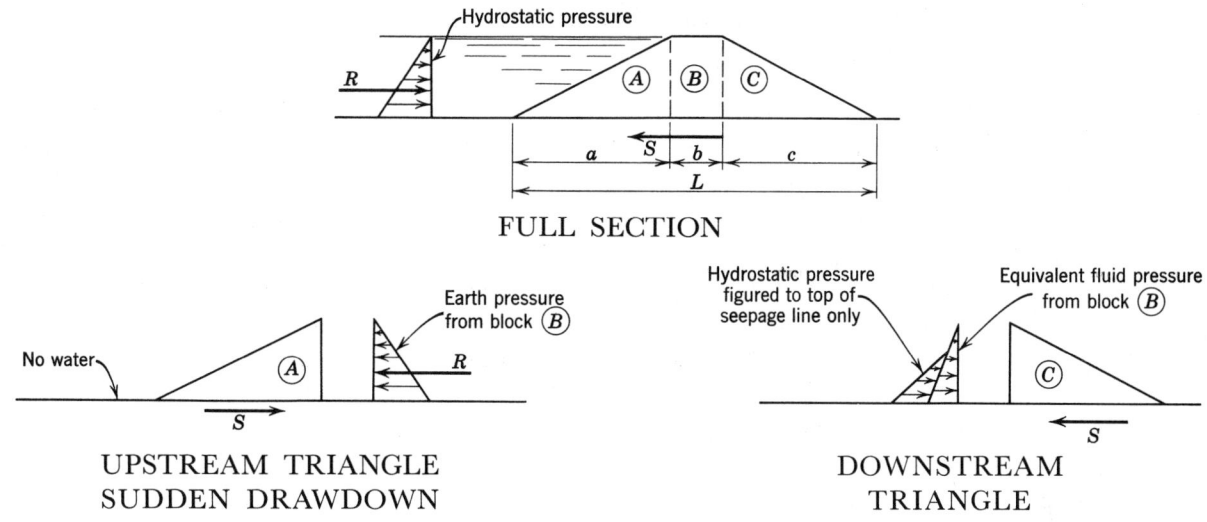

PLATE VII.   FORCES ON AN EARTH DAM.

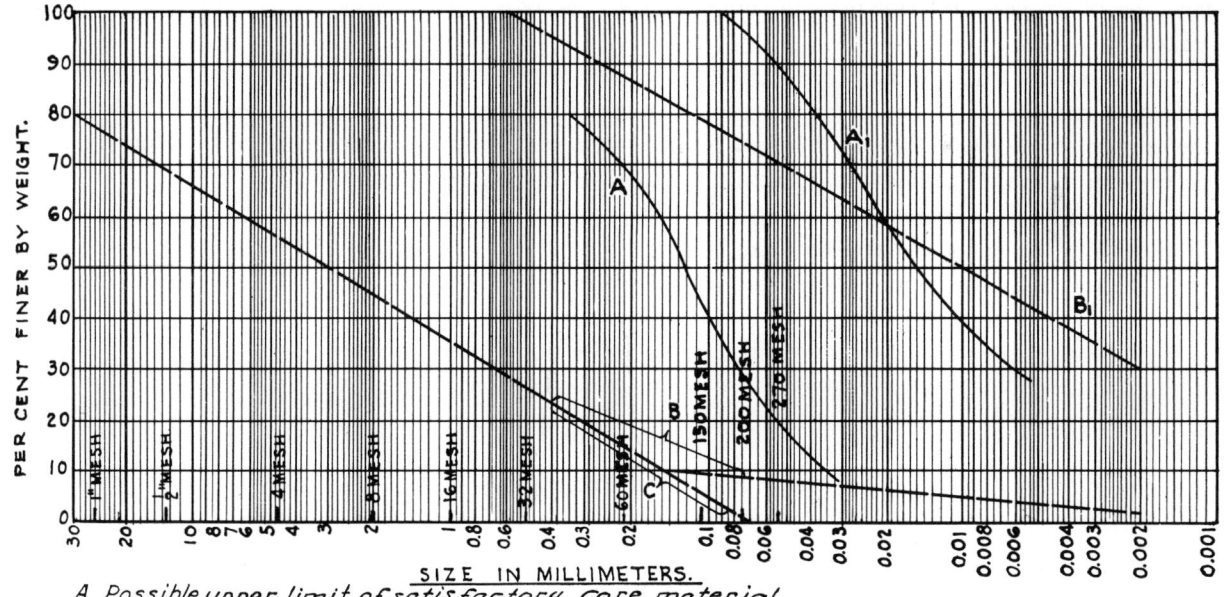

A. *Possible upper limit of satisfactory core material.*
A_1. *Probable upper limit of safe core material (Urquhart).*
B-B_1 *Proposed limits for ungraded materials suitable for impervious section for rolled fill dams (Lee)*
C-B_1 *Approximate limit of materials for impervious sections of rolled fill dams (Justin).*

FIG. 2.   CHART FOR SELECTION OF MATERIALS.*

Selection of Materials by PRA Groups.   See p. 13–39 for definitions.

Homogeneous Type: A–1, A–2 plastic.   Better grades of A–6 and A–7.

Core Type: Core: A–1, A–2 plastic, A–4 plastic, better grades of A–6 and A–7.   Faces: Non-plastic A–2 and A–4.   Do not use A–3, A–5, A–8, or highly plastic A–6 or A–7.

---

* From *Low Dams,* National Resources Comm.

Seepage in Earth Dams

An earth dam will always have water present in some sections. The amount of the water that passes through is called seepage. The height to which the water rises inside the dam is called the seepage line. Water may rise above the seepage line by capillary action. The location of this line has an effect upon the stability of the structure, as shown in the stability analysis, Plate VII.

For a dam of homogeneous material upon an impervious foundation, seepage will pass through the dam, appearing on the downstream face and eroding it. Even with a pervious foundation, seepage will appear on the downstream face unless a cutoff has been placed down to an impervious foundation. In this case the downstream portion of the foundation acts as a drain. These principles are true regardless of how well the embankment is built, because the seepage has no other place to go.

The problem then is to reduce the seepage as much as possible with the material which may be economically obtained and to prevent damage to the structure from that seepage.

The flow net shows the paths of seepage through the dam and foundation. Several different conditions are shown in Plate VIII. These flow nets should be studied in conjunction with the typical dam sections shown on Plate VI so as to facilitate the attempts to control seepage with material available.

Damage to downstream slope will occur from two causes. The first is erosion of the bank by trickling of water on the downstream slope. The remedy is lowering the line of seepage; see Plate VIII.

The second cause of damage is boils. Fine soils are easily carried into suspension, so that the emerging seepage will carry away the soils. When this carrying out of the soil occurs back under the embankment, the condition is called piping. A remedy lies in using a reverse filter on the toe, permitting the water to flow away, leaving the soil in place. See Plate X.

The rule for filter material is based on 15% size, meaning that 15% by weight of particles are smaller than the size given and 85% are larger.

To determine the required size, step up the grain size by 9.

Layers of material should be 12 in. thick minimum.

Example

Given:

Silt grain size	= 0.01 mm.	
First layer fine sand	= 0.09 mm.	based on
Second layer coarse sand	= 0.81 mm.	15% size
Third layer gravel	= 7.3 mm.	

Note that in any layer the ratio of the 85% size to the 15% size should not exceed 5.

Quantity of seepage follows Darcy's law. It is necessary to know the effective grain size and the porosity. The effective grain size is that size which is coarser than 10% and finer than 90% of the grain sizes in the material. It is determined by sieve analysis; see Chapter 13, Soil Mechanics. The porosity is determined from the void ratio as follows:

Determination of voids ratio = e.

Example

Weight of soil = 120 lb. per cu. ft.
Specific gravity of grains = 2.70.
2.70 × 62.4 = 169 lb. per cu. ft. = theoretical weight of solid material.
120/169 = 0.71 cu. ft. = volume of soil material.
1.00 − 0.71 = 0.29 cu. ft. = volume of voids.
0.29/0.71 = 0.41 = voids ratio.

Porosity $= \dfrac{e}{1 + e} = \dfrac{0.41}{1 + 0.41} = 0.29$, or the same as the volume of voids.

Darcy's law states:

$\qquad\qquad Q = kAH/L$ for flow of water through soil.

where $\qquad Q$ = volume of water, cubic feet per minute.

$\qquad\qquad k$ = coefficient of permeability, Table II.

$\qquad\qquad A$ = area in square feet of cross section.

$\qquad H/L$ = hydraulic gradient, where H is the head of water and L is the length of the flow path.

Determination of Seepage Line

The determination of the seepage line is important to an engineer. Usual solutions are by guess or models.

The following solution proposed by A. Casagrande is theoretical and not to be relied on because soils lack uniform flow properties in all directions. However, it is included as a scientific guess.

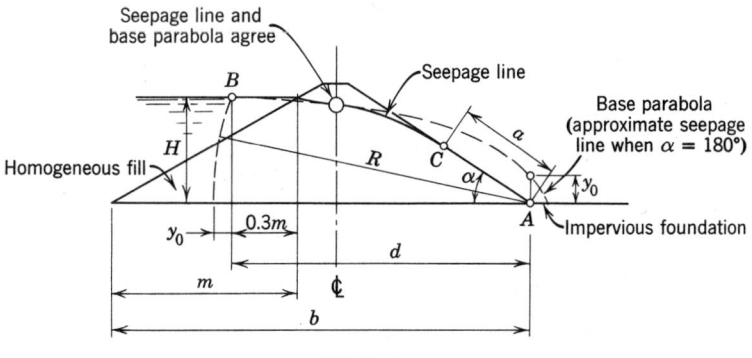

FIG. 3.

Procedure to find *d*: Lay off

$$d = b - 0.7m$$

Location of *C*: Solve equation $a = \sqrt{d^2 + H^2} - \sqrt{d^2 - H^2}\,\cot \alpha$

For other points, compute values as indicated in drawing.

Quantity of seepage per foot of dam

$\qquad\qquad Q = k\,(\sqrt{H^2 + d^2} - d) \qquad$ when $\alpha > 30°$

$\qquad\qquad Q = ka \sin^2 \alpha \qquad\qquad\quad$ when $\alpha < 30°$

For values of *k*, see Table II.

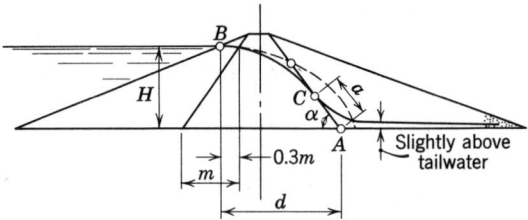

FIG. 4. LOCATION OF SEEPAGE LINE FOR COMPOSITE FILL.

A pervious foundation does not alter the seepage characteristics of a dam but additional seepage through the foundation must be anticipated.

Determination of Seepage by Means of Flow Nets

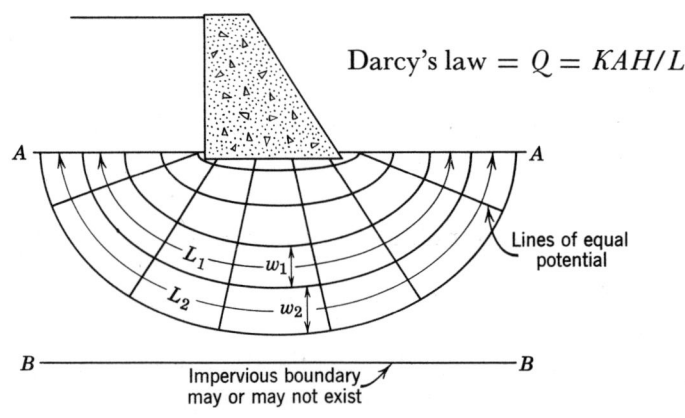

Darcy's law $= Q = KAH/L$

FIG. 5.

Concept: Divide flow net path into widths of approximately equal flow. From Darcy's Law, $w_1/w_2 = L_2/L_1$.

Seepage: Seepage in any path, say $w_1 = kw_1H/L$.

Flow Net: Flow net is constructed by sketching in the probable paths of seepage lines under a structure.

(1) To assist, one has the boundaries *A-A* and *B-B*. Flow lines end at right angles to *A-A* and are parallel to *B-B*.

(2) Equal potential lines, not discussed here, drawn at right angles to flow lines represent a further aid in drawing flow nets.

Red Lights

1. Accumulation of flow lines as per Fig. 6, may cause a washout.

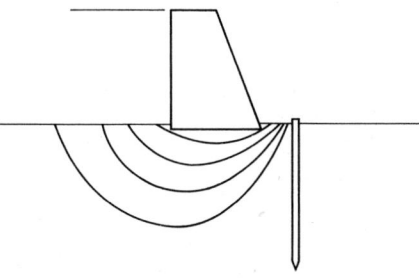

FIG. 6.

2. Seepage lines intersecting the downstream slope of earth dams may cause erosion.   See dotted line Fig. A, Plate VIII.

NOTE: Full lines represent flow lines after addition of special feature; dotted lines before.

The lines of percolation tend to slough off slope because of saturation.
Remedy: A reverse filter, or rock toe with a drain.

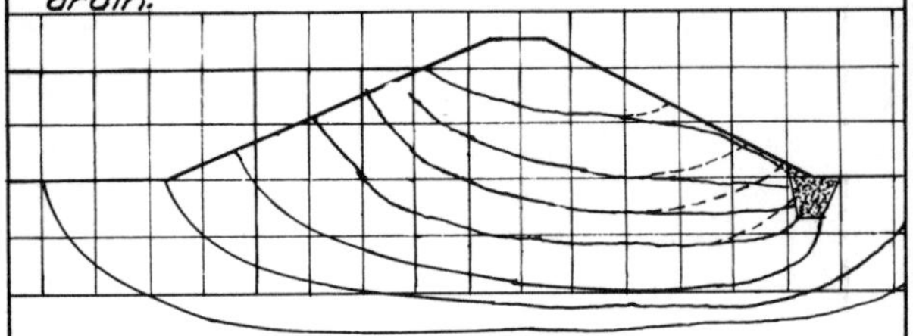

FIG. A - EFFECT OF FILTER AT TOE OF SLOPE.*

Additional fill placed on top of down-stream slope does not remedy a saturated toe.

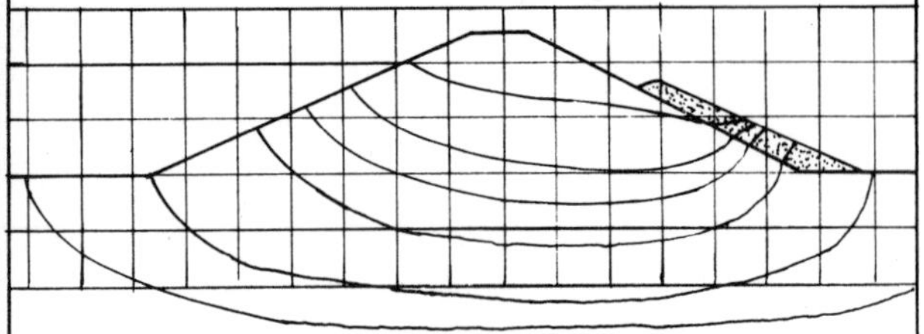

FIG. B - INCORRECT REMEDY EFFECT OF ADDED MATERIAL.*

Note improvement in flow lines at toe.

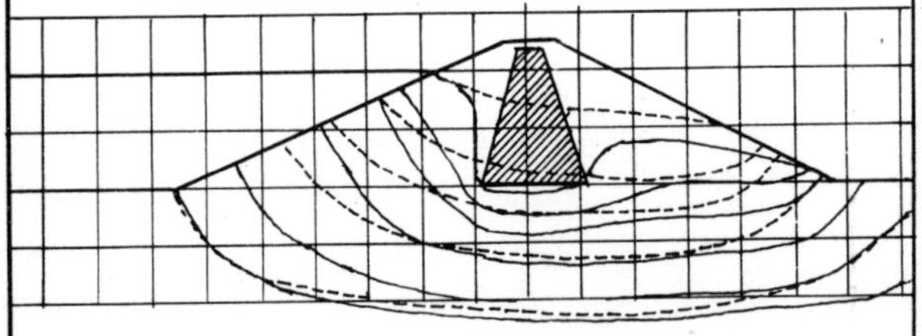

FIG. C - EFFECT OF IMPERVIOUS CORE ON PATH OF PERCOLATION.*

Increased flow concentration at toe is offset by reduced flow pressure.

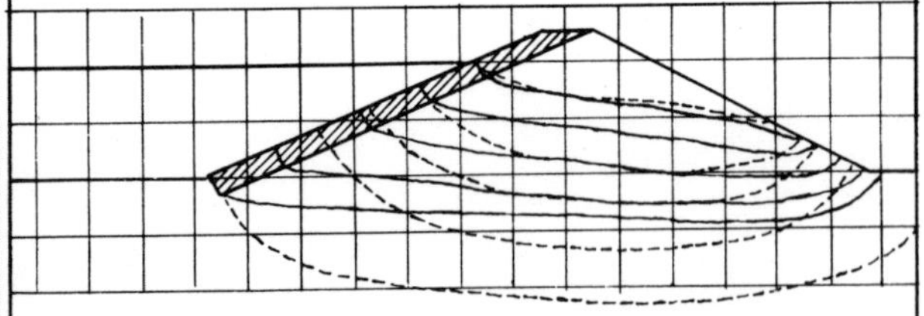

FIG. D - EFFECT OF IMPERVIOUS BLANKET ON UPSTREAM SLOPE.*

Increased flow concentration at toe is offset by reduced flow pressure.

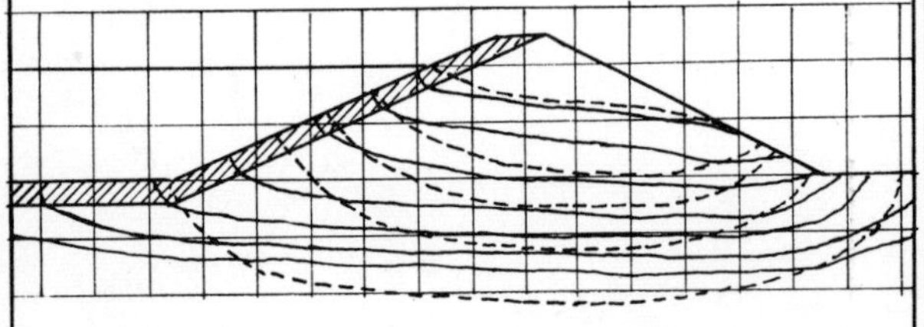

FIG. E - EFFECT OF IMPERVIOUS BLANKET ON UPSTREAM SLOPE & BOTTOM.*

Permeable embankment acts to support the core wall, and as a drain for water percolating through the core.

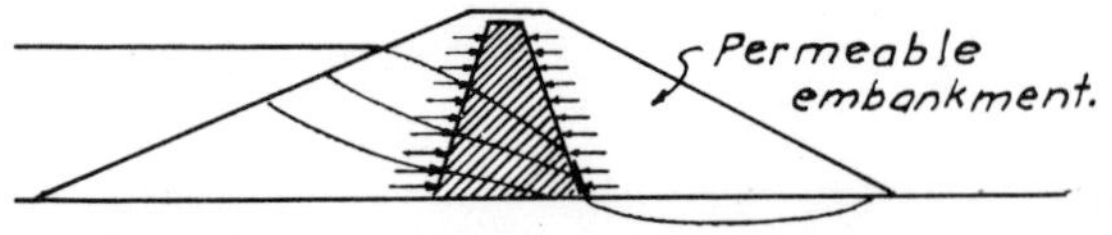

Permeable embankment.

FIG. G - SHOWING HOW CORE WALL IS SUPPORTED BY ADJACENT SLOPES.

Where foundation is pervious, a reverse filter and drain below ground level to carry off water stabilizes embankment by lowering the water table.

Lines of seepage

For design of reverse filter - see Plate X.

Pervious foundation

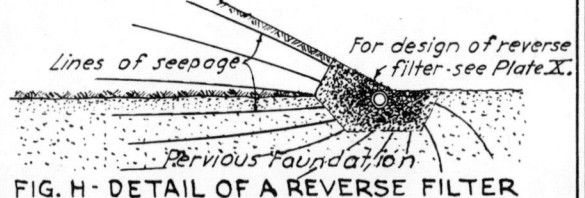

FIG. H - DETAIL OF A REVERSE FILTER AT TOE OF SLOPE.

A slight amount of settlement causes pressure on sheet-piling breaking it or shearing the masonry.

The effect of the cut off is to lengthen the path of seepage.

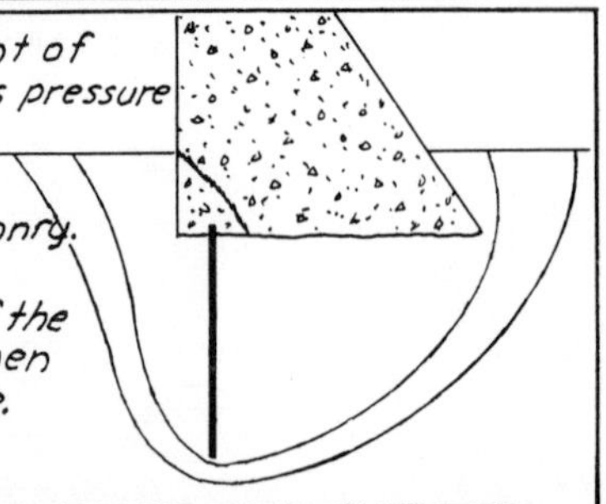

FIG. J - DANGER OF SHEET-PILE CUT OFF UNDER HEEL OF DAM.

*Adapted from Low Dams by National Resources Comm.

PLATE VIII.

TABLE II - COEFFICIENTS OF PERMEABILITY (k) in ft./min. for 60°F.

EFFECTIVE SIZE	Porosity = $\frac{e}{1+e}$						EFFECTIVE SIZE	Porosity = $\frac{e}{1+e}$				
	30 percent	32 percent	34 percent	36 percent	38 percent	40 percent		42 percent	44 percent	46 percent	48 percent	50 percent
0.01	0.00003	0.00004	0.00005	0.000060	0.000072	0.000085	0.01	0.000101	0.000123	0.000149	0.000181	0.000215
0.02	.00013	.00016	.00020	.000239	.000286	.000339	0.02	.000405	.000492	.000597	.000724	.000861
0.03	.00030	.00036	.00045	.000538	.000645	.000763	0.03	.000911	.00111	.00134	.00163	.00194
0.04	.00053	.00065	.00079	.000958	.001145	.001355	0.04	.00162	.00197	.00239	.00290	.00344
0.05	.00082	.00101	.00124	.001495	.001790	.002120	0.05	.00253	.00307	.00373	.00452	.00538
0.06	.00118	.00146	.00178	.002150	.002580	.003050	0.06	.00364	.00442	.00537	.00652	.00775
0.07	.00161	.00198	.00243	.002930	.003510	.004155	0.07	.00496	.00602	.00732	.00887	.0105
0.08	.00211	.00259	.00218	.003825	.004585	.005425	0.08	.00647	.00787	.00956	.0116	.0138
0.09	.00266	.00328	.00402	.004845	.005800	.006860	0.09	.00820	.00995	.0121	.0147	.0174
0.10	.00328	.00405	.00496	.005980	.007170	.008480	0.10	.0101	.0123	.0149	.0181	.0215
0.12	.00473	.00583	.00713	.008620	.01032	.01220	0.12	.0146	.0177	.0215	.0261	.0310
0.14	.00643	.00794	.00972	.01172	.01404	.01662	0.14	.0198	.0241	.0293	.0355	.0422
0.15	.00739	.00912	.01115	.01345	.01611	.01910	0.15	.0228	.0277	.0336	.0407	.0484
0.16	.00841	.01036	.01268	.01531	.01835	.02170	0.16	.0259	.0315	.0382	.0463	.0551
0.18	.01064	.01311	.01605	.01940	.02320	.02745	0.18	.0328	.0398	.0484	.0586	.0697
0.20	.01315	.0162	.01983	.02390	.02865	.03390	0.20	.0405	.0492	.0597	.0724	.0861
0.25	.020	.0253	.03100	.03740	.04480	.05300	0.25	.0632	.0768	.0933	.113	.134
0.30	.0296	.0364	.04460	.05380	.06450	.07630	0.30	.0911	.111	.134	.163	.194
0.35	.0403	.0496	.0608	.07330	.08790	.1039	0.35	.124	.151	.183	.222	.264
0.40	.0527	.0648	.07940	.09575	.1145	.1355	0.40	.162	.197	.239	.290	.344
0.45	.0665	.0820	.1005	.1211	.1450	.1718	0.45	.205	.249	.302	.366	.436
0.50	.0822	.1012	.1240	.1495	.1780	.2120	0.50	.253	.307	.373	.452	.538
0.55	.0994	.1225	.1500	.1810	.2165	.2565	0.55	.306	.372	.452	.547	.651
0.60	.1182	.1458	.1784	.2150	.2580	.3050	0.60	.364	.442	.537	.652	.775
0.65	.1390	.1710	.2095	.2530	.3030	.3580	0.65	.428	.519	.631	.765	.909
0.70	.1610	.1983	.2430	.2930	.3510	.4155	0.70	.496	.602	.732	.887	1.05
0.75	.1850	.2278	.2785	.3365	.4030	.4770	0.75	.569	.691	.840	1.02	1.21
0.80	.2105	.2590	.3175	.3825	.4585	.5425	0.80	.648	.787	.956	1.16	1.38
0.85	.2375	.2925	.3580	.4325	.5175	.6125	0.85	.731	.888	1.08	1.31	1.55
0.90	.2660	.3280	.4018	.4845	.5800	.6860	0.90	.820	.995	1.21	1.47	1.74
0.95	.2965	.3650	.4470	.5400	.6460	.7650	0.95	.913	1.11	1.35	1.63	1.94
1.00	.3282	.4050	.4960	.5880	.7170	.8480	1.00	1.01	1.23	1.49	1.81	2.15
2.00	1.315	1.620	1.983	2.390	2.865	3.390	2.00	4.05	4.92	5.97	7.24	8.61
3.00	2.960	3.640	4.460	5.380	6.450	7.630	3.00	9.11	11.1	13.4	16.3	19.4
4.00	5.270	6.480	7.940	9.575	11.45	13.55	4.00	16.2	19.7	23.9	29.0	34.4
5.00	8.220	10.12	12.40	14.95	17.90	21.20	5.00	25.3	30.7	37.3	45.2	53.8

TABLE III — TEMPERATURE CORRECTIONS TO TABLE II.
See below for use of table.

TEMP. IN °F.	t_c
32	0.64
35	.67
40	.73
45	.80
50	.86
55	0.93
60	1.00
65	1.08
70	1.15
75	1.23
80	1.30
85	1.39
90	1.47
95	1.55
100	1.64

Use of Table III.

If temperature is other than 60°F., multiply k value in Table II by value of t_c opposite applicable temperature in Table III.

* Adapted from *Low Dams* by National Resources Committee.

EMBANKMENT SHRINKAGE

CASE I – *Yield of borrow in finished embankment.*

Volume = $\frac{Weight}{Density}$: *Volume varies inversely as density.*

Assume $\begin{cases} borrow\ pit\ dry\ density = 110\ lbs.\ per\ cu.ft. \\ embankment\ dry\ density = 125\ lbs.\ per\ cu.ft. \end{cases}$

Then 1 cu.yd. of borrow will yield 110/125 cu.yd. embankment.

CASE II – *Shrinkage after embankment compaction.*
This will be zero if embankment is compacted to maximum density.
In ordinary practice, i.e. power equipment wheel compaction - no rollers,
no moisture control - it may be taken as:
  Sand and gravel - 1 to 2%* —   Clay or loam - 2 to 3%*
Certain deposits such as expansive clays swell in embankments.

CASE III – *Loss by waste, of improper material such as top soil or muck,
should be allowed for.*

TABLE IV – VOLUME OF BORROW REQUIRED FOR 1 CU.YD. OF EMBANKMENT.
(Empirical rules for use where densities are not obtainable. Power
equipment wheel compaction, not rolled.)

Gravel	1.09*	1.12**	Light sandy earth	1.14*	1.20**
Gravel and sand	1.10*	1.13**	Vegetable surface soil	1.18*	1.24**
Clay and clayey earth	1.11*	1.15**	Ledge rock		0.70**

PERMEABILITY See also Tables II and III.

TABLE V – PERMEABILITY DATA.‡

	Turbulent flow →	COEFFICIENT OF PERMEABILITY (K) in cm. per sec. (Log scale)					Perfect validity of Darcy's law
k =	10^2 10^1 1.0	10^{-1} 10^{-2} 10^{-3}	10^{-4} 10^{-5} 10^{-6}			10^{-7} 10^{-8} 10^{-9}	
DRAINAGE PROPERTY	Good drainage		Poor drainage			Practically impervious	
APPLICATION IN EARTH DAMS AND DIKES	Pervious sections of dams and dikes		Impervious sections of earth dams and dikes				
TYPES OF SOIL	Clean Gravel	Clean sands; Clean sand & gravel Mixtures	Very fine sands; Organic & inorganic silts; mixtures of sand, silt & clay; glacial till; stratified clay deposits; etc.			"Impervious" soils e.g. homogeneous clays below zone of weathering	
			"Impervious soils" which are modified by the effects of vegetation and weathering				
DIRECT DETERMINATION of coefficient of permeability	Direct testing of soil in its original position (e.g. well points) if properly conducted - reliable - considerable experience required						
	CONSTANT HEAD PERMEAMETER Little experience required						
		Reliable Little experience required	FALLING HEAD PERMEAMETER Unreliable Much experience necessary for correct interpretation			Fairly reliable Considerable experience necessary	
INDIRECT DETERMINATION of coefficient of permeability	COMPUTATION from the grain size distribution (e.g. Hazen's formula) only applicable to clean cohesionless sands & gravels						
			HORIZONTAL CAPILLARITY TEST Very little experience necessary. Especially useful for rapid testing of a large number of samples in the field without Lab. facilities			COMPUTATIONS from consolidation tests; expensive Lab. equip. & considerable experience required	

* From Am. C.E. Handbook by Merriman & Niggin. ** In accordance with modern highway practice.
‡ Adapted from Publication Nº 268, Harvard Grad. School of Eng.

PLATE IX.

"While nature is a fickle jade, she is far kinder to those who study her laws." *Lazarus White and Edmund Astley Prentis.*

Quick material occurs where particles are floated by upward hydraulic force. This occurs in sand approximately where:

$$\frac{Loss\ of\ Head}{Horizontal\ Distance} = 1\ (See\ Plate\ III\ for\ Flotation\ Gradient).$$

Quick material tends to lose its supporting power.

Bulls liver is fine sand which retains water and is quaky - 0.005 to 0.01 m m., requires only a small volume of water to boil. Coarse sands require a large volume of water to boil.

Flow nets are obtained by models and/or by analysis. This preparation requires special skill.

The reverse filter allows added stability under greater head of water.

Used to assist in excavation below ground water level.

Use with caution.

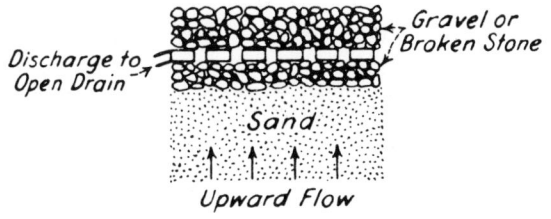

FIG. A · REVERSE FILTER.*

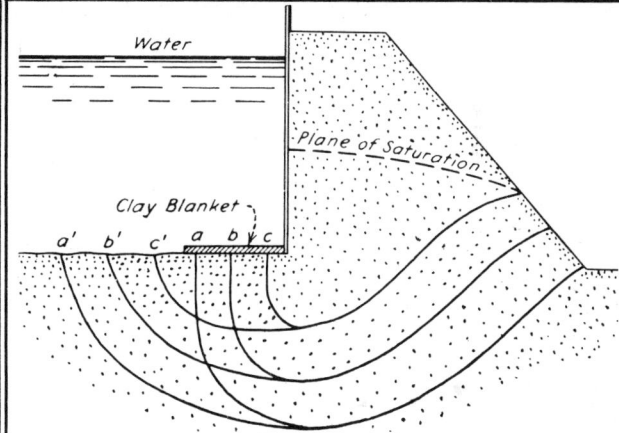

FIG. B · ILLUSTRATING SMALL EFFECT OF CLAY BLANKET IN A COFFERDAM.*

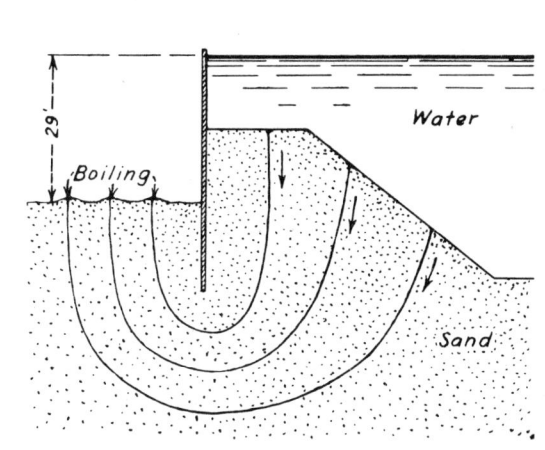

FIG. C · ILLUSTRATING INCORRECT PLACING OF BERM IN A COFFERDAM.*

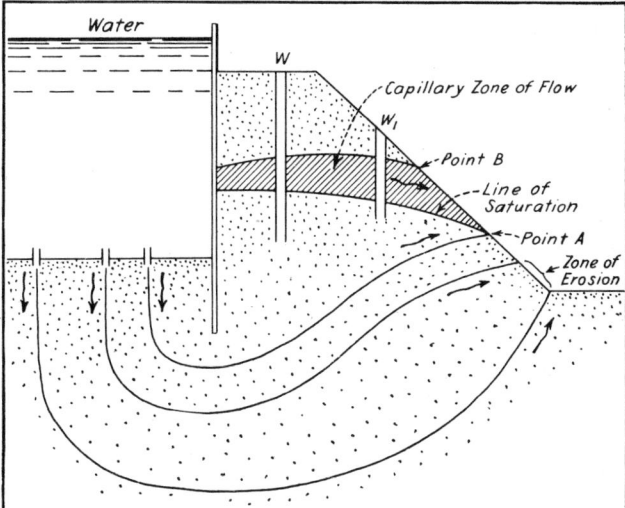

FIG. D · ILLUSTRATING CORRECT PLACING OF BERM IN A COFFERDAM.*

*Adapted from White & Prentis, Cofferdams, By permission of Columbia University Press.

PLATE X.

Stability of Earth Dams

Discussion

A sudden drawdown affects the upstream triangle, since the earth cannot drain as fast as the reservoir. The pressure from the saturated earth is greater than that from the dry earth of construction. The downstream triangle must likewise be analyzed for the earth pressure from the upstream side plus hydrostatic pressure within the dam up to the seepage line. In the following problem illustrating these forces a factor of safety of 2 for the total shear and a factor of safety of 1.5 for the maximum shear have been used. If the more exact method of the most dangerous circle were used, see p. 14–3 on embankments, the factor of safety of 1.5 could be used.

Problem. Check of Dam Stability

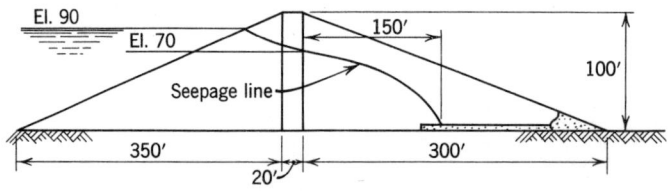

FIG. 7.

Given: Dam of homogeneous granular material with filter.

Damp weight of soil	120 lb./cu. ft.
Saturated weight of soil	135 lb./cu. ft.
Buoyant weight of soil	72.5 lb./cu. ft.

Angle of internal friction $\phi = 28°$ $\sin \phi = .470$ $\dfrac{1 - \sin \phi}{1 + \sin \phi} = .36$

$$\tan \phi = .531$$

Analysis of downstream triangle

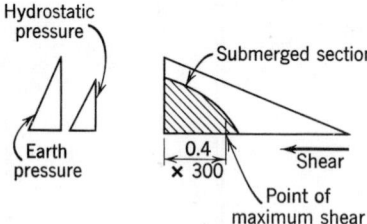

Earth pressure   FIG. 8.

Mean weight $= \dfrac{30 \times 120 + 70 \times 72.5}{100} = 86.8$ lb./cu. ft.

Pressure $= \frac{1}{2}wh^2 \dfrac{1 - \sin \phi}{1 + \sin \phi} = \frac{1}{2} \times 86.8 \times 100^2 \times .36 = 158{,}000$ lb.

Water pressure $= \dfrac{1}{2} \times 62.5 \times 70^2 = 154{,}000$ lb.

Total horizontal force $= 158^k + 154^k = 312^k$

Resisting forces

Area of triangle = $\dfrac{100 \times 300}{2}$ = 15,000 sq. ft.

Area of submerged parabola $70 \times 150 \times \dfrac{2}{3}$ = 7,000 sq. ft.

Moist material 8,000 sq. ft.

Total vertical force 8000×120 = 960,000

7000×72.5 = 508,000

 1,468,000 lb.

Total resisting force = $1468^k \tan \phi$ *

$= 1468 \times 0.531 = 780^k$

Factor of safety = $780/312$ = 2.50

Maximum unit shear occurs at the 0.4 point and is twice the average

$$\frac{312}{300} \times 2 = 2.08^k/\text{sq. ft.}$$

At this point the vertical load is $50 \times 120 + 10 \times 73 = 6730$

Horizontal resistance is $6730 \times \tan \phi = 3570$

Factor of safety $\dfrac{3570}{2080} = 1.71$ *

The downstream slope could be shortened if the soil can stand a steeper slope. With $\phi = 28°$ it probably could be.

Analysis of upstream triangle

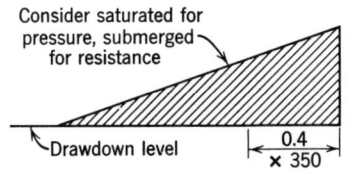

FIG. 9.

Pressure = $\frac{1}{2} \times 135 \times 100^2 \times 0.36 = 246,000$ lb.

Resistance: Vertical load = $\dfrac{350}{2} \times 100 \times 72.5 = 1,270,000$

Resisting force = $1270^k \times \tan \phi = 674^k$

Factor of safety $674/246$ = 2.73

Maximum shear $\dfrac{246}{350} \times 2 = 1.41^k/\text{sq. ft.}$

Resistance $60 \times 73 \times \tan \phi = 2.32$ lb./sq. ft.

Factor of safety = $2.32/1.41$ = 1.65

---

* The value of the unit shear should, of course, be checked by shear test; see p. 13–18.

Shear and Settlement below the Dam

The earth dam is an embankment and should be treated as such. The allowable pressure on soils has been given on p. 3–5. The underlying soil should be checked for shear by the most dangerous circle method. A more complete analysis of embankments is given in Chapter 14. The following formula by Leo Jorgenson is often used to check shear in soft, plastic soils. It holds true only when a is less than $\frac{1}{2}L$.

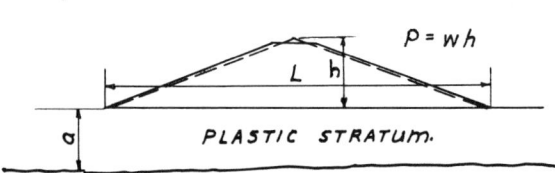

$$S = \frac{P \times a}{L} \quad \text{(Applies only to plastic soils).} \, \circledast$$

Assumes equivalent $\triangle$ cross-section.
S = Maximum unit shear - lb. per sq. in.
P = Maximum unit pressure - lb. per sq. in.
For very approx. limits for S see Table $\overline{VI}$.

FIG. 10 – FOUNDATIONS OF PLASTIC MATERIAL.

TABLE $\overline{VI}$. SOIL SHEAR VALUES.		
SOIL.	COHESION PER SQ. FT.	ANGLE OF INTERNAL FRICTION, ϕ
Clay - Liquid. **	100	0°
" - Very Soft **	200	2°
" - Soft **	400	4°
" - Fairly Stiff **	1,000	6°
" - Very Stiff **	2,000	12°
Sand - Wet **	0	10°
" - Dry or Unmoved **	0	34°
Silt. ***	0	20°±
Cemented Sand & Gravel-Wet.*	500	34°
" " " " - Dry.*	1000	34°
Shear Strength = Cohesion + W tan ϕ. Apply a safety factor of 2. Actual determination from soil analysis is advisable.		

$\circledast$ From The Application of Theories of Elasticity and Plasticity to Foundation Problems by Leo Jürgenson, J. Boston Soc. C. Es. July 1934.   ** Adapted from Hogentogler, Engineering Properties of Soils, McGraw-Hill, Based on quick shear test.* *** By author.

Settlement of the dam may occur from consolidation of a soft layer below. It may be computed on the basis of soil consolidation tests of samples as follows:

Basis for computing settlement:

$$\text{Settlement} = \frac{e_1 - e_2}{1 + e_1} \times h$$

where e_1 = void ratio before consolidation.
e_2 = void ratio after consolidation.
h = thickness of layer in feet.

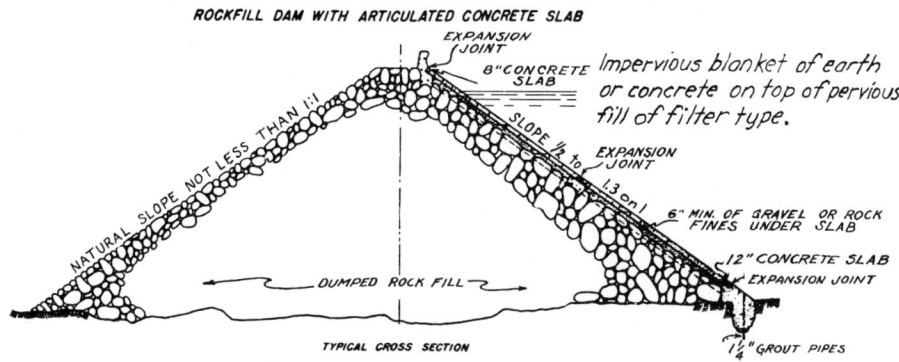

FIG. 11.   ROCK FILL DAMS.*

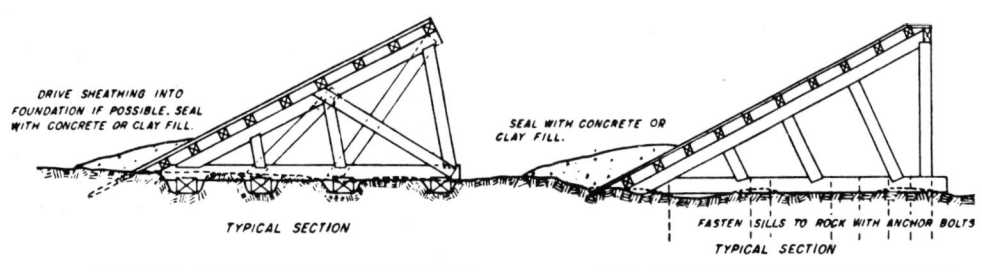

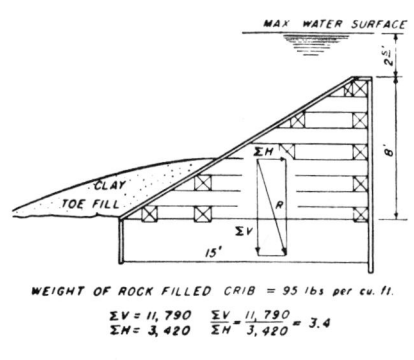

FIG. 12.   LOG CRIB DAMS.*

* Adapted from Low Dams by National Resources Comm.

RESERVOIRS

Earth reservoirs are designed in the same way as earth dams. Often, however, reservoirs are covered tanks as shown in Fig. 13.

Note: For Figs. D–M see Plate XI.

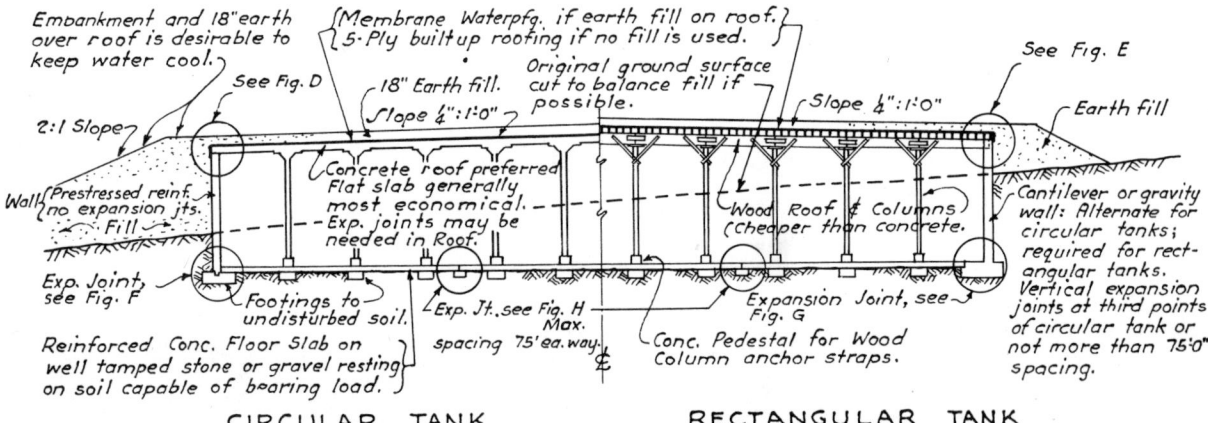

SECTION THRU TANK TYPE RESERVOIR—CIRCULAR OR RECTANGULAR

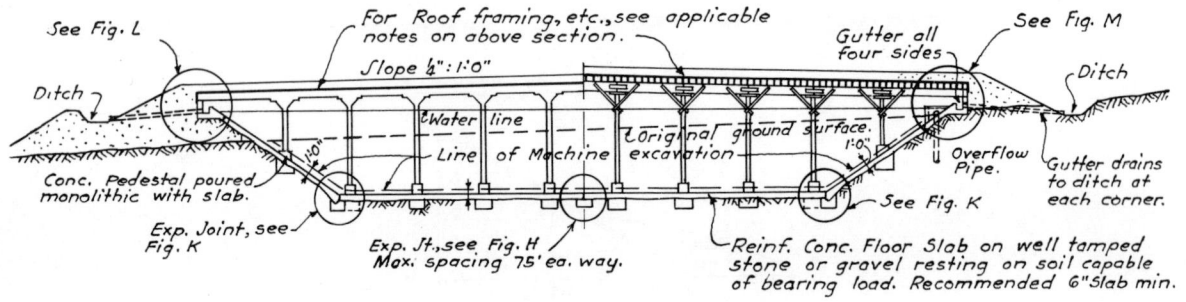

SECTION THRU PAVED CAVITY TYPE RESERVOIR

FIG. 13.

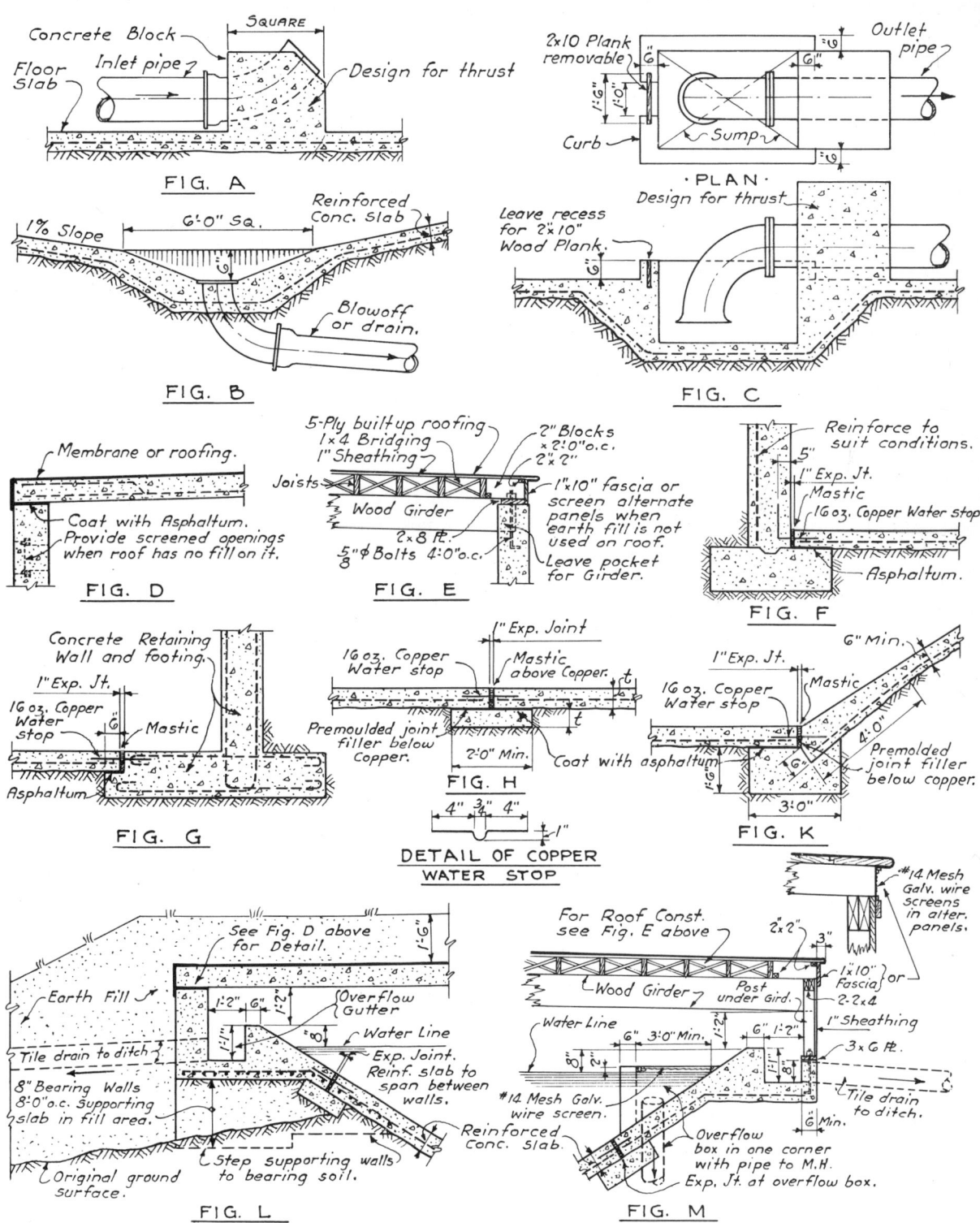

FIG. A

FIG. B

PLAN

FIG. C

FIG. D

FIG. E

FIG. F

FIG. G

FIG. H

DETAIL OF COPPER WATER STOP

FIG. K

FIG. L

FIG. M

NOTE: For location of above Figures see Fig. 13.

PLATE XI.

DISCUSSION

Seepage. In earth dams an impervious core wall may be used to prevent loss through the dam. This core wall should extend downward far enough to seal the dam. No matter how good the core wall is, some water will be lost through the dam. This water, as it emerges on the downstream side, will cause boils in silty soils, quickly eroding the base of the bank. The use of proper filters permits the water to escape without disturbing the soil.

Even with masonry dams, water may pass under or around them, causing loss of water and boils. Sometimes a filter is needed here. Cutoffs driven under the heel lengthen the line of flow, resulting in less loss. The figures showing the flow nets should be studied to see the possible routes of escaping water.

In selecting the site, investigate the reservoir area for possible routes of water loss. Limestone layers may contain channels and sink holes permitting loss of water.

The leakage under the dam causes uplift as mentioned before. Also, this leakage may wash out certain soluble rocks or fine sands undermining the dam. The amount of this leakage varies in some proportion to the head.

Choice of type of dam requires an economic study. Soils and geologic studies also are required, particularly for the higher dams. Obviously, the higher the dam the more strongly a rock foundation and masonry dam are indicated. However, earth dams on soil foundations have been built up to a height of 425 ft.*

Geological consultation may be of great value to the engineer to understand the geological formation of the site, but the decisions which involve the mechanics of solids, soils, and hydraulics should be made by the engineer.

RED LIGHTS

1. Watch out for weak planes of slip, such as thin layers of silt or sand, which may irrigate the soil and weaken its shearing resistance.

2. Water seeping through cut slopes or sudden drawdowns such as a tidal drop produce unbalanced hydraulic pressure as well as weakening the shearing resistance.

3. The angle, ϕ, of internal friction is lower for saturated soils than for moist soils, thus increasing active pressure and decreasing passive resistance.

4. Concrete will heat in setting; low-setting cements, class II, are desirable.

5. Avoid "creep" of water through soil of concrete dam foundation which may develop into a "sleeve" or destructive current.

6. Do not neglect upward pressure on a masonry dam foundation.

7. Design upstream face for sudden drawdown which may cause upstream slide before pore water in dam has drained off.

8. Avoid overtopping of earth dams by adequate spillway.

9. Avoid seepage through surface of downstream slope by filters or flattening slope.

10. Protect surface against wave erosion.

11. Provide against settlement fissuring an embankment.

---

* Mud Mountain, Wash., from *Engineering for Dams,*—Vol. 3, by Justin, Hinds, and Creager, John Wiley & Sons, 1945.

12. Avoid settlement due to squeezing out of water in deep layers of clay or plastic material by the excess weight of the structure imposed. This is more likely to occur under large fills of considerable area than under buildings where the added weight at lower depth may be inconsiderable because of distribution.

13. Overloading of foundation by an embankment of soft material or peat or dense silt matter will cause a flow out and rise, popularly known as a mud wave.

8

Evaluation of Bearing
Power of Soil

FOUNDATION REPORT CHECK LIST

I. *Site History.*
  (*a*) Geological history.
  (*b*) Points of interest in the past on site usage.

II. *Site Plan.*
  (*a*) Location of existing structures.
  (*b*) Location of physical features such as:
    Outcropping rock.
    Swales.
    Forestation.
    Water bodies.
  (*c*) Location of test pits, borings, load tests, or other subsurface explorations.

III. *Subsurface Exploration.*
  (*a*) Log of borings and test pits.
  (*b*) Analysis and description of samples.
  (*c*) Soil profile.
  (*d*) Results of test loads.
  (*e*) Indications of preload as based on undisturbed samples.
  (*f*) Indications of behavior of existing structures either on the site or adjoining the site.
  (*g*) Data on ground water, past and present.

IV. *Economic Studies.*

  Different types of foundations which appear to be adapted to this site should be made the subject of tentative designs and cost estimates to assist in selection of the proper type of foundation.

V. *Suggestions and Recommendations.*

EVALUATION

The bearing power of soil may be evaluated by:

1. Reference to Plate I after identification. Identification may be made by (*a*) visual inspection; (*b*) screen tests. See p. 13–36.

2. Observed penetration of standard spoon with standard ram. See Plate I.

3. Plate load test. See p. 15–31.

4. Extrusion theory. See p. 13–22.

Fig. 1, Plate I, is a study of the pressures on sand which are sufficient to limit the settlement of a footing to 1 in. This appears to be ultraconservative in the lower limits of N.

TABLE-I CLASSIFICATION OF SUPPORTING SOILS

Class	Material	Maximum allowable presumptive bearing values in tons per square foot
1	Hard sound rock	60
2	Medium hard rock	40
3	Hardpan overlaying rock	12
4	Compact gravel and boulder-gravel formations; very compact sandy gravel	10
5	Soft rock	8
6	Loose gravel and sandy gravel; compact sand and gravelly sand; very compact sand-inorganic silt soils	6
7	Hard dry consolidated clay	5
8	Loose coarse to medium sand; medium compact fine sand	4
9	Compact sand-clay soils	3
10	Loose fine sand; medium compact sand-inorganic silt soils	2
11	Firm or stiff clay	1.5
12	Loose saturated sand-clay soils; medium soft clay	1

Explanation of Terms
Compaction Related to Spoon Blows; Sand

Descriptive Term	Blows/Foot	Remarks
Loose	15 or less	These figures approximate for medium sand, 2½-inch spoon, 300-pound hammer, 18-inch fall. Coarser soil requires more blows, finer material, fewer blows.
Compact	16 to 50	
Very compact	50 or more	

Consistency Related to Spoon Blows; Mud. Clay, Etc.

Descriptive Term	Blows/Foot	Remarks
Very soft	push to 2	Molded with relatively slight finger pressure.
Soft	3 to 10	
Stiff	11 to 30	Molded with substantial finger pressure; might be removed by spading.
Hard	30 or more	Not molded by fingers, or with extreme difficulty; might require picking for removal.

Soil Sizes

Descriptive Term	Pass Sieve Number	Retained Sieve Number	Size Range
Clay	200	Hydrometer	.006 mm.
Silt	200	analysis	.006 to .074 mm.
Fine sand	65	200	.074 to .208 mm.
Medium sand	28	65	.208 to .589 mm.
Coarse sand	8	28	.589 to 2.362 mm.
Gravel	—	8	2.362 mm.
Pebble	—	—	2.362 mm. to 2½"
Cobble	—	—	2½" to 6"
Boulder	—	—	6"

TABLE-II PROPOSED BEARING VALUES FOR CLAY [**]

N = number of blows per foot in standard penetration test.
q_u = unconfined compressive strength in tons per sq. ft.
q_d = ultimate bearing capacity of continuous footing in tons/□′
q_{ds} = ultimate bearing capacity of square footing in tons/□′
q_a = proposed normal allowable bearing value in tons/□′ (G_s = 3)
q_a' = proposed maximum tolerable bearing value in tons/□′ (G_s = 2)
G_s = factor of safety with respect to base failure.

1. Standard Penetration Test = 140″ weight, 30″ drop, 2 o.d. sampler

Description of Clay	N	q_u	q_d	q_{ds}	q_a Square 1.2q_u	q_a Cont. 0.9q_u	q_a' Square 1.8q_u	q_a' Cont. 1.3q_u
Very Soft [*]	Less than 2	less than 0.25	less than 0.71	less than 0.92	less than 0.30	less than 0.22	less than 0.45	less than 0.32
Soft [*]	2 to 4	0.25 to 0.50	0.71 to 1.42	0.92 to 1.85	0.30 to 0.60	0.22 to 0.45	0.45 to 0.90	0.32 to 0.65
Medium	4 to 8	0.50 to 1.00	1.42 to 2.85	1.85 to 3.70	0.60 to 1.20	0.45 to 0.90	0.90 to 1.80	0.65 to 1.30
Stiff	8 to 15	1.00 to 2.00	2.85 to 5.70	3.70 to 7.40	1.20 to 2.40	0.90 to 1.80	1.80 to 3.60	1.30 to 2.60
Very Stiff	15 to 30	2.00 to 4.00	5.70 to 11.40	7.40 to 14.80	2.40 to 4.80	1.80 to 3.60	3.60 to 7.20	2.60 to 5.20
Hard	Over 30	Over 4.00	Over 11.40	Over 14.80	Over 4.80	Over 3.60	Over 7.20	Over 5.20

[*] If clay is normally loaded settlement can be important even under smallest allowable soil pressure.

FIG. I SAND BEARING CURVES [**]

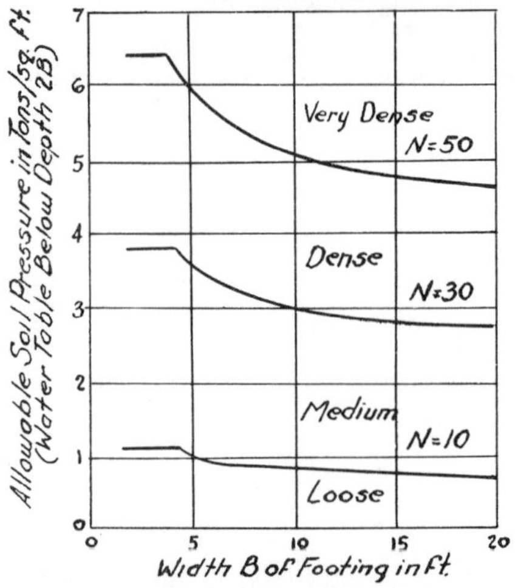

Allowable Soil Pressure in Tons/sq. ft. (Water Table Below Depth 2B)

Very Dense N=50
Dense N=30
Medium N=10
Loose

Width B of Footing in ft.

[*] Adapted from N.Y.C. Building Code, 1951
[**] From "Soil Mechanics in Engineering Practice" Terzaghi & Peck, John Wiley, 1948

PLATE I.

TABLE III

SUPPLEMENTARY BEARING VALUES

Type of Rock	Bearing [1] Capacity	Remarks
Igneous [2] such as trap, granite, basalt, lava	20–60	Usually *hard*.[3] Does not erode or dissolve readily. Subject to cleavage planes and bed planes at all angles.
Sedimentary [4] such as		
Limestone	10–20	*Medium hard*[3] as in limestone to *soft*[3] as in
Shale	8–10	chalks and shales. Subject to dissolving ero-
Chalk	8	sion, forming of caves. Soft layers and seams,
Coral	8	soft overburden. Bed planes generally hori-
Sandstone	10–20	zontal.
Metamorphic[5] such as		
Gneiss	20–40	Gneiss and schist have igneous characteristics;
Schist	20–40	slate and marble have sedimentary.
Marble	10–20	
Slate	8	

---

[1] Bearing capacity of rocks suggested by author. Tons per square foot.
[2] *Igneous:* derived from the interior of the earth in a molten condition by heat, pressure, and volcanic action.
[3] Approximate correlation to the *hard, medium hard,* and *soft* classification given before.
[4] *Sedimentary:* deposited in layers by water and cemented by the pressure of overburden.
[5] *Metamorphic:* heat, pressure, and chemically active fluids have acted to impart new characteristics to the rocks.

CLASSIFICATION — VISUAL AND SIEVE

Soil Bearing Classification. Soil is usually identified for foundation purposes as:

Hardpan. Hardpan overlying rock is a natural deposit of a hard cemented mixture of sand and pebbles or of sand, pebbles, and clay, with or without boulders, and difficult to remove by picking.

Gravel. Rounded or water-worn pebbles. No cohesion. No plasticity. Gritty and granular. Crunchy under foot. As a soil, over 1/10 in. in size.

Sand. Granular, gritty, loose grains, passing No. 10 * and retained on No. 270 sieve. Individual grains readily seen and felt. No plasticity or cohesion. When dry, a cast formed in the hands will fall apart. When moist, a cast will crumble when touched. The coarse grains are rounded; the fine grains are visible and angular.

Silt. Fine, barely visible grains, passing No. 270 sieve and over 0.005 mm. in size. Merges upward into a fine sand and downward into a clay. No cohesion. A dried cast is easily crushed in the hands. Permeable; movement of water through voids occurs easily and is visible. When mixed with water the grains will settle in from 30 minutes to 1 hour. Feels gritty when bitten. Will not form a ribbon. Difficult to distinguish fine sand from silt and fine silt from clay.

---

* ASTM Sieve Designation.

Clay. Invisible particles under 0.005 mm. Grains are submicroscopic in size but still minerals the same as sand. Cohesive. Highly plastic when moist. When pinched between the fingers will form a long, thin, flexible ribbon. Can be rolled into a thread to a pin point. When bitten with the teeth will not feel gritty. Will form hard lumps or clods when dry. Impermeable; no movement of water apparent through voids. Will remain suspended in water from 3 hours to infinity.

Muck and Organic Silt. Thoroughly decomposed material with considerable mineral soil material. Usually black, with a few fibrous remains. Odorous when dried and burnt. Found as deposits in swamps, peat bogs, and muskeg. Easily identified. May contain some sand or silt.

Peat. Partly decayed plant material. Mostly organic. Highly fibrous with visible plant remains.

Varved clay consists of alternate layers of gray inorganic silt and darker layers of clay. Layers thicker than 0.5 in. rarely occur. Likely to have the objectionable qualities of both clays and silts.

For a scientific soil classification see also Chapter 13, Soil Mechanics.

IDENTIFICATION OF ROCK

Granite is a coarse-grained, hard, igneous rock in which the different minerals give a speckled appearance.

True granite contains the following elements:

Quartz—a clear, hard crystal.

Feldspar, which looks like a yellowish tooth.

Hornblende—hard, black, shiny.

Mica—thin, flaky, transparent.

Pyrite, which looks like a yellowish metal.

Bastard granite contains some but not all of these crystals.

Both granites are excellent foundation materials.

Gneiss may be either sedimentary or igneous rock which has been metamorphosed, that is, compressed and worked under sufficient pressure and heat so that the structural changes were by plastic flow rather than by cracking.

In gneiss, the interlocking minerals are for the most part visible to the naked eye. The gneisses are banded. Gneiss is a satisfactory foundation material.

Gneisses merge into schists as the texture becomes finer.

Schists with a large percentage of mica are known as mica schists. As a foundation material they are subject to cleavage.

Trap rock is heavy, dark, and igneous. The name is derived from a word meaning "step," inasmuch as the rock tends to break into steplike blocks. Trap rock is an excellent foundation material.

Basalt is a dark igneous rock ranging from dark gray to black. Its texture is very fine. Basalt is an excellent foundation material.

Marble is a metamorphosed limestone and in its broken state shows shiny, smooth, crystalline surfaces. It is vulnerable to dissolving in certain atmospheres or water. Its hardness is medium. Marble may be made from either calcitic or dolomitic limestone. The dolomitic limestone does not effervesce with dilute acid. Marble has excellent durability and workability for buildings.

Limestone is calcium carbonate rock of sedimentary origin. It is somewhat vulnerable and may be distinguished from magnesium carbonate limestone by the fact that it effervesces under a dilute solution of acid, which is not the case with the dolomite. Individual grains cannot be distinguished. Limestone is soft, easily worked, and a reasonably good foundation rock, but vulnerable.

Sandstone, as its name implies, is made up of sand cemented with silica or lime. In general, the grains are distinguishable. Its reliability as a building material can be ascertained only after investigation; for instance, brownstone is a sandstone which has not always proved reliable.

Slates are metamorphosed shale and have cleavage planes along which the stone is split for commercial purposes. These cleavage planes occur at an angle to the bed planes. Slates are a satisfactory building material, particularly for roofs.

Shale comes from silt and clay and occurs in beds which tend to "shale" off. It is softer than limestone and unreliable as a building material.

Caution: Sedimentary stone should be laid on natural beds.

Definition: Porphyritic texture means a texture in which the larger minerals appear to be embedded in a matrix.

SCHIST   GNEISS

FIG. 2.

GRANITE   TRAP   BASALT

 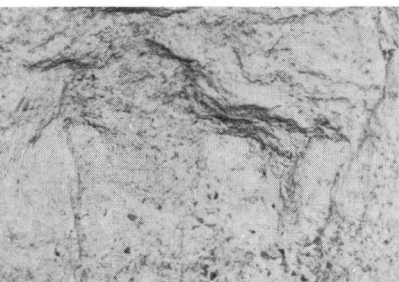 

WHITE MARBLE   LIMESTONE   SANDSTONE

FIG. 3.

EFFECT OF EXPOSURE TO AIR ON CERTAIN WORK

Some shales tend to explode in a series of minute scalings, probably because of compressed gases in the shale which split off the surface after the release of the overburden pressure.*

Some of the sedimentary and metamorphic rocks tend to weather rapidly when exposed. In using such rocks it is necessary to place the footings and partially backfill as soon as the bearing surface is exposed and approved by the engineer. Sedimentary rock tends to disintegrate if not laid on natural bed.

Rocks containing pyrites, such as brownstone, break down easily.

VARIATIONS FROM STANDARD CLASSIFICATION

In addition to the preceding soil classifications there are the following:

Weathered rock usually refers to surface weathering and erosion by water and wind. It is the main source of soil. The process is both mechanical and chemical, and is due to frost, solution of soluble minerals, oxidation, and vegetable growth. The result is a series of fine spalls interlacing the soil. Generally weathered rock is not very deep, and can be easily removed exposing good rock.

Kaolinized rock is rock in which the cementing feldspar has been changed to kaolin, a form of clay. It is the result of deep weathering caused by percolation through the seams of rock by ground water from above or by charged vapors from below. It may extend to great depths. The softened rock maintains much of its original appearance. It may be removed or penetrated by steel piles. It is not good for foundations.

Top soil is usually richly organic. It is not good for foundation but should be stripped and saved for grading.

Fill is man made. It usually contains organic material and any form of trash or refuse. It is not used for foundations.

Quicksand is a condition caused by the upward flow of water through sand. Quicksand is unsuitable for foundations but may be quickly compacted by removing the flow of water.

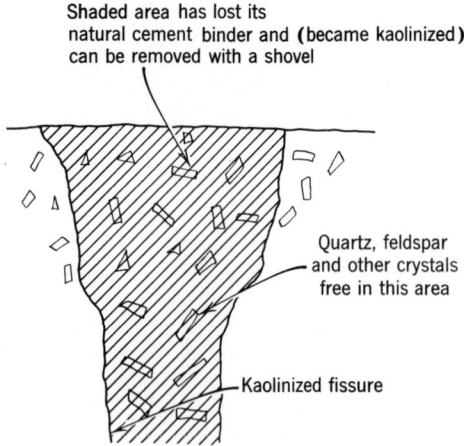

FIG. 4. GRANITE WITH DECOMPOSED FISSURE.

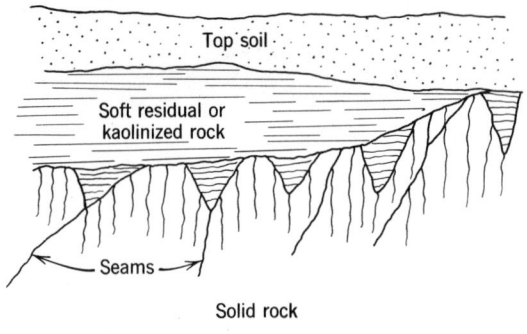

FIG. 5. KAOLINIZED ROCK.

Note: Kaolinized rock is rock which has lost its natural cement binder and is being reduced to clay.

* New Brunswick, N. J.

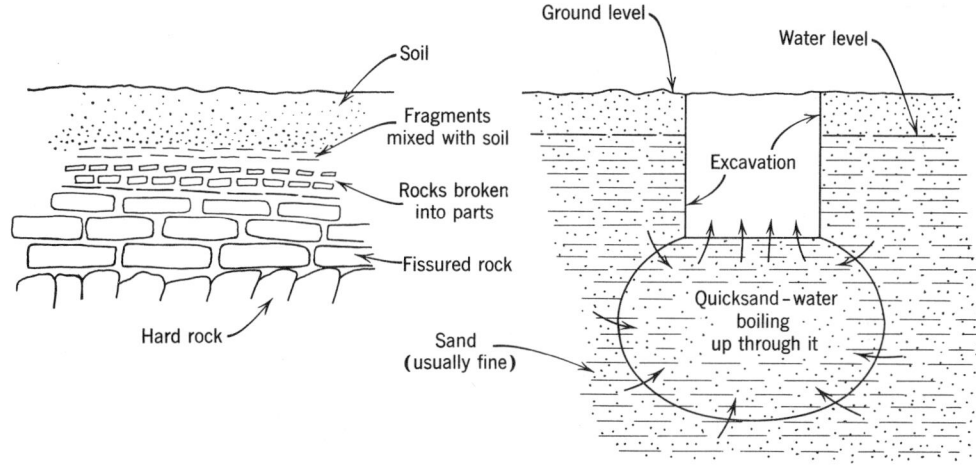

FIG. 6. WEATHERED ROCK.

FIG. 7. QUICKSAND.

Decomposed Rock.   The engineer will encounter deposits of decomposed rock which will vary widely as follows:

Soft igneous-gneis.   Occurs in New York City vicinity as if the leaching process came from above.   It is in pockets usually 1 to 40 ft. deep and deeper near geological faults.

Soft rock shows alternate layers of decomposed strata but still retains the integrity of ledge rock. Building code allows a safe bearing pressure of 8 tons per square foot.

Settlement may be considerable, depending on voids and depth of stratum.

Recommendations are not to depend on it if it is decomposed beyond the limit of structural integrity.   It may be broken down into sand or clay.   Remove or drive piles.

Granite and similar igneous rocks seem to leach out through faults as from below.   The end product is clay, but the intermediate product is a soft, flaky material.

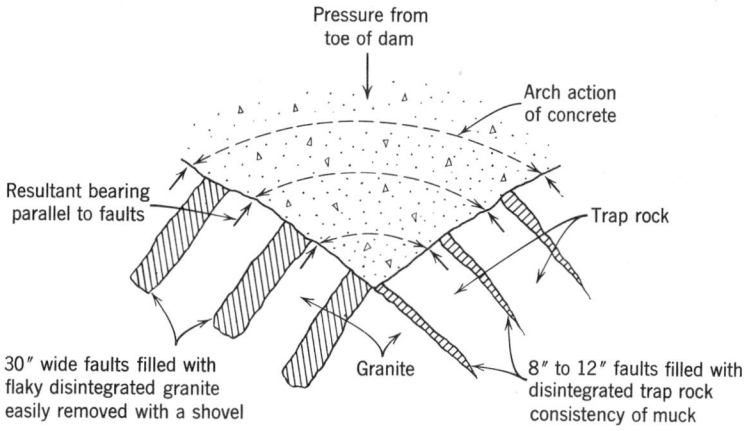

FIG. 8.   CONDITION AT TOE OF SACO RIVER DAM.

An example of treatment of decomposed rock.

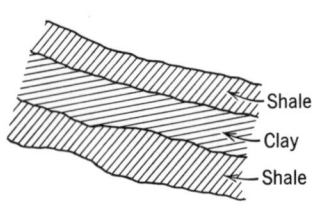
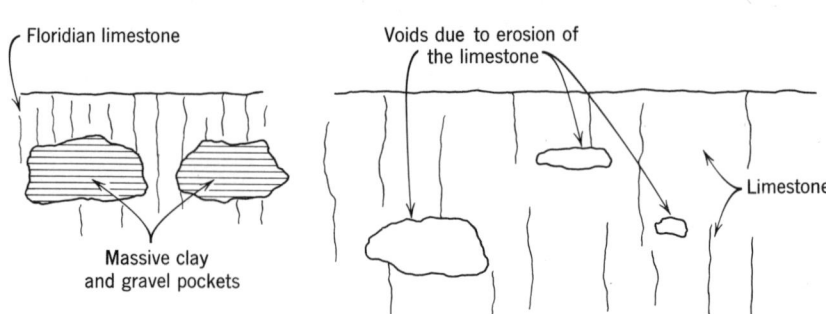

CLAY SEAMS IN SHALE　　CONDITION AT MIAMI　　CAVERNOUS LIMESTONE

Use low soil pressure, or　　Use low foundation　　Fill voids with concrete or bridge over.
carry foundation through;　pressures or carry foundation
prevalent in coal measures.　through.

FIG. 9.　SOFT STRATA AND VOIDS IN SEDEMENTARY ROCKS.

SOIL LOAD TESTS

Soil load test is conducted in accordance with Fig. 10.

Apply sufficient load uniformly on platform to produce a center load of 4 times proposed "design load per square foot." Center load equals load of platform times $(a/a + b)$.

Read settlement every 24 hours until no settlement occurs in 24 hours.

Add 50% more load and read settlement every 24 hours until no settlement occurs in 24 hours.

Settlement under proposed load should not show more than ¾ in., or increment of settlement under 50% overload should not exceed 60% of settlement under proposed load.

If the above limitations are not met, repeat test with reduced load.

Figure 11 represents an alternative setup which may be used with the same procedure.

Pile Load Test. Test equipment may be similar to that shown for soil load test.

Test load is twice proposed load.

Apply in seven increments equal to ½, ¾, 1, 1¼, 1½, 1¾, and 2 times the proposed load.

Record settlement or rebound to nearest 0.001 ft. after every increment or decrement in loading.

After proposed working load has been applied and after each increment thereafter, keep the test load in place until there is no settlement for a 2-hour period.

Keep total test load in place until settlement does not exceed 0.001 ft. in 48 hours.

Remove test load in decrements of not more than ¼ of the total load with intervals not less than 1 hour.

Record rebound 24 hours after total load is removed.

Allowable pile load is ½ that which causes a net settlement of not more than 0.01 in. per ton of total test load or is ½ that which causes a gross settlement of 1 in., whichever load is less.

The settlement of a footing on clay will not be the same as that of the load test on the basis of the same unit load. It can be estimated thus:

$$\text{Settlement} = \text{Load test settlement} \times \frac{\text{Width of footing}}{\text{Width of test plate}}$$

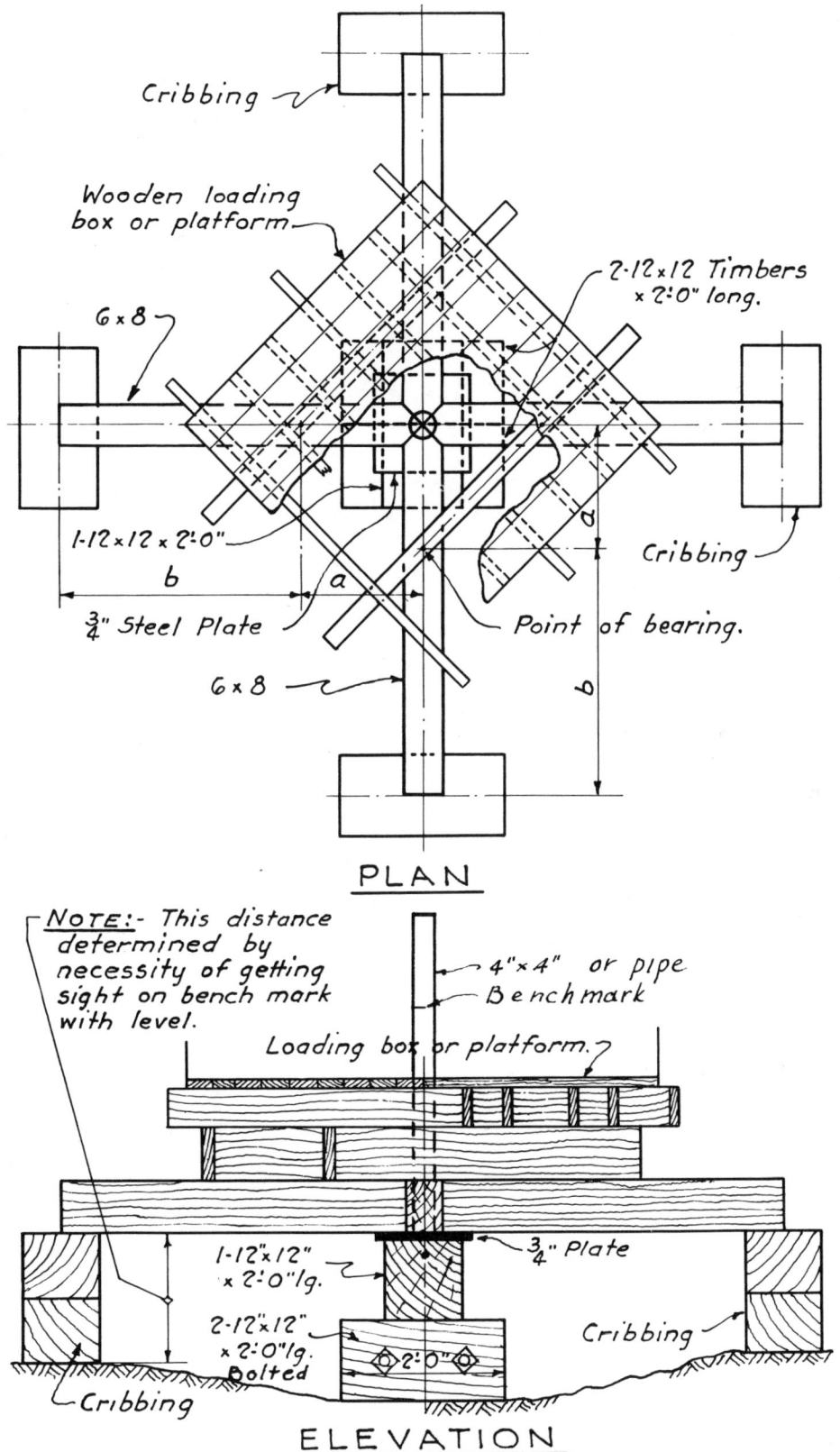

FIG. 10. METHOD OF CONDUCTING SOIL LOAD TEST.

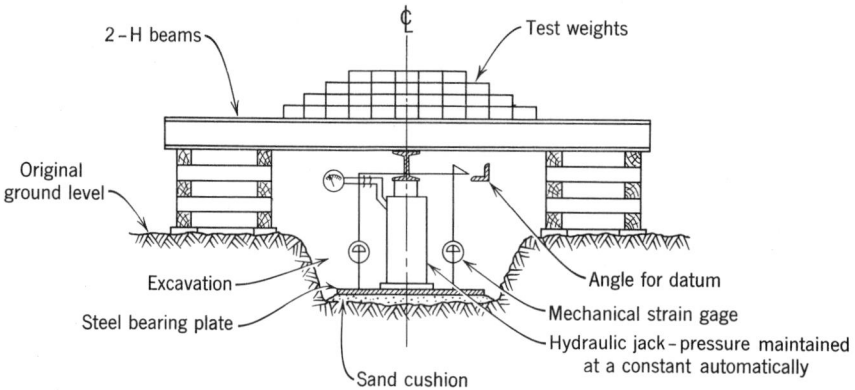

2 – H beams   Test weights

Original
ground level

Excavation
Steel bearing plate
Sand cushion
Angle for datum
Mechanical strain gage
Hydraulic jack – pressure maintained
at a constant automatically

FIG. 11.   REACTION TYPE LOAD TEST.

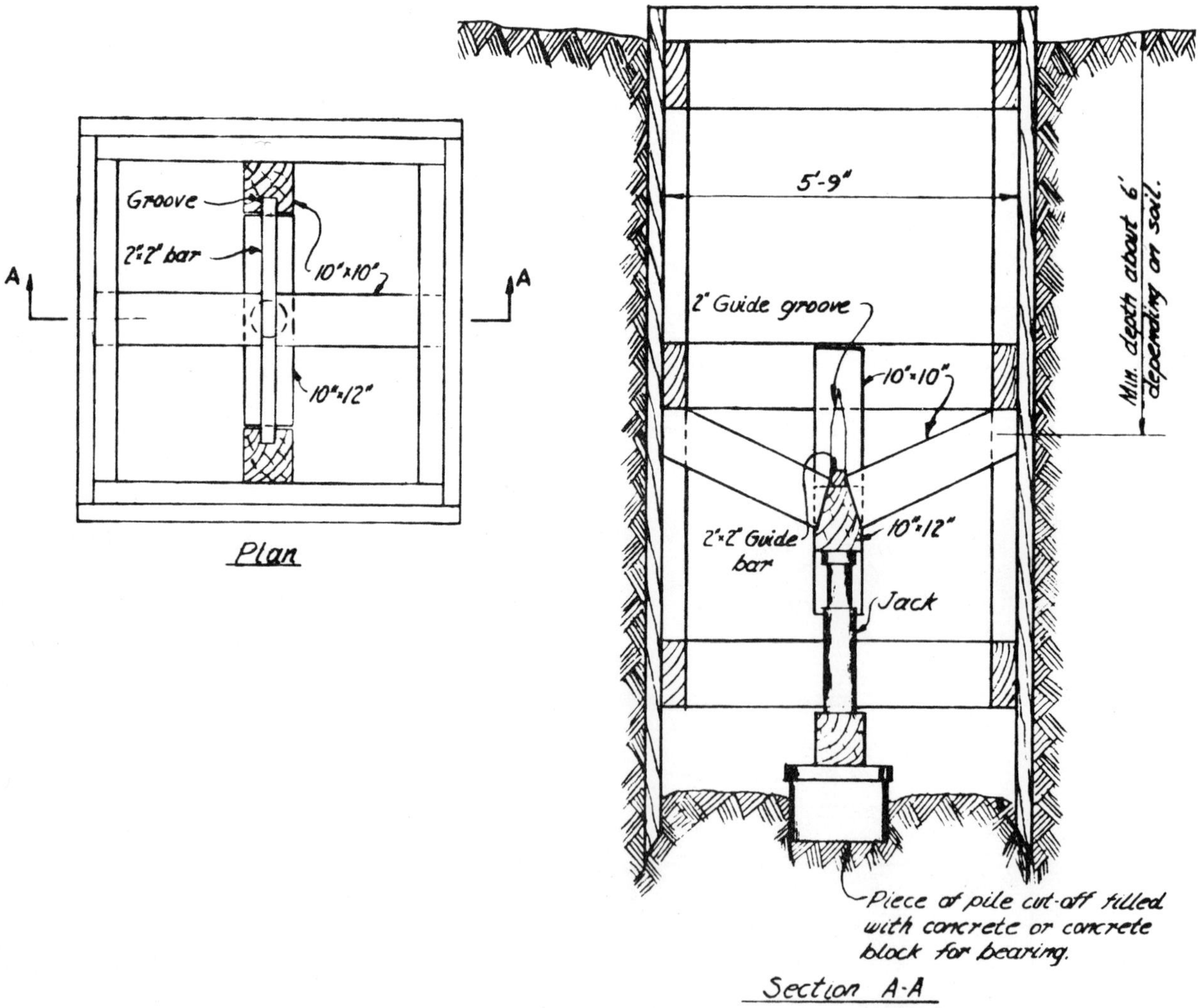

Groove
2"x2" bar
10"x10"
10"x12"

A   A

Plan

5'-9"

2" Guide groove
10"x10"
2"x2" Guide bar
10"x12"
Jack

Min. depth about 6'
depending on soil.

*Piece of pile cut-off filled
with concrete or concrete
block for bearing.*

Section A-A

FIG. 12.   SOIL BEARING TEST IN BOTTOM OF PIT.*

Avoids necessity of test load.

* Adapted from *Underpinning* by Prentis and White, Columbia University Press.

RED LIGHTS

1. The results of economizing on subsurface exploration can result in the loss of many times any economy effected.
2. Soil values are indeterminate. Therefore, use extreme conservatism in assuming a safe value; e.g., use 3 tons where indications are that a 4-ton pressure might be safe.
3. Beware of soft strata at lower depths. It is better to drive piles through than to take a chance.
4. Never build over black organic matter.

BORINGS

Borings are a tool to supplement the evaluation of the soil by enabling the engineer to inspect the subsoil by taking samples. Thus weak layers and soft spots below the bearing stratum are disclosed, and rock cores may be taken. Plate II illustrates the general types of borings.

The number of blows per foot of penetration of the sampling spoon furnishes important information about the compactness of soil as evaluated in Table I. The boring results are recorded on a boring log, Fig. 13, for handy reference.

In the interest of clarity, the techniques of taking undisturbed samples for laboratory tests are covered in Chapter 15, Field Practice.

TYPICAL BORING LOG †† STRUCTURES.

LOCATION ANTIGUA STRUCTURE HANGAR (See key plan) SHEET No. 1 OF 2

BORING No. 1 DATUM BORING INSPECTOR SMITH DATE 1-3-41.

MISCELLANEOUS DATA.
- LENGTH OF HOLE 26'0
- ROCK 5'0"
- WT. OF HAMMER 300 lbs.
- AVER. FALL OF HAM. 30"
- EL. OF GRD. WATER +68.4.

Stratification: Elevation	Depth	Legend	Description of Materials (Type, Color & Consistency)	Casing: Blows	Penetration	Sampler or Spoon: Blows	Penetration	Sample No.*	Remarks**
73.7	0		Surface						
		2'6"	Brown Sandy Loam						Few Roots
			Trace of Gravel.			6	12	1D	Dry & Friable
71.2	2'6"								
				8	12"	32	18"	2D	Fairly Firm.
		6'6"	Fine Brown Sand	10	12"				Cohesionless.
66'	G.W.		Trace of Gravel.	16	12"				Resistance
				16	12"	28	12"	3D	increases with
64.7	9'0"								depth.
		2'6"	Firm, Hard, Yellow,						Becomes Plastic
			Silty Clay.	18	12"	20	18"	4D	when worked.
62.2	11'6"								
		8'6"	Compact Gravel,	380	12"	60	3"	5D	Chips of black slate
52.7	21'0"		Silt & Sand "Hardpan"						embedded in silt.
		5'6"	Buff-colored						Casing & Rods
			Limestone.					6C	Refused at 21'0"
			Hard 80% Core						Bottom of Hole
47.7	26'0"		recovery.						at 26'0".

Note: Additional data may include: Keyplan with contours, stations coordinates and building outline; Benchmarks, date, drilling rig, casing dia.; Atterberg limits, Mech. Analysis, density, water content.

* Write sample No. at corresponding depth. Designate dry samples by *D*. Wash samples by *W*. Undisturbed samples by *U*. Rock cores by *C*.

** When drilling cores in rock, record the percentage of recovery in each foot of penetration.

†† Caribbean Architect-Engineer.

FIG. 13. TYPICAL BORING LOG.

Note: 300-lb. hammer shown above may be used but is not as common as 140-lb. hammer.

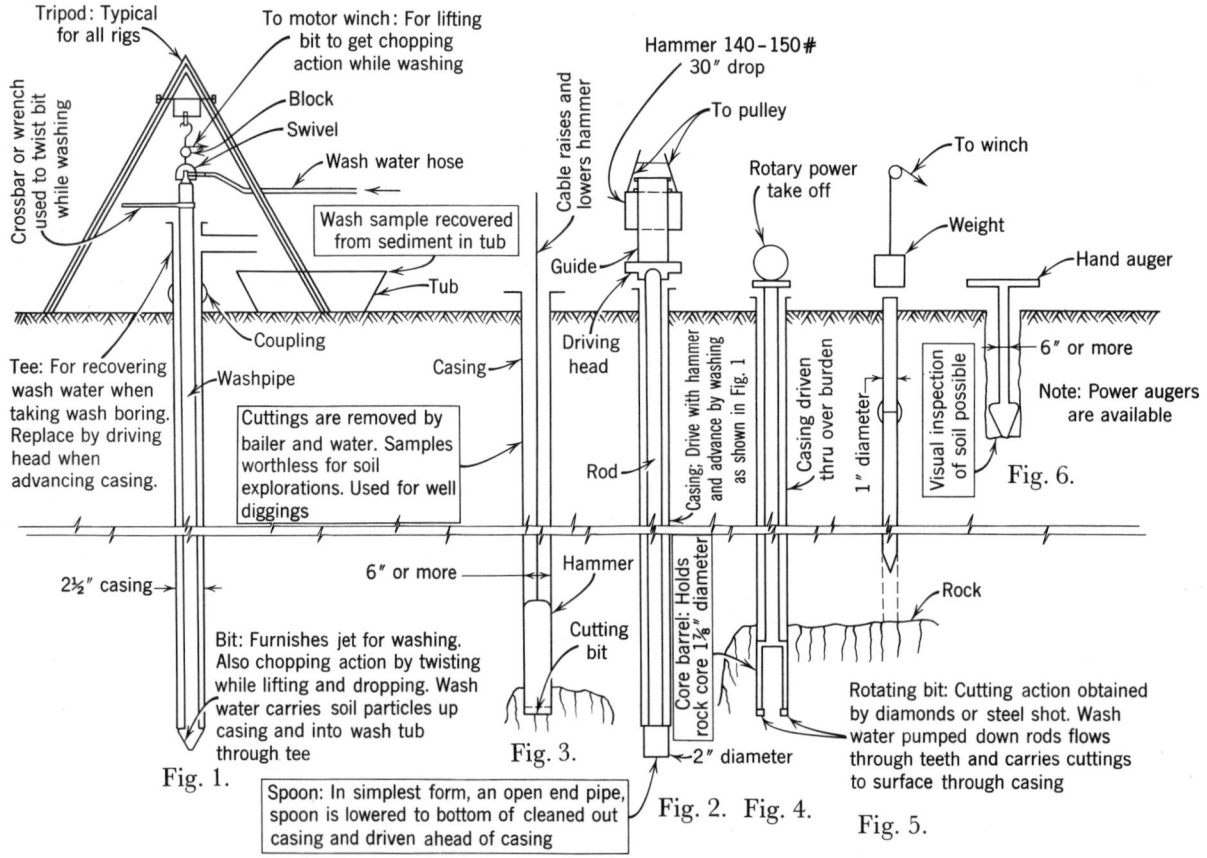

Fig. 1. Wash Borings   Fig. 3. Churn Drilling   Fig. 5. Sounding Rod
Fig. 2. Dry Sample   Fig. 4. Rock Core Boring   Fig. 6. Earth Auger

PLATE II. TYPES OF BORINGS.

Notes to Plate II

Fig. 1. Not recommended. Sample worthless and often confusing. Used mainly to drive casing preparatory to Figs. 2 and 4.

Fig. 2. Used for obtaining sample and measuring resistance. Most common type of soil boring.

Fig. 3. Not recommended for soil exploration. Used mainly for well drilling and quarry blasting.

Fig. 4. Preferred for rock sampling.

Fig. 5. Used for supplementary exploration, especially to locate top of rock.

Fig. 6. Used for subgrade exploration for highway and airfield work and for shallow foundations.

SPACING AND DEPTH OF BORINGS AND TEST PITS OR TEST HOLES

Highways. At 100-ft. stations plus additional necessary at culverts, bridges, weak zones, wide cuts and fills, muck deposits, borrow pits, and sources of base material. Depth not less than 3 ft. below subgrade. Locate ground water table, seepage sources, and direction of flow.

Airfields. At 100-ft. to 1000-ft. spacing on center line, edge of pavement, and edge of shoulders. Depth not less than 4 to 6 ft. below subgrade in cut or ground surface in fill. Not less than twice diameter of tire contact areas or less than frost penetration. Locate ground water table and seepage data. Make field load-bearing tests at time of survey (from 5 to 10 usual for each airfield).

Bridges, Dams and Piers. Borings spaced as needed to bedrock or well below foundation level. Make borings at least 20 ft. into solid rock. Make one or more borings at each pier 50 ft. minimum into solid rock. Use open-pit exploration on land and in shallow water. Make soil bearing tests and pile loading tests.

Building Foundations, Towers, Chimneys, etc. Borings spaced not over 50 ft. center to center. Depth 15 ft. to 20 ft. minimum below foundation level, with at least one deep boring to search for hidden weak deposits. Core borings into rock greater than minimum design depth of rock required.

Sewers, Drains, and Tunnels. On center line recommend 100- to 200-ft. intervals, except in rock, 10 to 50 ft., to catch its irregular surface for pay lines and to make certain of adequate rock cover for tunnels, also to avoid risk of preglacial gorges. Depth below anticipated or preliminary subgrade in good soil or rock nominally 5 ft. or more to allow for latitude in final design affecting subgrade elevations; in poor or unstable soils, explore to necessary depth requisite for determining kind of foundation such as bearing piles, replacement of poor soil, or consolidation by surcharge.

RED LIGHTS

A weakness in test borings is that the sampling is usually done by a mechanic instead of the engineer.

Frequency of samples should be such as to detect a thin layer.

Sounding under individual footings to detect a fissured or eroded cavity should be made for limestone or other soluble rocks.

Call for undisturbed samples, p. 15–28, where it is desired to make laboratory tests for time settlement, density, or shearing strength.

Borings may be stopped by rock. This should be drilled to differentiate between bedrock and boulders.

For special conditions for permafrost foundations, see p. 19–18.

Test pits, since they allow visual inspection and facilitate sampling, are to be preferred to borings, within practical limitations such as depth. Test pits dug by movable equipment such as a back hoe are preferable to fixed and sheathed test pits. Movable equipment in making test pits makes it more practicable for an engineer to supervise the sampling.

9

Waterproofing

The main methods of waterproofing are:

1. Gravity drainage.
2. Hydrolithic.
3. Membrane.
4. Cement base paint.
5. Integral.

GRAVITY DRAINAGE

Wherever conditions permit, this method is the most satisfactory and usually the most economical. An example of gravity drainage is given in Fig. 1.

GRAVITY DRAINAGE — BUILDING FOUNDATION

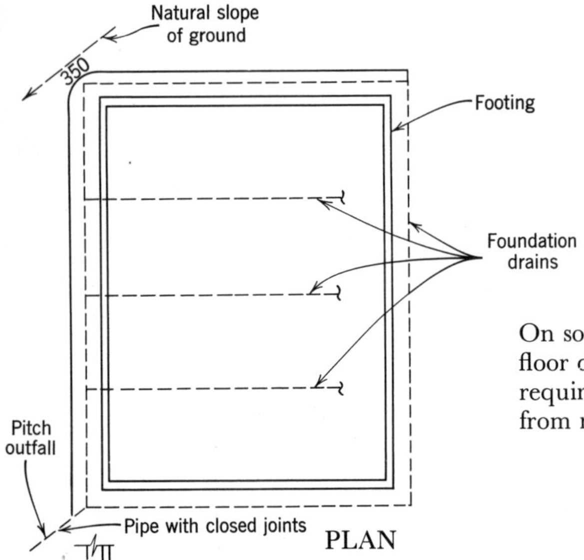

Natural slope of ground

350

Footing

Foundation drains

Pitch outfall

Pipe with closed joints

PLAN

Sump

Pump

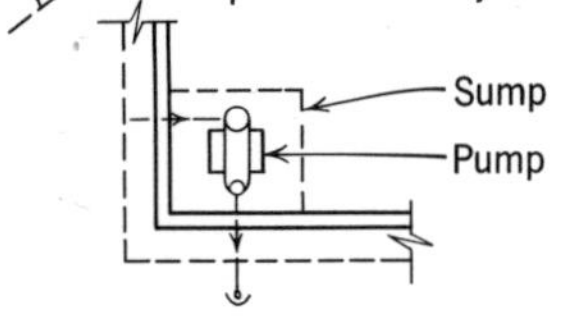

DRAIN WITH SUMP

Note: If gravity outflow is not practical or possible, a sump has to be used with a pump, as shown in the sketch

Nomograph for computing required size of circular drain, flowing full: $n = 0.015$

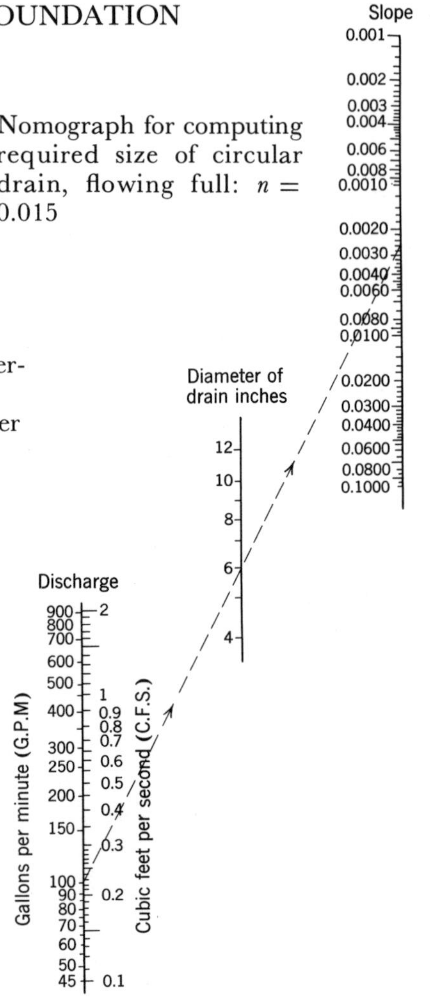

On some buildings under-floor drains may be required to prevent water from rising under floor

Slope
0.001
0.002
0.003
0.004
0.006
0.008
0.0010

0.0020
0.0030
0.0040
0.0060
0.0080
0.0100

0.0200
0.0300
0.0400
0.0600
0.0800
0.1000

Diameter of drain inches
12
10
8
6
4

Discharge

Gallons per minute (G.P.M)
900 / 2
800
700
600
500
400 / 1
 / 0.9
 / 0.8
300 / 0.7
250 / 0.6
200 / 0.5
 / 0.4
150 / 0.3
100
90 / 0.2
80
70
60
50
45 / 0.1

Cubic feet per second (C.F.S.)

Example

Given: Inflow of 100 g.p.m. established by a pumping test during excavation.
Length of drain is 350 ft.
Friction factor for pipes $= n = 0.015$.

Find: Underdrainage design required to keep cellar dry.

Solution: Assume a 6-inch pipe. From nomograph required slope for 100 g.p.m. $= 0.0024$. Hydraulic drop should, therefore, be $350 \times 0.0024 = 0.84$ ft. Bottom of drain is $0.5 + 0.84 = 1.34$ ft. below surface of floor.

Notes: 1. It would be possible to assume a 4-in. pipe with a larger slope or a larger diameter pipe and a smaller hydraulic slope. Selection of the drain size will depend on cost differential between a large pipe and more excavation or a smaller pipe and the necessity of lowering the footings. (See sketch.)

2. Suggested pipe materials in order of preference:

    (*a*) Porous concrete, $n = 0.015$.
    (*b*) Perforated concrete, $n = 0.015$.
    (*c*) Perforated metal, $n = 0.019$.
    (*d*) Open joint concrete, $n = 0.015$.
    (*e*) Open joint clay, $n = 0.019$.
    (*f*) Vitrified clay, $n = 0.013$.

3. Lay underdrainage pipe horizontally.
4. Minimum size of drain pipe, 4 in.

RED LIGHT:

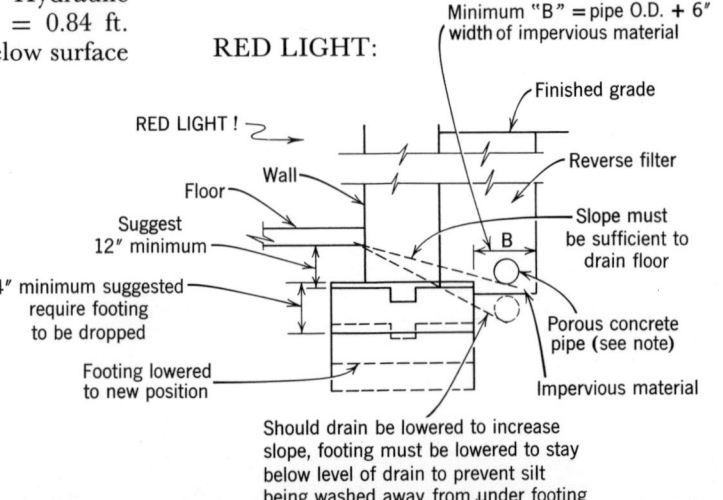

Minimum "B" = pipe O.D. + 6" width of impervious material

RED LIGHT !

Finished grade

Reverse filter

Wall

Floor

Suggest 12" minimum

Slope must be sufficient to drain floor

B

4" minimum suggested require footing to be dropped

Porous concrete pipe (see note)

Footing lowered to new position

Impervious material

Should drain be lowered to increase slope, footing must be lowered to stay below level of drain to prevent silt being washed away from under footing

FIG. 1. BUILDING FOUNDATION DRAINAGE.

HYDROLITHIC METHOD

The hydrolithic method of waterproofing basement walls and floors employs the art of placing properly bonded cement mortar coatings on the inside surfaces of floors and walls. It is in use with general success, being particularly favored because a leak, if one occurs, can be easily located and repaired. It is also an expensive method, because it usually requires a series of operations which include the chipping of the wall or floor surfaces for bonding the several applications of cement coatings required.

One variation of the method is the use of a powdered iron in the cement mortar which, when it corrodes, expands and forms a dense coat.

The cement or hydrolithic coating is effective under high heads.

For details see Fig. 2.

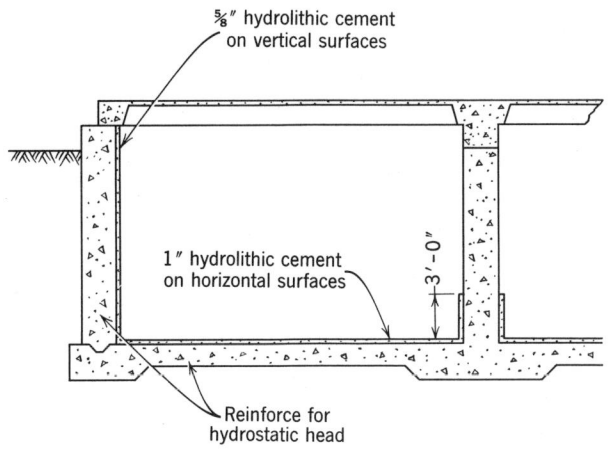

TYPICAL METHOD OF APPLICATION

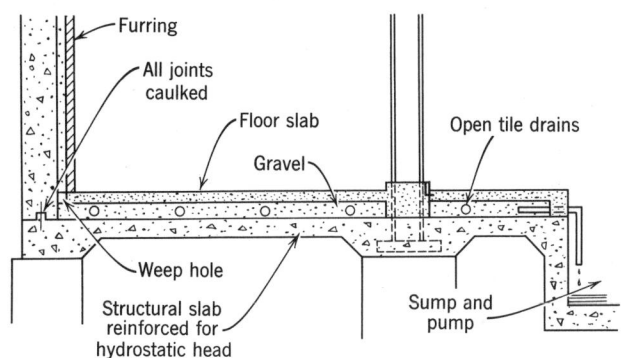

SPECIAL APPLICATION TO AVOID HYDROLITHIC COST

FIG. 2.   APPLICATION OF HYDROLITHIC WATERPROOFING.

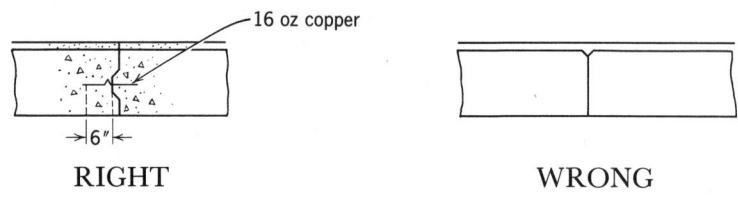

FIG. 3.   DETAIL OF CONSTRUCTION JOINT.

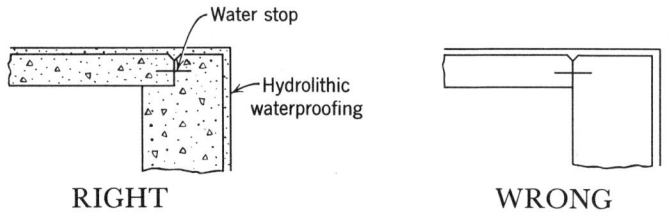

FIG. 4.   JOINT AT PIT WALL.

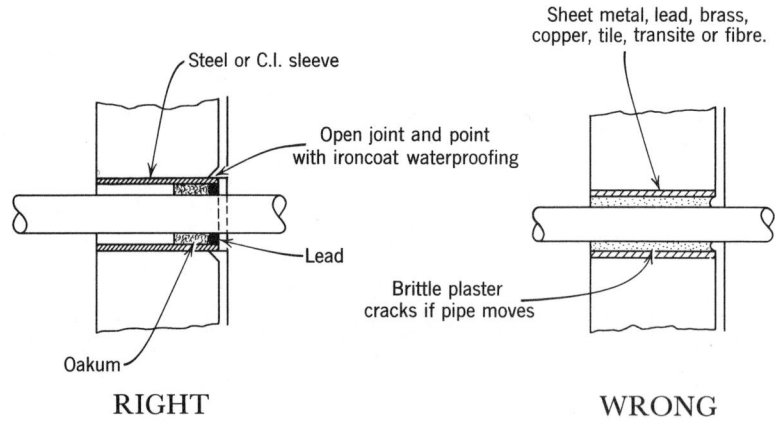

FIG. 5.   DETAIL AT SLEEVE.

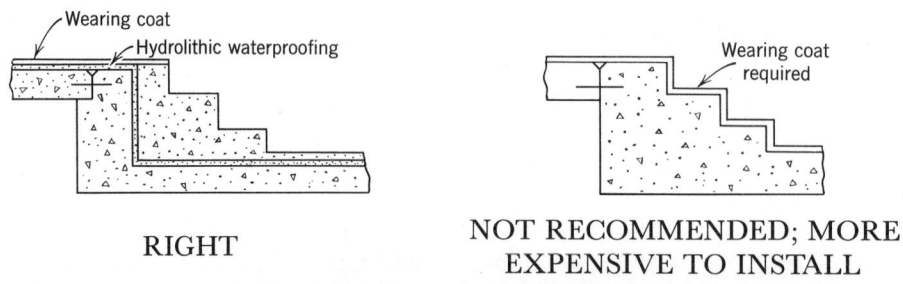

FIG. 6.   DETAIL OF STEPS.

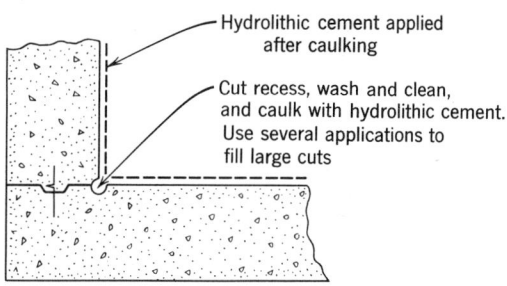

FIG. 7. TYPICAL JOINT CAULKING PRIOR TO APPLYING HYDROLITHIC CEMENT.

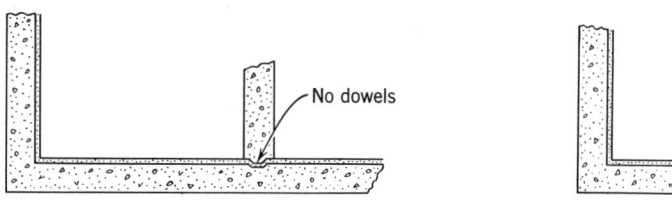

Good: More expensive. *Better:* Less expensive.

FIG. 8. DETAIL AT INTERIOR WALLS.

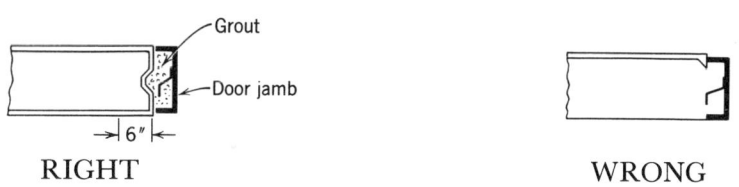

RIGHT WRONG

FIG. 9. DETAIL AT DOORBUCK.

RIGHT WRONG

FIG. 10. DETAIL AT FIRST FLOOR.

Note: All right if dowel is omitted because waterproofing is not punctured.

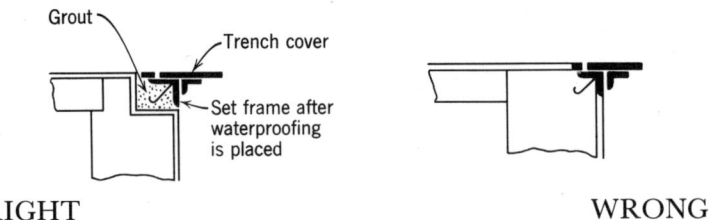

RIGHT   WRONG

FIG. 11.   DETAIL AT PIT OR TRENCH.

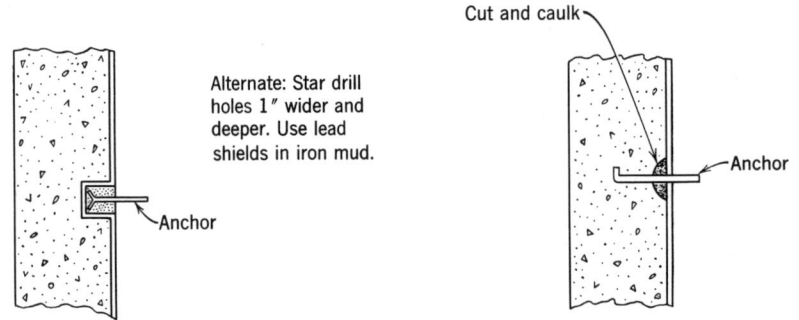

SOMETIMES USED   PERMISSIBLE AND PRACTICAL

FIG. 12.   DETAIL AT ANCHOR BOLTS.

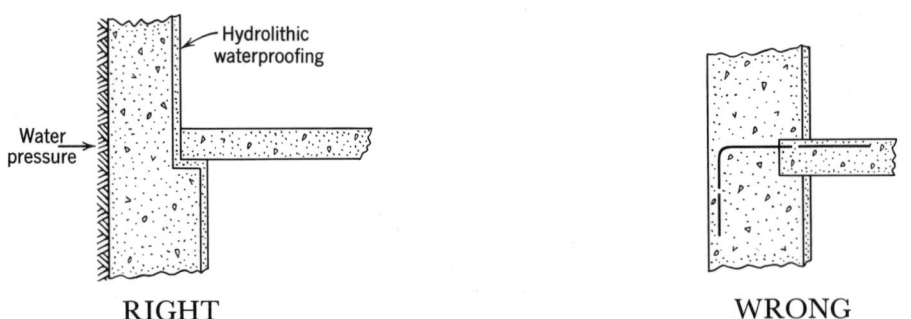

RIGHT   WRONG

FIG. 13.   DETAIL AT INTERMEDIATE FLOOR.

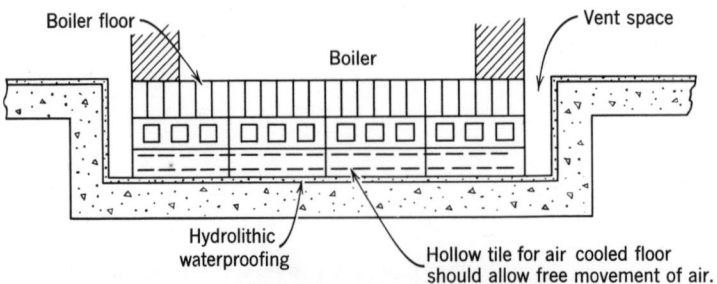

FIG. 14.   DETAIL AT BOILER PITS.

MEMBRANE

Membrane waterproofing is like a sandwich; that is, a bituminous membrane is sandwiched between two layers of masonry.

On account of the laminated construction, this method is expensive. Because of the fact that the waterproofing can not be tested for effectiveness until inside masonry is in place, it is extremely difficult to locate leaks which may occur as the result of oversight in construction. Nevertheless, this method is used a great deal and is generally accepted as providing satisfactory protection against leakage.

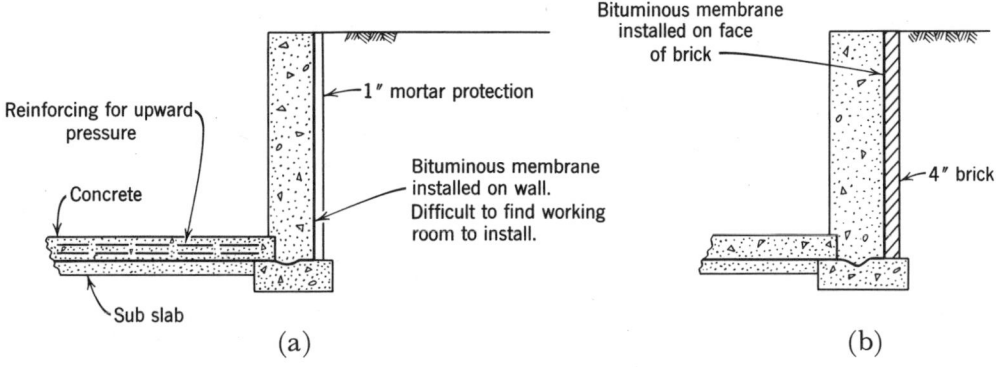

FIG. 15.   WALL DETAILS.

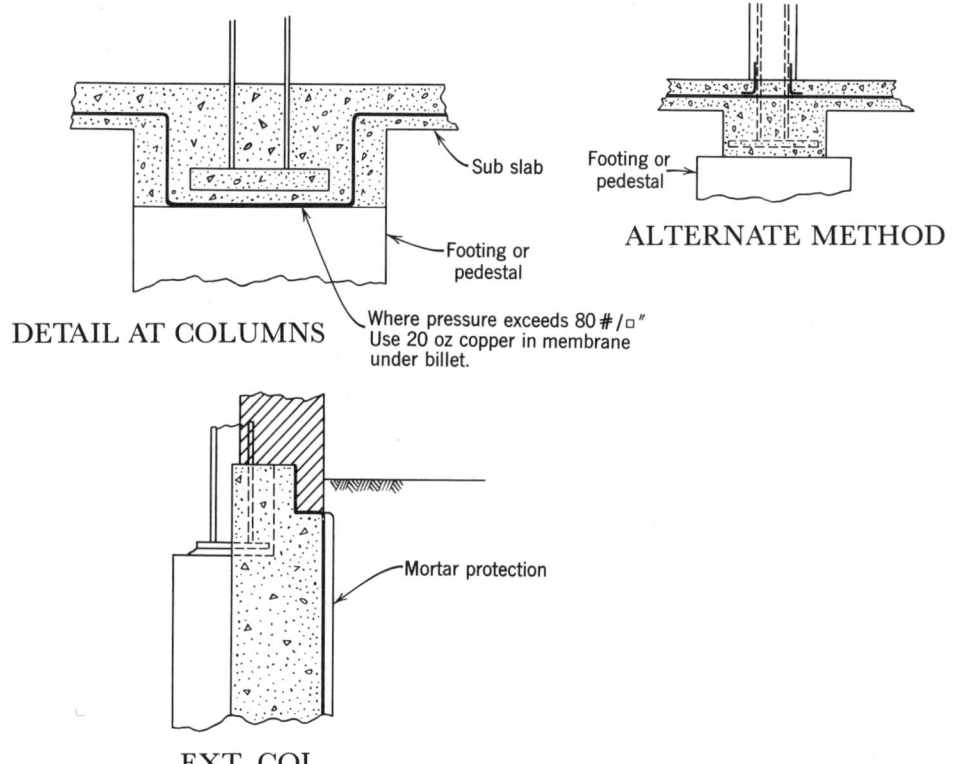

FIG. 16.   COLUMN DETAILS.

WATERPROOFING EXPOSED DECKS

Since all concrete is porous to some extent, it is necessary to provide waterproofing to prevent the entry of undesirable water. Sidewalk vaults, cut-cover subways, and bridges need waterproofing to prevent deterioration of the supporting steel as well as to prevent undesirable dampness. Thin sections of concrete such as stadium slabs deteriorate under the action of explosions caused by rusting of the reinforcing steel.

Waterproofing for such installations has consisted essentially of a membrane covered by a protective slab. This type of construction leaves much to be desired. Water may enter through the joints and through the slab itself and then freeze, rupturing the membrane. Leaks are difficult to locate for repair, requiring removal and replacement of the protective slab.

The joints are particularly susceptible to leakage. They extrude in the summer, wear down (or are cut flush), and then contract in the winter. After a few years, the more volatile components of the bituminous material evaporates and the filler becomes hard and brittle. Some commercial caulking compounds are better than others, but all must be maintained. The slab should be made of dense concrete to reduce infiltration. The use of low-strength concrete for protective slabs results in greater infiltration.

Another approach is to cover the membrane with as little protection as possible so that repairs may be easily made. The use of wooden duckboards will keep traffic from damaging the membrane. Traffic board or asphalt plank will serve the same purpose better.

A new system combines membrane and wearing surface. It uses a synthetic rubber membrane overlaid by a rubber-bound mineral plating.

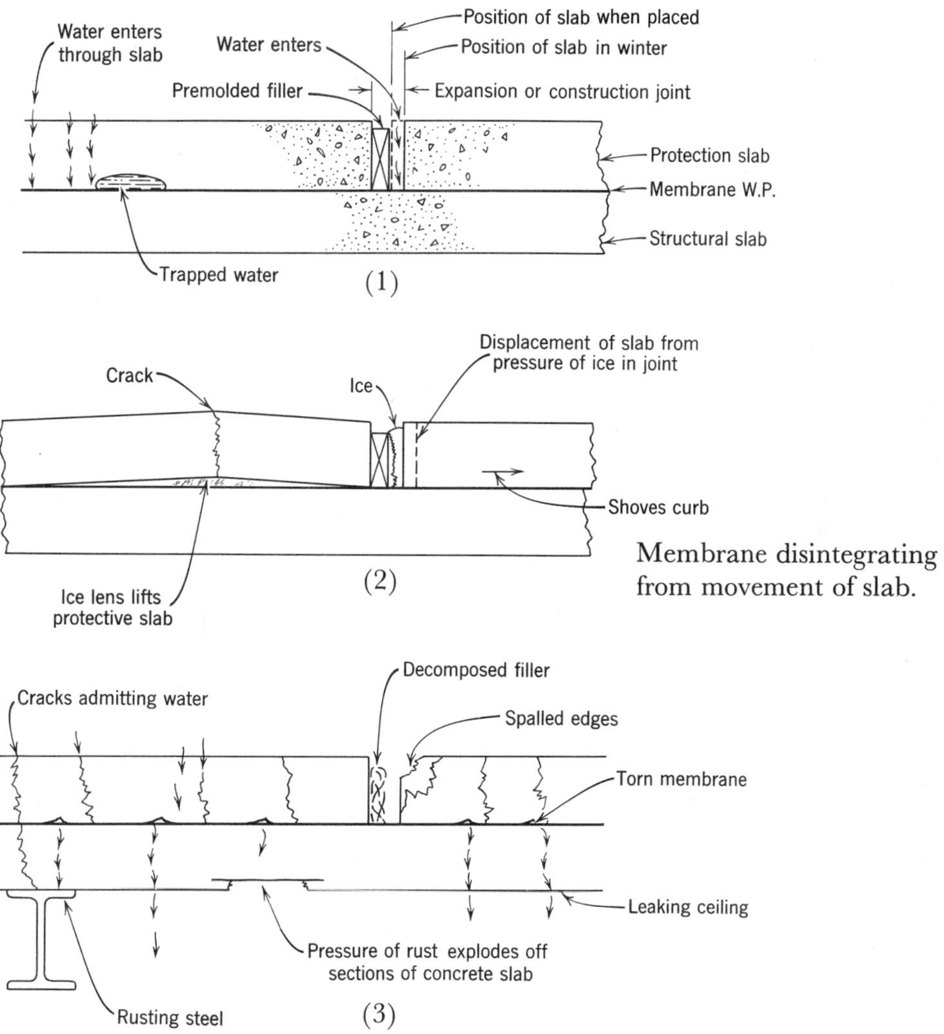

Water enters through slab

Water enters

Position of slab when placed

Position of slab in winter

Premolded filler

Expansion or construction joint

Protection slab

Membrane W.P.

Structural slab

Trapped water

(1)

Crack

Ice

Displacement of slab from pressure of ice in joint

Shoves curb

Ice lens lifts protective slab

(2)

Membrane disintegrating from movement of slab.

Cracks admitting water

Decomposed filler

Spalled edges

Torn membrane

Leaking ceiling

Pressure of rust explodes off sections of concrete slab

Rusting steel

(3)

FIG. 17. STEPS IN THE DECOMPOSITION OF WATERPROOFING PAVING CAUSED BY IMPOUNDING WATER UNDER CONCRETE SLAB.

Note: Leak is inaccessible.

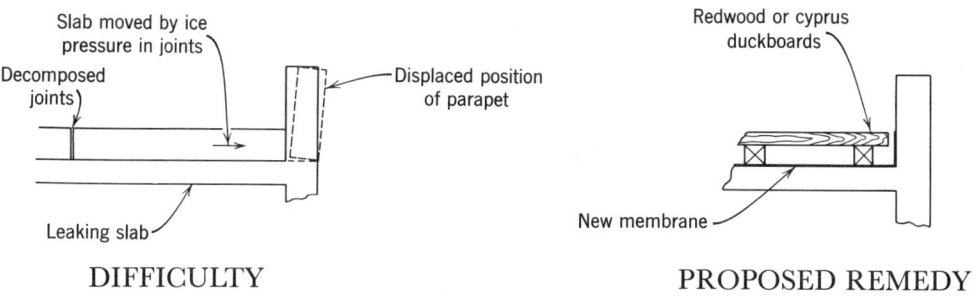

Slab moved by ice pressure in joints

Decomposed joints

Displaced position of parapet

Leaking slab

Redwood or cyprus duckboards

New membrane

DIFFICULTY

PROPOSED REMEDY

FIG. 18. BRIDGE AT ASBURY PARK.

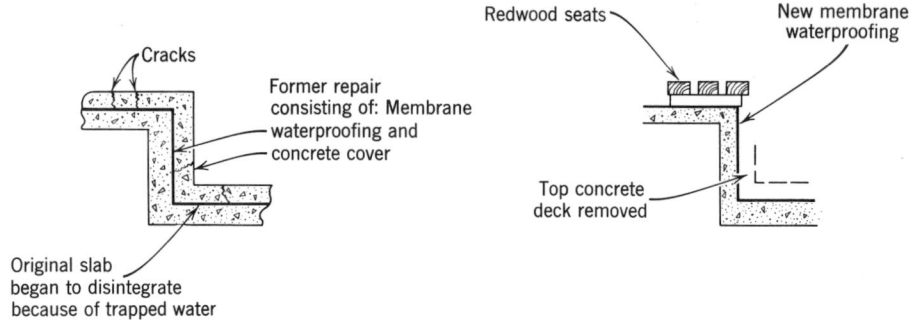

UNSUCCESSFUL REMEDY   REMEDY *

FIG. 19.   PALMER STADIUM, PRINCETON, N. J.

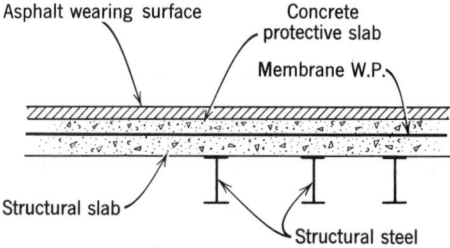

FIG. 20.   PARK AVENUE OVER NEW YORK CENTRAL RAILROAD.

Continued cutting out of protective slab to replace leaking waterproofing has been required.

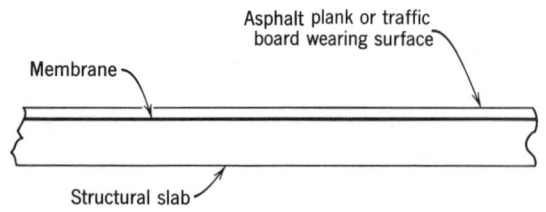

FIG. 21.   SUGGESTED METHOD
OF PLACING WATERPROOFING
AND PROTECTION.

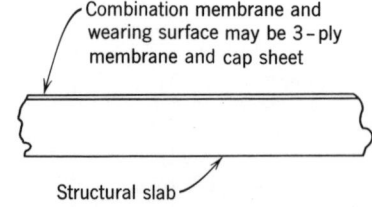

FIG. 22.   ALTERNATIVE METHOD
OF COMBINATION MEMBRANE
AND WEARING SURFACE.

* Marquette Stadium, Milwaukee, and the Philadelphia Municipal Stadium have been treated accordingly.

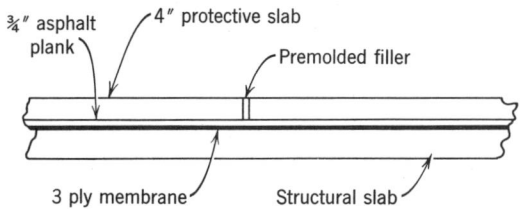

FIG. 23.   HEAVY-DUTY TYPE OF CONSTRUCTION USED IN NEW YORK CITY
GARAGES AND BUS TERMINALS.

CEMENT BASE PAINT

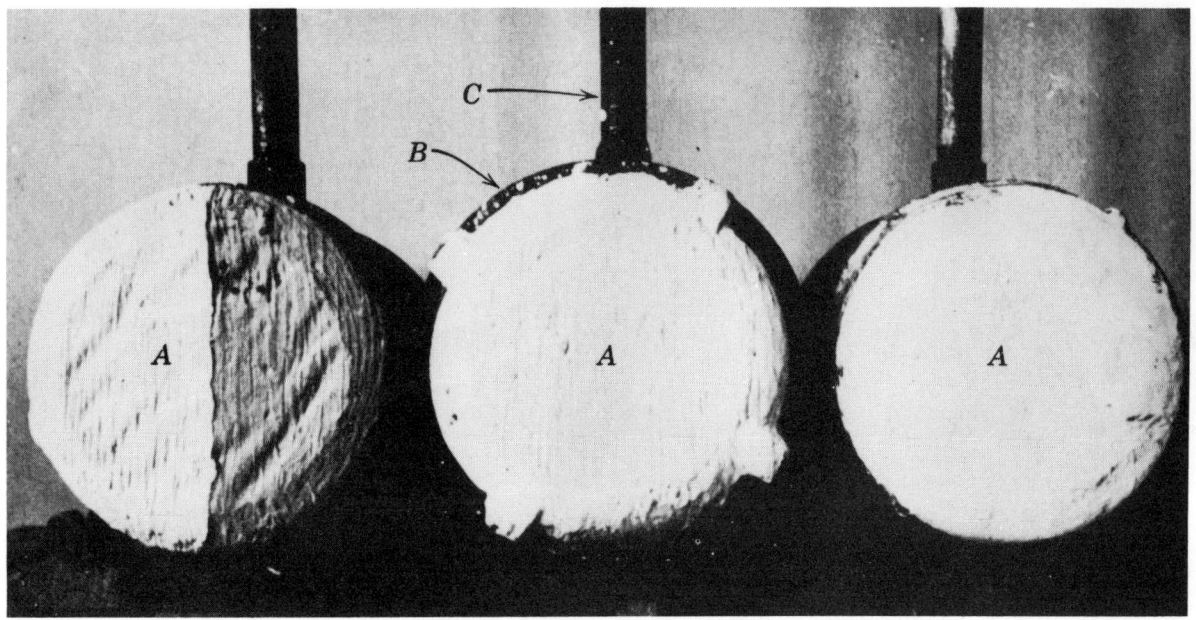

CEMENT BASE PAINT TESTS

A = porous concrete diaphragm waterproofed with coating of cement base paint.
B = pipe section containing water.
C = small pipe to apply head.

Certain cement base paints may be applied to the inside face of walls for waterproofing as a substitute for the cement or iron coat methods.

Contrary to common belief, the cement base paint coatings present important possibilities in waterproofing of basements under a very considerable head of water.   This was demonstrated by experiments made by the author, in which heads up to 8 ft. were successfully contained when the porous concrete diaphragm was only 2¼ in. thick.   See Fig. 24.   These paints should be applied under correct technical specifications.

The paints basically contain portland cement and a finer material such as lime which are scrubbed into the masonry, filling the voids.

INTEGRAL

Admixtures are added to concrete to produce a denser and consequently less permeable wall. These admixtures are basically solutions of calcium chloride in water with a touch of coloring. Some contain soapy compounds, and some add fines such as slaked lime more or less filling the pores of the concrete. The benefits are limited by the fact that these mixtures do not fill voids, cracks, or porous concrete but will fill capillary passages.

The proper design of concrete mixes and the proper placement of concrete do more to ensure dense concrete than any admixture. The presence of calcium chloride in the concrete acts as an accelerator and may cause "flash set," especially in hot weather. The accelerated set of the concrete causes greater heat of hydration with danger of shrinkage or temperature cracks, destroying the waterproofing quality of the concrete.

GENERAL SELECTION

Membrane waterproofing is most suitable for roofs, sidewalks, and other installations where the pressure is downward. Hydrolithic waterproofing is most often used for floors, walls, or other installations where the pressure is upward or inward. Cement base paints are used to reduce costs over the hydrolithic method. Integral waterproofing is best used for damp-proofing.

Eighty per cent of the cost of resisting hydraulic head consists of constructing a reinforced-concrete vault which is free from settlement and shrinkage cracks and whose construction joints are caulked.

It should not be forgotten that a saving can often be attained by the use of a gravity drain as shown in Fig. 1 or a well-caulked job with a subfloor drain, Fig. 2.

Silicone exterior masonry water repellent can be applied to finished brickwork and stucco walls to prevent entry of water and to protect masonry joints, thus preventing effloresence and retarding staining.

Effloresence is caused by water which has somehow entered the wall, leaching out soluble material in the brick and depositing it on the surface.

Secondary water damage can occur as the result of condensation, capillary action, or water vapor pressure. See Figs. 25, 26, and 27.

Condensation occurs when a moist air strikes a cold surface and its temperature is reduced to the dew point.

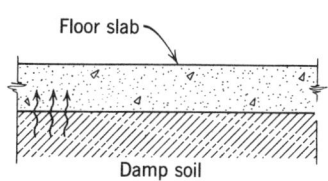

CAPILLARY ACTION OF
FLOOR ON DAMP SOIL,
GRANULAR OR PLASTIC

(*a*)

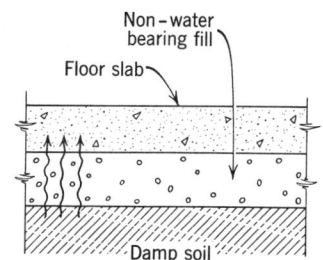

WATER VAPOR PENETRATING
FLOOR SLAB THROUGH FILL

(*b*)

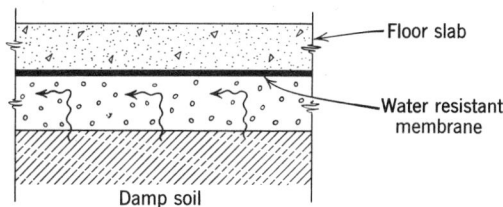

VAPOR AND CAPILLARY ACTION BOTH STOPPED BY MEMBRANE

(*c*)

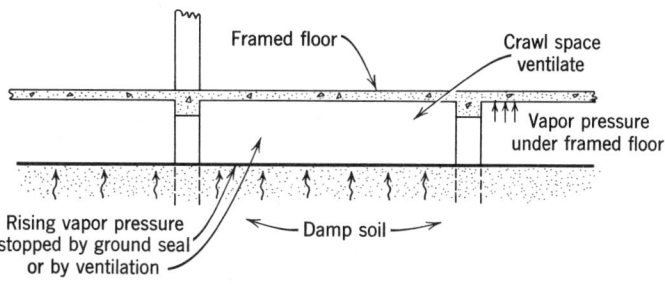

VAPOR PRESSURE UNDER A FOUNDATION

(*d*)

FIG. 25.

Water may be drawn upward by capillary action 1 ft. in coarse sand and 3 ft. in fine sand. In clay, it may be drawn up higher. A water seal should therefore always be provided under a floor slab unless it is well above the reach of capillary action.

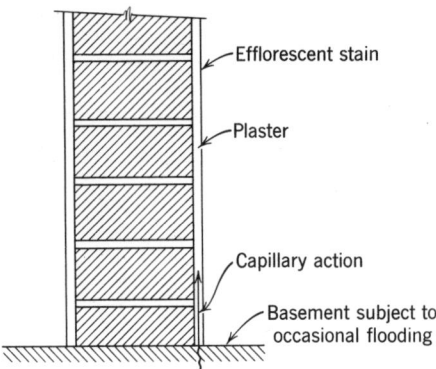

FIG. 26.   DAMAGE BY CAPILLARY ACTION.

Correction: Prevent flooding.

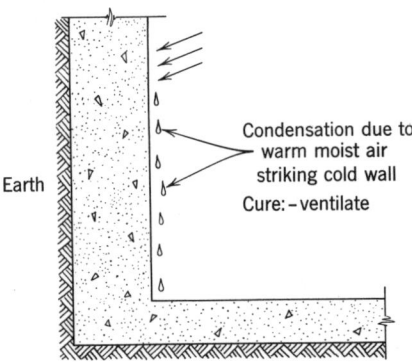

FIG. 27.   CORRECTION FOR CONDENSATION.

RED LIGHTS

A structure must be strong enough to withstand hydrostatic pressure.   Otherwise it will crack, with resulting loss of waterproofing and with damage to structure.

Check structure for uplift due to hydrostatic head.

Pressure must be temporarily relieved by well points, sumps, and drains, or by other methods prior to placing the waterproofing.   Otherwise, the waterproofing will be damaged in installation.

Hydrolithic waterproofing is applied on the *inside* of the surface, and satisfactory bond must be developed to resist hydrostatic pressure.   Precaulking of joints is essential.

Membrane waterproofing must be applied on the *outside* and protected from backfill by a veneer wall.

Cement base paints must be applied to thoroughly dampened masonry.

In using integral waterproofing, the water in the concrete must be reduced by the amount of water in the admixture solution or the concrete strength will be impaired.

Avoid boils in fresh concrete which may cause leaks.   Head should be lowered before placing of concrete slab and applying waterproofing.

Bituminous surface coating will blister under small hydraulic head (unlike cement base paints).

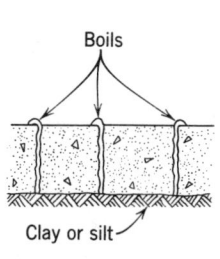

FIG. 28.

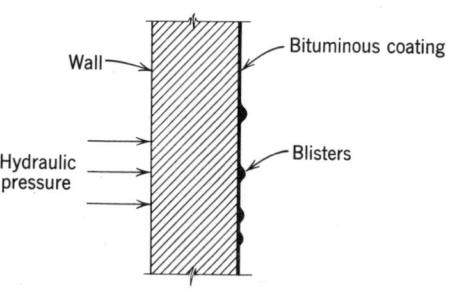

FIG. 29.

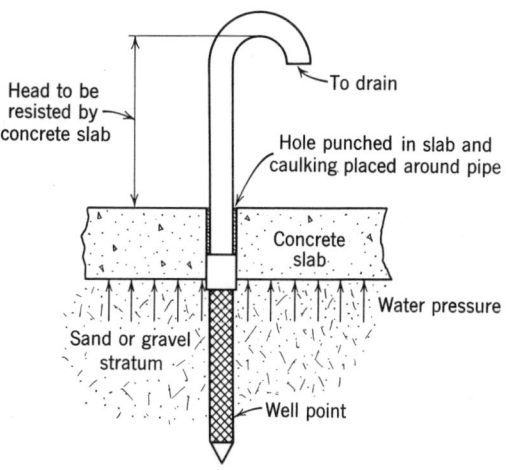

Partial relief of pressure on existing slab or
method of limiting pressure on new work.

FIG. 30.   WELL POINT IN FLOOR SLAB.

10

Construction Methods

UNDERPINNING

Underpinning is the art of placing new foundations under old. It may be **necessitated by a** present or future overload of existing foundations or by a desire to excavate **below the bottom of** the foundation.

The underpinning engineer is required to be on the alert to protect the structure to be under-pinned from damage due to loss of elevation from such causes as:

(*a*) Deformation of temporary supporting beams or needles due to loading; Fig. 17.

(*b*) Settlement of foundations of temporary supports such as needles or shores; Fig. 4.

(*c*) Settlement of new permanent structure due to elastic beam deformation; Fig. 20.

(*d*) Settlement in transferring load from temporary to permanent support; Fig. 20.

Sometimes a pneumatic shield may be used in place of underpinning adjacent to open trenches. See p. 11–21.

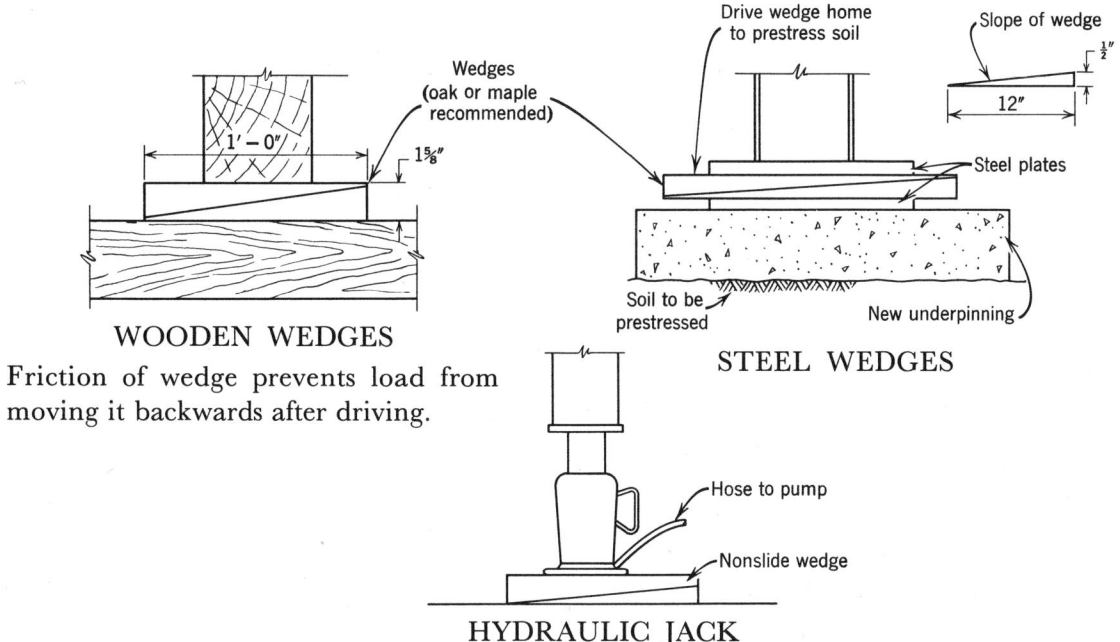

FIG. 1. LIFTING AND PRELOADING DEVICES USED IN UNDERPINNING.

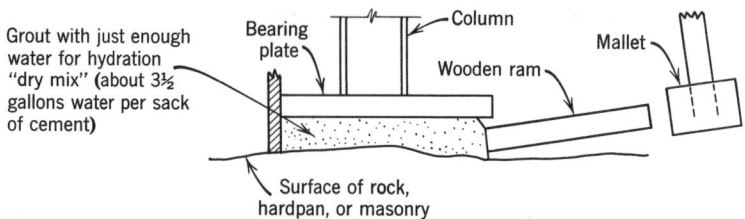

Grout with just enough water for hydration "dry mix" (about 3½ gallons water per sack of cement)

Bearing plate

Column

Mallet

Wooden ram

Surface of rock, hardpan, or masonry

FIG. 2.   DRY PACKING.

Note: Support bearing plate on steel wedges before dry packing.

Dry packing may also be used for needling.

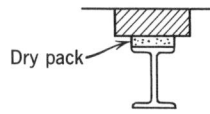

Dry pack

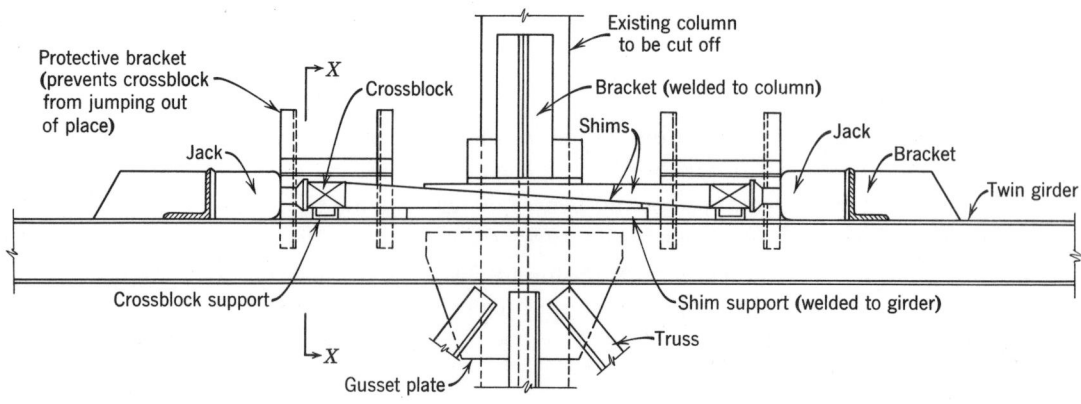

Protective bracket (prevents crossblock from jumping out of place)

Crossblock

Existing column to be cut off

Bracket (welded to column)

Shims

Jack

Jack

Bracket

Twin girder

Crossblock support

Shim support (welded to girder)

Truss

Gusset plate

ELEVATION

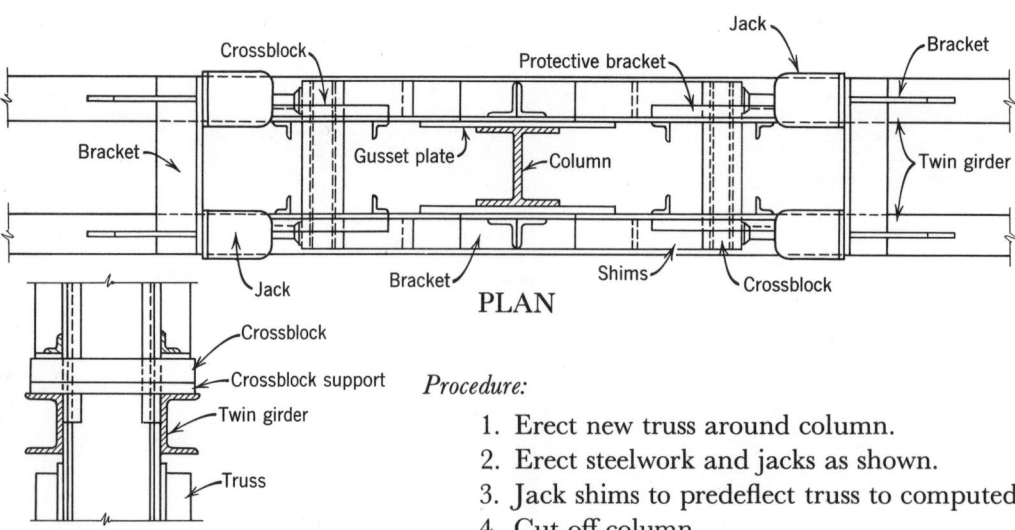

Crossblock

Protective bracket

Jack

Bracket

Bracket

Gusset plate

Column

Twin girder

Jack

Bracket

Shims

Crossblock

PLAN

Crossblock

Crossblock support

Twin girder

Truss

Section X–X

Procedure:

1. Erect new truss around column.
2. Erect steelwork and jacks as shown.
3. Jack shims to predeflect truss to computed deflection.
4. Cut off column.

FIG. 3.   PREDEFLECTION OF A NEW TRUSS WITH STEEL SHIMS.

(To receive load due to cutting off column below.)

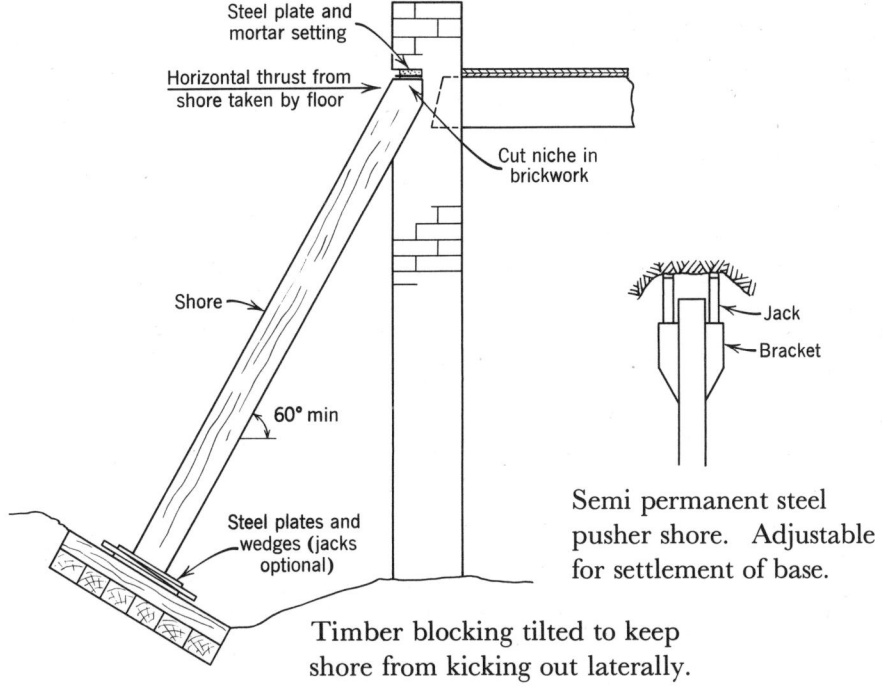

Steel plate and mortar setting

Horizontal thrust from shore taken by floor

Cut niche in brickwork

Shore

60° min

Jack

Bracket

Steel plates and wedges (jacks optional)

Semi permanent steel pusher shore. Adjustable for settlement of base.

Timber blocking tilted to keep shore from kicking out laterally.

FIG. 4. PUSHER SHORE.

May be used to protect existing wall from blasting or partial undermining due to excavations.

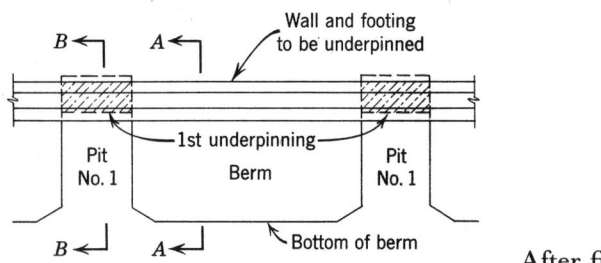

STAGE I. PLAN.

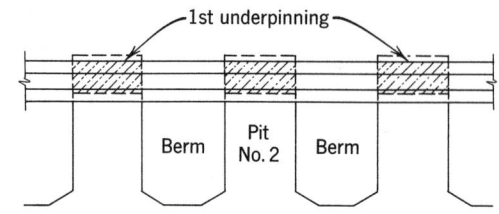

After first underpinning is set, dig pits 2, and underpin.

STAGE II. PLAN.

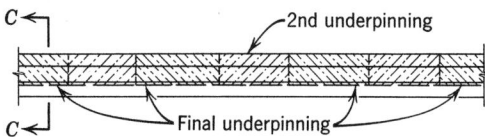

After second underpinning is set, remove remaining berms and underpin intermediate spaces.

STAGE III.

FOUNDATION PLAN.

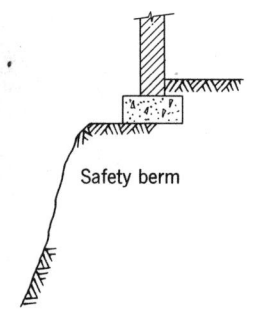

SECTION *A-A*

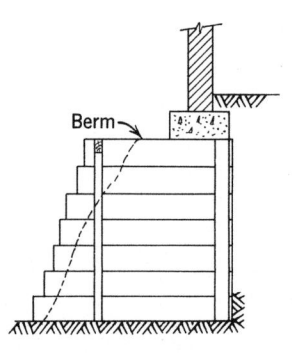

Back and sides supported by breast
boarding if nature of soil requires.

SECTION *B-B*

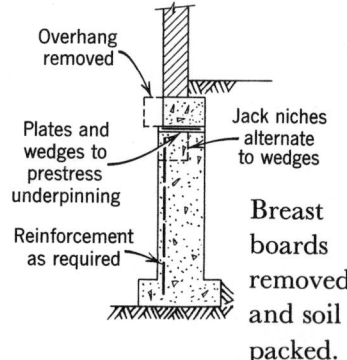

SECTION *C-C*

FIG. 5.   UNDERPINNING ADJOINING BUILDING BY METHOD OF APPROACH PITS.

(Stealing and filling.)

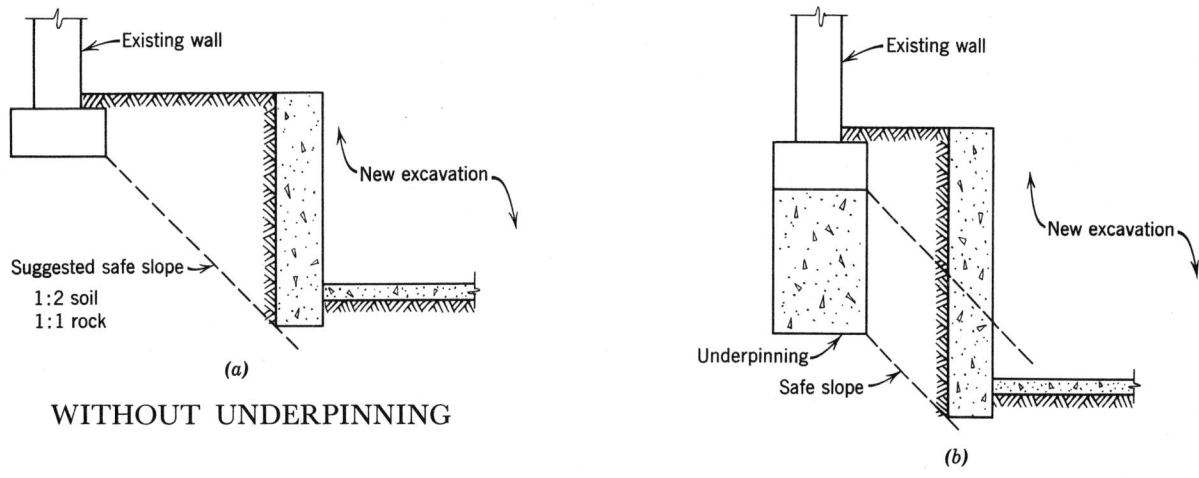

(a)

WITHOUT UNDERPINNING

(b)

UNDERPINNING NECESSARY

FIG. 6. MINIMUM APPROACH TO EXISTING FOOTING.

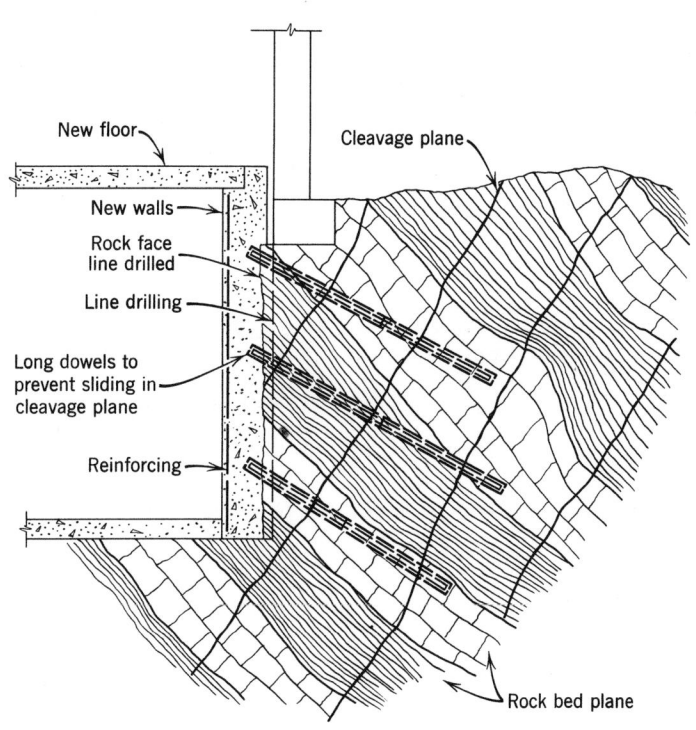

FIG. 7. DOWELING ROCK TO PREVENT SLIDING ON CLEAVAGE PLANE.

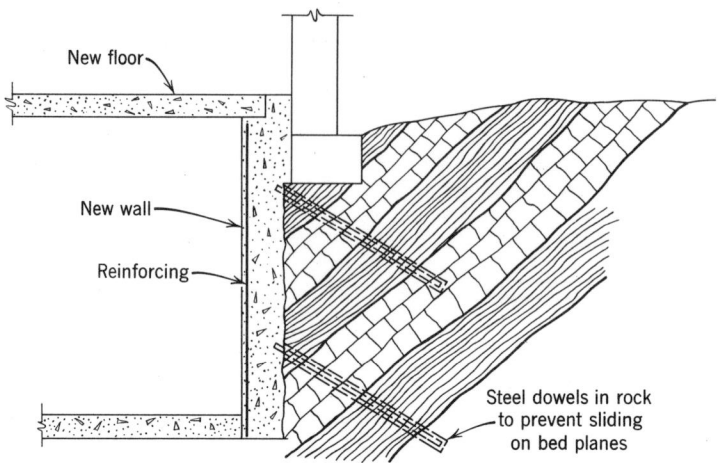

FIG. 8.   UNFAVORABLE ROCK STABILIZED WITH LONG DOWELS GROUTED IN AND HELD BY NEW WALL.

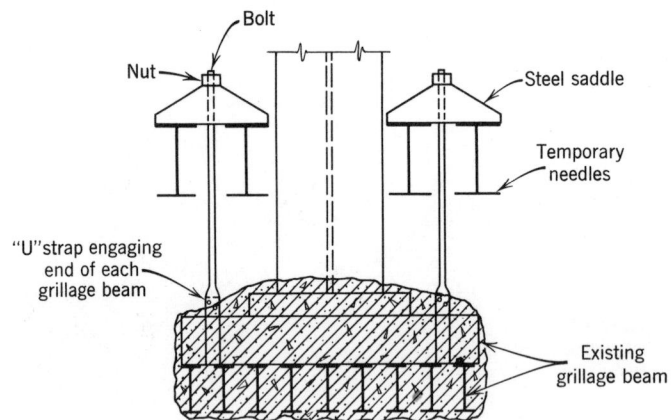

FIG. 9.   METHOD OF SUSPENDING EXISTING GRILLAGE FOR NEW CONSTRUCTION UNDERNEATH EXISTING COLUMN, ST. GEORGE HOTEL, BROOKLYN, N. Y.

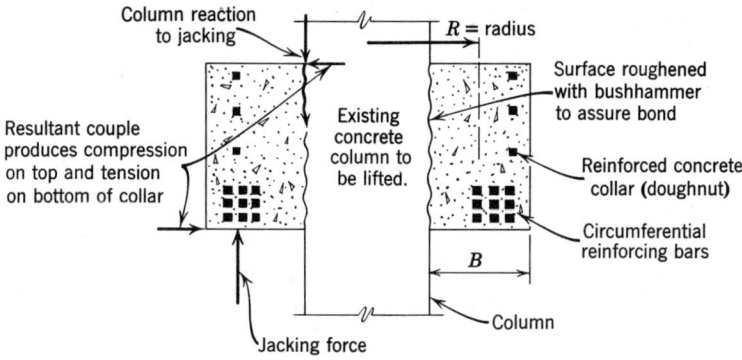

As the collar shrinks, its circumference is reduced, which causes it to grip the column; but shrinkage also causes the radial thickness to become less and loosen the grip. If C is the coefficient of shrinkage, then net movement of the inside surface of the concrete collar due to both shrinkage actions $= R \times C - \frac{1}{2} B \times C$. This value is always positive, so that the bond is actually improved by the shrinkage of the concrete.

FIG. 10. REINFORCED-CONCRETE COLLAR (DOUGHNUT) FOR JACKING OF COLUMN.

(For design of concrete collar see problem 1.)

Problem 1. Design of Concrete Collar (Doughnut)

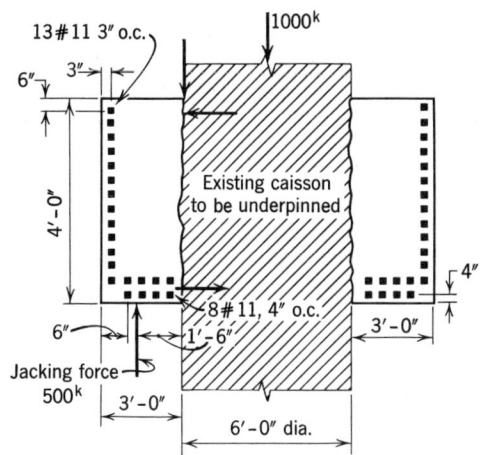

Given: Caisson Load $= 1000$ kips

Find: Dimensions and reinforcement of collar

Assume:

    Shrinkage coefficient for
Concrete $= 3 \times 10^{-4}$ in./in.

    Modulus of elasticity for concrete $= 3,000,000$ p.s.i.

    Bond of rough concrete on concrete $= 0.5$

    $f_{\text{yield}} =$ yield stress of steel reinforcement $= 40,000$ p.s.i.

    2 jacks used.

FIG. 11. CONCRETE COLLAR SHOWING REINFORCING.

Design: Assume dimensions of collar as shown, and check for stresses.

Net radial shrinkage $=$ Thickness of collar $\times$ coefficient of shrinkage
$$= 3 \times 12 \times 3 \times 10^{-4} = 0.0108 \text{ in.}$$

Unit shrinkage $= \dfrac{0.0108}{36} = 3 \times 10^{-4}$ in./in.

Shrinkage stress $= 3 \times 10^{-4} \times 3 \times 10^{6} = 900$ p.s.i.

Shrinkage force or grip acting on inner surface of collar $= 900 \times 6\pi \times 4 \times 144 = 9760$ kips

Friction resistance on collar $= 9760 \times 0.5 = 4880$ kips.

Steel reinforcement against shrinkage:

$$\text{Area of steel required per inch depth of collar} = \frac{900 \times 36}{40,000} - 0.81 \text{ sq. in./in.}$$

$\therefore$ Total steel required $= 48 \times 0.81 = 38.9$ sq. in.

Only half this amount will be used, assuming the friction of the contact area of caisson and collar will prevent excessive cracking of the collar.

Use therefore 13 No. 11 bars as shown above.

Reinforcement for jacking load:

Assume $f_s = 20,000$ p.s.i. and $f_c = 1350$ p.s.i.

Moment due to jacking load $= 500 \times 1.5 = 750$ kip-ft.

Check for compressive stress in concrete: *

$$f_c = \frac{2 \times 750,000}{0.35 \times 3 \times 3.67^2 \times 144} = 740 \text{ p.s.i.} \quad \text{(o.k.)}$$

Amount of steel reinforcement required:

$$A_s = \frac{750,000}{20,000 \times 3.67 \times 0.87} = 11.8 \text{ sq. in.}$$

Use 8 No. 11 bars as shown above.

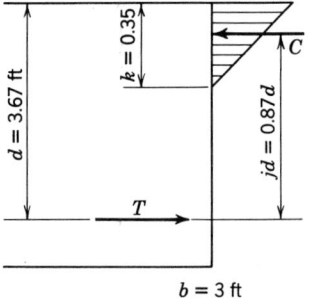

$b = 3$ ft

---

*$M = \tfrac{1}{2} f_c k b d^2$

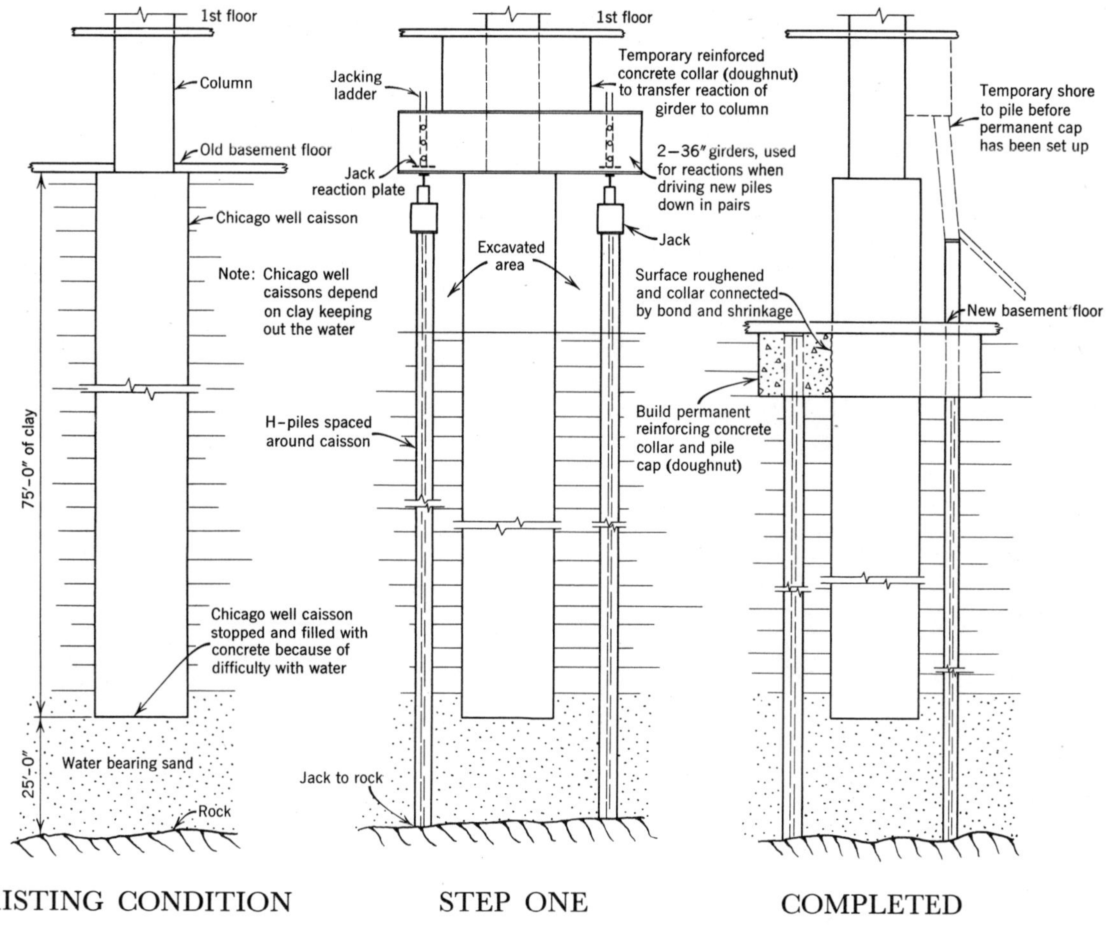

1st floor

Column

Old basement floor

Jack reaction plate

Chicago well caisson

Note: Chicago well caissons depend on clay keeping out the water

75'-0" of clay

H-piles spaced around caisson

Chicago well caisson stopped and filled with concrete because of difficulty with water

25'-0"

Water bearing sand

Rock

1st floor

Jacking ladder

Temporary reinforced concrete collar (doughnut) to transfer reaction of girder to column

2-36" girders, used for reactions when driving new piles down in pairs

Jack

Excavated area

Surface roughened and collar connected by bond and shrinkage

Build permanent reinforcing concrete collar and pile cap (doughnut)

Jack to rock

Temporary shore to pile before permanent cap has been set up

New basement floor

EXISTING CONDITION   STEP ONE   COMPLETED

FIG. 12.   UNDERPINNING CAISSON NOT CARRIED TO ROCK.

(Garage of Carson, Pirie & Scott Company, Chicago, Ill.)

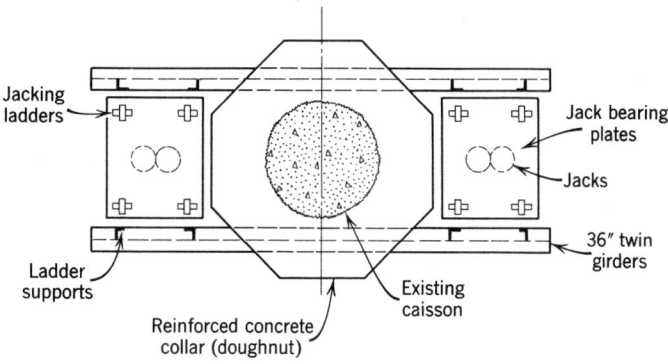

Jacking ladders

Jack bearing plates

Jacks

36" twin girders

Ladder supports

Reinforced concrete collar (doughnut)

Existing caisson

FIG. 13.   TOP VIEW OF UNDERPINNING ARRANGEMENT SHOWN IN FIG. 12.

(For typical reinforcement of collar, see Fig. 11.)

Jacking ladders permit adjustment of jack bearing plates when limit of jack is reached.

FIG. 14. JACKING OF PILES ON OPPOSITE SIDES OF COLUMN.

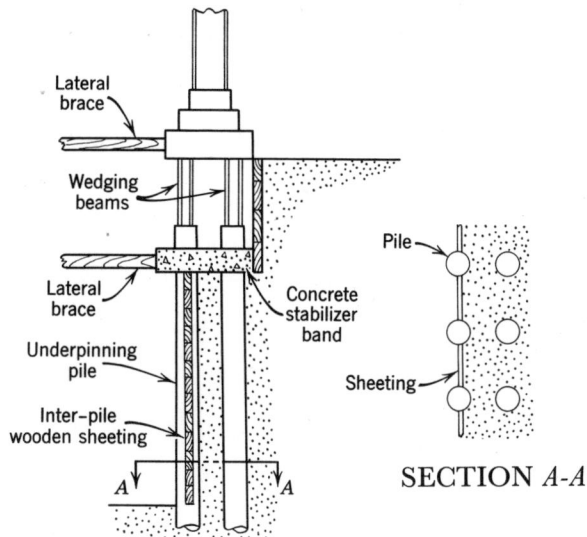

FIG. 15. CROSS SECTION SHOWING INTERPILE SHEETING.

(From *Underpinning* by Prentis and White, by permission of Columbia University Press.)

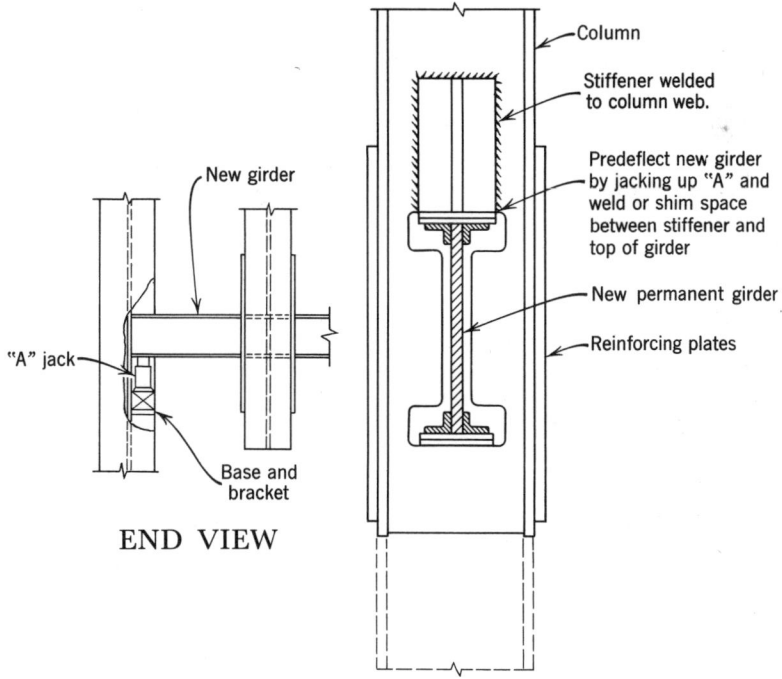

FIG. 16. CUTTING OFF STEEL COLUMN WITHOUT NEEDLING.

Procedure:

1. Reinforce flanges by welding plates.
2. Burn I-shaped hole into web of column.
3. Insert specially designed narrow flanged steel girder.
4. Weld stiffener to column web. Connection designed to take full load of column.
5. Predeflect girder and secure ends ready to take the load.

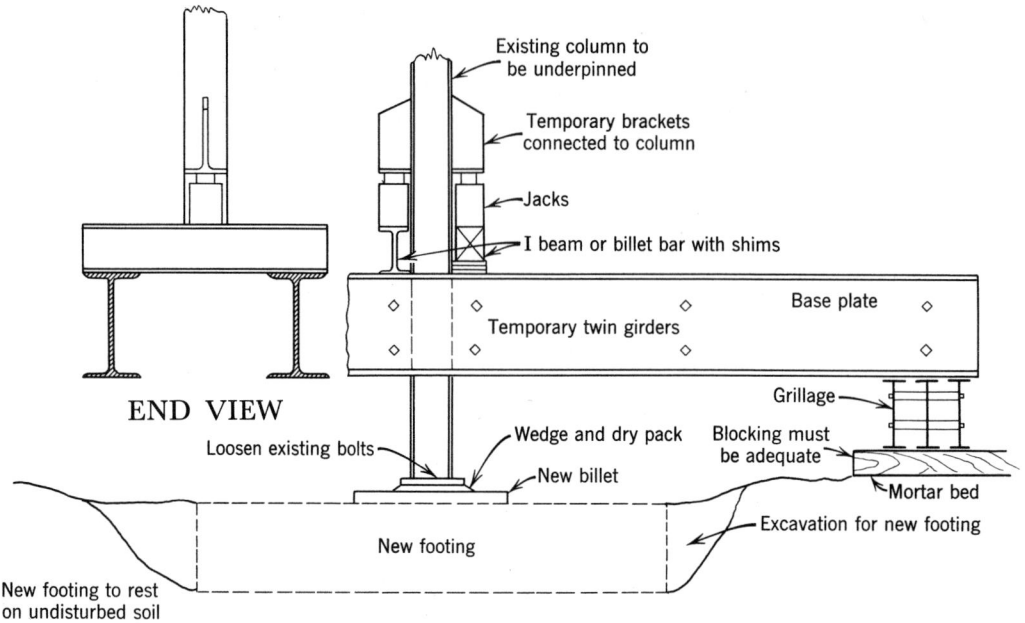

FIG. 17.   UNDERPINNING EXISTING STEEL COLUMN.

(Placing new foundation under existing column.)

Procedure:

1. Important: Design all elements including welds of seats to columns for the load to be lifted. Compute required deflection of temporary girder.

2. Connect brackets to column. Set up grillage, blocking, and girders.

3. Place jacks and load temporary girder to computed required deflection to lift column load. Leave space between base plate and footing. Remove footing.

4. Excavate, and place new footing.

5. Wedge and dry-pack between footing and column base plate to consolidate new footing on soil.

6. Release jacks, and remove brackets, girders, etc.

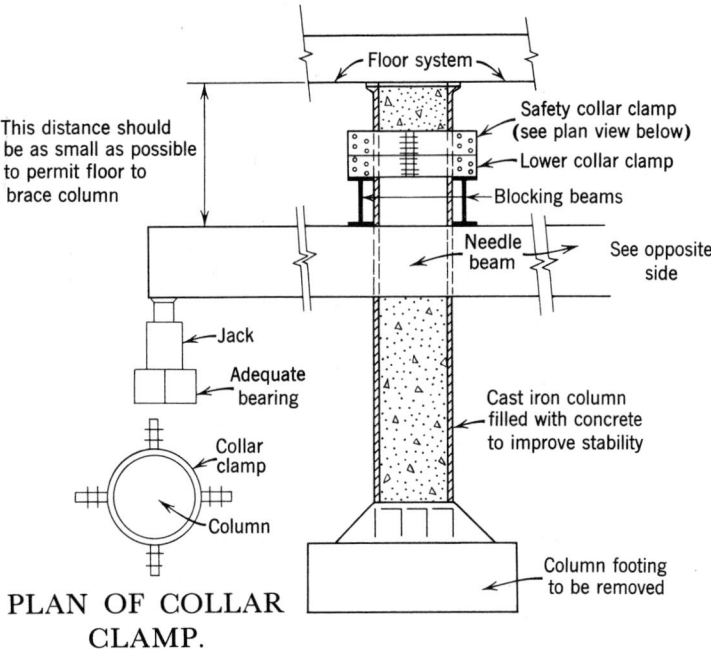

This distance should be as small as possible to permit floor to brace column

Floor system

Safety collar clamp **(see plan view below)**

Lower collar clamp

Blocking beams

Needle beam

See opposite side

Jack

Adequate bearing

Collar clamp

Column

Cast iron column filled with concrete to improve stability

Column footing to be removed

PLAN OF COLLAR CLAMP.

FIG. 18.   GRIPPING CAST-IRON COLUMN FOR NEEDLING.

Notes on design:

1. Compute load on column; design needles and clamps.

2. Carrying capacity of clamp results from friction resistance on column (not subject to exact computation).

3. Clamp lower collar.

4. Predeflect needles to column load.

5. Clamp upper collar for safety factor.

6. Burn off column, and install permanent support.

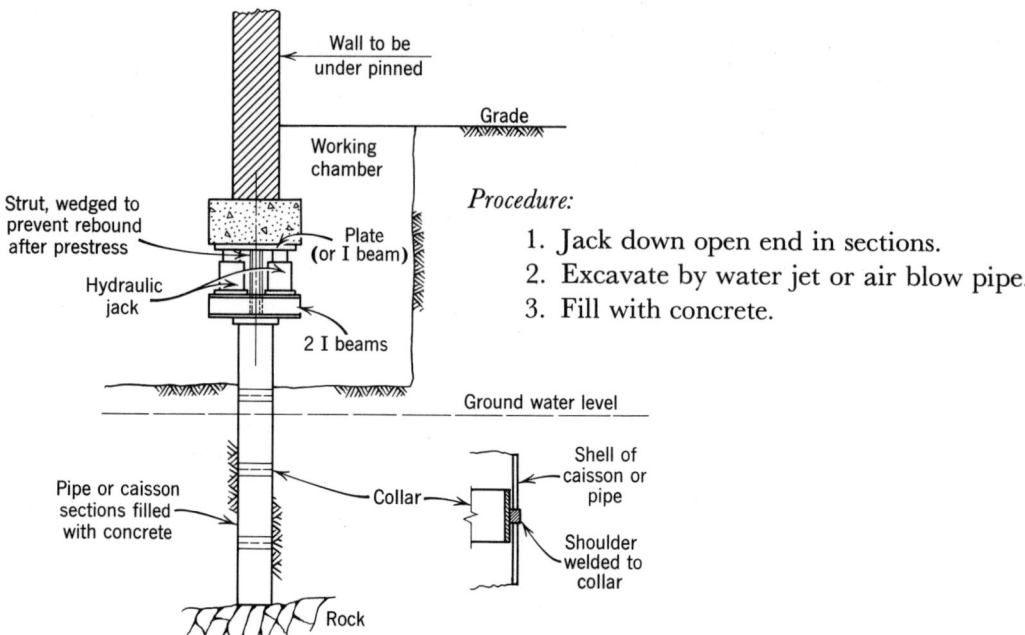

FIG. 19.　UNDERPINNING WITH PIPE SECTIONS.

Pretest; i.e., jacking load is also a test.

Procedure:

1. Jack down open end in sections.
2. Excavate by water jet or air blow pipe.
3. Fill with concrete.

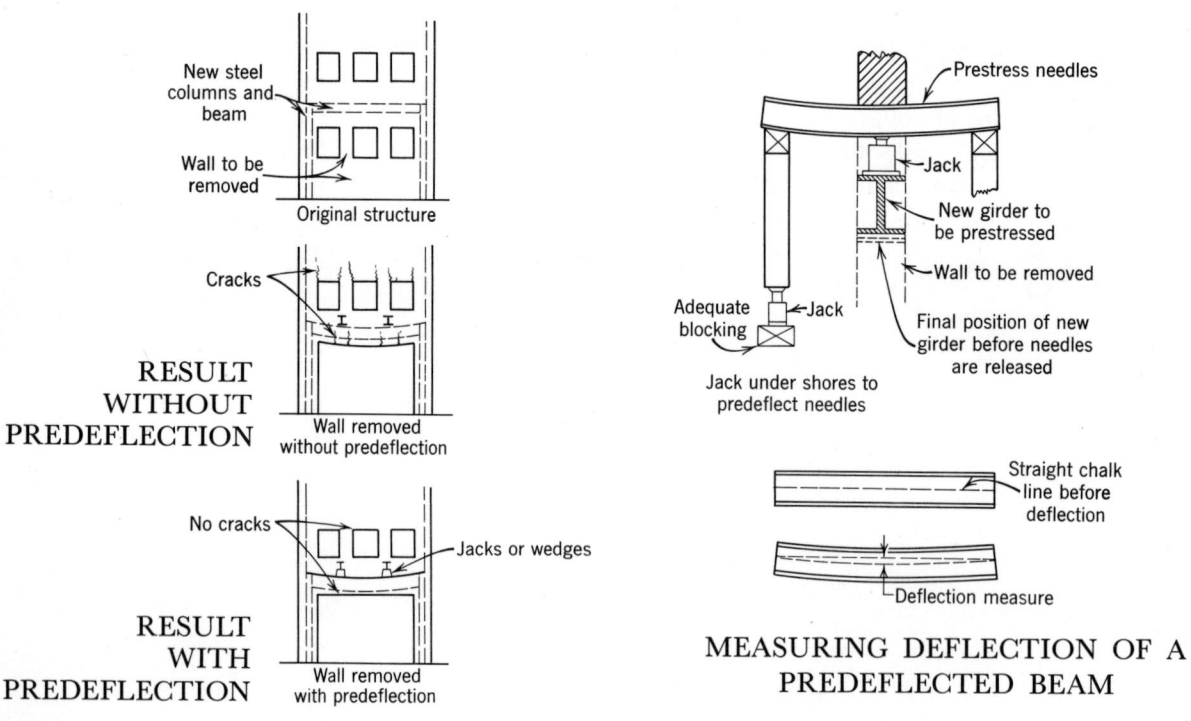

FIG. 20.　PRESTRESSING STRUCTURAL MEMBERS IN REMODELING OPERATIONS.

(Masonry cracks prevented by proper construction procedure.)

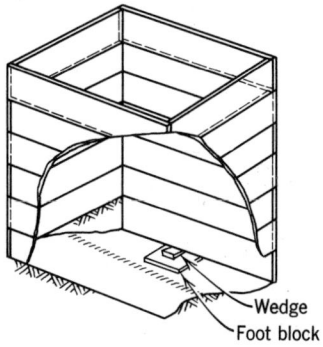

Wedge
Foot block

Fig. A. Showing how Pit Boards are Set.

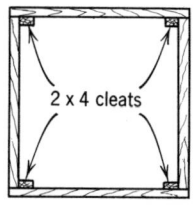

2 x 4 cleats

Fig. B. Plan of Fig. A.

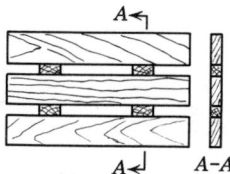

Fig. C. Louvers. Type with Cleats between.

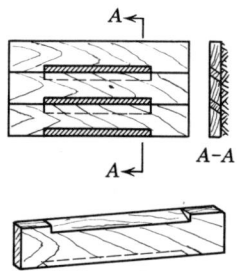

Fig. D. Louvers. Type with Notches Cut in Board.

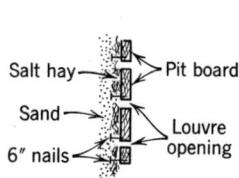

Salt hay
Sand
6″ nails
Pit board
Louvre opening

Fig. E. Nails and hay used to prevent runs in pits. The hay, held in position by the nails, acts somewhat as a shelf to hold material packed on it through the louvres, and prevents run. Any lost ground can be repacked through the louvres.

FIG. 21. HORIZONTAL SHEETING, OR BOX SHEETING, OF UNDERPINNING PIT.

(From *Underpinning* by Prentis and White, by permission of Columbia University Press.)

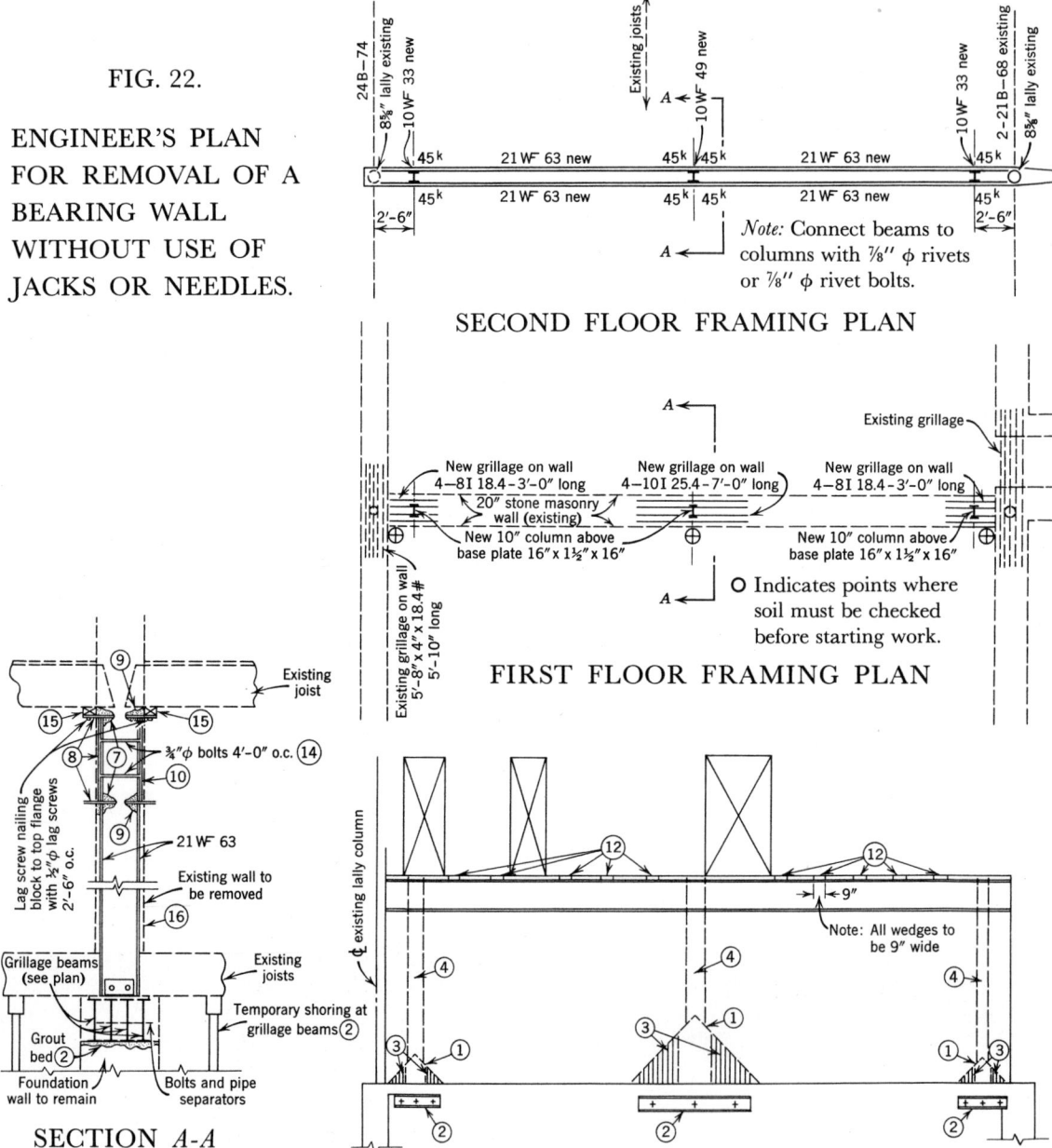

FIG. 22.

ENGINEER'S PLAN
FOR REMOVAL OF A
BEARING WALL
WITHOUT USE OF
JACKS OR NEEDLES.

SECOND FLOOR FRAMING PLAN

Note: Connect beams to columns with ⅞″ ϕ rivets or ⅞″ ϕ rivet bolts.

FIRST FLOOR FRAMING PLAN

O Indicates points where soil must be checked before starting work.

SECTION *A-A*

ELEVATION OF WALL

Note: All wedges to be 9″ wide

GENERAL PROCEDURE:

1. Cut triangles in bottom of wall.
2. Place grillage on grout bed after existing first-floor joists have been shored as per. sect. *A-A.*
3. Partially fill in bottom of wall.
4. Cut wall above vertically for columns.
5. Erect columns.
6. Drill 1½″ ϕ holes in wall for ¾″ ϕ bolts for new beams.
7. Cut notches on one side of wall.
8. Place beam on notched side of wall, and dry-pack top and bottom.

9. Cut notches on other side of wall.
10. Place beam on other side but do not dry-pack.
11. Cut holes for wedges, insert wedges, and remove dry packing at bottom of beam.
12. Predeflect both beams ⅛″ by means of wedges.
13. Dry-pack both beams.
14. Insert ¾″ ϕ bolts.
15. Place nailing block along beams, and spike joists to nailing block.
16. Remove wall below.

Check soil where indicated on plan and notify engineer before starting work.

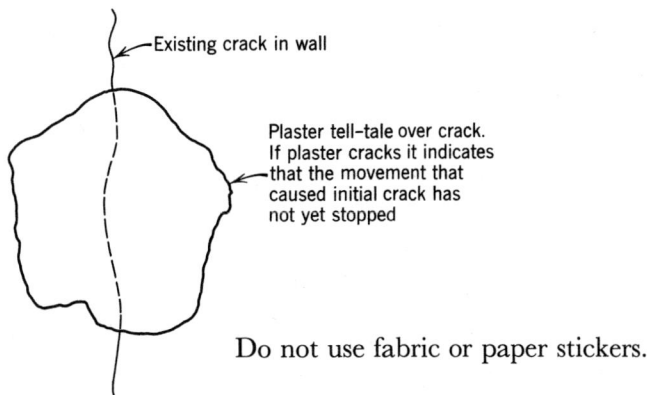

Existing crack in wall

Plaster tell-tale over crack. If plaster cracks it indicates that the movement that caused initial crack has not yet stopped

Do not use fabric or paper stickers.

FIG. 23.   TELL-TALE OVER CRACK.

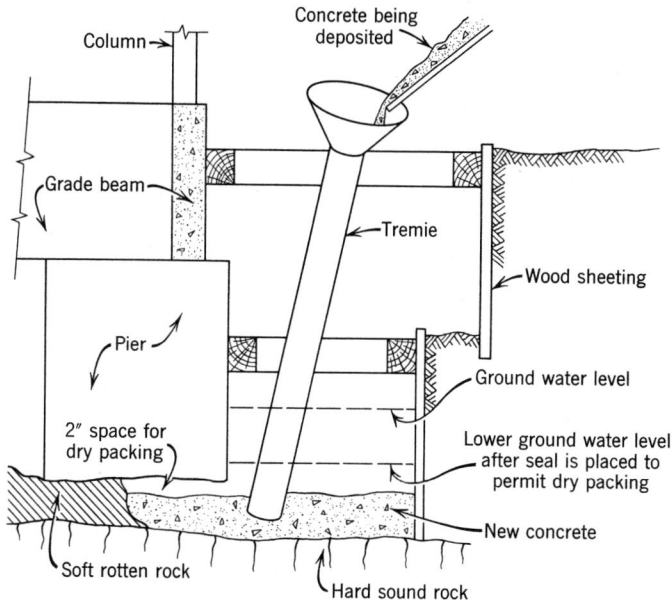

Concrete being deposited

Column

Grade beam

Tremie

Wood sheeting

Pier

Ground water level

2" space for dry packing

Lower ground water level after seal is placed to permit dry packing

New concrete

Soft rotten rock

Hard sound rock

Note: When water was pumped down more water ran in through seams in soft rotten rock, tending to disintegrate the fresh concrete.

FIG. 24.   UNDERPINNING PIER UNDER WATER.

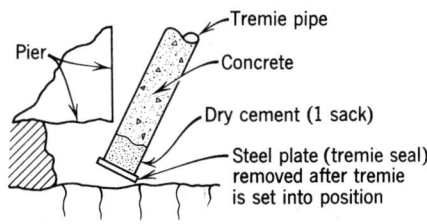

Tremie pipe

Pier

Concrete

Dry cement (1 sack)

Steel plate (tremie seal) removed after tremie is set into position

FIG. 25.   DETAIL OF PLACING TREMIE.

GROUTING

Pressure grouting is used for the following purposes:
1. Filling of fissures in a rock foundation.
2. Filling cavities around a pipe shaft or tunnel.
3. Filling deep fissures or seams to prevent seepage around or under a dam.
4. Filling cavities in limestone foundation under or near foundation.
5. Stabilizing dry sands that were unexpectedly encountered in tunneling work by means of chemical injections through pipes driven ahead of the tunnel face. The trickling dry sand may increase the pressure on the timbering and destroy all relieving effects of arching.
6. Filling depressions in clayey subsoils on which existing railway roadbeds rest. The depressions may become filled with water, which then produces a mushy condition at the contact surfaces between subsoil and ballast, and by repeated train passages the depressions become enlarged (pumping).

The grout is usually composed of cement and water, although emulsified asphalts have been used particularly in railroad sub-base stabilization.

A similar process has been developed using solutions of sodium silicate (water glass) and calcium chloride injected separately into soils. Upon contact these chemicals are supposed to combine to form a hard gel. This method may be of some value, but cement grout should usually accomplish as good results and do so more economically.

In some places, asphalt grouting may prove successful, as in the Hales Bar Dam on the Tennessee River. Water was flowing with appreciable velocity through large fissures in the rock, and common cement grouting was washed away as fast as it could be placed. The grouting was finally accomplished by pumping hot asphalt to the open fissures. The asphalt was kept in fluid condition by an electrically heated wire. When the asphalt reached the open fissures it cooled and hardened and was not washed away by the water.

Pressure grouting equipment consists of a pump to force the grout (a commercial mud jack machine developing about 250 lb. pressure is often used; see Fig. 27), and a steel pipe to be driven into the soil or rock to deliver the grout.

Pressure grouting is applicable to:

Igneous rock, siliceous sandstones, and other non-cavernous rock through which the grout could not be washed away. Generally portland cement grout is used.

Gravel and sandy soils. Generally portland cement grout or two chemical systems have been used.

Silty soils. Asphalt compounds have generally been used with equipment similar to that used with cement pressure grouting. The emulsified asphalt is maintained at atmospheric temperature, and it sets by losing the free water.

Pressure grouting is not applicable to:

Carbonate rocks or claybound or carbonate-bound sandstones. New channels may be leached as fast as old ones are closed unless special cutoff walls are used for stopping or reducing the flow.

Clays and other impervious soils which resist the penetration of the grout.

Discussion

Grouting has on occasion been used successfully. It has the drawback of working blind. There is little control of where the grout is going, making it impossible to ensure complete filling of all voids. It has had its greatest success in preventing seepage where 100% sealing is not required. Caution must be used in saturated soils, as heave may be caused by the grout's being forced in faster than the water can be drained.

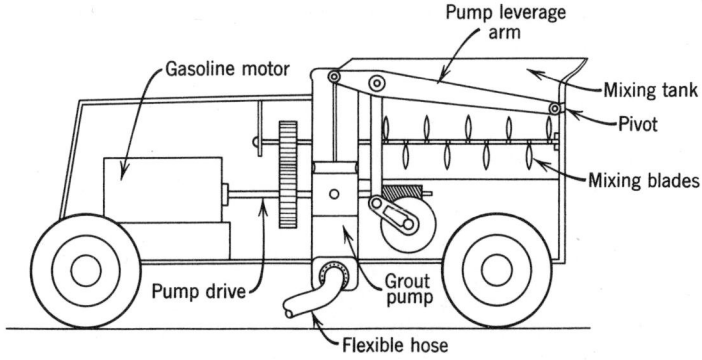

FIG. 26.   PRESSURE GROUTING MACHINE.*

MUD JACKING

Mud jacking consists of forcing a slurry of topsoil, water, and a small amount of portland cement under a concrete slab to fill the voids and force the slab upwards.   Twelve-inch pavements have been raised several inches in this manner.   Holes $2\frac{1}{2}$ to $2\frac{5}{8}''$ ϕ are drilled in the pavement, and the slurry is forced in.   Holes not being filled are closed with wood plugs.   The pressure (over 100 p.s.i. at the jack) forces the slurry under the slab and then forces the slab up.

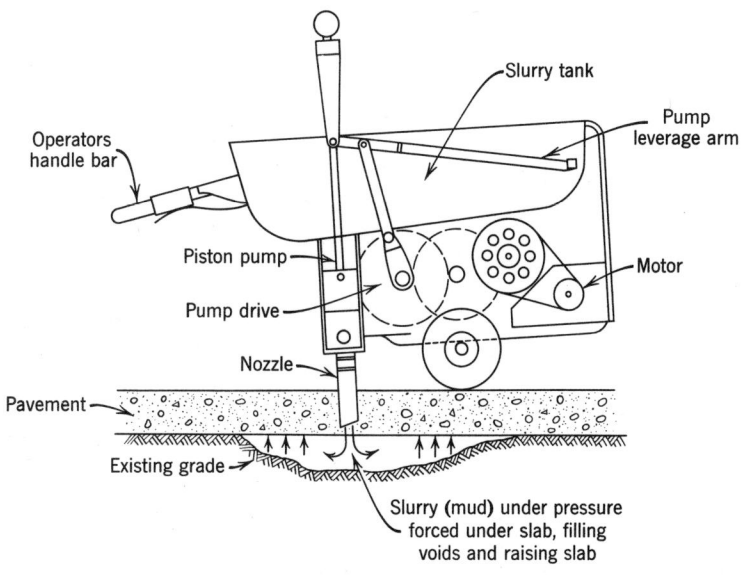

FIG. 27.   MUD JACK.*

* Courtesy Koehring Co. *Mud Jack* is a registered trade mark.

Discussion

Applicability of mud jacking depends upon the cause of settlement. Unless the settlement is complete, mudjacking is only a temporary relief measure. Most common applications of mudjacking have been: settled approaches to highway structures, settled floors on ground in buildings where walls and columns are on piles, highway slabs undermined by pumping.

Mud used is generally made of screened topsoil. Sands will not pump well. Clays take too long to dry and have too high a shrinkage factor. Silty loams work best though the organic material in topsoil seems to improve the pumping qualities. Portland cement is added to hasten early consolidation of the slurry and reduce shrinkage. Rich mixtures also tend to pump easier.

Operation is generally done by a specialty contractor experienced in the work. Slabs with little void space under are difficult to lift as there is no room to place mud to exert pressure. Once started up though, the slab may be raised as easily as any other. Different holes are alternately filled so as to bring the slab up as evenly as possible.

Holes are drilled to fit the standard nozzles. Since the mud flows out in a circular pattern under the floor, the holes should be laid out in a circular pattern about each other.

VIBRATION

Pile Driving and Blasting

Driving piles close to existing structures on sensitive foundations may cause cracks and/or settlement.

Sensitive Foundations Include:

Sands and granular soils if loose. For instance, a sand weighing less than 95 lb. per cu. ft. should be looked on as likely to give trouble. The same is true for other light soils.

Oversaturated soils where trapped water carrying part of the load may be suddenly released by vibration.

Peats and organic strata. Easily subject to further compaction.

Weak foundations, such as dry rubble or rubble with weak mortar.

Overloaded foundations, such as, say, 10 tons per sq. ft. on a clay soil.

Foundations lacking continuous strength, such as a block or brick foundation as contrasted with a reinforced-concrete foundation.

Weakened substructure or superstructure walls, such as bulged, or cracked walls, walls out of plumb.

Previous settlement, structure showing signs of previous settlement.

TABLE I *

NATURAL FREQUENCY OF VIBRATOR ON VARIOUS TYPES OF SOIL

Supporting Soil or Rock	*Frequency, cycles per second*
Loose fill	19.1
Dense artificial cinderfill	21.3
Fairly dense medium sand	24.1
Very dense mixed-grained sand	26.7
Dense pea gravel	28.1
Soft limestone	30.0
Sandstone	34.0

Note: These frequencies are for a specific machine under specific conditions and are not fundamental properties of the soils themselves. However, they are included as being approximate frequencies under which vibration conditions may occur.

Avoidance of Damage

Reinforce existing foundations by underpinning wall:

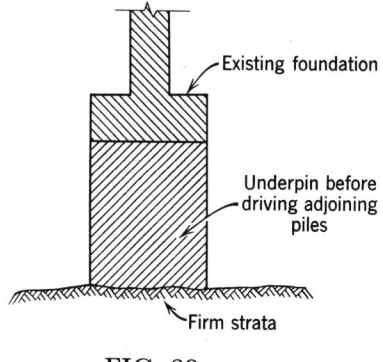

FIG. 28.

Shore or needle adjoining walls during driving.

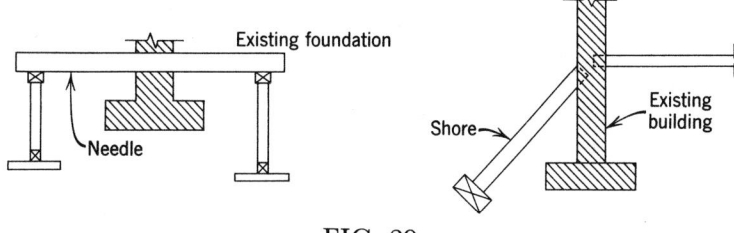

FIG. 29.

---

* From H. Lorenz, "Neue Ergebnisse der dynamischen Baugrund *forschung*," *Z. Ver. deut. Ing.*, Vol. 78, pp. 379–385, 1934.

Use jacked cylinders in place of driven piles for piles near the existing foundations.

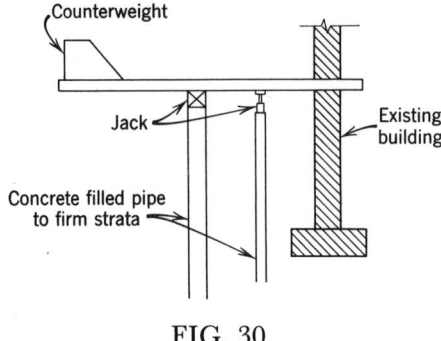

FIG. 30.

Piles under existing building: See p. 1–11.

Blasting may cause settlement in the same way as pile driving.   The methods of protection against damage are similar to those given above.

Machine vibration may cause settlement of loose soils.   Possible corrective methods are: Compact the soil or carry down foundations to a firm stratum.   Provide elastic dampening pads.

Machine Foundations.   When it is desired to prevent a vibrating machine from transmitting the vibrations to a floor, or vice versa, methods of approach are shown in Fig. 31.

Insulating Columns from Vibration.   In the case of the Grand Central Terminal there was the problem of preventing train vibration from being transmitted to the tall building constructed in the "air rights" over the tracks through the supporting columns.

This could be prevented (*a*) if the decks were built free from the columns, and (*b*) if a lead cushion were inserted under the column bases to prevent vibrations from coming through the rock into the columns.   See Fig. 31.

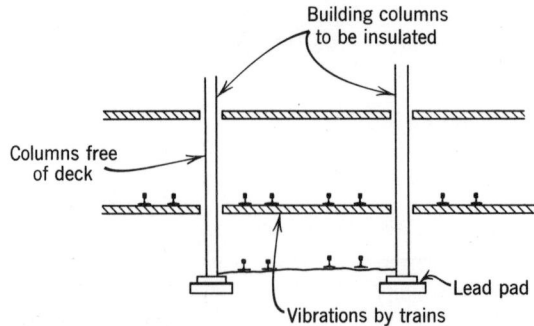

FIG. 31.   INSULATION OF GRAND CENTRAL TERMINAL.

Elimination of Vibration in Tall Buildings in Grand Central Terminal Area

The following data on elimination of vibration in the Grand Central Terminal were obtained for the author by Richard E. Dougherty, formerly Engineering Vice President of the New York Central System, who quotes Mr. Robert Crane, Chief Engineer of the New York Central System, as follows:

"Regarding use of lead mats under column bases at Grand Central Terminal for reduction of vibration: During construction the Main Station Building columns were not provided with lead mats under the grillages; consequently vibration is noticeable throughout the building during train movements.

"Following tests made at Columbia University, lead mats were installed under the steel grillages of building columns in all later buildings erected in the Grand Central Terminal Area. This form of vibration mat, together with complete separation of viaduct and railroad structures from the building framing system, has resulted in high-class hotel, office, and residential buildings, directly over our railroad tracks, free of any noticeable vibration."

RED LIGHT

Use of open-ended pipe or cylinder if jetted into running sand may cause loss of material under adjoining footings.

Tell Tales

Place tell tales on all cracks of existing building and watch for signs of trouble during driving. Tell tales should be of plaster of paris or cement, not paper or fabric. *Survey of existing building* should be made before starting operations. See Chapter 17.

Discussion

Elastic Vibration

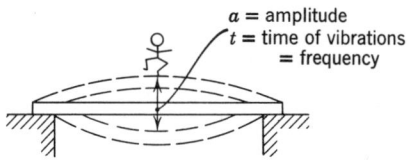

FIG. 32.

A child bouncing on a plank is an illustration of elastic vibration. The *amplitude* of the plank vibration is *a*. The elapsed time between jounces of the child is the *period* or *frequency* of the vibration.

If the child regulates the time of his jounce to the natural frequency of the plank he produces resonance, and he bounces higher and higher. If a block of soft rubber were introduced on top of the plank, deflections due to the child's bounces would be reduced, and also the resonance would be broken up.

Vibrations are transmitted to a foundation by elastic chain action. See Fig. 33.

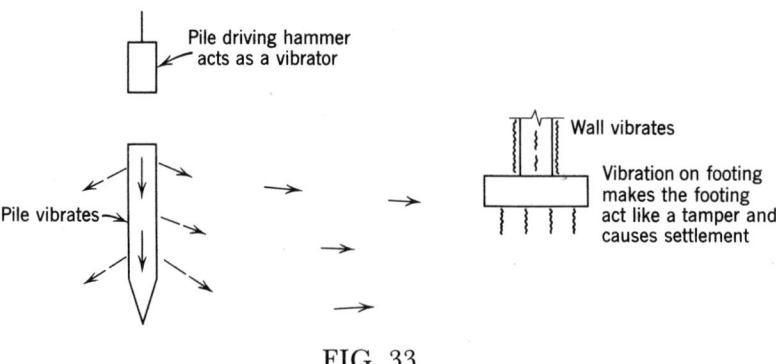

FIG. 33.

Note that in Fig. 33 the effect of the soil hitting the footing is the same as if the footing were dancing up and down on the soil, and that the footing acts like a *tamper,* which is why vibration under footings is to be feared.

Consolidation of Granular Soils by Vibration

How this may occur is shown in Fig. 33.

Legal and Realistic Considerations

Approaches to Evaluating Shock.   Measurements by accelerograph or seismograph.

Figures 34 and 35, together with the data obtained from the seismograph or accelerograph, will give some line on the dangers being caused by blasting or pile driving.

Procedure: Drive experimental piles or make experimental blasting shots at various distances from the structure.   Determine, from the seismograph or accelerograph, the acceleration or displacement and frequency of the building.   Keep the energy ratio less than 3.

GROUND VIBRATION DUE TO BLASTING

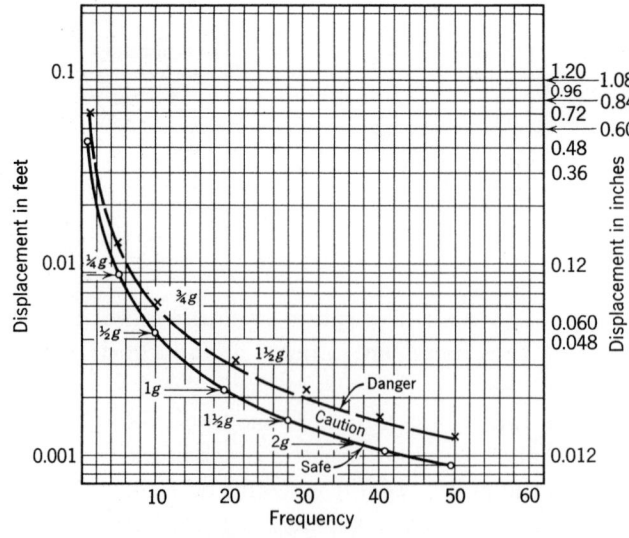

FIG. 34.   ENERGY RATIO LIMIT CHART, DISPLACEMENT vs. FREQUENCY.*

---

* From F. J. Crandell.

GROUND VIBRATION DUE TO BLASTING

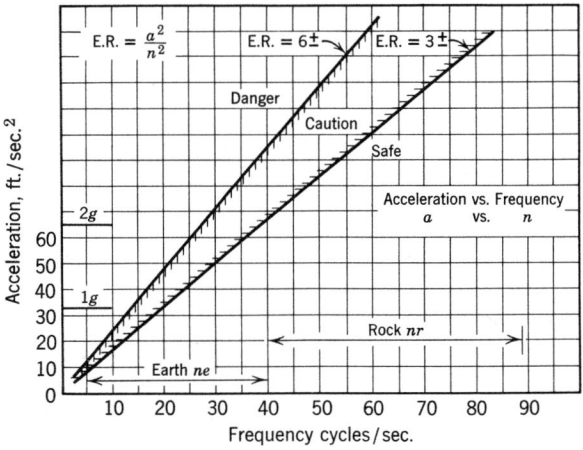

FIG. 35.   ENERGY RATIO LIMIT CHART.*

Practical Elimination of Resonance

Note that in a pile-driving or blasting operation resonance is not a problem, as the blows are single, isolated blows.   Trains, trucks, and dynamos create a chain of elastic vibration from the agitator through the ground through the column or footing in the building.   By the laws of choice and chance, resonance is extremely unlikely except in the simpler set-up such as a supporting floor vibrating a precision machine.   Here, scientific study may yield practical results.

Sound

Sound may be mistaken for vibration.   Sound will not vibrate a glass of water.

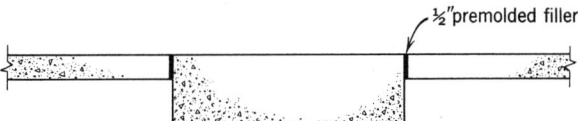

FIG. 36.   FOUNDATION FOR LIGHT HIGH-SPEED MACHINE.

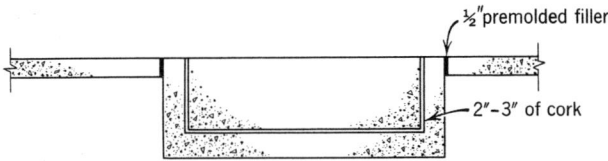

FIG. 37.   FOUNDATION FOR HEAVY HIGH-SPEED MACHINE.

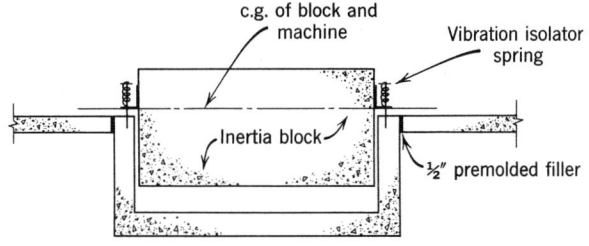

FIG. 38.   FOUNDATION FOR HEAVY LOW-SPEED MACHINE.

---

* From F. J. Crandell.

SHEET PILING

Sheet piling is used primarily to keep back earth or water during excavation.

Timber sheet piling, the simplest type, has limitations on driving and often must be pre-excavated or jetted to position. For that reason, it is not recommended for use where loss of earth from behind it is of importance.

Interlocking steel sheet piling is often used. It has a tight fit, resistance to abuse in driving, and good beam strength. The different mills furnish various rolled and fabricated shapes for different uses. See Fig. 2.

Master piles are steel H piles driven deep with sections of sheet piling between acting as catenaries. Arch and Z sections cannot be used for such purposes, as they will twist and break the interlocks when subjected to tension. See Fig. 6.

Soldier piles are H piles driven on fairly wide centers and used to restrain horizontal wood sheeting dropped between the flanges. See Fig. 7.

Caulking Sheet Piling

Sheet piling is not watertight. When the piling is driven through water, the amount of water seeping through can be reduced greatly by placing cinders, sawdust, manure, or fine sand in the water. The leakage through carries the particles into the joints and seals them. Timber sheeting also swells when wet, helping to close the joints.

Caulking is of particular importance in the case of fine running sands.

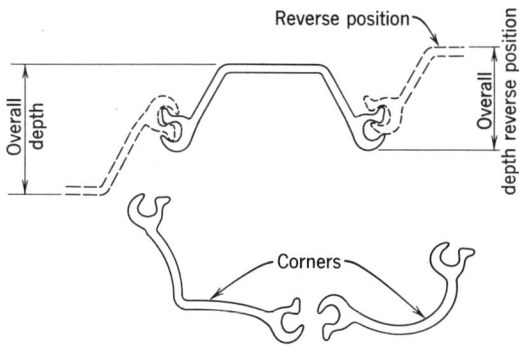

Arch web steel sheet piling. Greater beam strength. May be driven reverse position to reduce overall depth.

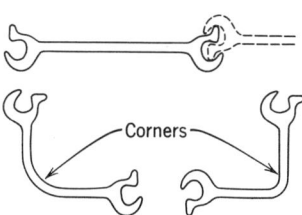

Straight web steel sheet piling: Weak in beam action. Can take tension for use in circular cellular construction.

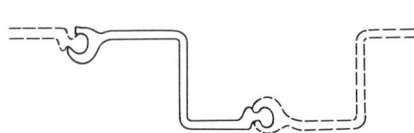

Z piling. Greatest strength.

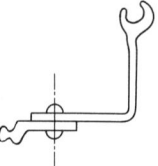

Corner piece fabricated. Other corners may be fabricated also.

FIG. 2. STEEL SHEET PILING.

For dimensions and properties, see p. 19–2.

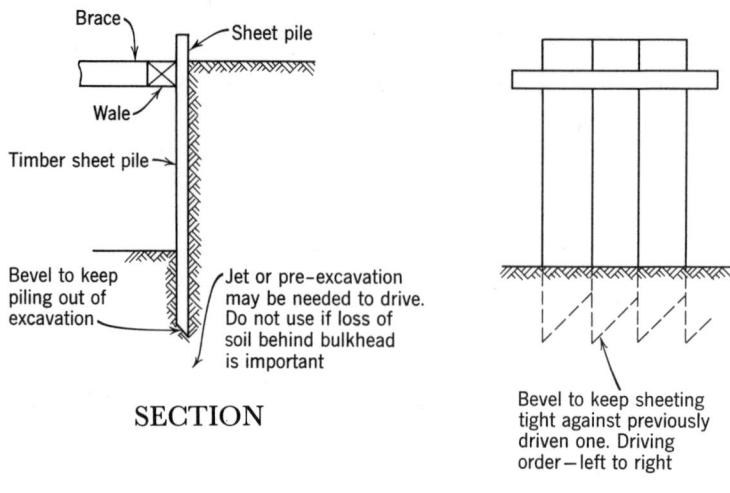

FIG. 3.   USE OF TIMBER SHEET PILING.

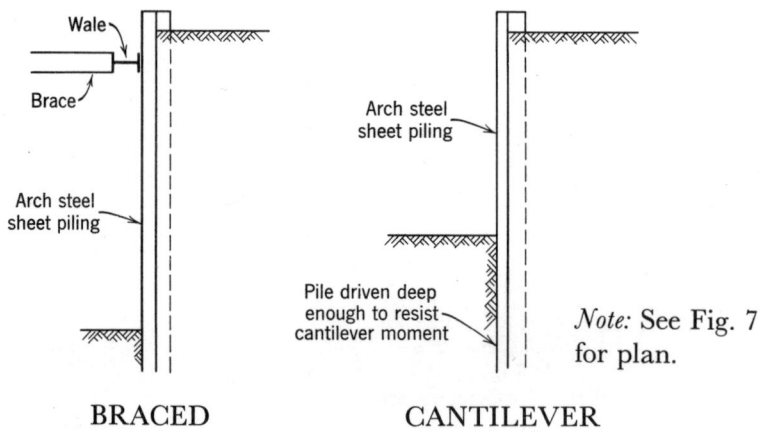

FIG. 4.   USE OF STEEL SHEET PILING.

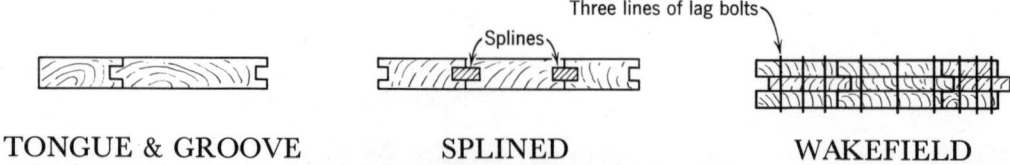

FIG. 5.   TIMBER SHEET PILES.

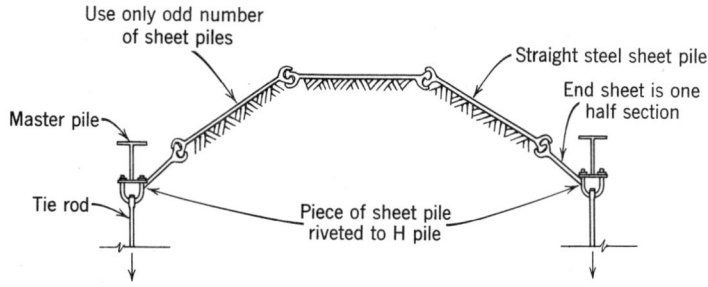

Note: Sheet pile need not be driven as deep as H piles.

FIG. 6. USE OF MASTER PILES.

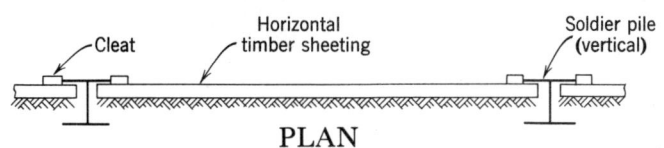

Timber short enough to fit in between pile flanges. Cleats hold timber in position.

PLAN

FIG. 7. USE OF SOLDIER PILES.

Deep building excavation

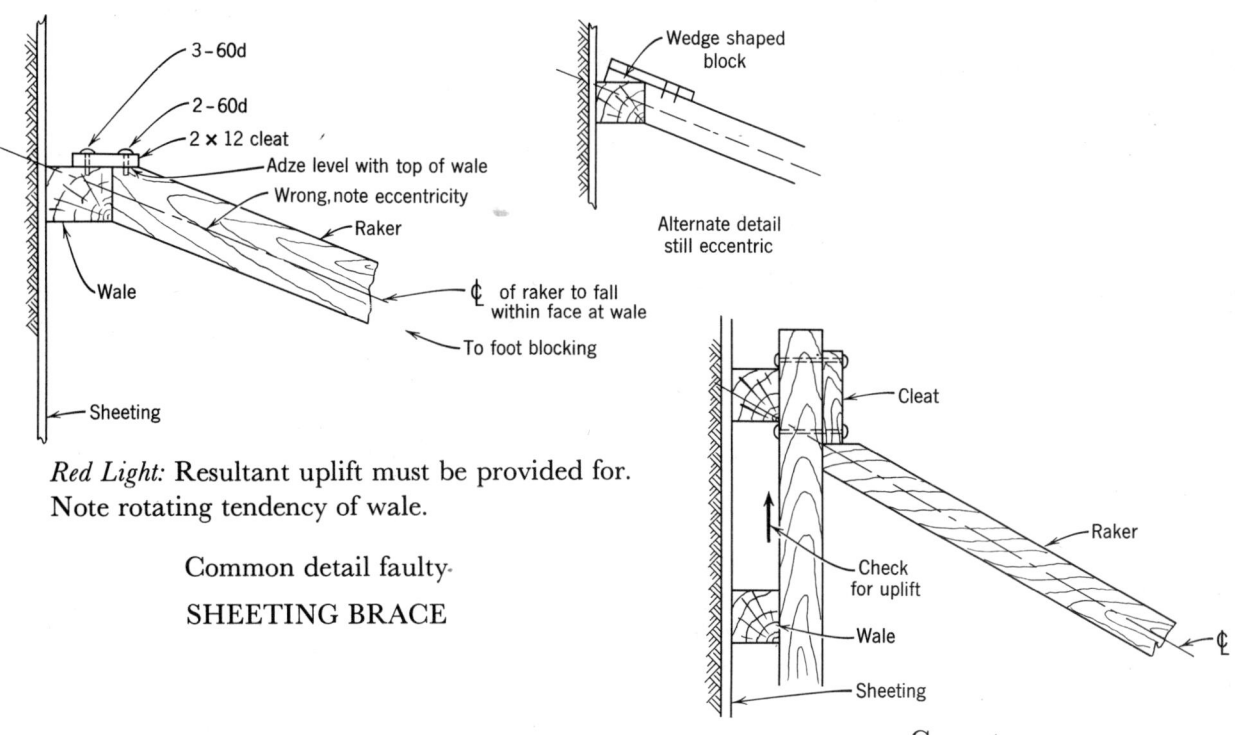

Red Light: Resultant uplift must be provided for. Note rotating tendency of wale.

Common detail faulty.
SHEETING BRACE

Correct
ALTERNATIVE SHEETING BRACE

FIG. 8. TYPICAL SHEETING BRACES.

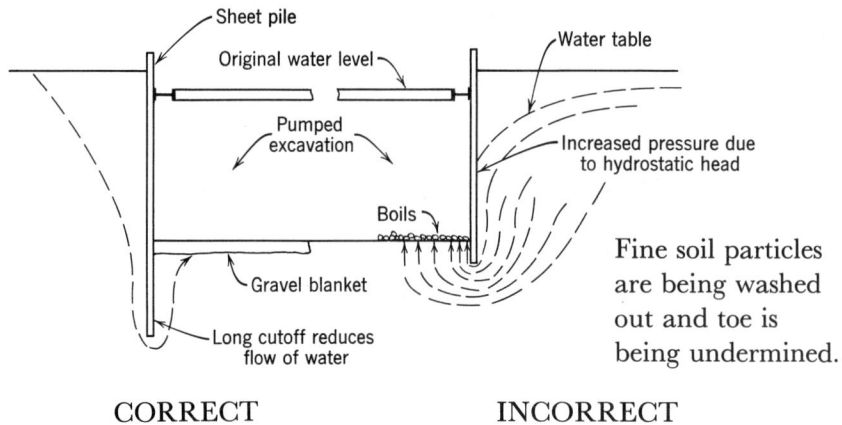

Fine soil particles
are being washed
out and toe is
being undermined.

CORRECT   INCORRECT

FIG. 9.   WATER IN EXCAVATION.

WELL POINTS

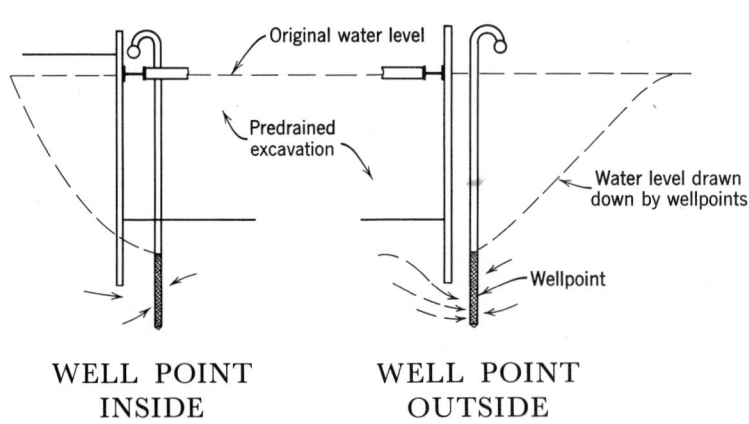

WELL POINT   WELL POINT
INSIDE   OUTSIDE

FIG. 10.   DRY EXCAVATION BY USE OF WELL POINTS.

Well points permit excavation by predraining the area to be excavated.   A well point is driven into the ground and attached to a pump.   For fine soils a sand filter is placed around the pipe and a clay plug is placed at the top of the filter.   The system then operates under a vacuum.   Well points cannot be used in very fine silts or clays.

TABLE III.

SOIL DEWATERING BY WELL POINTS

Soil	Normal Well Point	Vacuum Well Point	Electro-osmosis	Remarks
Rock fill and open gravel	Cannot be used as water yield is too high			Underwater excavation and construction often used
Graded gravel	Use. High water yield may require multistage installation			
Coarse sand	Use. High water yield. Limit 15 ft. of water per stage			Yield may exceed that of graded gravel
Medium sand	Use. Limit 17½ ft. of water per stage			
Fine sand	Use. Limit 22 ft. of water per stage. Low water yield	May be required for very fine sands		Approaches limit of gravity drainage
Sandy silt	Not applicable	Use provided sufficient sand is present. Sand lenses will help. Low water yield	May be indicated where sand content is small	
Silt		Not applicable	Indicated. Very low yield. More information is needed	Small water content removed increases stability greatly
Clay			Not applicable	Water generally not a problem
Muck Peat mud			Not applicable	Requires special studies and methods. Very poor material

Well Point Spacing and Pump Capacity Estimating Data

TABLE IV

Class	Soil	Grain Diameter, mm.	Capacity Each Griffin Well Point, gal. per min.	
A	Coarse sand	1.0–0.5	30–16	*Note:* uniformity of grain
B	Medium sand	0.5–0.25	15– 5	sizes governs variation
C	Fine sand	0.25–0.1	5– 1	in gallons per minute.

TABLE V

Model 108 Pump Capacity at Varied Suction Lifts			*Maximum Griffin Well Points for One Model 108 Pump.*		
			Soils Classed below		
Suction Lift, ft.	Gal. per Min.	% of Maximum Gal. per min.	A	B	C
10	2500	100	83	166*	500†
15	2170	85	72	144*	434†
20	1840	73	61	122*	368†
25	1380	55	46	92*	276†

* In actual practice use 75% of theoretical number of well points.
† In actual practice use 60% of theoretical number of well points.

TABLE VI

To Estimate Distance between Well Points: 8-in. header line located at elevation 2 ft. above water level. Soil classified in Table IV. Header surrounds excavation.

Depth Water, ft.	Depth Excavation, ft.	Length Riser, ft.	Soil A, ft.	Soil B, ft.	Soil C, ft.
5	7	11	4	8	6
10	12	16	3	4	6
12½	14½	19	2	4	5
15	17	21	2	3	4
17½	19½	24	*	3	3
20	22	26	*	*	3
22	24	28	*	*	3

* Use 2-stage system, suction lift above practical limits.

Example: Given 12½ ft. of water and medium sand. Select well points with 19 ft. long riser spaced 4 ft. on center. (Soil B is medium sand from Table IV.)

Excavation in Water

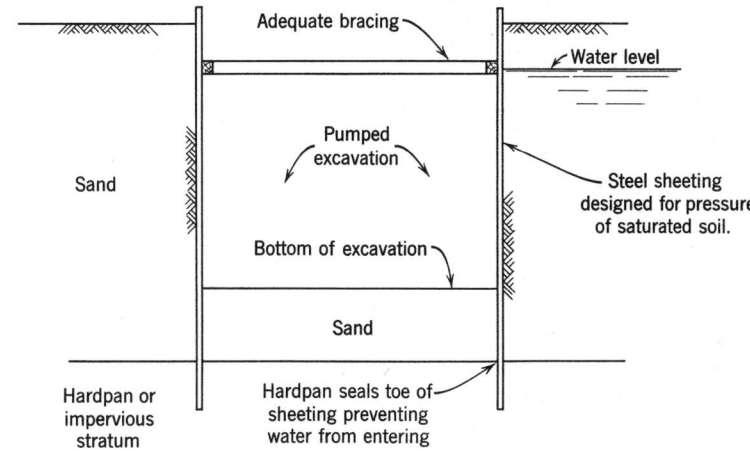

FIG. 11.   EXCAVATION IN WATER BY SEALED SHEETING.

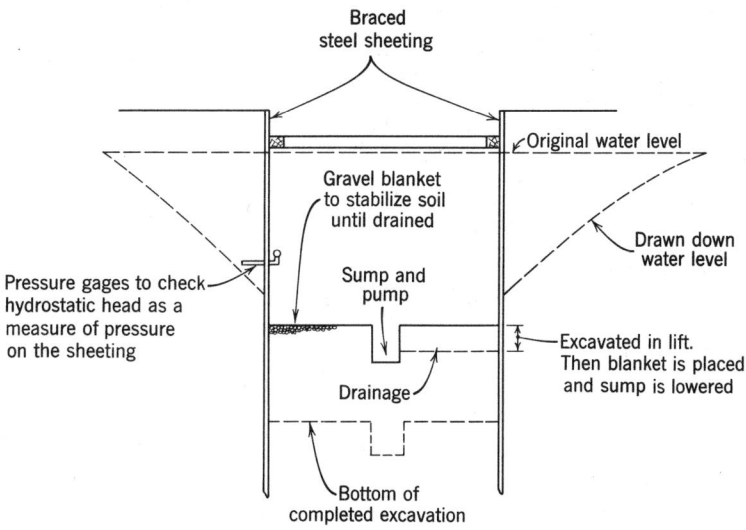

FIG. 12.   EXCAVATION BY PREDRAINAGE.

For detail of sump see Fig. 13.

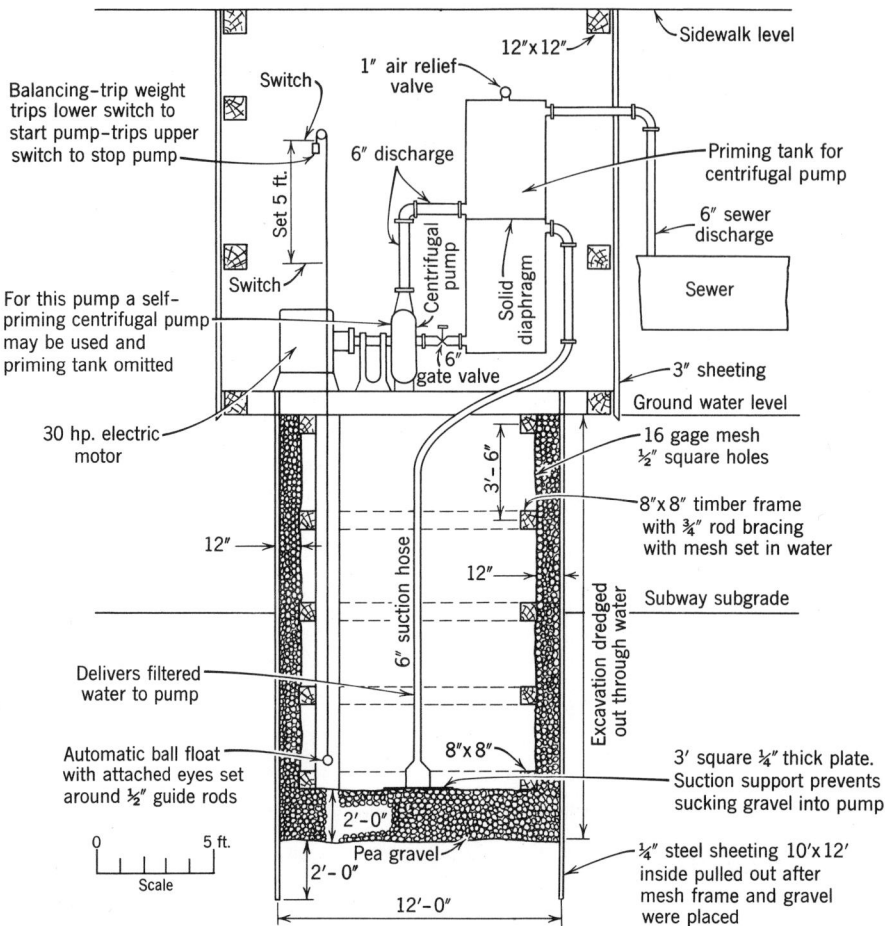

FIG. 13.   PRE-DRAINAGE SUMP AND AUTOMATIC PUMPING PLANT.

From *Underpinning* by Prentis and White, by permission of Columbia University Press.

COFFERDAMS

Cofferdams are dams placed about an area to allow temporary dewatering. They may be of the double-wall type as shown in Fig. 14, or of the single-wall type. The latter consists of an enclosure of sheet piling heavily braced. The double-wall dam gives the advantage less leakage and freedom from cross bracing.

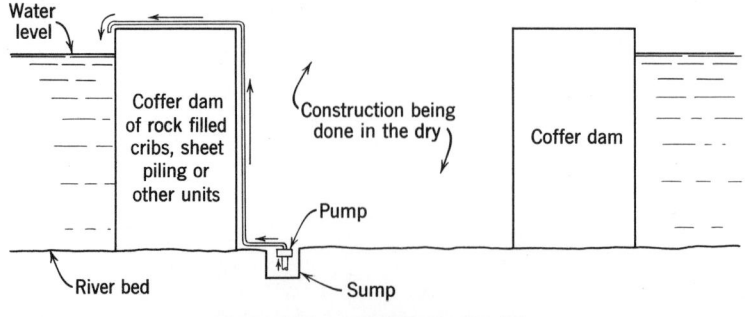

FIG. 14.   COFFERDAM.

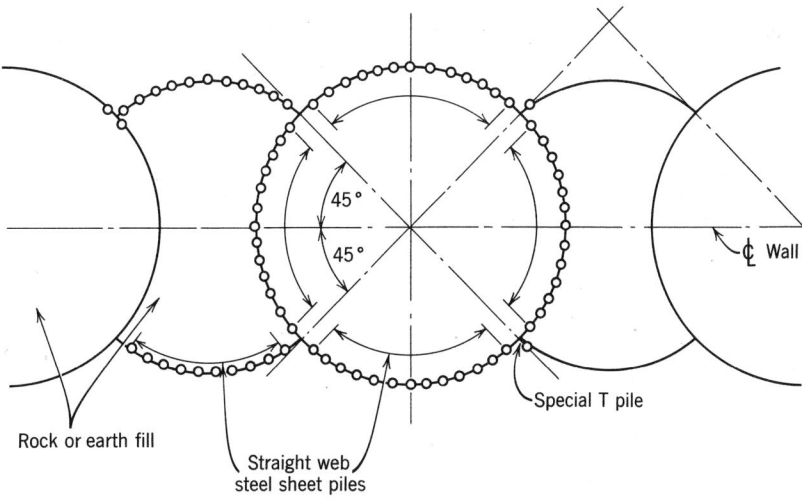

FIG. 15.   CELLULAR STEEL SHEET PILE WALL.

Used for cofferdams, breakwaters, piers.

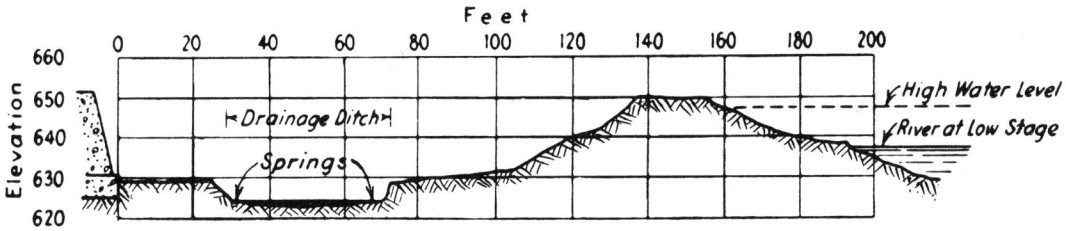

FIG. 16.   EARTH DIKE (for cofferdam).*

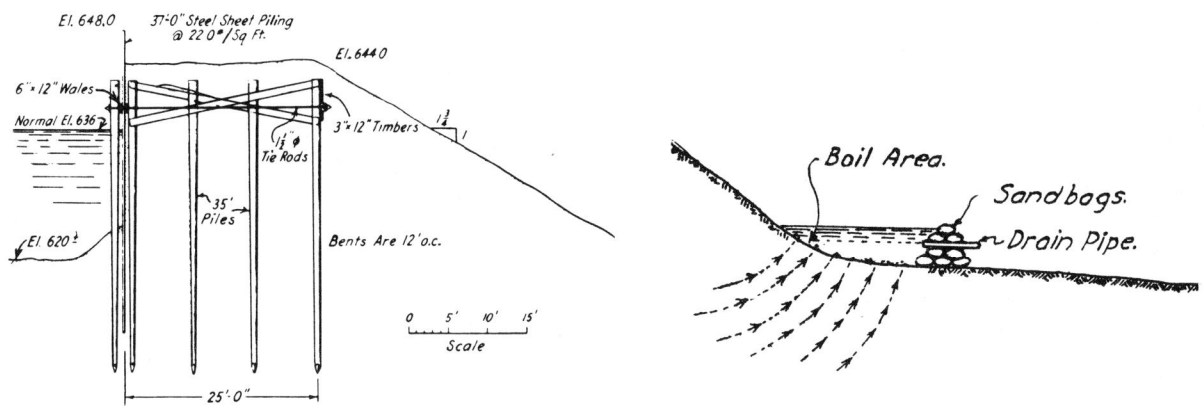

FIG. 17.   TYPICAL COFFERDAM.*   **FIG. 18.   CORRECTION OF A BOIL.***

*Adopted from White and Prentis, *Cofferdams,* by permission of Columbia University Press.

PRESSURES ON TRENCH SHEETING

Observed pressures on the sheeting of trenches do not follow the general results obtained from the Coulomb or Rankine equations. The pressure on the bracing at mid-height is more than at the bottom, a condition well known to experienced contractors and foremen. Sheeting is flexible, supported rigidly at the bracing points. In sand the deflection of the sheeting under load results in a redistribution of pressures because of arching, Fig. 20.

There is little evidence that arching occurs in clays, but there is some transfer of shearing stress to the soil below the base. Since the permanency of this transfer is questionable, both temporary and permanent values have been given. For very soft clays, organic silts, and muck this transfer should be neglected.

Because of the lack of accuracy of the assumptions, it is customary to disregard the effect of continuity in the sheeting when determining the thrusts on the braces.

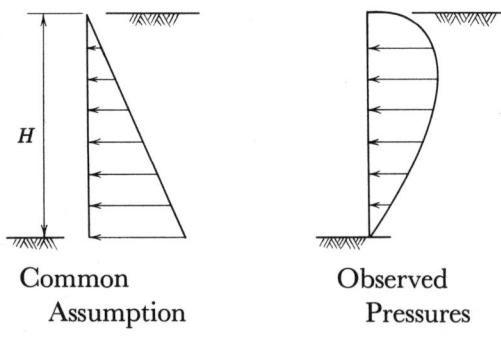

Common Assumption   Observed Pressures

FIG. 19.   PRESSURES ON BRACED SHEETING.

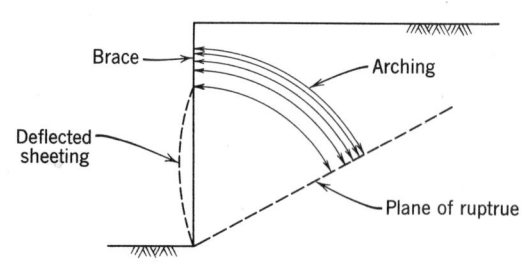

FIG. 20.   EXPLANATION OF ARCHING.

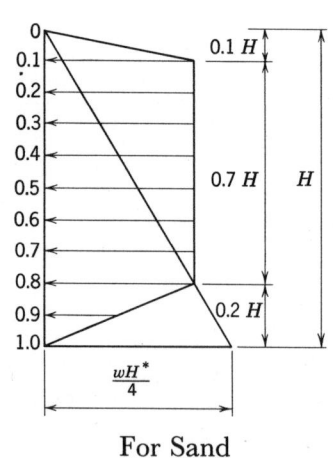

For Sand

w = unit weight of soil.
* = given.

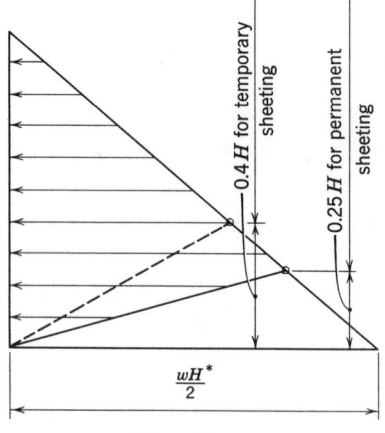

For Clay

FIG. 21.   RECOMMENDED PRESSURES FOR DESIGNING BRACED SHEETING.

By permission, from *Soil Mechanics, Foundations and Earth Structures* by Tschebotarioff, copyright, 1953, by McGraw-Hill Book Co., Inc.

RED LIGHTS

1. Avoid loss of material from under adjoining footing from pumping or natural flow.

2. Avoid settlement of adjacent structures due to permanent drainage and consolidation of surrounding soil.

3. Structural failure of shoring or sheeting may cause slides or cave-ins.

4. Note that the distribution of forces in Fig. 19 points to the importance of heavy top bracing.

5. Deflection of top of sheeting may cause a lateral shift of earth and injure adjacent subsurface structures.

6. Soft clays may bulge up under sheeting; see p. 13–23.

DEEP FOUNDATIONS

Chicago Well Method

This method was developed for use in medium to stiff clays which can hold a face of about 6 ft. The shaft is excavated in lifts of about 6 ft. After the first lift is excavated, the sheeting is placed and held in position by two wedged steel bands. Succeeding lifts are similarly excavated and sheeted down to the bearing stratum. The shaft is filled with concrete. Some loss of ground is bound to occur because of the plastic flow of the clay. See Fig. 22.

Gow Caisson Method

This method, sometimes called the Boston caisson, is used in softer clays. Successive steel shells are driven into the soft clay, which is excavated after the driving of each shell. These shells may be driven through previous seams if the end can be sealed in impervious soil. The excavation is stopped at a point short of the bottom of each shell to prevent the flow of clay up into the excavated shaft. The shaft is carried down to good bearing. Where a firm layer of clay overlaps the bearing stratum, the shaft may be "belled out" by undercutting. The entire shaft is filled with concrete, withdrawing the steel shells. See Fig. 23.

Pneumatic Caissons

When the soil is too soft to permit excavation by the Gow method, air pressure may be used to help keep back the soil. In cases of ground water air pressure will keep water out of the shaft. Everything entering or leaving the shaft must pass through air locks to prevent loss of pressure. Personnel must not only pass through air locks but also remain in them while the pressure is released slowly over a period of time. For high pressures this decompression time may be so long that a workman can work only 1 hour out of 8. Because of the high cost of labor and the large amount of hand work involved, the pneumatic caisson is not used as much as formerly. See Fig. 24 and Table VII.

Spliced Piles

The length of pile that can be handled by a pile driver ranges from 60 to 90 ft. Timber piles cannot be obtained commercially much over 60 ft. For deep foundations the trend is now toward long spliced piles. Steel piles over 300 ft. have been driven.

TABLE VII

WORKING UNDER COMPRESSED AIR
Work Periods for Each 24 Hours *

Pressure		Hours			
Minimum Number of Pounds	Maximum Number of Pounds	Maximum Total	Maximum 1st Shift	Minimum Rest Interval in Fresh Air	Maximum 2nd Shift
Normal	18	8	4	½	4
18	26	6	3	1	3
26	33	4	2	2	2
33	38	3	1½	3	1½
38	43	2	1	4	1
43	48	1½	¾	5	¾
48	50	1	½	6	½

* New York State Labor Law 1946.   Title 3—Section 425–431.

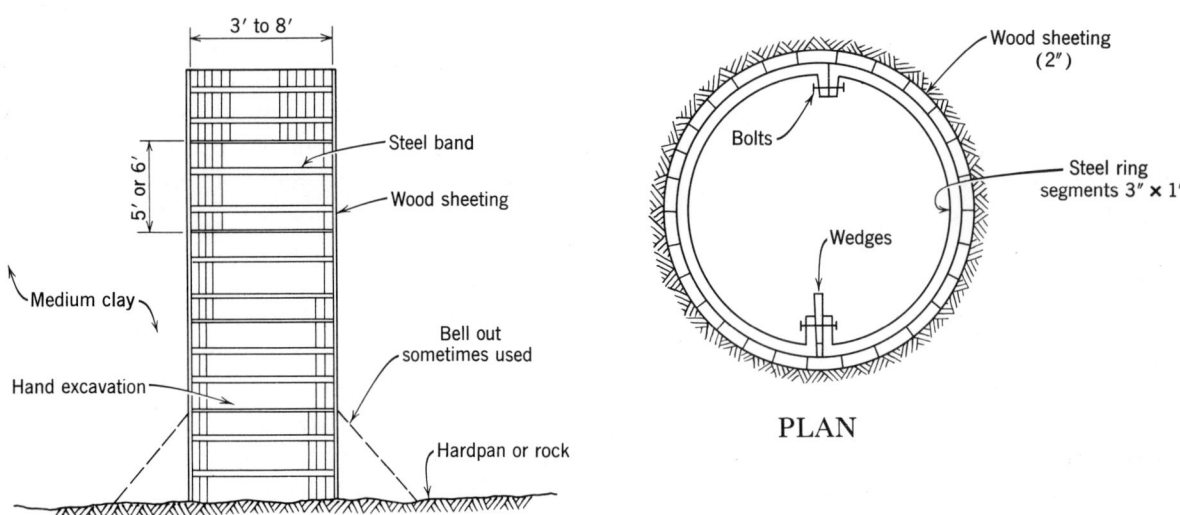

FIG. 22.   CHICAGO WELL METHOD.

Fill with concrete and remove bands as concreting progresses.

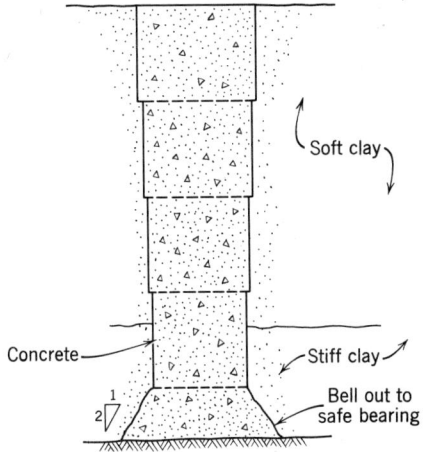

Completed   Hardpan or rock.
Rock with capacity
of over 45 tons
does not need bell.

FIG. 23.   GOW CAISSON.

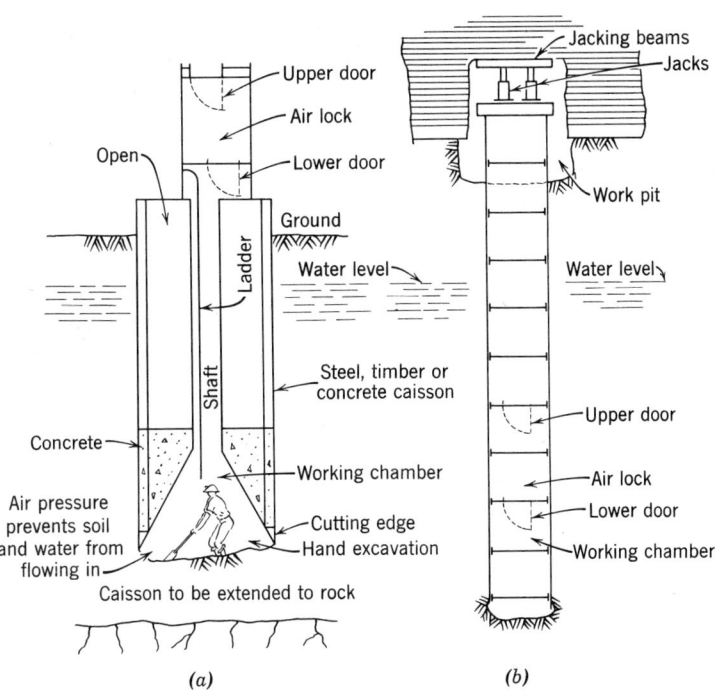

FIG. 24.   PNEUMATIC CAISSONS.

(a) Steel, timber, or concrete caissons for new foundations below ground water.   (b) Steel caisson underpinning old wall.

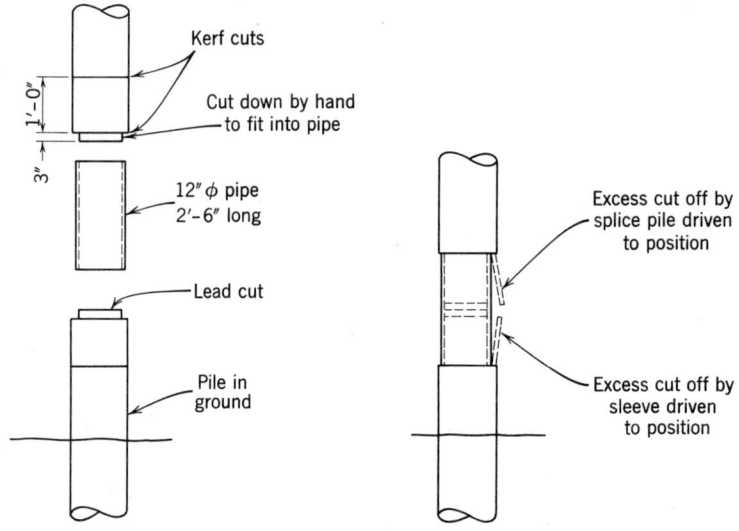

PARTS OF SPLICE   COMPLETED SPLICE

FIG. 25.   DETAIL OF TIMBER PILE SPLICE.

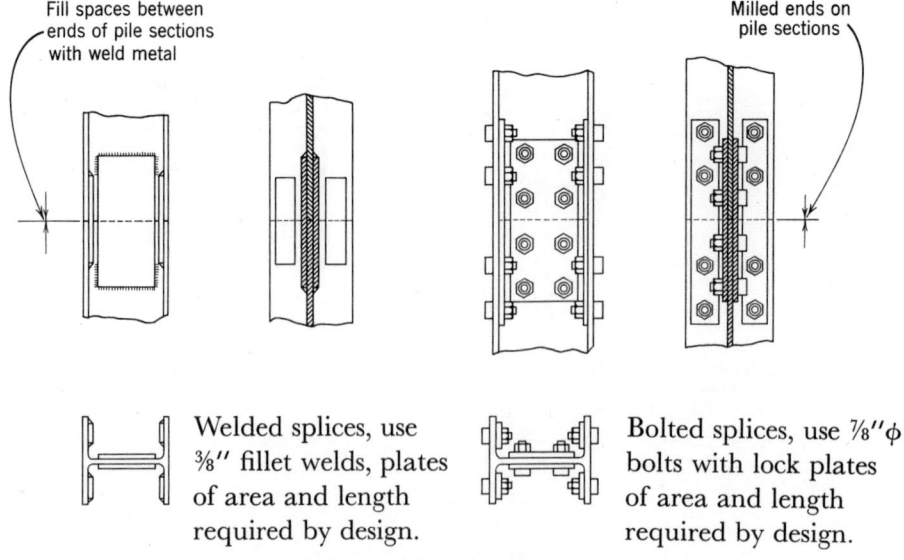

Welded splices, use ⅜″ fillet welds, plates of area and length required by design.

Bolted splices, use ⅞″ϕ bolts with lock plates of area and length required by design.

FIG. 26.   TYPICAL DETAILS OF PILE SPLICES.

Courtesy U. S. Steel Corp.

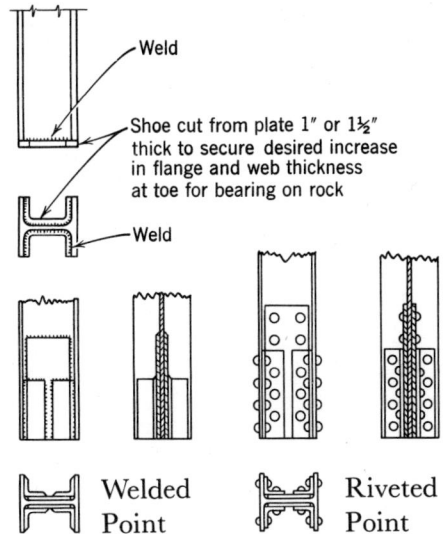

Welded Point   Riveted Point

Sufficient area of plates and angles added to bring pressure between gross area of steel and rock down to a range of 3000 lbs. to 6000 lbs. per sq. in. Welds or rivets proportioned to develop stresses of 10,000 lbs. per sq. in. on added steel areas. This is to insure against angles and plates tearing loose during driving.

FIG. 27. BUILT-UP PILE POINTS FOR DRIVING TO SOLID ROCK.

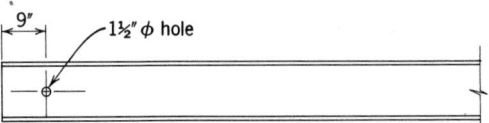

If ordered, piles can be furnished with handling holes as shown at one or both ends of section.

FOLLOWER SECTIONS

For CBP 83 use CB 83 58 lb.
For CBP 103 use CB 103 89 lb.
For CBP 124 use CB 124 106 lb.
For CBP 145 use CB 145 136 lb.
For CBP 146 use CB 146 176 lb.

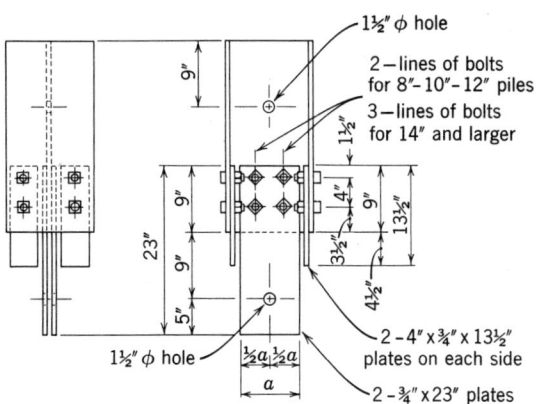

FIG. 28.
FOLLOWER-TYPE DRIVING CAP.

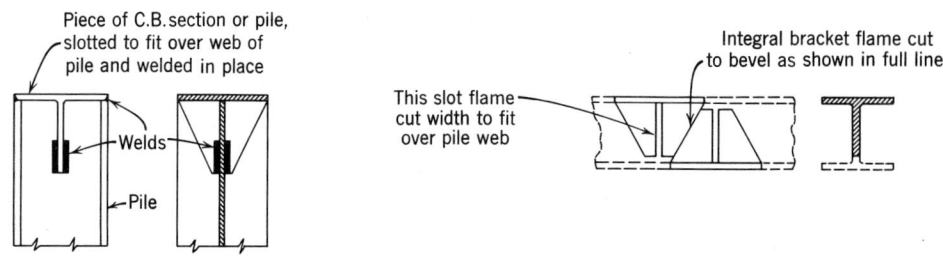

DETAIL OF CAPS CUT OUT OF SECTION OF CBP PILE

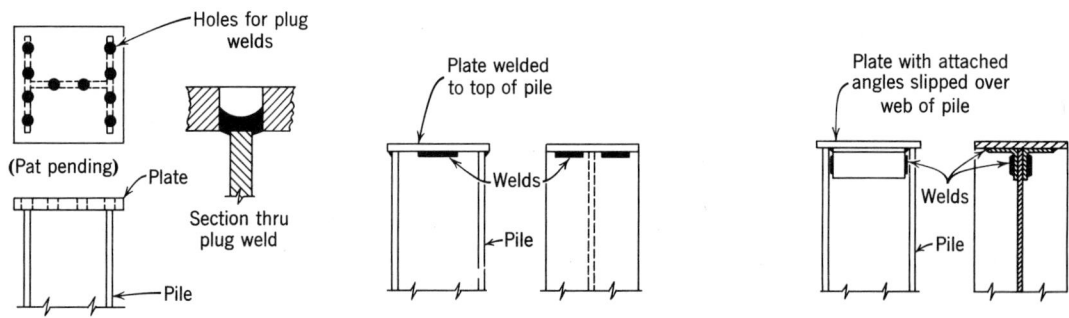

TYPICAL PLATE CAPS FOR PILES

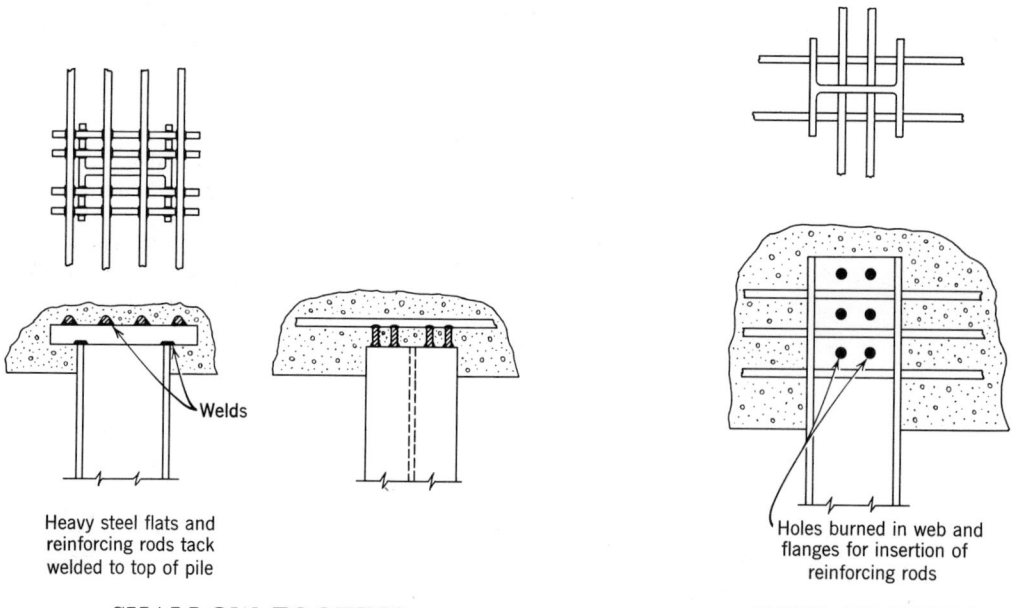

SHALLOW FOOTING   DEEP FOOTING

ALTERNATIVE METHOD OF CAPPING PILES

FIG. 29.   PILE CAP DETAILS.

Courtesy U. S. Steel Corp.

SHIELD TUNNELING

Shield tunneling with or without compressed air has been used to prevent the loss of ground. In subaqueous work it has been used to push the ground aside, Fig. 30. The amount of the face exposed varies with the nature of the soil and the amount of air. In running soils, the face is timbered. Boards are removed to permit partial excavation which is retimbered. The pressure of compressed air reduces the amount of water inflow and helps reduce loss of ground. In theory the volume of tunnel is the same as the volume of excavation, so that there is no loss of ground disturbing the adjacent foundations. In practice there is some loss of ground because of plastic flow of the soil. In the Chicago Subway excavation, noticeable settlements occurred in the street above.

Shield Used in Place of Underpinning

Singstad and Baillie contribute the following:

"In 1928–30, two 18 ft. 3 in. outside diameter cast-iron-lined rapid-transit tubes were constructed under Fulton Street, Manhattan, from South Street to Church Street, about 3100 ft., in soft ground below the water table, using the shield and compressed air method. The tubes were driven 55 ft. deep to pass under existing subways and tunnels at William Street, Broadway, and Church Street and two levels of new subway on Nassau Street, and, because of the narrow street width, were necessarily driven within inches of the lines of many important buildings. With the approval of the supervising engineers of the Board of Transportation, the Contractor for this work, Mason & Hanger Co., Inc., elected to depend entirely on the shield method to maintain the support and stability of the buildings; no direct underpinning was employed during shield driving, and only relatively minor settlement of the buildings occurred."

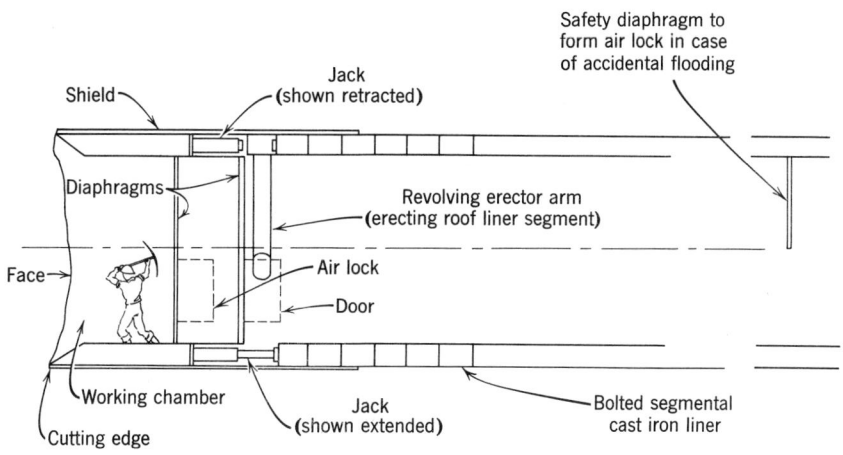

FIG. 30.   PNEUMATIC TUNNEL SHIELD.

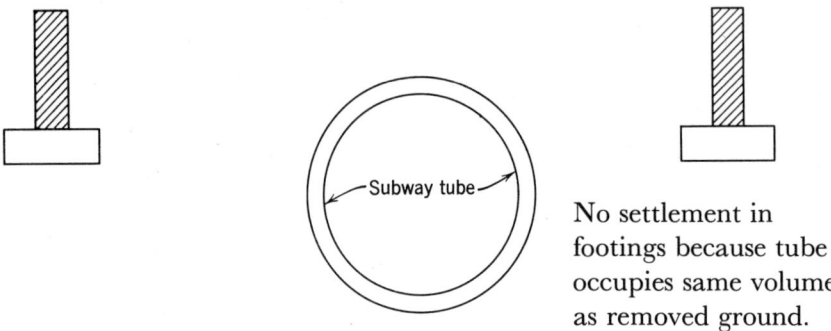

No settlement in footings because tube occupies same volume as removed ground.

FIG. 31.   TUNNELING NEAR BUILDINGS WITH A PNEUMATIC SHIELD.

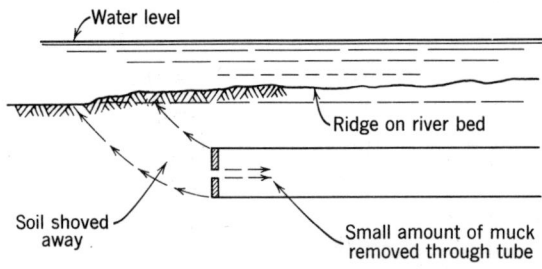

FIG. 32.   REDUCTION OF MUCK VOLUME BY DISPLACEMENT OF SOIL FOR TUNNELS IN MUD OR SOFT CLAY.

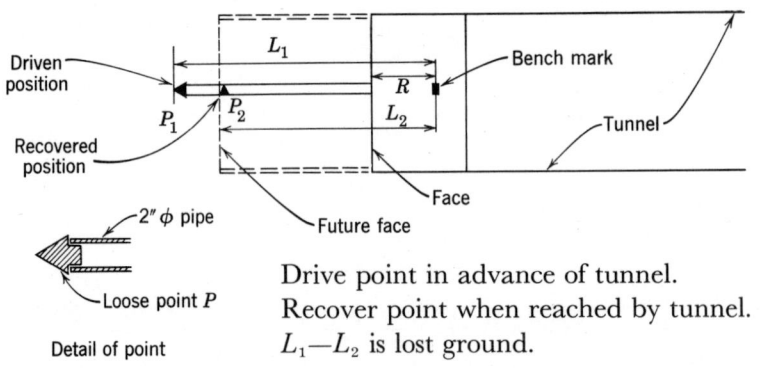

Drive point in advance of tunnel.
Recover point when reached by tunnel.
$L_1 - L_2$ is lost ground.

FIG. 33.   ESTIMATING LOST GROUND IN TUNNELING.*

* By Terzaghi, "Liner-Plate Tunnels on the Chicago (Ill.) Subway," *Trans.* A.S.C.E., 1943.

RED LIGHTS

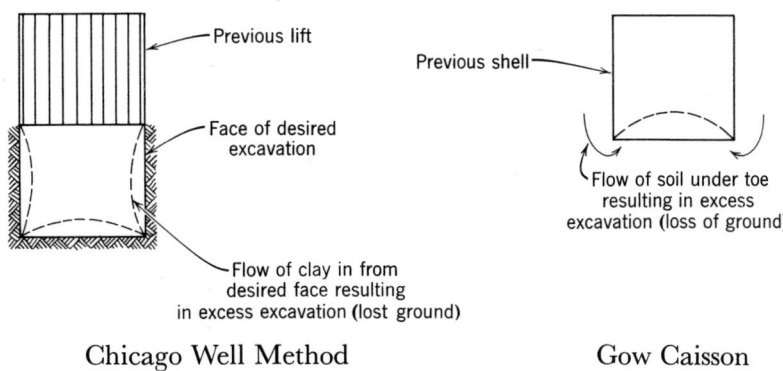

Chicago Well Method   Gow Caisson

FIG. 34.   LOST GROUND.

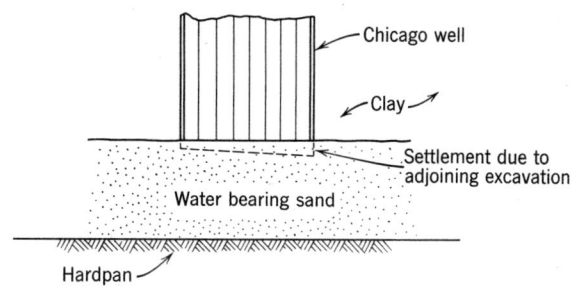

FIG. 35.   CAISSON STOPPED SHORT OF BEARING BECAUSE IT WAS UNABLE
TO PENETRATE ADVERSE LAYER.

See p. 10–9 for an example repaired by pile underpinning.

EXAMPLES OF DEEP FOUNDATIONS

Jefferson Memorial, Washington, D. C.

Steel pipe piles, 24 in. in diameter, were driven 125 ft. through river silt and then drilled into the bed rock. They were then cleaned out and filled with concrete.

M.I.T. Library, Cambridge, Massachusetts

Gow caissons, Fig. 23, were carried down through clay to rock.

Phoenix Insurance Co. Office Building, Hartford, Connecticut

A cast-in-place pile (Western Projectile Pile) was driven 125 ft. through compressible strata.

Mexico City and New Orleans

Many buildings are on piles driven 100 to 200 ft. to thin layers of gravel. Many buildings have been placed on mats with doubtful success because of heavy settlements.

Chicago

The fact that the city is underlain by clay has led to the development of the Chicago well method, Fig. 22, of digging caissons to rock. This method will not work in water-bearing strata.

Floating Foundation for Tappan Zee Bridge, on the New York Thruway across the Hudson River

Mr. Emil H. Praeger contributes the cut-away section in Fig. 36 which shows floating caissons taking advantage of the buoyancy of the displaced soil, which in effect meant a substantial reduction in the number of long piles required to support this structure.

New York City

In past years pneumatic caissons have been used to reach rock below soft overburden. This method has not been used so much recently. Most recent buildings have been placed on bed rock in open excavation or on long piles.

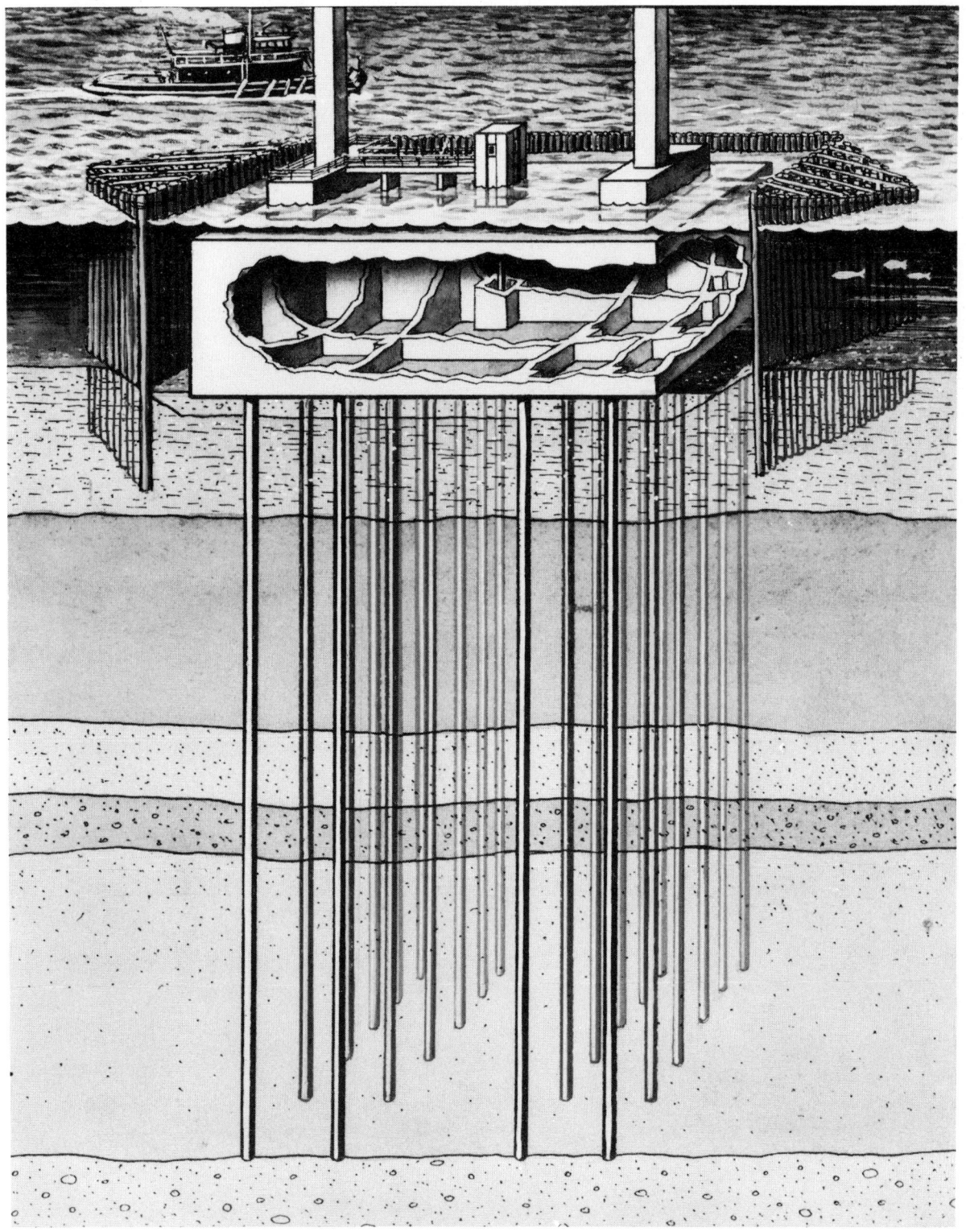

FIG. 36. FLOATING FOUNDATION FOR TAPAN ZEE BRIDGE.

DISCUSSION

The trend of deep foundations is toward steel pipe driven through water or poor soil, cleaned out by an air jet, and filled with concrete. Steel H piles and cast-in-place concrete piles are often used. Pneumatic caissons are limited in pressure, and the high cost of labor for working in high pressures results in their being obsolete. Piles over 300 ft. long have been driven recently.*

---

* Highway bridge, Meadville, Pa., 304.3 ft.

12

Foundations for Light Masonry

Foundations for light masonry differ from other foundations in that a compromise is made between initial cost and the possible detrimental results of the savings. A calculated risk is taken that the structure may be destroyed by weathering. Of course no risk is taken as regards safety of human life.

Frost

To be safe from frost the footings should be below the maximum anticipated frost. In light construction this depth is reduced. Ice lenses and frost heaves do not occur in sandy or clayey soils but rather in silts and loam. Therefore frost protection is waived in sand and clay soils. For house foundations advantage is taken of the fact that heat is dissipated from the house to reduce the frost. Occasionally difficulty is experienced with frost damage.

Earth Pressure

The maximum earth pressure as figured by conventional methods rarely occurs. This condition is especially true in clays and other cohesive soils. Garden and driveway walls often take advantage of this fact. Most have stood satisfactorily for many years, though failures have been noted.

SMALL BUILDING FOUNDATIONS

Foundation walls of small houses are often built of concrete or cinder block. The overturning moment on an unbound wall is $Wh^3/6$. In other words, it varies as the cube of the depth: $36W$ for a 6-ft. wall, $85W$ for an 8-ft. wall, and $167W$ for a 10-ft. wall.

This overturning moment may be reduced by:

1. Load from above.
2. Floor joists which shore it at the top provided that they do not run parallel to the wall.
3. Returns, cross walls, and end walls. Block walls with broken joints have strength to span as a horizontal beam.

The following points are against the safety of a block wall:

1. It may be overturned more easily.
2. Frost shove may require a greater mass or a concrete wall.
3. Not so water resistant as a concrete wall unless waterproofed on inside.
4. In large buildings a concrete wall may be used as a reinforced-concrete girder to span over inequalities of soil.

Conclusion

Block walls may be suitable for shallow basements. Long runs should be reinforced for shrinkage. (See also Chapter 3.) The main reason for using block walls is economic. A 12-in. block wall costs $1.10 per sq. ft.; a 10-in. reinforced concrete one, $2.80 per sq. ft. although 12-in. unreinforced concrete walls placed with metal forms are comparable in cost to block walls.

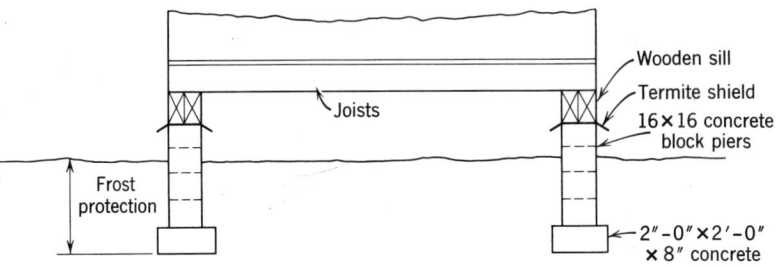

FIG. 1.   SMALL UNHEATED BUILDING.

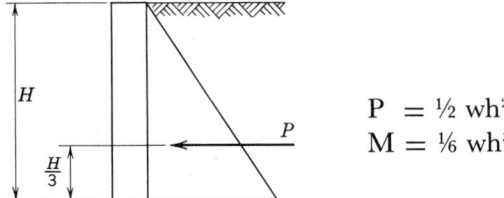

$$P = \tfrac{1}{2}\,wh^2$$
$$M = \tfrac{1}{6}\,wh^3$$

FIG. 2.   EFFECT OF HEIGHT ON OVERTURNING OF FOUNDATION WALL.

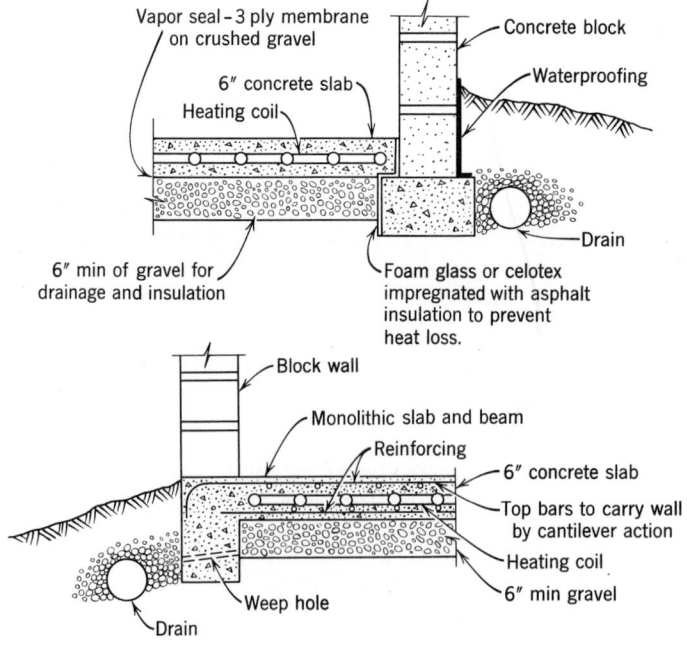

FIG. 3.   CONCRETE SLAB FLOOR ON GROUND ABOVE FROST LINE
WITH HEATING COILS EMBEDDED.

(Use same detail for vapor seal if not heated.)

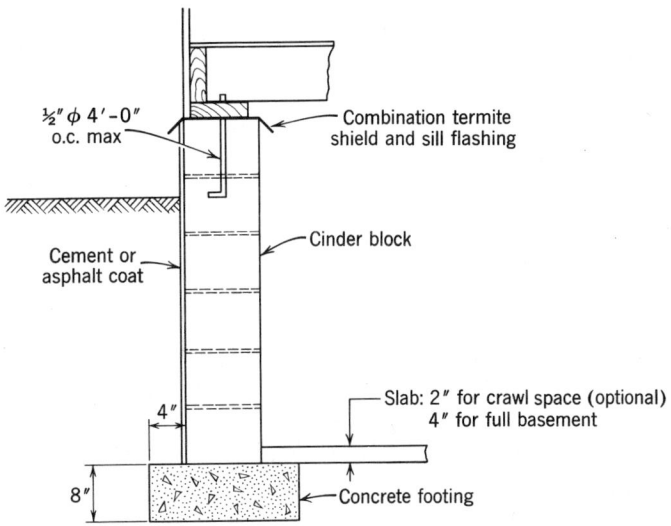

FIG. 4.   TYPICAL HOUSE FOUNDATION WALL.

(Not to be used below permanent ground water.)

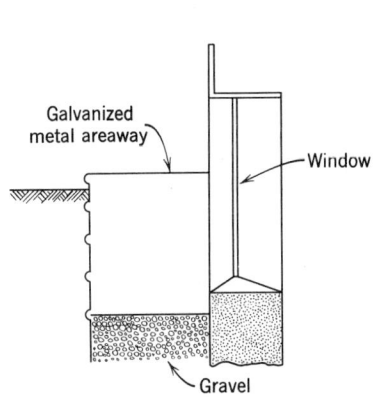

FIG. 5.   BASEMENT AREA.

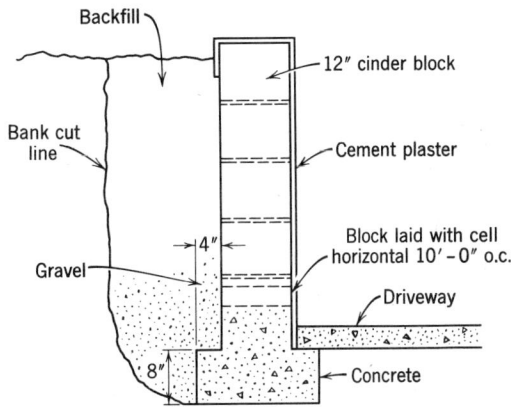

FIG. 6.   DRIVEWAY RETAINING WALL.

(Has been used up to 4'-0".)

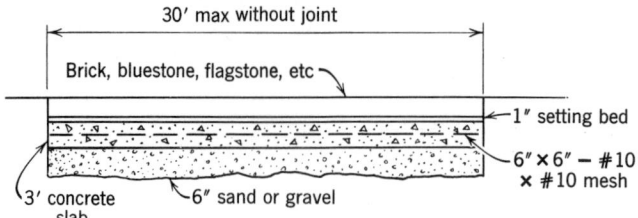

Case I.   Free Floating.

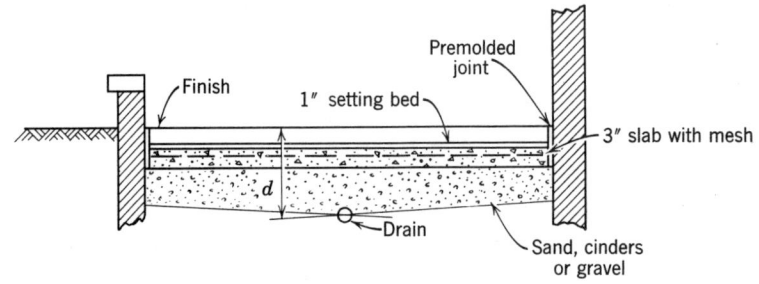

Case II.   Enclosed.

FIG. 7.   DETAILS OF TERRACES AND WALKS.

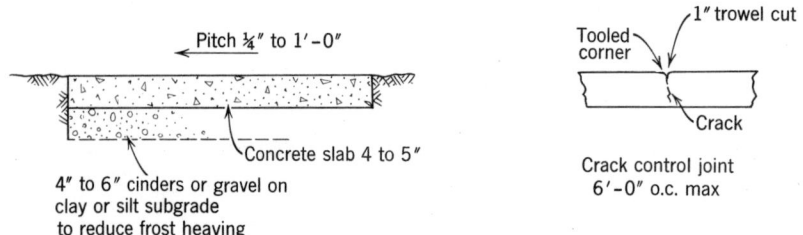

FIG. 8.   SIDEWALK DETAIL.

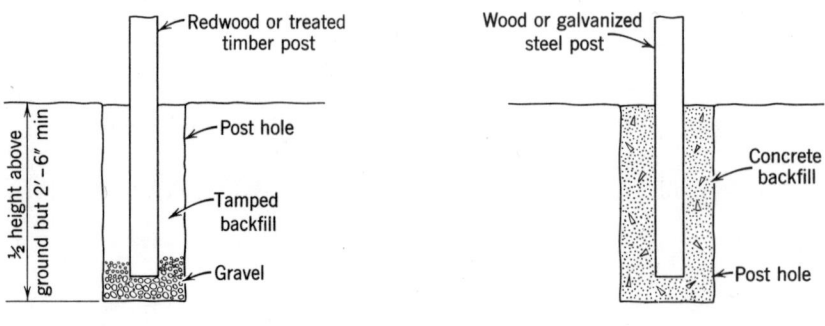

Good Detail   Better Detail

FIG. 9.   POST HOLE DETAILS.

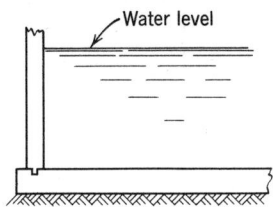

Case I. Pool on Ordinary Soil. Keep Pool Filled in Winter to Prevent Frost Heave on Bottom.

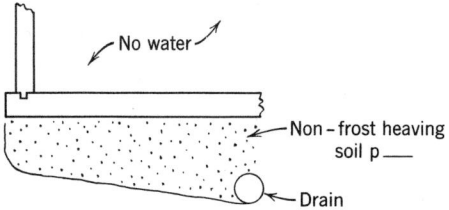

Case II. Pool on Non-Frost-Heaving Soil May Be Empty in Winter.

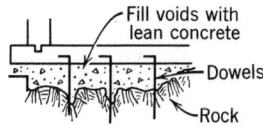

Case III. Pool on Rock. Anchor against Upheaval.

FIG. 10. OUTDOOR SWIMMING POOLS.

Freezing of water in the pool may cause damage to the concrete. Possible counter measures are:

1. Use of floating logs (doubtful value).
2. Use of granite gutter and life rail.

Bituminous Curb

Granite Block Curb

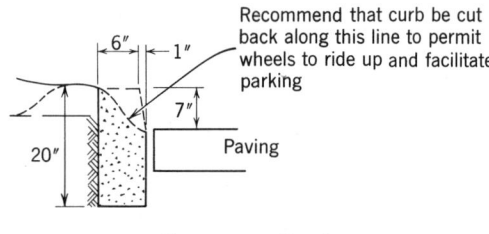

Concrete Curb
(Heavy Duty)

FIG. 11.   ROADWAY CURBS.

RED LIGHT

Roots will cause cracks and heaving of shallow foundations.

13

Soil Mechanics

SOIL BEHAVIOR—AN INTRODUCTION TO SOIL MECHANICS

Shearing Resistance vs. Stability of Soils

All stability in soils is derived from shearing strength.

Corollaries. (*a*) Ability of soils to support spread footings is directly proportional to their shearing strength.

(*b*) The steepness of the safe slope of embankments depends on the shearing strength of the soil.

(*c*) The safety of the supporting soil under the embankment from mud wave action depends on the shearing strength of the soil.

Shearing Resistance—Granular vs. Cohesive Soils

As granular soils have internal friction resistance, their shearing strength increases in relation to the normal pressure to which they are subjected.

Granular soils have no cohesion.

Clays are cohesive soils and have no angle of internal friction. They have a resistance to shearing due to their cohesive or molecular strength.

Hence their shearing strength is the same regardless of the normal pressure to which they are subjected.

Soil mixtures of clay and sand partake of both cohesive and internal friction resistance. Thus, most sands have some cohesion; most clays have some internal friction.

Corollaries. (*a*) The safe slope of a granular bank does not decrease as the height increases because its shearing strength increases to resist the increasing shearing stresses as the bank becomes higher.

(*b*) The safe slope of a clay bank becomes flatter as the bank becomes higher because its shearing strength does not increase to resist the corresponding increasing shearing stress.

Field Test for Shearing Strength

(*a*) The so-called unconfined compression test is very simple and may be improvised in the field. (See p. 3–18).

(*b*) For granular soils, the angle of repose is approximately equal to the angle of internal friction.

(*c*) Load tests are of little value except on cohesive soils.

Judging Strength of Soils

(*a*) Classification is by grain size such as clay, silt, sand, and gravel. It is usually used in connection with empirical tables to give strength for building foundations.

(*b*) Refinement of this classification is the measurement of resistance to a standard driving spoon which is correlated with the empirical strength table. (See p. 8–2).

(*c*) Load tests on soils and piles. (See p. 8–8).

(*d*) For determining the wheel bearing capacity of composite sections of flexible pavements and bases, there is the California Bearing Ratio, which is the resistance of a standard plunger to being forced into a layer of the base or subbase compared to its resistance to being forced into a standard layer of broken stone. Empirical curves are available. (See p. 4–30).

(*e*) For rigid pavements, a plate loaded according to a standard procedure gives a value known as the modulus of subgrade reaction, K, which is used in connection with established formulas to estimate the bearing capacity of concrete pavements. (See pp. 3–83 & 4–26).

(*f*) In general, the heavier the unit weight of soil, the greater the strength.

(*g*) In general, the less voids, the greater the strength.

Worked-Over Clays

Clays are subject to remolding; that is, an apparently stiff clay if worked will give off water and become soft. This is because a certain amount of water is fixed or attracted to the submicroscopic particles of clay, and the adhered water is broken off by working. If the clay is allowed to rest, the water will re-adhere and the clay will regain some of its stiffness.

Corollaries. (*a*) Piles driven into clay, if left overnight, will set up and be difficult to start.

(*b*) Freezing and thawing works the clay and weakens it, causing settlement or slides.

Settlement of Footings on Clays

Clay settlement varies directly with water content and inversely with the cohesive strength.

For a given unit pressure and a given clay, a definite amount of settlement may be expected.

For instance, clay sample 1 under pressure of 2 tons to the square foot might have an expected total settlement of 2 in. After this settlement has taken place and the pressure is increased to 3 tons, there would be a certain additional settlement of, let us say, 1½ in.

There are also definite periods of time for these settlements to become complete.

The settlement is caused by the squeezing out of water.

Corollaries. (*a*) The larger the footing, the greater the settlement, because the area of the bulb of pressure will increase in proportion to the sizes of the footings. See Fig. 1.

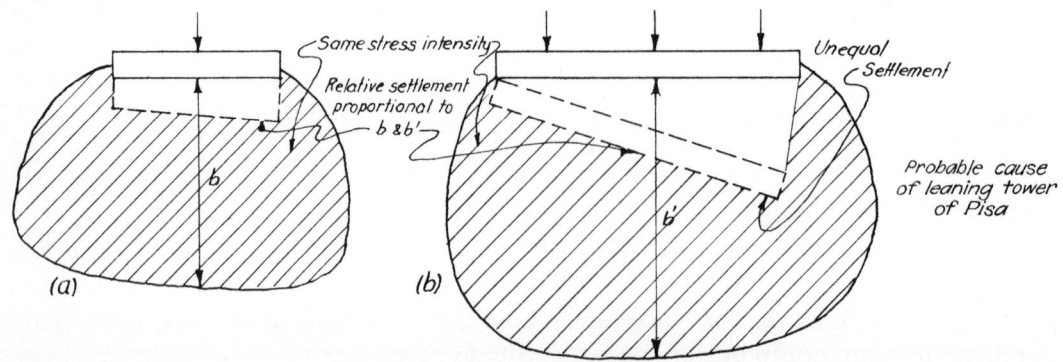

FIG. 1. EFFECT OF INCREASED FOOTING SIZE ON COHESIVE SOILS.

(*b*) While increase in width of footing increases the amount of settlement in the relation of *b'* to *b*, it does not increase the danger of failure because the intensity of shearing stresses in 1 (*a*) is no greater than in 1 (*b*).

(*c*) However, unequal settlement as shown in 1 (*b*) might produce critical shearing stresses, or a vicious cycle of rotation.

Shrinkage

Clays tend to hold free water in addition to their adhered water. They do not drain, nor do they dry out rapidly.

Granular soils do not hold water readily.

Corollaries. (*a*) Clays are subject to a large amount of shrinkage, but the loss of water that causes this shrinkage is slow.

(*b*) These shrinkages might amount to as much as 20% in volume.

(*c*) Granular soils do not shrink much when drying, and they shrink more rapidly.

Settlement of Footings on Sands

Compressibility of sands and silts varies with density.

Pore Water Pressure

When granular soils are saturated with water and the water is trapped, the footing may be supported on hydraulic pressure. This is called pore water pressure. Examples are boils or soft spots in a subgrade, or a ground with quakes under the passage of trucks.

Corollaries. (*a*) Soils under pore water pressure have greatly reduced shearing strength.

(*b*) The seepage out of pore water under pressure will cause settlement.

(*c*) Drainage to relieve the water is indicated.

Compaction-Optimum Moisture

For most soils there is a percentage of moisture at which the soil will compact to its greatest density.

This optimum moisture may run from 8% for sands, 15% for silts, to 15–20% for clays.

Corollaries. (*a*) Water content should be controlled in making fills.

(*b*) Reduction of water in clays is very difficult. Suggestions for doing this are as follows:

Spread out in thin layers to dry.

Choose a borrow dryer than optimum moisture.

Modern construction equipment supplemented by rollers is recommended for consolidation of fills.

(*c*) Deep trenches with clay backfill may require puddling, which will result in considerable shrinkage, or power tampers may be used to break up the lumps.

(*d*) Sand backfill may be inundated in compacting around a foundation wall, which will leave the sand loose and subject to settlement, but it may be of benefit as it will improve the drainage around the basement walls.

(*e*) For pavements and floor fills, optimum moisture and heavy rolling and tamping are the only answers.

(*f*) A well-graded gravel may be compacted with a bulldozer in 12-in. layers.

Soil Investigations

(*a*) Borings giving the material and the resistance to driving with a standard spoon.

(*b*) Undisturbed samples which can be tested for density, shearing resistance, and settlement.

(*c*) Atterberg Limit Tests, which are tests of fluidity and sensitivity to vibration. Their use includes determination of resistance of soils to frost, soil classification, compressibility, and shrinkage. See p. 3–18.

Capillary Action

Soils possess capillary action similar to that in a dry cloth with one end immersed in water.

Corollaries. (*a*) Coarse gravel: no capillary action.

(*b*) Coarse sand: up to 12 in.

(*c*) Fine sands and silts: up to 3 ft., low in clay.

(*d*) Pure clay: low value.

Frost Action

Most damage from frost action occurs at the time of thawing.

Corollaries. (*a*) With granular soils and mixtures, frost aided by capillary action may suck up water and cause actual ice lenses. When this material thaws, the soil is overirrigated and incapable of supporting a load. A pore water condition may result.

(*b*) With a clay soil, the heave may be less because the clay soil does not readily suck up water from below on account of its imperviousness, but when it thaws the frozen clay will lose its strength as when it is worked.

(*c*) Frost boils in pavement occur from similar causes.

Prevention

All structural foundations to extend below frost. Subgrades of roads to have a gravel capillary cut-off.

Quicksand

Quicksand occurs where a current of water passing upward through a soil is of sufficient velocity to cause a flotation or boiling up of the particles.

Corollaries. (*a*) The bearing value of the material is destroyed.

(*b*) Material may be carried off from under a structure or adding material.

(*c*) Correct by lowering head of water.

Sand Filters

Water passing out of a fine soil into a coarse aggregate may tend to carry material with it and clog the drain.

Corollary. The grains around the drain should be graded so that there is no abrupt change in size. See p. 3–06.

Vibration

Vibration may cause damage to structures by:

(*a*) Pile driving, which

1. May endanger tender adjoining masonry.
2. May start overloaded skin friction piles down.
3. May cause cracks in plaster or masonry.

(*b*) Effect of resonance: The natural period of the earth crust may vary between 1000 and 2000 cycles per minute, and machinery, for instance, vibrating within these limits might cause trouble.

(*c*) Truck vibrations may act similarly to pile driving.

(*d*) Blasts are not continuous, and a large part of the effect of blast is an air wave. However, blasts are a distinct danger.

Precautions. (*a*) Shore weak masonry and foundations.

(*b*) Insulate foundations of vibrating machinery.

(*c*) Open windows during blasting.

(*d*) Line hole rock supporting adjacent buildings.

(*e*) Shore exposed rock faces.

(*f*) Protect client by preconstruction survey of adjoining properties together with photographs.

Effect of Water on Soils

Water in soil is the all-round enemy of the engineer and constructor. Some of the troubles caused by water are:

(*a*) Frost failures.

(*b*) Settlement due to drying out of water in soil.

(*c*) Reduction of the bearing power of soil due to weakening of the shearing strength.

(*d*) Removal of soil under foundations due to pumping operations or flow.

(*e*) Cavitation and piping in dams.

(*f*) Construction difficulties.

(*g*) Dampness in basements.

(*h*) Pressure on structure.

(*j*) Corrosion of steel.

Water is fought by:

(*a*) Gravity drainage.

(*b*) Ordinary pumping.

(*c*) Pumping with well points in soils that are somewhat granular.

(*d*) Sealing of the casing of well points to produce better vacuum.

Advantages of Water:

(*a*) Protection of timber below water line.

(*b*) Prevention of shrinkage in soils due to drying out.

Flow through Soils

Flow through soils is dependent on the hydraulic gradient and the fineness of the material, and can be estimated. See p. 3–31.

(*a*) The uplift on the base of a dam should be estimated.

(*b*) Piping which is a channelized outflow of soil carried away by this seepage must be controlled.

DISCUSSION OF FUNDAMENTAL THEORIES OF COMPUTING STRESSES IN SOILS

Elastic Theory

The Elastic Theory is based on the following assumptions:

1. Soil is perfectly elastic and homogeneous.

2. A load impinging on any point of any elastic mass causes definite deflections and stresses throughout the entire mass. Figure 2.

3. It is possible to compute by means of equations derived by Boussinesq the compressive, tensile, and shearing stresses at any point caused by a force applied at any other point.

The common loading conditions and resulting stresses are shown in Figs. 2–5.

Because soil is far from being perfectly elastic, engineers are reluctant to accept this theory. However, it has its uses if for no other reason than to check computations based on other theories. It has a particular application to settlement as giving the approximate pressure at lower depths.

Granular-Plastic Theory

This common approach consists in analyzing soils as an equivalent liquid, or sections of soils as free bodies. For instance, the Rankine approach for a retaining wall reduces the earth pressure to the equivalent liquid pressure.

The sliding block treatment for an embankment, or the most dangerous circle treatment, consists in treating a section of earth as a free body.

Special Approaches

These might include, for example, the measurement of flow through soils by means of the coefficient permeability and Darcy's law (see p. 13–20), the design of filters (see p. 7–17), and the classification of soils for frost upheavel, either by grain size or by Atterberg limits.

Self-Ownership by the Engineer of Designing Processes

It is important that the engineer be able to understand and set up his own problems, because to accept abstruse solutions by theorists blindly is neither necessary nor safe.

ELASTIC THEORY:- Based on Boussinesq equation.
CAUTION:- In applying this to soils, it is to be remembered that it is based on a foundation of homogeneous, isotropic material of infinite depth, modulus of elasticity independent of depth, which are not the usual properties of soils.

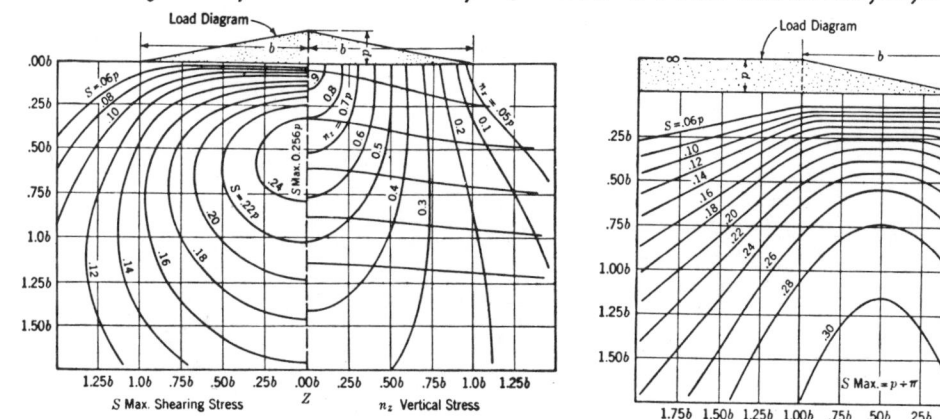

FIG. 2 TRIANGULAR LOADING.   FIG. 3 - TERRACE LOADING.

DISTRIBUTION OF SHEARING STRESSES UNDER EMBANKMENTS.*

S = Shear per sq. ft.; p = Load per sq. ft. on foundation at ℄ of dam.
Foundation of homogeneous isotropic material, infinite depth.

USE OF DIAGRAMS:* Given:- Embankment 100 ft. high; foundation material = fine silt with tan ϕ = 0.4 and C = 0, weight = $120^\#$/cu.ft. , b = 200 ft.
Required:- Factor of Safety at depth 0.5 b. Solution:- In Terrace loading - Fig. 3 diagram at 0.5b, max. unit shear = $0.25 p = \frac{0.25 \times 100 \times 120}{2000} = 1.5$ tons/sq.ft. Unit Shearing strength = W. tan ϕ + C. W = unit weight x total depth at point of max. unit shear (midpoint of slope = 100 + 50) ∴ Unit shearing strength = $\frac{150 \times 120}{2000} \times 0.4 + 0 = 3.6$ tons/sq.ft. factor of safety = $\frac{3.6}{1.5} = 2.4$.

MIN. FACTOR OF SAFETY:- Try solution at other depths, 0.25 b, 0.375 b, 0.75 b, etc.

Notes: 1.- Justin, Hinds & Creager prefer using Terrace Loading rather than Triangular loading for dam embankments.
2.- Applicable only to homogeneous isotropic foundations of infinite depth.
3.- Applicable to fill such as on soft harbor foundations. Test as in Fig. 6 below.

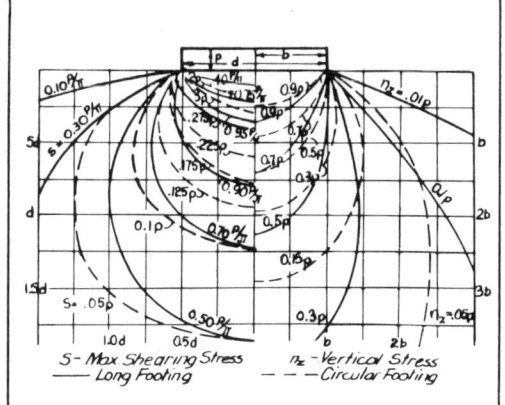

P - Lbs. per sq. ft. distributed Load.
FIG. 4 DISTRIBUTION OF SHEARING STRESSES
UNDER A LONG FOOTING* (for circular figs.

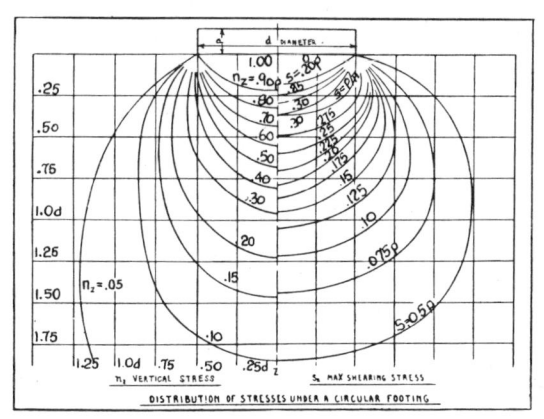

Unit shear and direct stress given for a circular footing.

FIG. 5

* From The Application of Theories of Elasticity and Plasticity to Foundation Problems by Leo Jürgenson, J. Boston Soc. Civil Engrs., July 1934, adapted by Justin, Hinds & Creager.

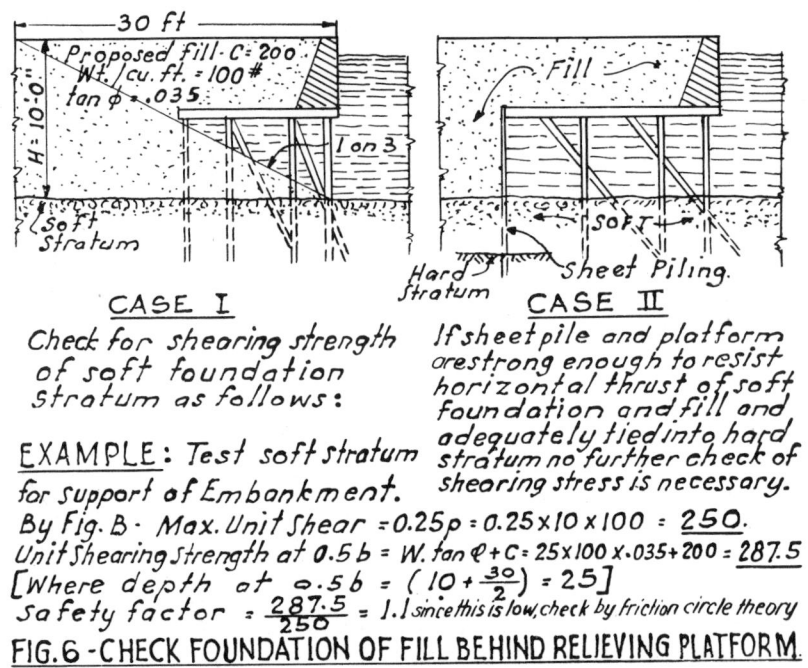

CASE I

Check for shearing strength
of soft foundation
stratum as follows:

EXAMPLE: Test soft stratum
for support of Embankment.
By Fig. B - Max. Unit Shear = 0.25p = 0.25 × 10 × 100 = __250__.
Unit Shearing Strength at 0.5b = W. tan φ + C = 25 × 100 × .035 + 200 = __287.5__
[Where depth at 0.5b = (10 + $\frac{30}{2}$) = 25]
Safety factor = $\frac{287.5}{250}$ = 1.1 since this is low, check by friction circle theory

CASE II

If sheet pile and platform
are strong enough to resist
horizontal thrust of soft
foundation and fill and
adequately tied into hard
stratum no further check of
shearing stress is necessary.

FIG. 6 - CHECK FOUNDATION OF FILL BEHIND RELIEVING PLATFORM.

(Adapted from Plummer and Dore, *Soil Mechanics and Foundations*, Pitman Publishing Corp.)

Granular-Plastic Theory

Certain problems in soil mechanics can be expressed as problems in the mechanics of solids and fluids.   Some of these problems are shown on the following pages.

Like all other problems they require certain empirical data, such as weights of material and shearing strengths.   This data may be approximated from those given on p. 13–12 or from shear tests, p. 13–17.

The need for empirical data is so great in the field of soil mechanics that a large number of standard laboratory and field tests are included in this book.

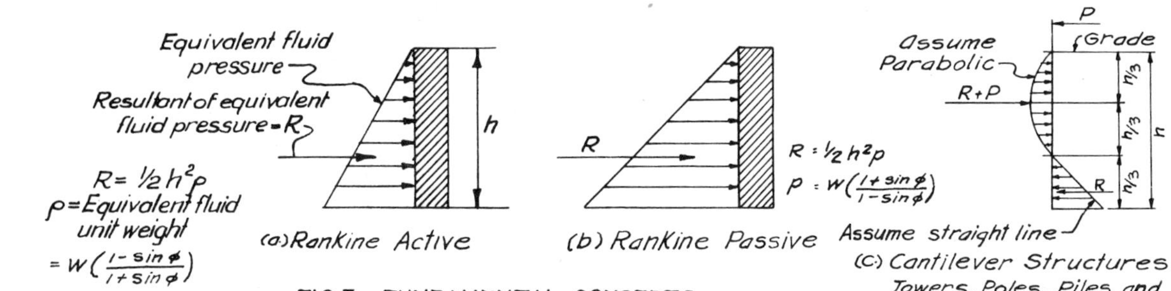

Equivalent fluid pressure
Resultant of equivalent fluid pressure = R
h
R = ½h²p
p = Equivalent fluid unit weight
= w((1 - sin φ)/(1 + sin φ))
φ = Angle of slope of repose
(a) Rankine Active
R
R = ½h²p
p = w((1 + sin φ)/(1 - sin φ))
(b) Rankine Passive
P
Grade
Assume Parabolic
R+P
h/3
h/3
h/3
h
R
Assume straight line
(c) Cantilever Structures
Towers, Poles, Piles and sheet piling

FIG. 7- FUNDAMENTAL CONCEPTS OF EARTH PRESSURES

Alternative trial plane to give max. F
45° + φ/2 Theoretical Assumption
Force to hold = F
ACTIVE
Shearing strength of the soil = S
Mud Wave
45° - φ/2 Theoretical Assumption
Shearing strength of the soil = S
Force to push up the wedge
PASSIVE
Cut and try distance to give min. F

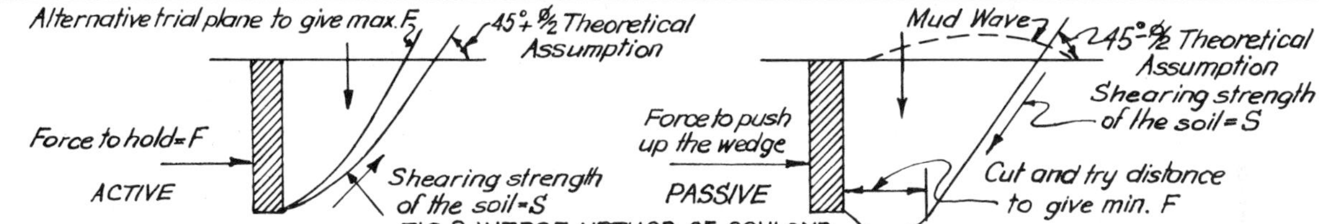

FIG. 8 WEDGE METHOD OF COULOMB

SUBMERGED SATURATED, AND MOIST WEIGHTS.

Moist weight increases if sample is saturated and decreases if submerged on account of flotation
Most unfavorable condition should be assumed.

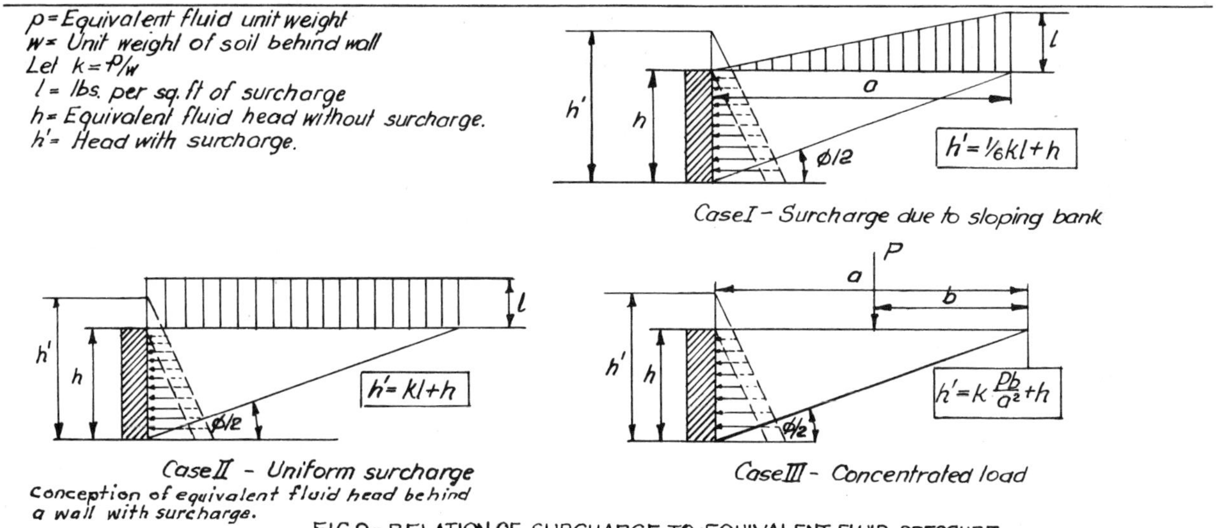

p = Equivalent fluid unit weight
w = Unit weight of soil behind wall
Let k = p/w
l = lbs. per sq. ft of surcharge
h = Equivalent fluid head without surcharge.
h' = Head with surcharge.
l
a
h'
h
φ/2
h' = ⅙kl + h
Case I - Surcharge due to sloping bank
l
h'
h
h' = kl + h
φ/2
Case II - Uniform surcharge
Conception of equivalent fluid head behind a wall with surcharge.
P
a
b
h'
h
h' = k Pb/a² + h
φ/2
Case III - Concentrated load

FIG. 9- RELATION OF SURCHARGE TO EQUIVALENT FLUID PRESSURE

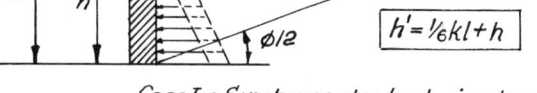

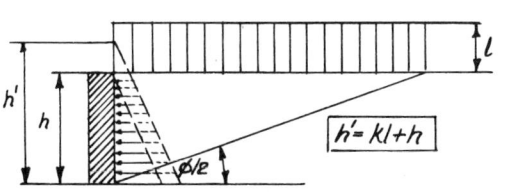

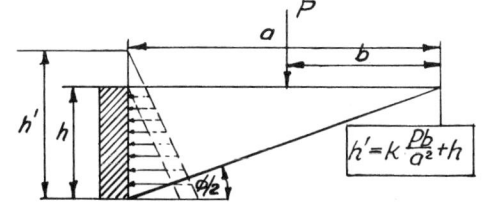

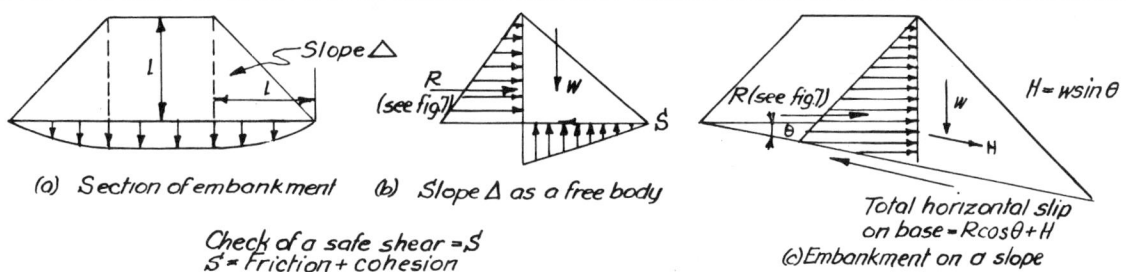

Slope △
l
l
(a) Section of embankment
R (see fig 7)
W
S'
(b) Slope △ as a free body
Check of a safe shear = S'
S' = Friction + cohesion
R (see fig 7)
W
θ
H
H = w sin θ
Total horizontal slip on base = R cos θ + H
(c) Embankment on a slope

FIG. 10 EMBANKMENT STABILITY- "SLIDING BLOCK" METHOD

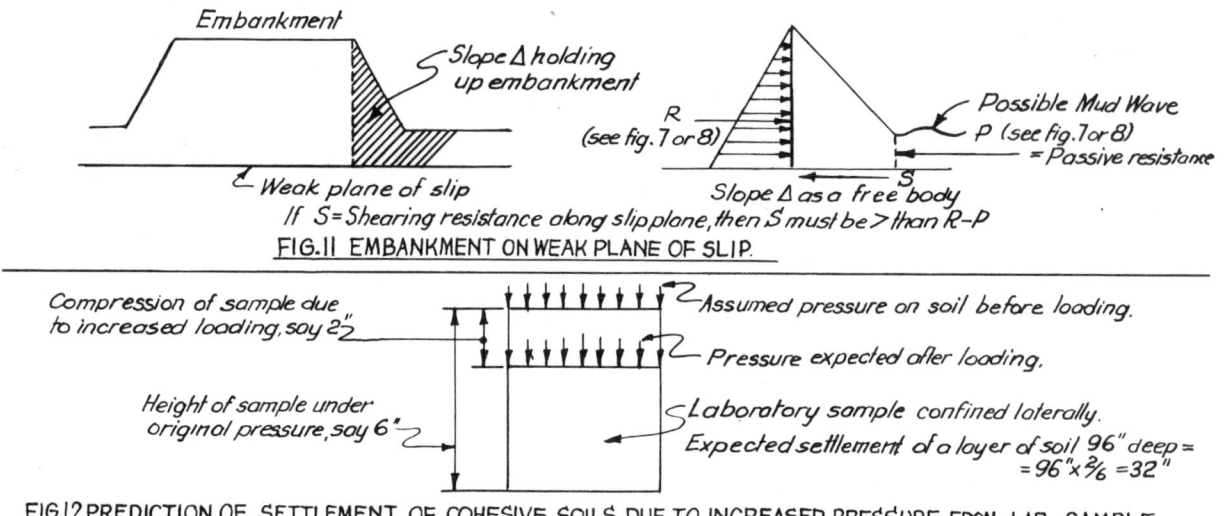

Embankment

Slope Δ holding up embankment

Weak plane of slip

R (see fig.7 or 8)

Slope Δ as a free body

Possible Mud Wave
P (see fig.7 or 8)
= Passive resistance

If S = Shearing resistance along slip plane, then S must be > than R - P

FIG.11 EMBANKMENT ON WEAK PLANE OF SLIP.

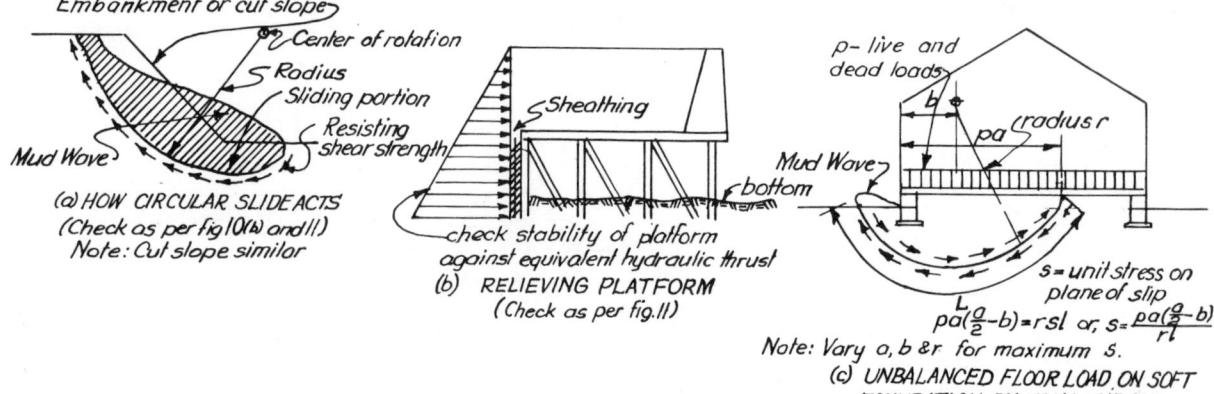

Compression of sample due to increased loading, say 2"

Height of sample under original pressure, say 6"

Assumed pressure on soil before loading.

Pressure expected after loading.

Laboratory sample confined laterally.

Expected settlement of a layer of soil 96" deep =
= 96" × 2/6 = 32"

FIG.12 PREDICTION OF SETTLEMENT OF COHESIVE SOILS DUE TO INCREASED PRESSURE FROM LAB. SAMPLE.

TIME OF SETTLEMENT: May vary as square of depth if water can flow out from top and bottom of stratum. If flow is from top or bottom only, time of settlement should be quadrupled.

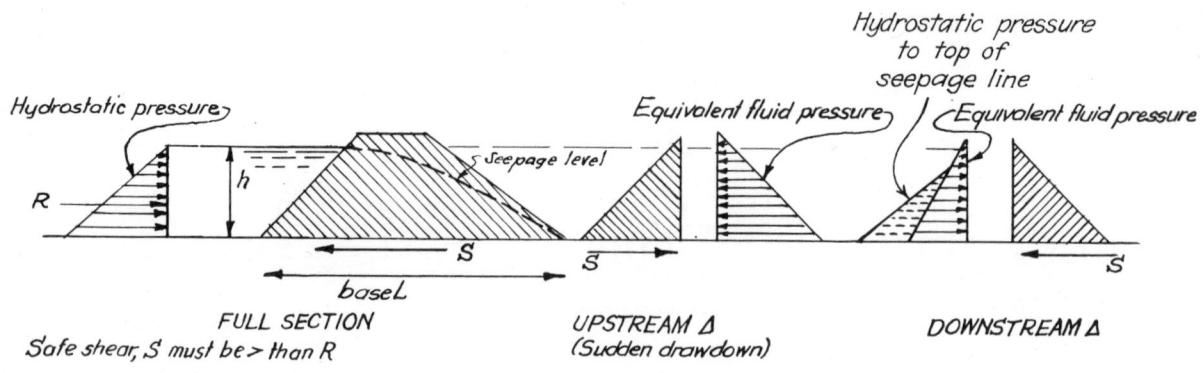

Embankment or cut slope

Center of rotation

Radius

Sliding portion

Resisting shear strength

Mud Wave

(a) HOW CIRCULAR SLIDE ACTS
(Check as per fig 10(a) and 11)
Note: Cut slope similar

Sheathing

check stability of platform against equivalent hydraulic thrust
(b) RELIEVING PLATFORM
(Check as per fig.11)

p - live and dead loads

b

pa (radius r

Mud Wave bottom

s = unit stress on plane of slip

$pa(\frac{a}{2} - b) = rsl$ or, $s = \frac{pa(\frac{a}{2} - b)}{rl}$

Note: Vary a, b & r for maximum s.
(c) UNBALANCED FLOOR LOAD ON SOFT FOUNDATION BY TRIAL CIRCLE.

FIG.13 TYPICAL PROBLEMS INVOLVING SLIDES

Hydrostatic pressure

R

h

seepage level

Equivalent fluid pressure

Hydrostatic pressure to top of seepage line

Equivalent fluid pressure

S

S

S

base L

FULL SECTION
Safe shear, S must be > than R

UPSTREAM Δ
(Sudden drawdown)

DOWNSTREAM Δ

FIG.14 STRESS DIAGRAMS FOR EARTH DAMS

I. ARBITRARY STRENGTH PER SQUARE FOOT

By Soil Classification, see pages

II. BY DISPLACEMENT:

For cohesive soils such as clays or clay mixtures.

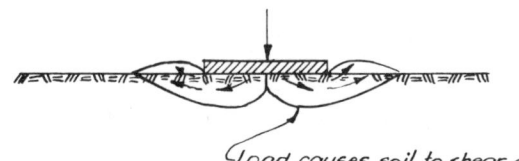

Load causes soil to shear on
such plane as this.

III ELASTIC THEORY: Assumes soil truly Elastic

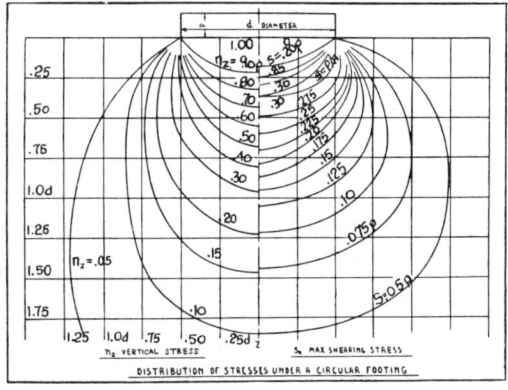

DISTRIBUTION OF STRESSES UNDER A CIRCULAR FOOTING

Unit shear and direct stress given for a circular
footing.

FIG. 15   DESIGN OF SPREAD FOOTINGS

D'ARCY'S LAW:
Seepage volume varies directly with area.

Volume of seepage $= kA\frac{h}{L}$

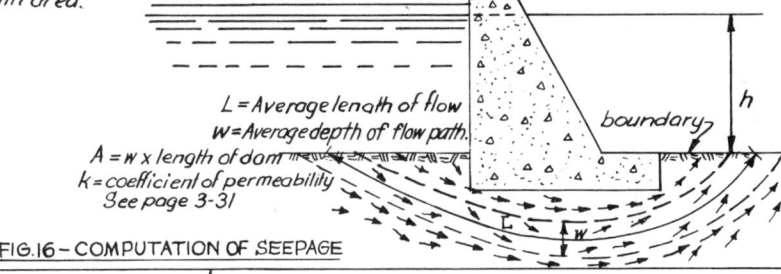

L = Average length of flow
w = Average depth of flow path.
A = w × length of dam
k = coefficient of permeability
See page 3-31

boundary

h

FIG.16 – COMPUTATION OF SEEPAGE

Flow lines without filter
Flow lines with filter
Filters tend to bend seepage
lines down.

Filter drain

Note: Filters are of sand and gravel and are graded from
coarse to fine to prevent the fine from the soil from being
carried into the filter and clogging it

FIG.17 CONTROL OF DAM SEEPAGE BY FILTERS

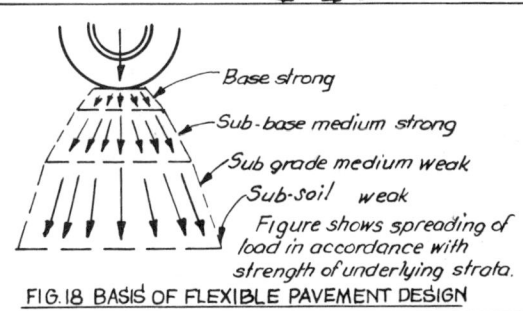

Base strong
Sub-base medium strong
Sub grade medium weak
Sub-soil weak
Figure shows spreading of
load in accordance with
strength of underlying strata.

FIG.18 BASIS OF FLEXIBLE PAVEMENT DESIGN

Design pavement for
flexural strength

The softer the subgrade
the bigger the dimple.
and, the greater the
flexural stress.

Intensity of dimple estimated from plate load test on
soil, called subgrade reaction.

FIG.19 BASIS OF RIGID PAVEMENT DESIGN.

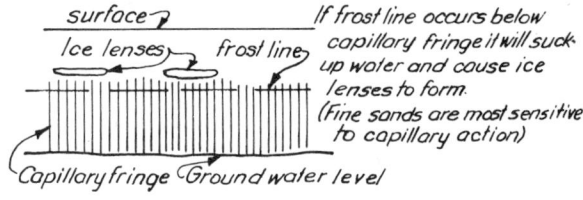

surface
ice lenses   frost line

If frost line occurs below
capillary fringe it will suck
up water and cause ice
lenses to form.
(Fine sands are most sensitive
to capillary action)

Capillary fringe   Ground water level

**FIG.20 RELATION OF CAPILLARY PROPERTIES TO FROST
BOILS IN HIGHWAYS.**

TABLE I – SLOPES OF REPOSE

KIND OF EARTH	SLOPE OF REPOSE	
	NON-SUBMERGED	SUBMERGED
Sand, clean	1 on 1.5	1 on 2
Sand and clay	1 on 1.33	1 on 3
Clay, dry	1 on 1.75	
Clay		1 on 3.5
Clay, damp, plastic	1 on 3	
Gravel, clean	1 on 1.33	1 on 2
Gravel and clay	1 on 1.33	1 on 3
Gravel, sand, and clay	1 on 1.5	1 on 3
Soft, rotten rock	1 on 1	1 on 1
Hard, rotten rock	1 on 1	
Hard rock, riprap		1 on 1
Bituminous cinders	1 on 1	
River mud		1 on 3 to 1 on 20
Anthracite Ashes	1 on 1.5 to 1 on 2	

Rule of thumb for submerged excavated slopes:
Sand— 1 on 2   Clay—1 on 1.5 to vertical
Stiff mud—1 on 1 to vertical   Sluiced Mud—1 on 10 to 1 on 20

TABLE II – UNIT WEIGHT OF SOILS

KIND OF EARTH	UNIT WEIGHTS—lb/cu.ft.
Moist Soils	110
Medium or stiff clay	120
Saturated earth	110 + % voids × 62.5 = say 132
Submerged earth	132 − 62.5 = say 70
Soft clay or mud	100

TABLE III – UNIT WEIGHTS AND C.B.R. VALUES FOR COMPACTED SOILS

SOLIDS AT OPTIMUM COMPACTION	WELL GRADED		NOT GRADED	
	UNIT WT.	C.B.R.*	UNIT WT.	C.B.R.
Sand and Silt	120	–	105	8-30
Sand and Clay (Binder)	125	20-60	105	8-30
Sands	120	20-60	100	10-30
Gravel	130	>50	115	25-60
Silts inorganic	–	–	100	6-25
Organic Silts	–	–	90	3-8

TABLE V – ROUGH DATA FOR EQUIVALENT FLUID PRESSURES OF SOILS

MULTIPLY UNIT WEIGHT BY "K"

KIND OF EARTH	"K"
Granular Sand	0.33
Mixtures of Clay and Granular Soils	0.50
Soft Clays, Silts, Organic Soils	1.00
Stiff Clays	1.00

TABLE IV – SOIL SHEAR VALUES

KIND OF EARTH	COHESION, lbs/sq.ft.	ANG. OF INT. FR.°
Clay – liquid†	100	0°
" very soft	200	2°
" soft	400-500	4°
" firm	1000	6°
" stiff	2000	12°
" very stiff	2000-4000	14
Sand wet	0	10°-15°
Sand dry or unmoved	0	34°
Silt	0	± 20°
Cemented Sand & Gravel – Wet	500	34°
" " " " – Dry	1000	34°

TABLE VI – EQUIVALENT FLUID PRESSURES FOR SOILS SUBMERGED IN SEA WATER**

SLOPE OF REPOSE OF EARTH	WEIGHT 'W' OF SUBMERGED EARTH LB./CU.FT.							
	40	44	48	52	56	60	64	68
1 on 1/2	66.2	66.4	66.7	66.9	67.1	67.3	67.6	67.8
1 on 3/4	68.2	68.9	69.3	69.8	70.2	70.7	71.1	71.6
1 on 1	70.9	71.6	72.2	72.9	73.6	74.3	75.0	75.7
1 on 1 1/4	73.2	74.2	75.1	76.0	76.9	77.9	78.8	79.7
1 on 1 1/2	75.4	76.6	77.7	78.9	80.0	81.2	82.3	83.5
1 on 1 3/4	77.5	78.8	80.2	81.5	82.9	84.2	85.6	86.9
1 on 2	79.3	80.8	82.3	83.9	85.4	86.9	88.4	90.0
1 on 2 1/2	82.3	84.2	86.0	87.8	89.7	91.5	93.3	95.2
1 on 3	84.8	86.9	88.9	91.0	93.1	95.2	97.2	99.3
1 on 3 1/2	86.8	89.0	91.3	93.6	95.9	98.2	100.0	102.0
1 on 4	88.4	90.8	93.3	95.7	98.1	101.0	103.0	105.0
1 on 5	90.9	93.6	96.3	99.0	102.0	104.0	107.0	109.0
1 on 6	104.0	108.0	112.0	116.0	120.0	124.0	128.0	132.0

To obtain equivalent fluid pressure for a given slope of repose, say 1¾:1, get the weight of the submerged soil from table VII, say 60, enter table VI at column marked nearest to this value. Obtain equivalent weight, 84.2 from row of given slope of repose.

TABLE VII WEIGHT OF SOLIDS SUBMERGED IN SEA WATER

MATERIAL	POUND PER CUBIC FOOT		
	MAXIMUM	MINIMUM	AVERAGE
Gravel and Marl		42.0	62.9
Gravel and Sand	73.0	42.0	62.4
Sand	66.0	42.0	58.3
Gravel, Sand, and Clay	80.9	51.2	70.0
Stiff Clay	64.8	38.4	47.8
Stiff Clay and Gravel	70.3	44.8	52.6

* C.B.R. = California Bearing Ratio.
† For classification see p. 8–2 (N.Y.C. Code).
**Adapted from "American Civil Engineers' Handbook" by Merriman & Wiggin.

Factual Data

To solve the soils problems we must have values for variable soils, just as we must have values for the strength of steel to proportion the size of members in a bridge truss.

Soils vary far more than steel in their properties, and most important decisions in determining soil problems should be based on tests. Nontheless, it is most important to have a perspective knowledge of properties to be expected from certain types of soil for use in solving suggested problems (see p. 13–12).

Also included is Casagrande's remarkable soil chart, an excellent contribution to soil mechanics perspective.

TABLE VIII

PERMEABILITY COEFFICIENTS OF DIFFERENT SOILS

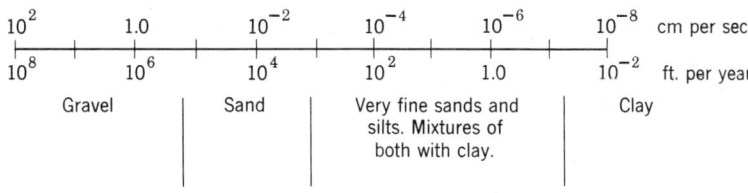

Permeability is the measure of the rate of flow through soils.

Discussion

Aids and Assumptions

1. The plane of rupture according to Rankine's theory is the plane along which the wedge of soil behind a retaining wall slips. It is generally assumed in cut-and-try analyses of retaining walls. The most common trial assumption is $45° + \phi/2$ for the active condition and $45° - \phi/2$ for the passive. See Fig. 8.

2. The reduction of soil pressure to an equivalent fluid pressure is made according to the equation

$$\text{Equivalent fluid} = \text{Unit weight of soil} \times \frac{1 - \sin \phi}{1 + \sin \phi}$$

or, as it is often written $= \text{Unit weight of soil} \times \tan^2(45 + \frac{\phi}{2})$

3. Shearing strengths of cohesive or semicohesive soils may be taken as one-half of the unconfined compression test strength. See p. 13–18.

4. Saturated soils act on the strata below with their submerged weights only, unless the water is trapped or perched above these lower strata. The hydrostatic pressure acts separately and does not bear on lower strata.

TABLE IX - CASAGRANDE

Major Division		Soil Group Symbols	Soil Groups & Typical Names	General Identification		Observations and Tests Relating to Material in Place	Principal Classification Tests on Disturbed Sample
				Dry Strength	Other Pertinent Examinations		
Coarse-Grained Soils.	Gravel & Gravelly Soils.	G W	Well-graded gravel and gravel-sand mixtures; little or no fines.	None.	Gradation, Grain shape.	Dry unit weight or void ratio; degree of compaction; cementation; durability of grains; stratification and drainage characteristics; ground-water conditions; traffic tests; large-scale load tests; or California bearing tests.	Sieve analysis
		G C	Well-graded gravel-sand-clay mixtures; excellent binder.	Medium to High	Gradation, grain shape, binder examination, wet & dry.		Sieve analysis, liquid and plast limits on binder.
		G P	Poorly graded gravel & gravel-sand mixtures; little or no fines.	None.	Gradation, grain shape.		Sieve analysis
		G F	Gravel with fines, very silty gravel, clayey gravel poorly graded gravel-sand-clay mixtures.	Very slight to high.	Gradation, grain shape, binder examination, wet and dry.		Sieve analysis liquid and plast. limits on binder if applicable.
	Sands & Sandy Soils.	S W	Well-graded sands & gravelly sands; little or no fines.	None.	Gradation, grain shape.		Sieve analysis.
		S C	Well-graded sand-clay mixtures; excellent binder.	Medium to high.	Gradation, grain shape, binder exam. wet & dry.		Sieve analysis, liqu plastic limits on bir
		S P	Poorly graded sands; little or no fines.	None.	Gradation, grain shape.		Sieve analysis.
		S F	Sand with fines, very silty sands, clayey sands, poorly graded sand-clay mixtures.	Very slight to high.	Gradation, grain shape, binder examination, wet and dry.		Sieve analysis, liquid and plast limits on binder if applicable.
Fine-Grained Soils (containing little or no coarse grained material).	Fine-grained soils having low to medium compressibility.	M L	Silts (inorganic) and very fine sands, Mo, rock flour, silty or clayey fine sands with slight plasticity.	Very slight to medium.	Examination wet (shaking test and plasticity).	Dry unit weight, water content, and void ratio. Consistency undisturbed and remoulded. Stratification. Root holes Fissures, etc. Drainage and ground-water condition. Traffic tests, large-scale load tests, California bearing tests, or compression tests.	Sieve analysis, liquid and plas limits, if applic able.
		C L	Clays (inorganic) of low to medium plasticity, sandy clays, silty clays, lean clays.	Medium to high.	Examination in plastic range.		Liquid and pla limits.
		O L	Organic silts and organic silt-clays of low plasticity.	Slight to medium.	Examination in plastic range, odor.		Liquid & plastic lim from natural condit and after oven-dr
	Fine-grained soils having high compressibility.	M H	Micaceous or diatomaceous fine sandy and silty soils; elastic silts.	Very slight to medium.	Examination wet (shaking test and plasticity).		Sieve analysis, liq & plastic limits i applicable.
		C H	Clays (inorganic) of high plasticity; fat clays.	High.	Examination in plastic range.		Liquid and pla limits.
		O H	Organic clays of medium to high plasticity.	High.	Examination in plastic range, odor.		Liquid and plastic from natural con and after oven-d
Fibrous organic soils with very high compressibility.		Pt	Peat and other highly organic swamp soils.	Readily identified.		Consistency, texture and natural water content.	

LEGEND FOR SOIL GROUP SYMBOLS.

C - Clay, plastic-inorganic soil.
F - Fines, material < 0.1 mm.
G - Gravel, gravelly soil.
H - High compressibility.
L - Relatively low to medium compressibility.
M - Mo, very fine sand, silt, rock flour.
O - Organic silt, silt clay or clay.
P - Poorly graded.
Pt - Peat, highly organic fibro
S - Sand, sandy soil.
W - Well graded.

SOIL CHART.

Value as Foundation when Not Subject to Frost Action	Value as Wearing Surface [*][†] — With Dust Palliative	Value as Wearing Surface — With Bit. Surf. Treat.	Potential Frost Action [†]	Shrinkage Expansion Elasticity	Drainage Characteristics	Compaction Characteristics & Equipment	Solids at Optimum Compaction. u, lb/cu.ft. [**] e, Void Ratio	California Bearing Ratio for Compacted and Soaked Specimen	Comparable Group in Public Roads Class (P.R.A.)
Excellent.	Fair to Poor.	Excellent.	None to very slight.	Almost none.	Excellent.	Excellent, Tractor.	$u > 125$ $e < 0.35$	> 50	A-3
Excellent.	Excellent.	Excellent.	Medium.	Very slight.	Practically impervious.	Excellent, Tamping Roller.	$u > 130$ $e < 0.30$	> 40	A-1
Good to excellent.	Poor.	Poor to Fair	None to very slight.	Almost none.	Excellent.	Good, Tractor.	$u > 115$ $e < 0.45$	25-60	A-3
Good to excellent.	Poor to Good	Fair to Good.	Slight to medium.	Almost none to slight.	Fair to practically impervious.	Good, Close Control Essential, Rubber Tired Roller, Tractor.	$u > 120$ $e < 0.40$	> 20	A-2
Excellent to Good.	Poor.	Good.	None to very slight.	Almost none.	Excellent.	Excellent, Tractor.	$u > 120$ $e < 0.40$	20-60	A-3
Excellent to Good.	Excellent.	Excellent.	Medium.	Very slight.	Practically impervious.	Excellent, Tamping Roller.	$u > 125$ $e < 0.35$	20-60	A-1
Fair to Good.	Poor.	Poor.	None to very slight.	Almost none.	Excellent.	Good, Tractor	$u > 100$ $e < 0.70$	10-30	A-3
Fair to Good.	Poor to Good.	Poor to Good.	Slight to high.	Almost none to medium.	Fair to practically impervious.	Good, Close Control Essential, Rubber Tired Roller.	$u > 105$ $e < 0.60$	8-30	A-2
Fair to poor.	Poor.		Medium to very high.	Slight to medium.	Fair to poor.	Good to Poor, Close Control Essential, Rubber Tired Roller.	$u > 100$ $e < 0.70$	6-25	A-4
Fair to Poor.	Poor.		Medium to high.	Medium.	Practically impervious.	Fair to Good, Tamping Roller.	$u > 100$ $e < 0.70$	4-15	A-4 A-6 A-7
Poor.	Very Poor.		Medium to high.	Medium to high.	Poor.	Fair to Poor Tamping Roller.	$u > 90$ $e < 0.90$	3-8	A-4 A-7
Poor.	Very Poor.		Medium to very high.	High.	Fair to poor.	Poor to Very Poor.	$u > 100$ $e < 0.70$	< 7	A-5
Poor to very poor.	Very Poor.		Medium.	High.	Practically impervious.	Fair to Poor, Tamping Roller.	$u > 90$ $e < 0.90$	< 6	A-6 A-7
Very poor.	Useless.		Medium.	High.	Practically impervious.	Poor to Very Poor.	$u > 100$ $e < 0.70$	< 4	A-7 A-8
Extremely poor.	Useless.		Slight.	Very high.	Fair to poor.	Compaction not Practical. Replace with Compactible Material.			A-8

Notes:

* Values are for subgrade and base courses, except for base courses directly under wearing surface.

† Values are for guidance only. Design should be based on test results.

** Unit weights apply only to soils with specific gravities ranging between 2.65 and 2.75.

MEANING OF ANGLE OF REPOSE, ANGLE OF INTERNAL FRICTION COHESION

The angle ϕ is used quite generally to describe the angle of repose or internal friction; see Fig. 21.

The angle of repose in granular soils, which is the natural slope of a bank, is approximately equal to the angle of internal friction.

In an ideal plastic material, which clay approximates, the internal pressure does not affect its shearing strength. Therefore, the angle of internal friction is zero. This shearing strength is called cohesion c.

In soils which are a mixture of granular and plastic material, both the angle of internal friction and cohesion are present. The cohesion is unaffected by the normal pressure, whereas the internal friction is affected. Approximate values are given in Table IV, factual data. More exact values are determined by test.

Soil shearing strengths are (see Figs. 22 and 23):

Granular soils $= N \tan \phi$
Mixed soils $= c + N \tan \phi$
Purely plastic soils $= c$

where N = normal compression stress.

Meaning of ϕ and c Symbols

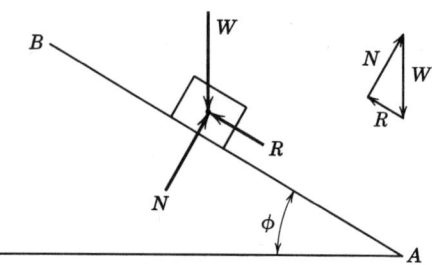

Note: ϕ may be used to indicate the angle of repose of a sand.

Select angle ϕ such that block just slides down slope AB. Then angle of friction between horizontal and plane is ϕ, and $\tan \phi = R/N$.

FIG. 21.   GENERAL DEFINITION OF FRICTION ANGLE.

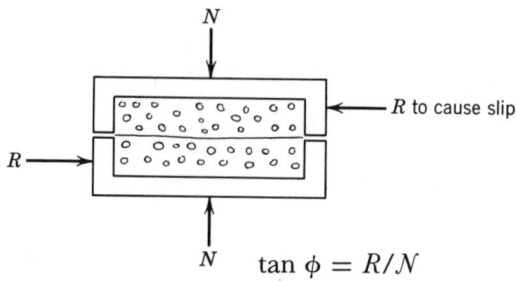

$\tan \phi = R/N$

FIG. 22.   IDEALIZED CONDITION DEFINING ANGLE OF INTERNAL
FRICTION FOR COHESIONLESS SOILS.

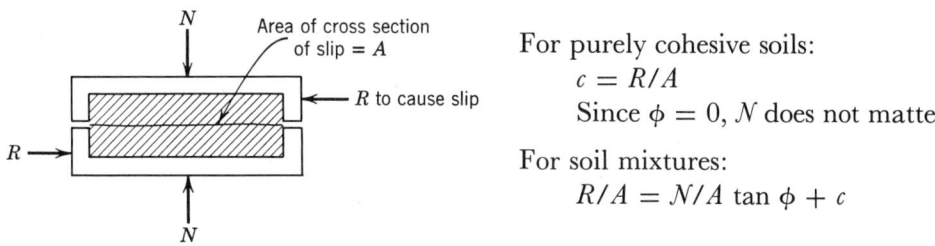

For purely cohesive soils:
$$c = R/A$$
Since $\phi = 0$, N does not matter

For soil mixtures:
$$R/A = N/A \tan \phi + c$$

FIG. 23.   CONDITION DEFINING COHESION FOR COHESIVE SOILS.

REMOLDED CLAYS

Some clays have the property of *remolding*.   When the clay is disturbed the bond between the particles is broken and the clays become soft.   In the remolded condition, the clays usually lose shearing strength and acquire greater compressibility.   Because of this property, undisturbed and therefore unremolded samples should be obtained for laboratory analysis if possible.

Clays may be intentionally remolded for the following purposes:

To obtain the characteristics of the remolded clay for evaluating clay fills which are, by their very nature, remolded.

To evaluate the shear value when it is impractical to obtain an undisturbed sample.   A disturbed sample may be consolidated to the amount of water in the ground layer and its properties extrapolated to obtain those of an undisturbed sample.

If the remolded sample is left undisturbed, it will recover most of the strength lost by remolding.   This recovery of strength accounts for piles driven into clays being difficult to start again after driving is suspended for a short period of time.

Sensitivity of a clay is the measure of the effect of remolding.   It is figured thus:

$$\text{Sensitivity} = \frac{\text{Unconfined compression strength before remolding}}{\text{Unconfined compression strength after remolding}}$$

Sensitivity for most clays ranges from 2 to about 4.   Sensitive clays range from 4 to 8, and extra-sensitive clays exceed 8.   For determination of unconfined compression strength see Fig. 24.

FACTOR OF SAFETY

Factor of safety for the bearing of the soil for a footing is customarily taken as 3.   The factor of safety for a fill, retaining wall, or dam in regard to sliding or overturning is customarily assumed as 1.5.

Red Light

The allowable bearing pressure may be governed by settlement considerations rather than ultimate resistance against failure directly under the footing.

Sensitive clays should be approached with caution, especially where possibility of slide or flow exists.

PURPOSE: To determine maximum shearing stresses, cohesion, and angle of internal friction from soil samples. To check general data given under "Factual Data".

I. UNCONFINED SHEAR TEST:

When Used: Field test for undisturbed soils. For clays and clayey mixtures. Cannot be used with materials without a binder.

Method: Specimen loaded to failure by weights added to loading arm
  Approximately: Shear = ½ x p.s.i. on specimen.
  Unconfined compression = p.s.i. on specimen.

Advantages: Test is easily performed; apparatus is portable and can be home-made. Test can be improvised. It could be made by adding water to a bucket resting on specimen. Unconfined shear test is more accurate for clays or mixtures of clay.

Note: Height of specimen = 2 x width

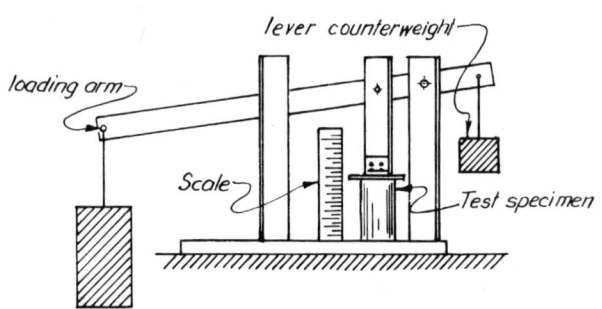

FIG. 24·UNCONFINED SHEAR TEST APPARATUS:

2. ANGLE OF REPOSE METHOD: For sands and free draining deposits of sand. Determine angle of repose which equals lower limit of angle of friction.

3. SHEAR BOX METHOD:

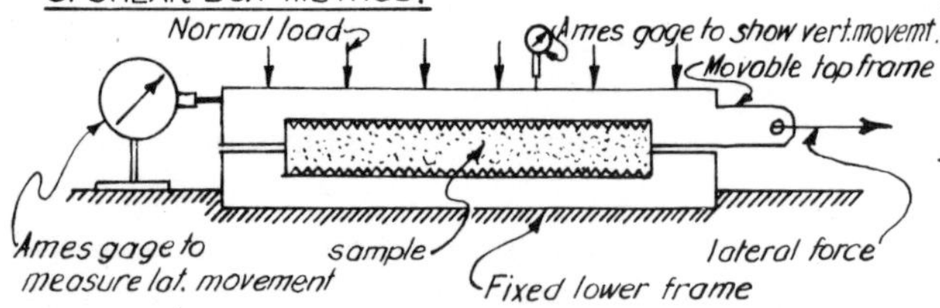

When Used: To simulate effect of material under pressure. Gives the maximum angle of internal friction. Use for free draining deposits, soil mixtures above ground water, or for clays.

Method: With a constant normal load a lateral force is applied until slip occurs. A curve as shown at left may then be plotted. For clays and mixtures a quick shear test may be desirable.

Advantages: Apparatus is portable and easy to set up.

FIG. 25 – SHEAR BOX

Note: Sample should be at field density

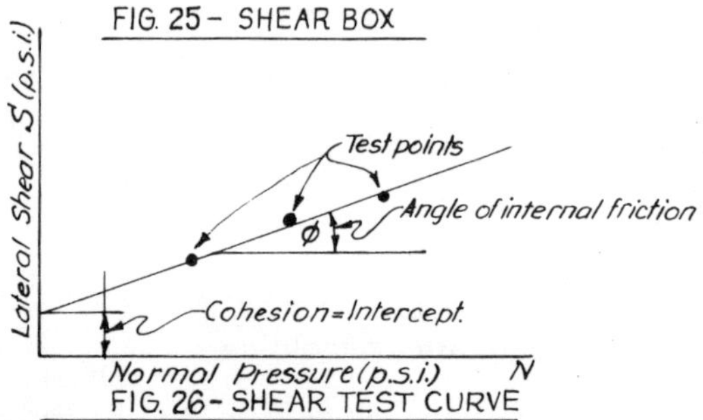

When Used: For silty soils generally. Can be used for all soils. Since apparatus is bulky, test is performed in a laboratory.

Method: Lateral hydrostatic pressure is maintained constant and a vertical force is applied until failure occurs. Test is repeated with increased lateral pressure and results are plotted as shown, based on Mohr's circle theorem.

Advantages: Test can be used for all soils, gives most accurate results as actual drainage conditions are simulated.

FIG. 26 – SHEAR TEST CURVE

4. TRIAXIAL SHEAR TEST:

P_{1-2} = lat. press. for runs 1&2 (p.s.i.)   N = normal pressure on soil (p.s.i.)
W_{1-2} = vert. press. for runs 1&2 (p.s.i.)   S = total shear strength (p.s.i.)
ϕ = Angle of internal friction (determined) $S = c + N \tan \phi$
c = cohesion (determined from diagram)

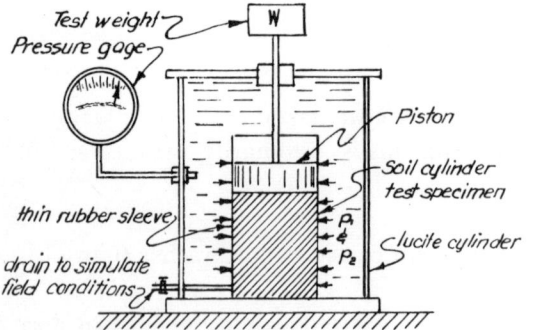

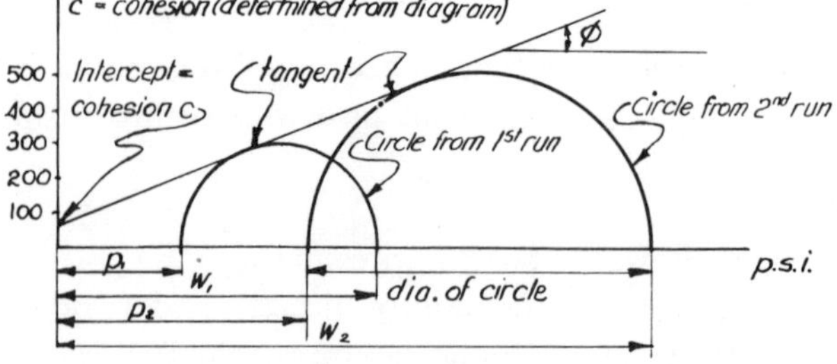

FIG.27-TRIAXIAL TEST APPARATUS

FIG.28-MOHR'S CIRCLE DIAGRAM

PERMEABILITY

Permeability is of great value in studying seepage under dams and time of consolidation of soils under pressure.

Permeability, measured by a coefficient of permeability k, is the ability of soils to pass water under a hydrostatic head. It is measured by permeameter, Fig. 29. The finer soils, silts, and clays are less permeable and fall into the classification of impervious.

The water passes between the soil particles through the voids. These voids can be measured by either the void ratio e, which is the ratio of voids to solids, or by the porosity n, which is the ratio of the voids to total volume. These may be interchanged according to the following equation:

$$n = \frac{e}{1 + e}$$

Since the permeameter test is rather complicated, and since k is a function of the effective size and the void ratio, k may be determined more easily from Table X. The void ratio is easily figured, and the effective size is determined from mechanical analysis, p. 13–36.

DETERMINATION OF VOIDS RATIO = e

EXAMPLE: Weight of Soil = 120 pounds per cubic foot.
Specific Gravity of grains = 2.70
2.70 x 62.4 = 169 lb./cu.ft. - Theoretical weight of solid material.
120/169 = 0.71 cu.ft. - Volume of Solid material.
1.00 - 0.71 = 0.29 cu.ft.- Volume of voids.

$$\frac{0.29}{0.71} = 0.41 = VOIDS\ RATIO.$$

PERMEABILITY

Darcy's Law : $Q = kA\frac{H}{L}$ for flow of water through soil.

WHERE:
Q = Volume of Flow in cu.ft. per min.
k = Coefficient of permeability·for values see Table 10.
A = Area in sq. ft. of cross-section under consideration.
$\frac{H}{L}$ = Hydraulic Gradient.

TABLE X-COEFFICIENTS OF PERMEABILITY (k) in ft./min. for 60°F.

EFFECTIVE SIZE	30 percent	32 percent	34 percent	36 percent	38 percent	40 percent	EFFECTIVE SIZE	42 percent	44 percent	46 percent	48 percent	50 percent
0.01	0.00003	0.00004	0.00005	0.000060	0.000072	0.000085	0.01	0.000101	0.000123	0.000149	0.000181	0.000215
0.02	.00013	.00016	.00020	.000239	.000286	.000339	0.02	.000405	.000492	.000597	.000724	.000861
0.03	.00030	.00036	.00045	.000538	.000645	.000763	0.03	.000911	.00111	.00134	.00163	.00194
0.04	.00053	.00065	.00079	.000958	.001145	.001355	0.04	.00162	.00197	.00239	.00290	.00344
0.05	.00082	.00101	.00124	.001495	.001790	.002120	0.05	.00253	.00307	.00373	.00452	.00538
0.06	.00118	.00146	.00178	.002150	.002580	.003050	0.06	.00364	.00442	.00537	.00652	.00775
0.07	.00161	.00198	.00243	.002930	.003510	.004155	0.07	.00496	.00602	.00732	.00887	.0105
0.08	.00211	.00259	.00218	.003825	.004585	.005425	0.08	.00647	.00787	.00956	.0116	.0138
0.09	.00266	.00328	.00402	.004845	.005800	.006860	0.09	.00820	.00995	.0121	.0147	.0174
0.10	.00328	.00405	.00496	.005980	.007170	.008480	0.10	.0101	.0123	.0149	.0181	.0215
0.12	.00473	.00583	.00713	.008620	.01032	.01220	0.12	.0146	.0177	.0215	.0261	.0310
0.14	.00643	.00794	.00972	.01172	.01404	.01662	0.14	.0198	.0241	.0293	.0355	.0422
0.15	.00739	.00912	.01115	.01345	.01611	.01910	0.15	.0228	.0277	.0336	.0407	.0484
0.16	.00841	.01036	.01268	.01531	.01835	.02170	0.16	.0259	.0315	.0382	.0463	.0551
0.18	.01064	.01311	.01605	.01940	.02320	.02745	0.18	.0328	.0398	.0484	.0586	.0697
0.20	.01315	.0162	.01983	.02390	.02865	.03390	0.20	.0405	.0492	.0597	.0724	.0861
0.25	.020	.0253	.03100	.03740	.04480	.05300	0.25	.0632	.0768	.0933	.113	.134
0.30	.0296	.0364	.04460	.05380	.06450	.07630	0.30	.0911	.111	.134	.163	.194
0.35	.0403	.0496	.0608	.07330	.08790	.1039	0.35	.124	.151	.183	.222	.264
0.40	.0527	.0648	.07940	.09575	.1145	.1355	0.40	.162	.197	.239	.290	.344
0.45	.0665	.0820	.1005	.1211	.1450	.1718	0.45	.205	.249	.302	.366	.436
0.50	.0822	.1012	.1240	.1495	.1780	.2120	0.50	.253	.307	.373	.452	.538
0.55	.0994	.1225	.1500	.1810	.2165	.2565	0.55	.306	.372	.452	.547	.651
0.60	.1182	.1458	.1784	.2150	.2580	.3050	0.60	.364	.442	.537	.652	.775
0.65	.1390	.1710	.2095	.2530	.3030	.3580	0.65	.428	.519	.631	.765	.909
0.70	.1610	.1983	.2430	.2930	.3510	.4155	0.70	.496	.602	.732	.887	1.05
0.75	.1850	.2278	.2785	.3365	.4030	.4770	0.75	.569	.691	.840	1.02	1.21
0.80	.2105	.2590	.3175	.3825	.4585	.5425	0.80	.648	.787	.956	1.16	1.38
0.85	.2375	.2925	.3580	.4325	.5175	.6125	0.85	.731	.888	1.08	1.31	1.55
0.90	.2660	.3280	.4018	.4845	.5800	.6860	0.90	.820	.995	1.21	1.47	1.74
0.95	.2965	.3650	.4470	.5400	.6460	.7650	0.95	.913	1.11	1.35	1.63	1.94
1.00	.3282	.4050	.4960	.5880	.7170	.8480	1.00	1.01	1.23	1.49	1.81	2.15
2.00	1.315	1.620	1.983	2.390	2.865	3.390	2.00	4.05	4.92	5.97	7.24	8.61
3.00	2.960	3.640	4.460	5.380	6.450	7.630	3.00	9.11	11.1	13.4	16.3	19.4
4.00	5.270	6.480	7.940	9.575	11.45	13.55	4.00	16.2	19.7	23.9	29.0	34.4
5.00	8.220	10.12	12.40	14.95	17.90	21.20	5.00	25.3	30.7	37.3	45.2	53.8

Porosity = $\frac{e}{1+e}$

TABLE XI- TEMPERATURE CORRECTIONS TO TABLE A.
See below for use of table.

TEMP. IN °F.	t_c
32	0.64
35	.67
40	.73
45	.80
50	.86
55	0.93
60	1.00
65	1.08
70	1.15
75	1.23
80	1.30
85	1.39
90	1.47
95	1.55
100	1.64

Use of Table XI:-
If temperature is other than 60°F., multiply k value in Table X
by value of t_c opposite applicable temperature in Table XI
For effective size see p. 13-36.

* Adapted from Low Dams by National Resources Committee.

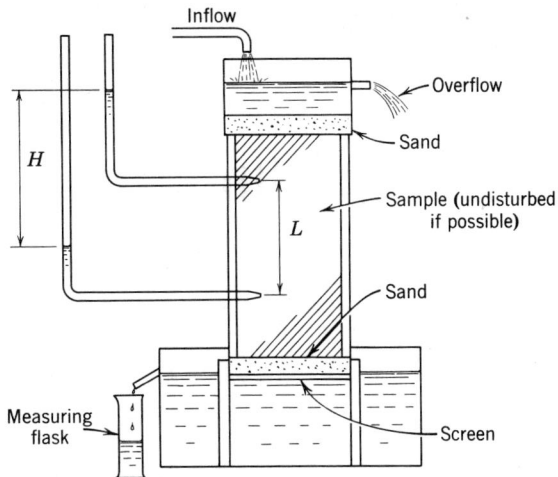

FIG. 29.   CONSTANT HEAD PERMEAMETER.

Cross-sectional area of sample = A.

Run permeameter for time t and collect quantity of water q; i.e., $Q = q/t$.

Then, coefficient of permeability k is, from Darcy's Law, $Q = KAH/L$, or, by algebra, $k = qL/HAt$.

TABLE XII- PERMEABILITY DATA.†

		COEFFICIENT OF PERMEABILITY (k) in cm. per sec. (Log scale)									Perfect validity of Darcy's Law
Turbulent flow											
k = 10^2 10^1	1.0	10^{-1}	10^{-2}	10^{-3}	10^{-4}	10^{-5}	10^{-6}	10^{-7}	10^{-8}	10^{-9}	

DRAINAGE PROPERTY: Good drainage | Poor drainage | Practically impervious

APPLICATION IN EARTH DAMS AND DIKES: Pervious sections of dams and dikes | Impervious sections of earth dams and dikes

TYPES OF SOIL:
- Clean Gravel | Clean sands; Clean sand & gravel Mixtures
- Very fine sands; Organic & Inorganic silts; mixtures of sand, silt & clay; glacial till; stratified clay deposits; etc.
- "Impervious" soils e.g. homogeneous clays below zone of weathering
- "Impervious soils" which are modified by the effects of vegetation and weathering

DIRECT DETERMINATION of coefficient of permeability:
- Direct testing of soil in its original position (e.g. well points) if properly conducted - reliable - considerable experience required
- CONSTANT HEAD PERMEAMETER Little experience required
- FALLING HEAD PERMEAMETER
  - Reliable little experience required
  - Unreliable Much experience necessary for correct interpretation
  - Fairly reliable Considerable experience necessary

INDIRECT DETERMINATION of coefficient of permeability:
- COMPUTATION from the grain size distribution (e.g. Hazen's formula) only applicable to clean cohesionless sands & gravels
- HORIZONTAL CAPILLARITY TEST Very little experience necessary. Especially useful for rapid testing of a large number of samples in the field without Lab. facilities
- COMPUTATIONS from consolidation tests; expensive lab. equip. & considerable experience required

‡ From Am. C. E. Handbook by Merriman & Wiggin . ** In accordance with modern highway practice.
† Adapted from Publication Nº 268. Harvard Grad. School of Eng.

For development of flow nets see Chapter 7.

THEORETICAL APPROACH TO SAFE FOUNDATION PRESSURE

The values for safe foundation pressures given in Table 8–I, need some further comment.

Table XII is based on the flow out from under a footing as shown in case 1, Fig. 30, and results in the following equations:

Circular or square footing ultimate bearing capacity = 7.4 × cohesion of soil = $7.4c$.

Continuous footing ultimate bearing capacity = $5.7c$.

Oblong footing B width L length = $5.7c (1 + 0.3B/L)$.

This same theory has been applied to the plastic flow of sand but is accepted with reservations by this author.

Obviously, if we assume case 1 to be correct, surcharge increases the resistance of the footing, but if we assume case 2, surcharge does not do so.

Attention is called to the fact that Table 8–I requires drastic reduction of soil pressures in cases of high water table.

The author has a feeling that a rigid interpretation of Fig. 8–I, especially in regard to the looser materials, tends to reductio ad absurdum.

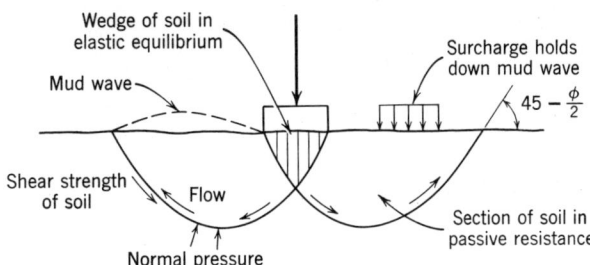

CASE 1.   Not likely to occur with granular soil.

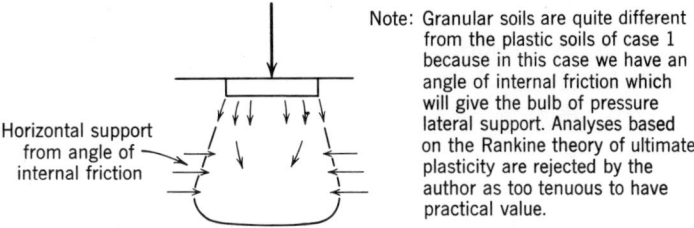

Note: Granular soils are quite different from the plastic soils of case 1 because in this case we have an angle of internal friction which will give the bulb of pressure lateral support. Analyses based on the Rankine theory of ultimate plasticity are rejected by the author as too tenuous to have practical value.

CASE 2.   Soil compacted and driven down and outward.   Likely behavior for a weak, granular soil.

FIG. 30.   MUD WAVES IN BUILDING CONSTRUCTION.

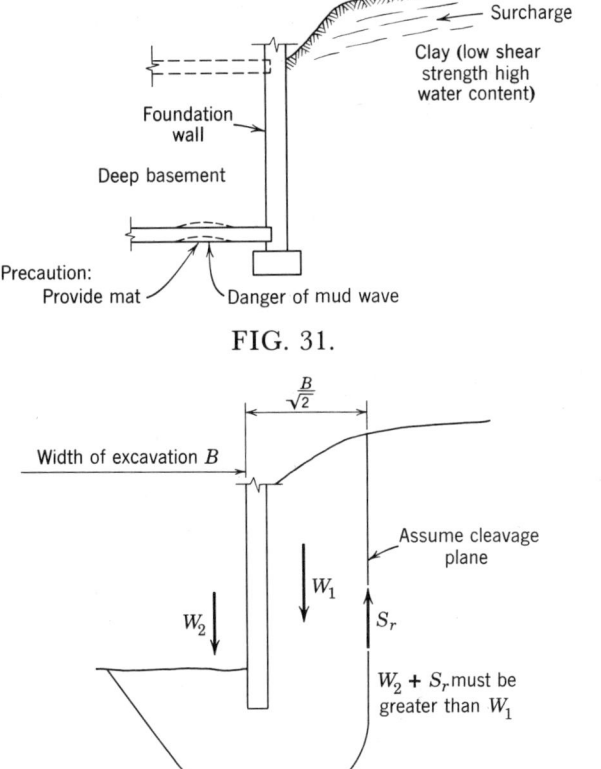

FIG. 31.

FIG. 32.   APPROXIMATE SOLUTION FOR FIG. 31.

See also Chapters 10 and 11.

Discussion

Sand

Chart, Fig. 8–1, is based on a dry moist sand and on test data.

If the sand is saturated, reduce the above value by 50%. However, if the footing is deep enough to give a surcharge effect, the reduction due to submergence may be compensated partially or in full.

This chart indicates that one should not rely on sand with an N of 5 or less, although Table 8–I (New York City Code) would allow considerable load for values of N below 5.

Silt

Silts with less than 10 blows are loose and are generally not as good as soft clay. Those which are medium or dense may be divided into rock flour types and plastic types. Figure the former as fine sands, the latter as clay, which is discussed next.

Clay

Table 8–II is set up to use the number of blows of resistance to driving and hence is a practical approach.

Comment: No allowance for surcharge is given in this table.

The "local shear failure" is one likely to occur in the softer clays and may be used as the safer value.

The footing width has an important effect on the amount of settlement. Wider footings settle more for the same unit bearing pressure.

The question of foundation settlement for clay is vital. See the following section.

SETTLEMENT—AMOUNT

Settlement studies are based upon the compression of an *undisturbed,* saturated, sample, usually plastic, in the laboratory, and the recording of the consolidation as the water is squeezed out. The results are then projected upon the foundation being considered.

Amount of Consolidation

The laboratory sample is placed in a consolidation machine, Fig. 33, and loaded in increments producing a load often of 0.20, 0.40, 0.80, 1.60, 3.20, and 6.40 tons per sq. ft. It is then unloaded in decrements of reverse order. Twenty-four hours should elapse between increments and decrements of load. Results are plotted in Fig. 34.

The amount of consolidation of the sample is proportional to the amount of consolidation to be expected in a thicker layer in situ.

Preconsolidation

Some soils have been preconsolidated by overburden or by loads now no longer present (eroded land or glaciers). For such loads, some additional foundation pressure may be added before consolidation begins. Cases have been reported of very high preconsolidation resulting from drying out of the soil (desiccation) or from decomposition of chemicals in it. This condition of preconsolidation or desiccation (Fig. 35) can be estimated by the shape of the curve, Fig. 34, if an undisturbed sample is available.

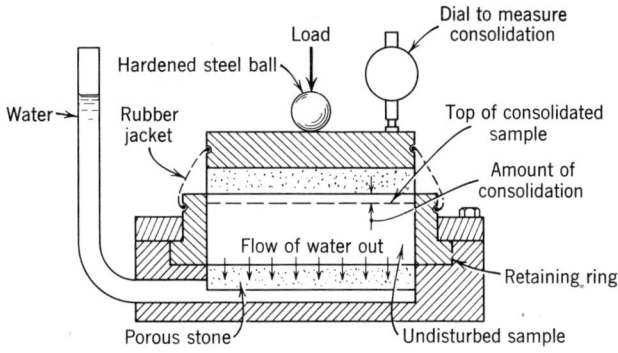

FIG. 33.   CONSOLIDATION TESTING MACHINE.

Purpose: To measure consolidation of soils for computing time and settlement values.   Pressure from load onto sample forces water out through the porous stones, causing the soil sample to consolidate.

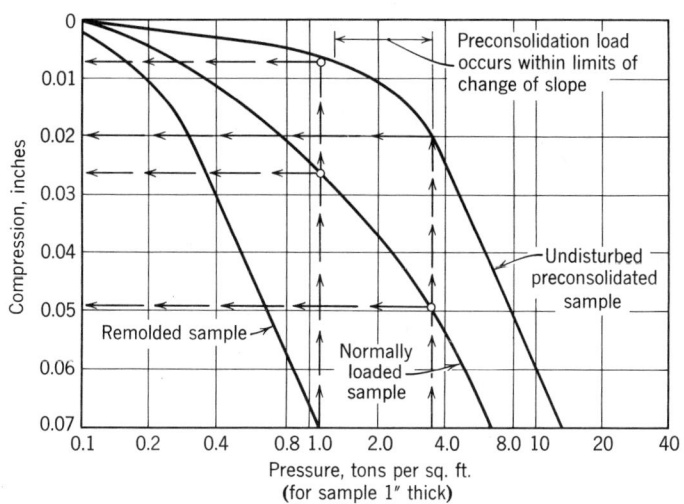

FIG. 34.   CURVES FOR CONSOLIDATION TESTS OF 1 IN. SAMPLE.

Note: Water content of preconsolidated clays is near the plastic limit, of normally loaded clays near the liquid limit.   For definition of liquid and plastic limit see p. 13–44.

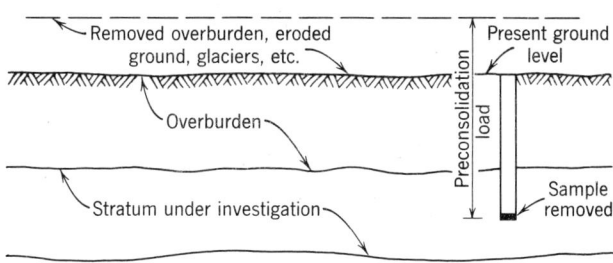

FIG. 35.   EXPLANATION OF THE TERMS OVERBURDEN AND PRECONSOLIDATION LOAD (DESICCATION).

Example 1

To compute expected settlement of a layer of clay.

Given: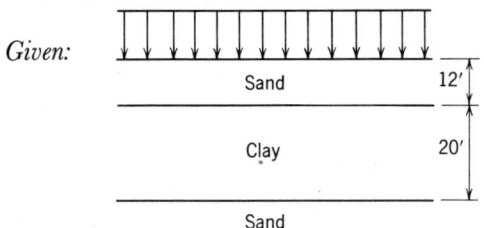

Additional Load 2.5 tons per sq. ft.
     Unit weight of soil, 100 lb. per cu. ft.
     No preconsolidation.

To Find: Settlement.

Obtain undisturbed sample. Run consolidation test. (Assume sample 0.9 in thick, and results are same as in Fig. 34.)

Compute load at center of clay layer:

$$\frac{22 \times 100}{2000} = 1.1 \text{ tons per sq. ft. at present}$$

$$1.1 + 2.5 = 3.6 \text{ tons per sq. ft. in future}$$

From curve, Fig. 34 (normally loaded sample),
Compression of sample at 3.6 tons = 0.051
Compression of sample at 1.1 tons = 0.026
     Net compressibility   = 0.025

$$\text{Expected settlement} = \frac{0.025 \times 20 \times 12}{0.9} = 6.94 \text{ in.}$$

If the soil was preconsolidated, use preconsolidated sample, Fig. 34.
Compression of sample at 3.6 tons = 0.020
Compression of sample at 1.1 tons = 0.007
     0.013

$$\text{Expected settlement} = \frac{0.013 \times 20 \times 12}{0.9} = 3.47 \text{ in.}$$

Approximate Settlement by Liquid Limit

The liquid limit (p. 13–44) can be used to give the approximate amount of settlement. This method has the advantage of being quick.

First, determine compression index.

     Compression index = 0.009 (Liquid limit -10%) = C *

Second, determine void ratio (p. 13–20). Then,

$$\text{Settlement} = \frac{\text{Thickness of Layer} \times \text{Compression index}}{1 + C} \times \log_{10} \frac{\text{Pressure} - \text{Increase in pressure}}{\text{Pressure}} *$$

---

* Evolved from Empirical data by A. W. Skempton and others.

Example 2

Clay layer 20 ft. thick; present load at center of layer 1.1 tons; future load 3.6 tons; void ratio 1.01; liquid limit 18.

$$\text{Compression index} = 0.009\,(18 - 10) = 0.072$$

$$\text{Settlement} = \frac{20 \times 12 \times 0.072}{1 + 1.01} \times \log_{10}\frac{3.6}{1.1}$$

$$= 4.32 \text{ in.}$$

Red Light

Not valid for extrasensitive clays, p. 13–17.

Failure to take into account long-time settlement of plastic soil has caused a large amount of damage in the way of cracked buildings, ruptured conduits, cracked or misplaced bridge abutments, fissured embankments, etc.

Discussion

Removal of Overburden

If 3 ft. of overburden were removed as for a basement and replaced by a mat averaging 300 lb. per sq. ft., the original pressure would be unchanged and there would be no settlement.

Spread Footings

In computing the probable settlement of a spread footing, it is necessary to arrive at an average pressure on the clay stratum. The bulb of pressure given in the elastic theory, p. 13–28, is useful for this purpose. Where the intensity of pressure varies considerably through a thick layer, it is helpful to divide the stratum into layers.

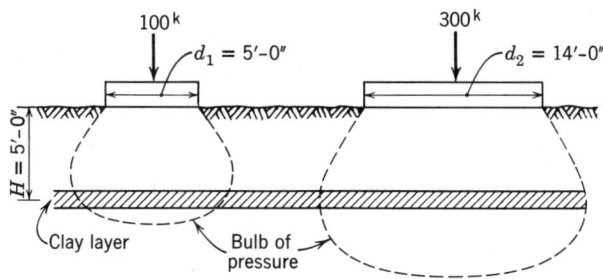

FIG. 36.   DESIGN FOR EQUAL SETTLEMENT.

Given: Safe bearing load 4000 lb. per sq. ft.

To design for equal settlement.

$$100^k \text{ footing } \frac{100}{4} = 25 \text{ sq. ft.} = 5'0'' \times 5'0''$$

Pressure 5 ft. down = H/d = 5/5 = 1. Determine factor = 0.30 $\pm$ from Fig. 36a.

Pressure = 0.3 × 4000 = 1200 lb. per sq. ft.

Select footing under 300^k load which gives a pressure of 1200 lb. per sq. ft. down 5 feet. Try several:

Contact Pressure	Area	Footing Size	Factor	Pressure at 5 ft.
4000	75	9 × 9	0.58	2320
3000	100	10 × 10	0.64	1920
2000	150	12–6 × 12–6	0.74	1480
1500	200	14–6 × 14–6	0.76	1140

Select a 14'0" × 14'0" footing.

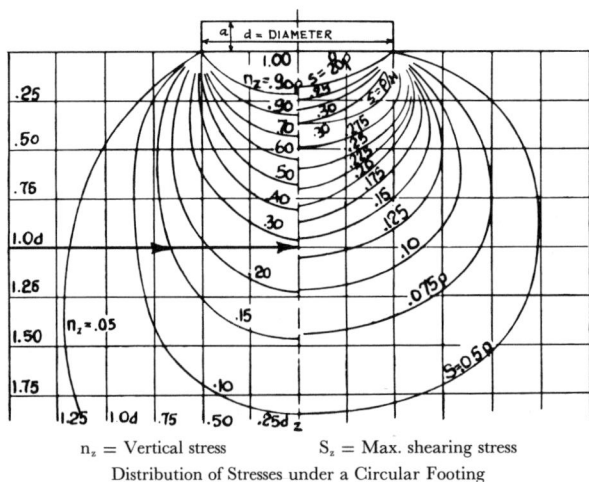

n_z = Vertical stress S_z = Max. shearing stress
Distribution of Stresses under a Circular Footing

FIG. 36a.   UNIT SHEAR AND DIRECT STRESS GIVEN FOR A CIRCULAR FOOTING.

SETTLEMENT—TIME

Discussion

Consolidation results from the squeezing out of water from clays by added load. Before the load was added, the clays contained a certain amount of adhered water. When the load was added, a certain amount of this adhered water was broken loose and squeezed out through the pores. The time it takes for this water to squeeze out through the pores represents the time of settlement.

An observation of the time elapsed in obtaining equilibrium due to loading an undisturbed sample can be extrapolated to a prediction of the time to consolidate a thick layer. Important considerations in making this extrapolation are the drainage boundaries of the layer under consideration. It has been determined empirically that the time for a given consolidation to take place varies as the square of the distance of travel, for example, in passing through a layer as the square of the thickness of the layer.

Figure 37 (a) has the same drainage conditions as the sample in the consolidation testing machine, Fig. 33, whereas, in the case of Fig. 37(b), the drainage travel is twice as much. Hence, the relative time of drainage is $(H/2)^2 : H^2$ or 1:4.

In sand pile drains, Fig. 38, the water being forced out by pressure must pass through a funnel, which increases the time of flow in the ratio of $(D/d)^2$.

DRAINAGE BOUNDARIES

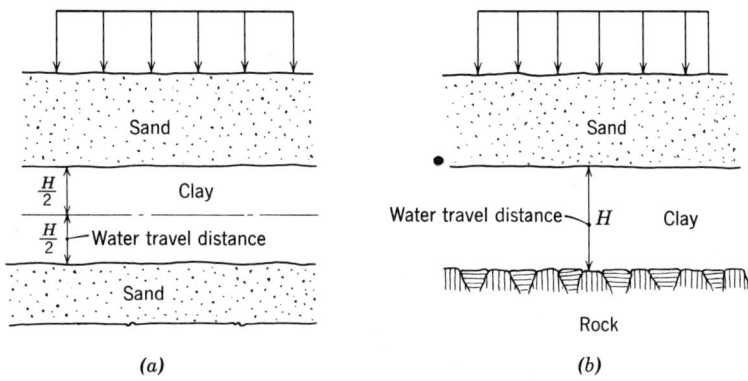

(a)   (b)

FIG. 37. DETERMINATION OF H FOR FIGURING TIME OF CONSOLIDATION.

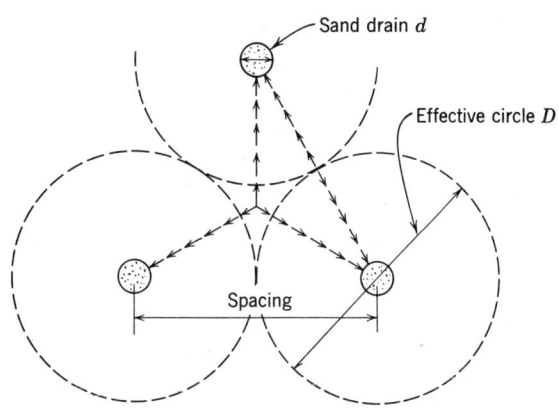

FIG. 38. USE OF SAND DRAINS HASTENS CONSOLIDATION
WHEN SPACING IS LESS THAN THICKNESS OF LAYER.

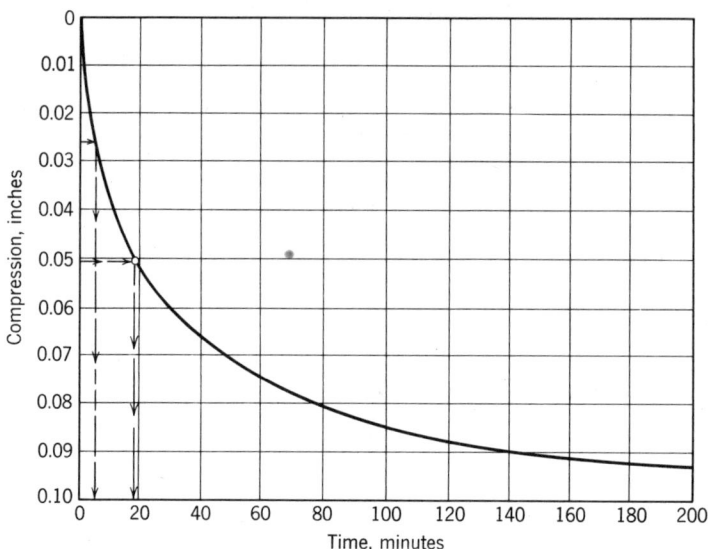

TIME SETTLEMENT

FIG. 39.   TIME COMPRESSION CURVE FOR NORMALLY LOADED SAMPLE.

(Prepared from consolidometer test.)

Example 3

Given: Same as example 1, p. 13–26.
From Fig. 39:

Time to consolidate sample 0.051 in. = 19 min.
Time to consolidate sample 0.026 in. =   5 min.
Time of additional consolidation = 14 min.

To figure time of settlement in field:

$$\text{Time} = 14 \times \frac{(20 \times 12)^2}{0.9^2} = 995{,}600 \text{ min.}$$

$$= 1.89 \text{ years.}$$

If lower layer is impermeable, time = $4 \times 1.89 = 7.6$ years.

Red Lights

The presence of undetected sand lenses or shafts will permit the escape of water and hasten the results over those expected.

Disturbed samples are remolded, and the effects of preconsolidation are overlooked.   Use only undisturbed samples, if possible.

Ignoring the buoyant effect of ground water upon the overburden will lead to erroneous results.

Use large-diameter sand piles.

Example 4

Effect of water table on stratum.

```
El. -0  _____                    _____
El. -10                                        Sand
          Sand                         - - - - - - - -
                                          Water table
El. -30  _____                    _____
          Clay                                 Clay
El. -40  _____                    _____
El. -45  __ Sand __ __ __                      Sand
        Water table
              (a)                              (b)
```

Pressure at center of clay stratum EL–35 when unit weight of soil is 100 lb. per cu. ft.

$$\text{Case } a \quad P = 35 \times 100 = 3500 \text{ lb. per sq. ft.}$$
$$\text{Case } b \quad P = 35 \times 100 - 25 \times 62.4 = 1940 \text{ lb. per sq. ft.}$$

COMPACTION CONTROL

Backfill under floors may require a compaction density of 95–100% of maximum density at what is known as optimum moisture content. Embankment or earth dams may require similar control. The shearing resistance of many soils may be governed by the degree of compaction. Table XIII gives some recommended values.

TABLE XIII
Relative Bearing Values and % Compaction Required

Max. Dry Density	Soil Rating	Recommended Compaction, %
90 lb. and less	N. G.	—
90 lb.–100 lb.	Very poor	95–100
100–110 lb.	Poor to very poor	95–100
110–120 lb.	Poor to fair	90–95
120–130 lb.	Good	90–95
130 lb. and over	Excellent	90–95

Note: Density or wt./vol. may be expressed as pounds per cubic foot or grams per cubic centimeter. Density in grams per cubic centimeter = bulk specific gravity.

Soil should be placed as dense as possible. Maximum density may be reached at a certain moisture content ("optimum moisture content"). This content is determined by laboratory procedure and checked in the field, as per the following tests.

PURPOSE: of Maximum Density - Optimum Moisture is to determine the % of moisture at which the Maximum Density can be obtained when soil is compacted in fill, earth dams, embankments, etc.

Purpose of the Proctor Needle test is to obtain a measure of the degree of compaction of a soil by measuring its resistance to penetration. Also a method of determining soil moisture. Cannot be used in soils with coarse particles. Used mostly in earth dam construction.

MAX. DENSITY - OPTIMUM MOISTURE,

as per A.S.T.M-D.698 - A.A.S.H.O.-D:T.99.

(a) Mold 1/30 Cu.ft.
(b) Rammer
(c) Sleeve
(d) Balance or Scale 25# cap. sen. to 0.01#
(e) Balance 100 g sensitive to 0.1g
(f) Drying oven 110 C. or 230 F.
(g) 12" Straightedge.

FIG. 40 APPARATUS NEEDED.
TESTING PROCEDURE:

6 lb. ± (3000 grams) of air dried soil slightly damp & passing the Nº 4 sieve is mixed thoroughly, then compacted in the mold of 1/30 of Cu.ft. capacity in 3 equal layers. Each layer receiving 25 blows from the rammer with a Controlled drop of 1 ft. The collar is removed and the soil struck off level and weighed.

(Wt. of soil plus mold - Wt. of mold) X 30 = Wet Weight per cubic foot or wet density.

A 100-g. sample from the Center of the mass is weighed, dried at 230 F. and moisture content determined.

Pulverize original 6 lb., add about 1% Water and repeat test. Repeat until soil becomes saturated (about 5 times) Plot Wet-Density Curve. See Fig. 36. Compute Dry Density by formula and plot curve:

$$\text{Dry Density} = \frac{\text{Wet Wt.} \text{ lb. per Cu. ft.}}{\% \text{ moisture} + 100} \times 100$$

In Fig. 41 - Enter at top of Dry Density Curve & read optimum moisture & max. wt. of soil 20.2% & 103.5 lb.

MODIFIED A.A.S.H.O. METHOD.**

Same as above except:
1. Rammer to weigh 10 lb.
2. Rammer to have controlled drop of 18".
3. Soil compacted in mold in 5 equal layers. 25 blows to each layer.

The highest dry density is recorded as lab. unit Wt.
NOTE: Modern Airfield compaction equipment can secure greater densities than can be obtained by the standard Proctor or A.A.S.H.O. Test. If field compaction or vibration will give greater densities on any job than the test, the higher density should be used to control compaction.

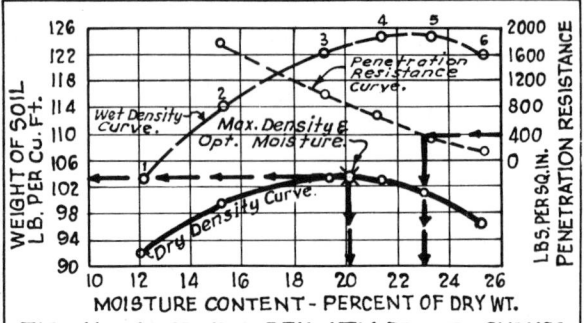

FIG. 41- MOISTURE-DENSITY PENET. CURVES.

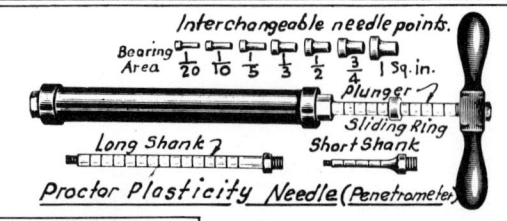

Interchangeable needle points.
Bearing Area 1/20 1/10 1/5 1/3 1/2 3/4 1 Sq. in.
Plunger
Long Shank   Sliding Ring   Short Shank

Proctor Plasticity Needle (Penetrometer)

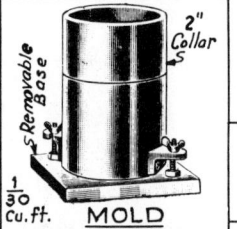

2" Collar
Removable Base
1/30 Cu. ft. **MOLD**
4" I.D. x 4 1/2" Deep.

Needle shanks are graduated at 1/2" intervals to indicate penetration. Plunger rod calibrated for every 10 lb. up to 110 lb. pressure. Ring indicates max. pressure.

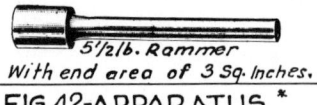

5 1/2 lb. Rammer
With end area of 3 Sq. Inches.

FIG. 42-APPARATUS.*

PROCTOR TEST:[†] 5 lb. of dry soil passing

a Nº 10 sieve is mixed thoroughly with just enough water to make it slightly damp, then compacted in the mold in 3 layers. Each layer is given 25 blows with the rammer dropped 1 ft. The soil is then struck off level with the cylinder, weighed, and the stability determined with the plasticity needle by measuring the force required to press it into the soil at the rate of 1/2" per sec. A small portion of the soil is oven dried to determine the moisture content. This procedure is repeated 3 to 6 or more times, each time adding about 1% more water until the soil becomes very wet. The density & plasticity needle readings are plotted against moisture content, see Fig. 41. Thus in Fig. 41 a needle reading of 400 gives a moisture content of 23%.

* Adapted from: Humboldt Mfg. Co., ** Engineering Manual, O.C.E., War Dept.,
† Engineering News Record, Aug. 31 to Sept. 28, 1933, R. R. Proctor.

PURPOSE: 1. To determine moisture content for optimum moisture and maximum density relations.

2. To determine the amount of water in aggregates for concrete, bituminous and other mixtures.

Gravelly Soils: Use Pycnometer Method - Fig. 43 or heat method described below.

Sandy Soils : Use Chapman Flask - Fig. 44 or heat method described below.

Silts and Clays: Use heat method described below.

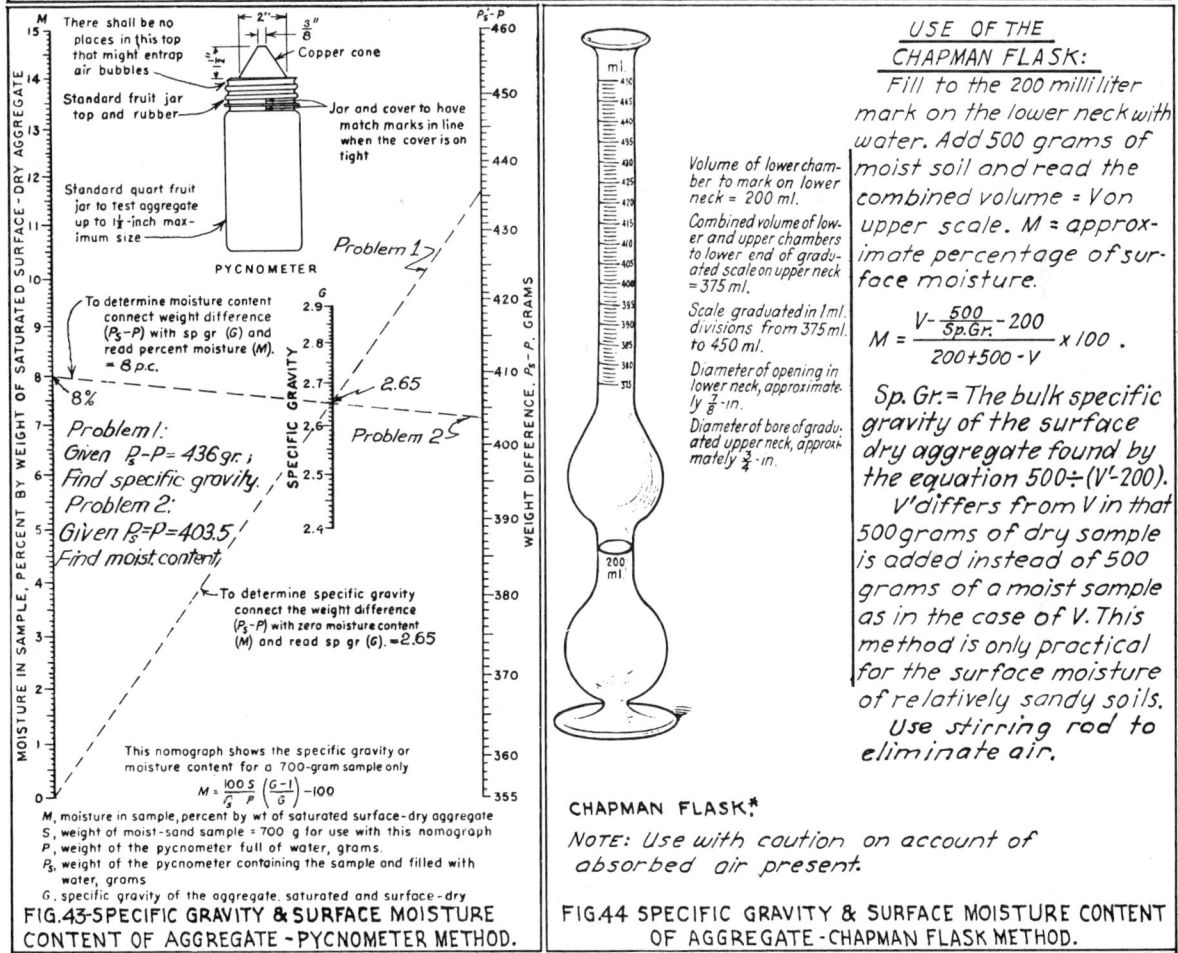

There shall be no places in this top that might entrap air bubbles.

Copper cone

Standard fruit jar top and rubber

Jar and cover to have match marks in line when the cover is on tight

Standard quart fruit jar to test aggregate up to 1½-inch maximum size

PYCNOMETER

To determine moisture content connect weight difference (P_s-P) with sp gr (G) and read percent moisture (M). = 8 p.c.

8%

2.65

Problem 1:
Given P_s-P = 436 gr.;
Find specific gravity.

Problem 2:
Given P_s=P=403.5;
Find moist content.

To determine specific gravity connect the weight difference (P_s-P) with zero moisture content (M) and read sp gr (G). =2.65

This nomograph shows the specific gravity or moisture content for a 700-gram sample only

$$M = \frac{100\,S}{S\,P}\left(\frac{G-1}{G}\right) - 100$$

M, moisture in sample, percent by wt of saturated surface-dry aggregate
S, weight of moist-sand sample = 700 g for use with this nomograph
P, weight of the pycnometer full of water, grams.
P_s, weight of the pycnometer containing the sample and filled with water, grams
G, specific gravity of the aggregate, saturated and surface-dry

MOISTURE IN SAMPLE, PERCENT BY WEIGHT OF SATURATED SURFACE-DRY AGGREGATE

SPECIFIC GRAVITY

WEIGHT DIFFERENCE, P_s-P, GRAMS

FIG.43-SPECIFIC GRAVITY & SURFACE MOISTURE CONTENT OF AGGREGATE - PYCNOMETER METHOD.

ml.

200 ml.

CHAPMAN FLASK.*

NOTE: Use with caution on account of absorbed air present.

Volume of lower chamber to mark on lower neck = 200 ml.

Combined volume of lower and upper chambers to lower end of graduated scale on upper neck = 375 ml.

Scale graduated in 1 ml. divisions from 375 ml. to 450 ml.

Diameter of opening in lower neck, approximately ⅞-in.

Diameter of bore of graduated upper neck, approximately ¼-in.

USE OF THE CHAPMAN FLASK:

Fill to the 200 milliliter mark on the lower neck with water. Add 500 grams of moist soil and read the combined volume = V on upper scale. M = approximate percentage of surface moisture.

$$M = \frac{V - \frac{500}{Sp.Gr.} - 200}{200 + 500 - V} \times 100\ .$$

Sp. Gr. = The bulk specific gravity of the surface dry aggregate found by the equation 500 ÷ (V'-200).

V' differs from V in that 500 grams of dry sample is added instead of 500 grams of a moist sample as in the case of V. This method is only practical for the surface moisture of relatively sandy soils. Use stirring rod to eliminate air.

FIG.44 SPECIFIC GRAVITY & SURFACE MOISTURE CONTENT OF AGGREGATE - CHAPMAN FLASK METHOD.

HEAT METHOD: FOR TOTAL MOISTURE CONTENT OR SURFACE MOISTURE CONTENT.

1. Obtain a representative sample. If a metric scale is available the sample should not be smaller than 100 grams. If an avoirdupois scale graduated by ½ ounces is used, the sample should contain at least 50 ounces.

2. Weigh sample and record weight.

3. Place sample in pan and spread to permit uniform drying. Set pan in oven or on top of stove in a second pan to prevent burning of soil.

4. Dry to constant weight when total moisture is to be found; dry until surface moisture disappears when surface moisture content is desired. Temperature should not exceed 105°C (221°F). Stir constantly to prevent burning.

5. After the sample has been dried to constant weight, remove from oven and allow to cool sufficiently to permit absorption of hygroscopic moisture. Weigh dried sample and record weight.

6. Compute the moisture content as follows:

$$\text{Percent Moisture} = \frac{\text{weight of wet soil - weight of dry soil}}{\text{weight of dry soil}} \times 100.$$

*From A.S.T.M. Specifications.

Purpose: 1. To obtain the natural density of soil in place (*a*) as an indication of its stability or bearing value as foundation; (*b*) to compute the shrinkage or swell when the soil is removed and placed in embankment at a higher or lower density. 2. To determine the percentage of compaction being obtained to check against requirements of specifications.

Method of Determining Weight Per Cubic Foot of Soil in Place

Calibrated Sand Method

The density of a soil layer may be determined by finding the weight of a disturbed sample and measuring the volume of the space occupied by the sample prior to removal. This volume may be measured by filling the space with a weighed quantity of a medium of predetermined weight per unit volume. Sand, heavy lubricating oil or water in a thin rubber sack may be used.

1. Determine the weight per cubic foot of the dry sand by filling a measure of known volume. The height and diameter of the measure should be approximately equal and its volume should be not less than 0.1 cu. ft. The sand should be deposited in the measure by pouring through a funnel or from a measure with a funnel spout from a fixed height. The measure is filled until the sand overflows and the excess is struck off with a straight-edge. The weight of the sand in the measure is determined and the weight per cubic foot computed and recorded.

2. Remove all loose soil from an area large enough to place a box similar to the one shown in Fig. 46, and cut a plane surface for bedding the box firmly. A dish pan with a circular hole in the bottom may be used.

3. With a soil auger or other cutting tools bore a hole the full depth of the compacted lift.

4. Place in pans all soil removed, including any spillage caught in the box. Remove all loose particles from the hole with a small can or spoon. Extreme care should be taken not to lose any soil.

5. Weigh all soil taken from the hole and record weight.

6. Mix sample thoroughly and take sample for water determination.

7. Weigh a volume of sand in excess of that required to fill the test hole and record weight.

8. Deposit sand in test hole by means of a funnel or from a measure as illustrated in Fig. 46 by exactly the same procedure as was used in determination of unit weight of sand until the hole is filled almost flush with original ground surface. Bring the sand to the level of the base course by adding the last increments with a small can or trowel and testing with a straightedge.

9. Weigh remaining sand and record weight.

10. Determine moisture content of soil samples in percentage of dry weight of sample.

11. Compute dry density from the following formulas:

$$\text{Volume of soil} = \frac{\text{Wt. of sand to replace soil}}{\text{Wt. per cu. ft. of sand}}$$

$$\% \text{ moisture} = \frac{\text{Wt. moist. soil} - \text{Wt. dry soil}}{\text{Wt. of dry soil}} \times 100$$

$$\text{Moist density} = \frac{\text{Weight of soil}}{\text{Volume of soil}}$$

$$\text{Dry density} = \frac{\text{Moist density}}{1 + \dfrac{\% \text{ of moisture}}{100}}$$

$$\% \text{ Compaction} = \frac{\text{Dry density}}{\text{Maximum density}} \times 100$$

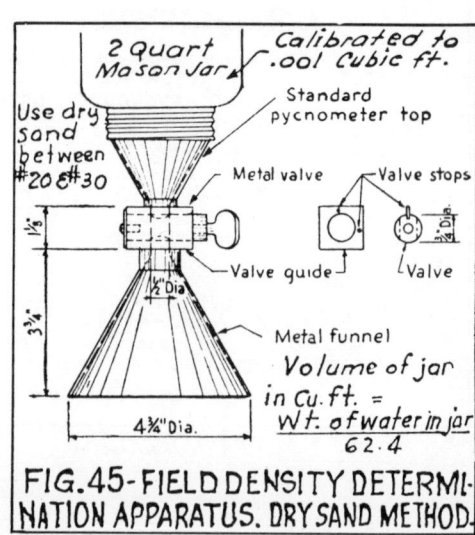

FIG. 45-FIELD DENSITY DETERMINATION APPARATUS. DRY SAND METHOD.

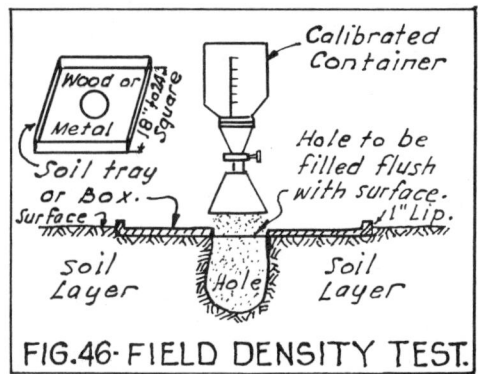

FIG.46· FIELD DENSITY TEST.

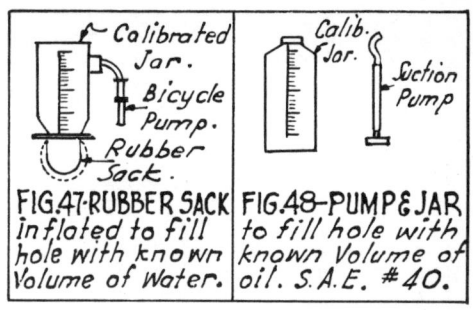

FIG.47·RUBBER SACK inflated to fill hole with known Volume of Water.

FIG.48–PUMP & JAR to fill hole with known Volume of oil. S.A.E. #40.

Example 5

Given:

Wt. per cubic foot of sand = 100 lb.
Wt. of moist soil from hole = 5.7 lb.
Moisture content of soil = 15%
Wt. of sand to fill hole = 4.5 lb.

Required: Density and % Compaction.

Solution:

Volume of soil $= \dfrac{4.5}{100} = 0.045$ cu. ft.

Moist density $= \dfrac{5.7}{0.045} = 126.7$ lb.

Dry density $= \dfrac{126.7}{1 + 15/100} = 110.0$ lb.

Given maximum density = 115 lb. (from density test).

% Compaction $= \dfrac{110}{115} \times 100 = 95.7\%$

Note: In gravel soils material over ¼ in. is screened out and correction made.

Chunk Sample Method

1. Cut sample 4″–5″ diameter full depth of layer.
2. Determine % moisture.
3. Trim sample and weigh to ½ oz.
4. Immerse sample in hot paraffin, remove, cool, and weigh again.
5. Compute volume of paraffin using 55 lb. per cu. ft.
6. Compute volume of sample by weighing in water (correcting for volume of paraffin).
7. Compute density data by formulas above.

The above method is adapted from *Public Roads,* Vol. 22, No. 12, by Harold Allen, Public Roads Administration.

SOIL CLASSIFICATION

Soils are generally classified as sand, clay, silt, etc., as outlined in Chapter 8. Such classification is generally made on the basis of grain size. In addition, there are several other classifications which depend on the grain size and also upon the use or the origin. A few of the more prominent classifications are given.

PURPOSE: 1. To identify homogeneous soils in the major divisions, see Table I-VII
2. To classify soil mixtures occurring in a natural state, Fig. 53.
3. To classify soil into the P.R.A. or Casagrande groups Tables XVI, XVII, & IX.
4. To design or control stabilized soil mixtures.
5. To determine frost heaving potentialities. See Tables XVI, XVII and IX.
6. To determine Effective Size (D_{10}) & Uniformity Coefficient (C_u.) for the design and control of filters and sub-drainage back fill.

MM	No.	INCHES
0.84	20	0.0331
0.42	40	0.0165
0.25	60	0.0098
0.105	140	0.0041
0.074	200	0.0029
0.053	270	0.0021

8" Frames, brass

FIG. 49 SIEVES

EQUIPMENT:
Balance sensitive to 0.1 gram
Mortar & rubber covered pestle.
Sieves: see left.
In addition it is desirable to have #4, #10, 3/8, 3/4 & 1 1/2 for coarse grain soil.

Grad. in grams of soil per liter of suspension.

Hydrometer analysis of grain size is based upon Stokes' Law:
"Particles of equal Specific Gravity settle in water at a rate which is in proportion to the size of the particle."
NOTE: This test requires Laboratory Technique.

FIG. 50 HYDROMETER TEST.

SIEVE ANALYSIS.

Size of sample to be 400 to 750 grams - the coarser the material the larger the sample required.

Take sample by quartering or with sample splitter.

Dry surface moisture by heating the quartered sample at less than 212°F., or boiling point of water at high altitudes, in open pan until surface water disappears & sample is apparently dry and will not lose more weight with additional heating.

Break up cakes with mortar & pestle.

Record dry weight of sample.

Proceed to pass material through screens by placing sample in a stack of sieves, largest size on top, & shake vigorously with horizontal rotating motion balancing on bumper or pad until no more material will pass through each screen.

Weigh amount retained on each sieve, compute per cent of total weight of sample and plot curve.

Washing is recommended for Nº 200 sieves and smaller.
Partly immerse the largest sieve in a pan of water and agitate. Take material and water from pan and repeat for next smaller size sieve. Agitate smallest size sieve in several water baths until water remains clear. Air-Dry portions retained in sieves, weigh & plot curve.

MECHANICAL ANALYSIS OF SOILS.

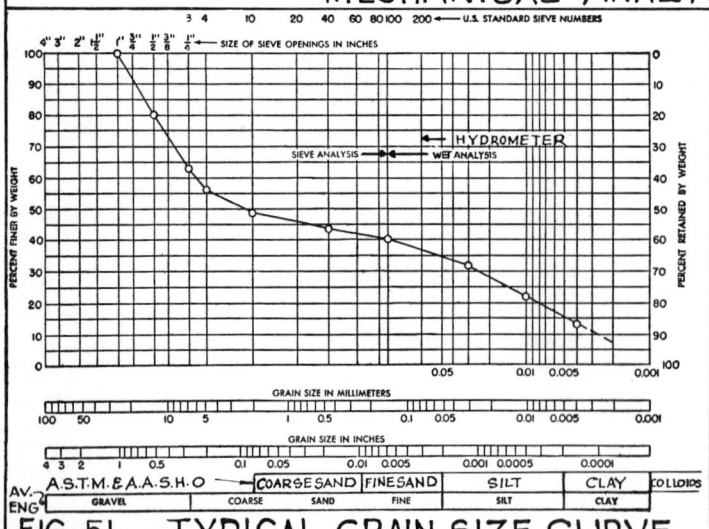

FIG. 51 -TYPICAL GRAIN SIZE CURVE.

EFFECTIVE SIZE (D_{10}): of a soil is the particle size that is coarser than 10% (by weight) of the soil, that is, 10% of the soil consists of particles smaller than the Effective Size (D_{10}) and 90% consists of larger particles. Example: in Fig. 52 Chart, Effective Size (D_{10}) is 0.02 mm.

UNIFORMITY COEFFICIENT (C_u) is computed by first determining the size that is coarser than 60% of the soil and dividing that size by the Effective Size (D_{10}), ie.,

$$C_u = \frac{60\% \ Size}{10\% \ Size}$$

Example: in chart, $C_u = \dfrac{0.5}{0.02} = 25$.

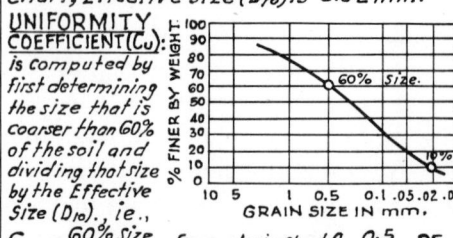

Note: The C_u of filter backfill should not be over 20. The D_{10} of non-frost heaving uniform soil is 0.02 mm. minimum.

FIG. 52 EFFECTIVE SIZE (D_{10}) & UNIFORMITY COEFFICIENT (C_u).

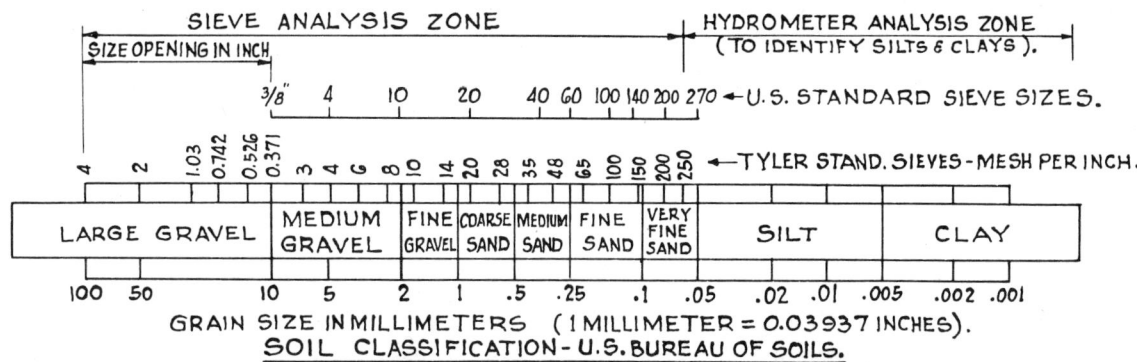

FIG. 53-IDENTIFICATION BY MECHANICAL GRAIN SIZE ANALYSIS.

NOTES: *Mechanical analysis is necessary to identify soils into the various divisions, and into PRA & Casagrande systems. In general, the value of soils as a foundation for structures and as a material of Construction is determined by the grain sizes and the gradation of the soil mixture. Other widely used grain size classifications are International,* Natl. PK. Serv., A.S.T.M.

TABLE XIV - CLASSIFICATION OF SOIL MIXTURES. *

CLASS	PER CENT		
	SAND	SILT	CLAY
SAND	80-100	0-20	0-20
SANDY LOAM	50-80	0-50	0-20
LOAM	30-50	30-50	0-20
SILT LOAM	0-50	50-80	0-20
SANDY CLAY LOAM	50-80	0-30	20-30
CLAY LOAM	20-50	20-50	20-30
SILTY CLAY LOAM	0-30	50-80	20-30
SANDY CLAY	50 70	0-20	30-50
CLAY	0-50	0-50	30-100
SILTY CLAY	0-20	50-70	30-45

NOTE: Determine proportions of Sand, Silt & Clay by sieve analysis or inspection.
(Natural soils seldom exist separately as gravel, sand, silt, clay, but are found as mixtures.)

USE OF CHART.

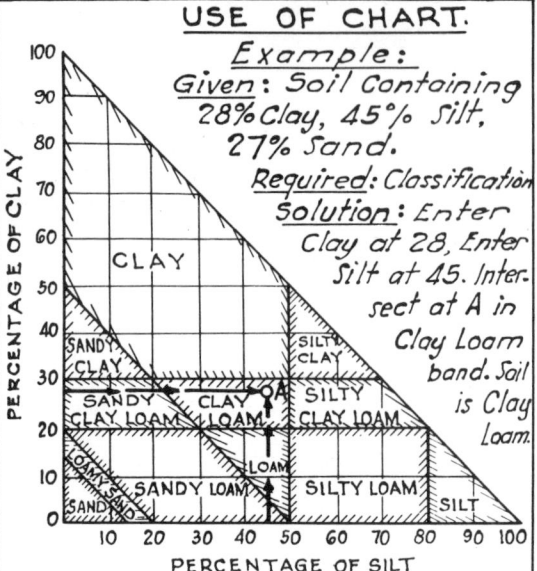

Example:
Given: Soil Containing 28% Clay, 45% Silt, 27% Sand.
Required: Classification
Solution: Enter Clay at 28, Enter Silt at 45. Intersect at A in Clay Loam band. Soil is Clay Loam.

FIG.54-RIGHT ANGLE SOIL CHART. *

Soil Profile: A vertical cross-section of the soil layers from the surface downwards through the parent material.

A HORIZON The upper layer, surface soil or topsoil. The upper part is designated A_o and is humus or organic debris. Indices are used for subdivision into transition zones as shown for A_1, A_2, etc. May range to 24" in depth.

B HORIZON The heavier textured under layer or subsoil. May range from 6" to 8' in depth. May be subdivided into transition zones B_1, B_2, etc., as shown. The products of the leaching or eluviation of the A horizon may be deposited in horizon B.

C HORIZON The unweathered or incompletely weathered parent material.

D HORIZON The underlying stratum such as hard rock, hardpan, sand or clay.

FIG. 55-CLASSIFICATION OF SOILS BY HORIZONS.*

Widely used in soil stabilization.

NOTES: Structures or pavements are not usually placed on A horizon soils. Also the organic content of these soils may adversely affect stabilization. In cuts the C horizon soil does not usually have as good bearing value as the more weathered B horizon. Foundations for heavy structures are preferably founded on the D horizon where it is bedrock or unyielding.

TABLE XV - CLASSIFICATION OF SOILS BY ORIGIN.

Residual:		Rock weathered in place - Wacke, laterite, podzols, residual sands, clays & gravels.
Cumulose		Organic accumulations - peat, muck, swamp soils, muskeg, humus, bog soils.
Transported	Glacial	Moraines, eskers, drumlins, Kames - till, drift, boulder clay, glacial sands & gravels.
	Alluvial	Flood planes, deltas, bars - Sedimentary clays & silts, Alluvial sands & gravels.
	Aeolian	Wind-borne deposits - Blow sands, dune sands, loess, adobe.
	Colluvial	Gravity deposits - Cliff debris, talus, avalanches, masses of rock waste.
	Volcanic	Volcanic deposits - Dakota bentonite, Volclay, volcanic ash, lava.
	Fill	Man made deposits - may range from waste & rubbish to carefully built embankments.

NOTE: In general, residual or glacial deposits are preferable for heavy foundations.
Important in soil surveys & Eng. Reports.

* Adapted from Soil Cement Laboratory Handbook, Portland Cement Assoc.
References: Engineering Geology; by Ries & Watson.

TABLE XVI - CHARACTERISTICS FOR IDENTIFYING P.R.A. SOIL GROUPS.*

Established by Public Roads Administration & Highway Research Board-Classification as shown is latest modification. Extensively used by engr's for highways, airfields & dams.

Characteristics	A-1 NON-PLASTIC	A-1 PLASTIC	A-2 NON-PLASTIC	A-2 PLASTIC	A-3	A-4 and A-4-7‡	A-5 and A-5-7‡	A-6	A-7	A-8
TEXTURAL CLASS	UNIFORMLY GRADED GRANULAR COARSE TO FINE		POORLY GRADED GRANULAR-COARSE AND FINE		CLEAN SAND OR GRAVEL	SILT OR SILT-LOAM	SILT OR SILT LOAM	PLASTIC CLAY	PLASTIC CLAY LOAM	MUCK & PEAT
Soil Constants										
Internal Friction	High	High	High	High	High	Variable	Variable	Low	Low	Low
Cohesion	High	High	Low	High	None	"	Low	High	High	Low
Shrinkage	Not detrimental		Not Significant	Detrimental if poorly graded	Not Significant	"	Variable	Detrimental	Detrimental	Detrimental
Expansion	None		None	Some	Slight	"	High	High	"	"
Capillarity	"		"	"		Detrimental	"	"	High	"
Elasticity	"		"	"	None	Variable	Detrimental	None	"	"
Capillary Rise	Low	High	36"Max.	Over 36"	6"Max.	High	High	High	High	"
Atterberg Limits										
Liquid Limit	25 Max.	35 Max.	35 Max.	40 Max.	Non Plastic	40 Max.	Over 40	35 Min.	35 Min.	35-400
Plasticity Index	6 Max.	4-9	NonPlastic	15 Max.	"	0-15	0-60	18 Min.	12 Min.	0-60
Shrinkage Limit	14-20		15-25	25 Max.	Not Essential	20-30	30-120	6-14	10-30	30-120
Field Moisture Equivalent	Not Essential	Not Essential	Not Essential	Not Essential	Not Essential	30 Max.	30-120	50 Max.	30-100	30-400
Centrifuge Moisture Equivalent	15 Max.		12-25	25 Max.	12 Max.	Not Essential	Not Essential	Not Essential	Not Essential	Not Essential
Shrinkage Ratio	1.7-1.9		1.7-1.9	1.7-1.9	Not Essential	1.5-1.7	0.7-1.5	1.7-2.0	1.7-2.0	0.3-1.4
Volume Change	0-10		0-6	0-6	None	0-16	0-16	17 Min.	17 Min.	4-200
Lineal Shrinkage	0-3		0-2	0-4	"	0-4	0-4	5 Min.	5 Min.	1-30
Grading (Grain Size)										
% Sand	70-85		55-80	55-80	75-100	55 Max.	55 Max.	55 Max.	55 Max.	55 Max.
% Silt	10-20		0-45	0-45		High	Medium	Medium	Medium	Not
% Clay	5-10		0-45	0-45		Low	Low	30 Min	30 Min.	Significant
% Passing Nº 10	20-100	40-100								
% Passing Nº 40	10-70	25-70								
% Passing Nº 200	3-25	8-25	Less than 35	Less than 35	0-10					

‡ A-4 or A-5 soil with A-7 characteristics.

TABLE XVII — CHARACTERISTICS AND PERFORMANCE OF P.R.A. SOIL GROUPS

SOIL GROUP	A-1 Non Plastic	A-1 Plastic	A-2 Non Plastic	A-2 Plastic	A-3	A-4 and A-4-7‡	A-5 and A-5-7‡	A-6	A-7	A-8
Stability	High	High when dry	High	Good when dry	Ideal when Confined	Good When dry	Doubtful	Good, when properly compacted or undisturbed		None
Base	Good	Fair	Fair	Fair	Excellent	N.G.	N.G.	N.G.	N.G.	N.G.
Sub-base	Excellent	Good	Excellent	Good	"	"	"	"	"	"
Sub-grade	"	"	"	"	"	Poor	Poor	Poor	Bad	"
Fills under 50'	"	Excellent	"	"	Good	Good to Poor	Poor to Very Poor	Bad	Fair to Poor	"
Fills over 50'	Good	Good	Good to Fair	Good to Fair	Good to Fair	Fair to Poor	Very Poor	Bad	Very Poor	"
Frost Action	Slight	Subject to	Slight	Subject to	None	Bad	Bad	Slight to Bad	Slight to Bad	Slight
Dry Density	over 130 lb.	over 130 lb.	120-130 lb.	120-130 lb.	120-130 lb.	110-120 lb.	80-100 lb.	80-110 lb.	80-110 lb.	under 90 lb.
Optimum Moisture	9%	9%	9-12%	9-12%	9-12%	12-17%	22-30%	17-28%	17-28%	—
Required Compaction	90-95%	90-95%	90-95%	90-95%	90-95%	95%	100%	100%	100%	Waste
Compaction Methods	Rolling with smooth face, tamping or rubber tire roller.				Tractor, Disking, Vibration.	Tamping or Sheeps-foot roller.	Tamping or Rubber tire roller.	Heavy Sheeps foot or tamping roller.		"
Compaction Abilities	Excellent	Excellent	Good with close control		Good	Poor to Good	Very Poor	Poor to Good	Poor to Fair	N.G.
Pumping Action	None	Slight	None	Slight	None			Bad	Bad	—
Bearing Value	Good to Excellent	Good to Excellent	Fair to Excellent			Poor to Fair	Poor	Poor	Poor	N.G.
Drainage	Drains Freely	Impervious	Fair to practically impervious		Drains Freely	Fair to Impervious	Fair to Impervious	Impervious	Poor	Poor
Flex. Pavement & Base Required	0"-6"	0"-6"	0"-6"	2"-8"	0"-6"	9"-18"	9"-24"	12"-24"	12"-24"	

‡ A-4 or A-5 soil with A-7 characteristics.

NOTES: A-1 to A-3 Soils: When used as base, Plasticity Index and Liquid Limit should not exceed 6 and 25 respectively. A-1 to A-3 Soils: Best for soil cement stabilizing, use 8 to 12% cement. Non-plastic A-1 to A-3 Soils: May require vibration and saturation for compaction. A-4 to A-7 Soils: Fills should be placed in dry season at not over optimum moisture content. A-4 Silts: Will settle rapidly in fills and are liable to erosion. A-5 Soils: Very difficult to compact because of expansion and rebound. A-6 Soils (clays): Will pump badly into porous bases, cracks and R.R. ballast. Fills will settle over long period of time. High banks in cuts and fills very liable to slide.

USE AND TREATMENT OF P.R.A. SOIL GROUPS

TABLE XVIII – FOR ROADS AND AIRFIELDS* See also Table XVII	
A-1 SOILS:	Well graded gravels & Sand-clays, as Florida sand-clay or Georgia Topsoil. Satisfactory treated Surface. Good base with thin pavement. Excellent fill. Frost heave & break-up in North if plastic. Use sub-drainage to lower water table. Stabilize; mechanically, chlorides or Portland Cement.
A-2 SOILS:	Poorly graded sands & gravels, as S. Carolina Topsoil or Bank Run. Good base for moderate flexible or thin rigid pavement. Good fill. Frost heave, break-up if plastic. Softens when wet if plastic. Use base course when subgrade P.I. > 6. Sub-drainage effective. Stabilize: with bitumen, chlorides, Cement or Admixture soils.
A-3 SOILS:	Clean sands & Gravels, as Florida Sand, glacial gravel, beach sand, wash gravel. Ideal base for moderate flexible or thin rigid pavement. Good fill. No frost heave or break up. Sub-drainage only thru impervious shoulders. Stabilize: with soil binder, bituminous, or chemical admixtures.
A-4 SOILS:	Silty soils as N.H. silt or Minn. Silt. No good for surface. Poor base. Absorbs water. Unstable when wet. Bad frost heave & break-up. Use Sub-drainage and/or base and Sub-base with flexible pavement. Use bituminous sub-grade prime. Use thick concrete pavement (7" to 10") with steel reinforcement and crack control.
A-5 SOILS:	Elastic silts as N. Carolina micaceous silt or Maryland micaceous sandy loam. Use Sub-drainage and/or granular base and Sub-base with bitum. Sub-grade prime. Use thick conc. pavement reinforced with crack Control.
A-6 SOILS:	Clays, as Miss. Gumbo, Missouri colloidal clay, sandy clays. Impermeable & stable when dry and undisturbed (hard clay). Plastic & absorbent if disturbed. Bad pumping into porous base, Macadam or pavement joints. Shrinks & cracks when dry. Use granular base & sub-base. Use sub-drainage only when made pervious by cracks, root holes & laminations. Frost heave slight when impermeable, bad when pervious. Use sub-grade prime. Use thick, strong, dense flexible pvmt. or reinf'd. Crack controlled concrete.
A-7 SOILS:	Expansive, plastic clays, as Adobe, Missouri Clay, Illinois or Red River Gumbo. Excessive volume change. Bad frost heave & break up. Sub-drainage not effective. Use thick, dense flexible pavement with base & sub-base over sub-grade prime or reinforced crack controlled concrete placed on impervious paper.
A-8 SOILS:	Muck & Peat. No good for construction purposes. Excavate to solid stratum & replace with selected fill. Displacement by superimposed fill is doubtful. Displacement by explosive under superimposed fill is sometimes effective.

USE AS FOUNDATIONS FOR STRUCTURES.

A-1 to A-3 Soils : <u>BEST</u>. A-6 & A-7 Soils : <u>NEXT BEST</u>, when hard, undisturbed & not plastic. A-5, A-8, Plastic A-6 & A-7 Soils : Require special treatment in each case.

USE IN EARTH DAM.†

HOMOGENEOUS TYPE LOW PERCOLATION.	IMPERVIOUS CORE TYPE. CORE.
Use: A-1, A-2 Plastic, A-4 Plastic, Better grades of A-6 & A-7.	Use: A-1, A-2 Plastic, A-4 Plastic, Better grades of A-6 & A-7.
FIG. 56 	POROUS FACES Non Plastic A-2 & A-4.  FIG. 57

<u>Do not use:</u> A-3, A-5, A-8 or Highly Plastic A-6 or A-7 in Dam Construction. A-4, A-6 & A-7 Soils: Use Controlled compaction to maximum density at optimum moisture content.

† Adapted from Hogentogler, Engineering Properties of Soil, Mc Graw-Hill.   Refs.-Highway Subgrades by A.G. Bruce, Principles of Highway Const., Public Rds. Adm., Highway Research Board – Wartime Road Problems. *See also Chapter 7.

STABILIZED SOILS: *Should be sealed when used as a wearing course. Stabilization is mostly used to form base courses for thin bituminous or Portland cement concrete pavements.*

MECHANICAL STABILIZATION: *Plot curve of soil on chart in Fig. 58. Curve should fall within shaded zone; otherwise coarse or fine material must be added to soil.*

CRITERIA FOR MECH. STABILIZATION:

Plasticity Index (P.I.) of fraction of soil passing Nº 40 sieve should be from 3 to 9 but not over 6 if bituminous surface treatment is to be added.

The fraction passing Nº 10 sieve should show no appreciable shrinkage.

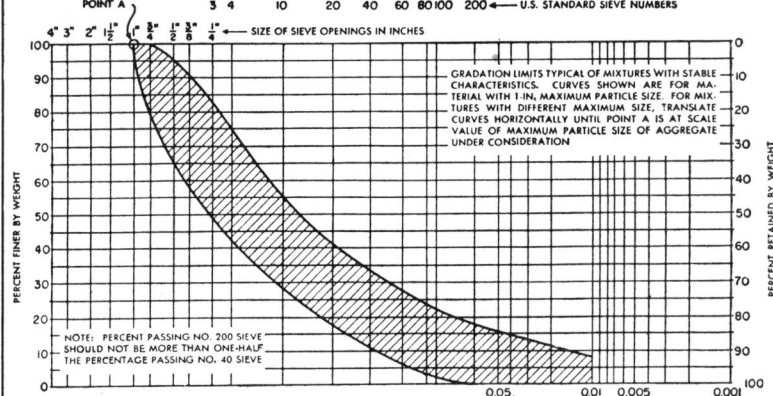

GRADATION LIMITS TYPICAL OF MIXTURES WITH STABLE CHARACTERISTICS. CURVES SHOWN ARE FOR MATERIAL WITH 1-IN. MAXIMUM PARTICLE SIZE. FOR MIXTURES WITH DIFFERENT MAXIMUM SIZE, TRANSLATE CURVES HORIZONTALLY UNTIL POINT A IS AT SCALE VALUE OF MAXIMUM PARTICLE SIZE OF AGGREGATE UNDER CONSIDERATION

NOTE: PERCENT PASSING NO. 200 SIEVE SHOULD NOT BE MORE THAN ONE-HALF THE PERCENTAGE PASSING NO. 40 SIEVE

FIG. 58-GRADATION LIMITS FOR STABLE MIXTURES.*

PORTLAND CEMENT STABILIZATION: *The amount of cement to be added should be determined by laboratory analysis, Fig. 59 to be used as a guide only.*

CRITERIA FOR CEMENT STABILIZATION.

Liquid Limit (L.L.) should not be more than 40.

Plasticity Index (P.I.) not more than 18.

Maximum depth of construction = 6".

Note: L.L. and P.I. values as recommended by the Portland Cement Assoc.

For cement treated base suggest A-3 type soil. See also Table XVIII

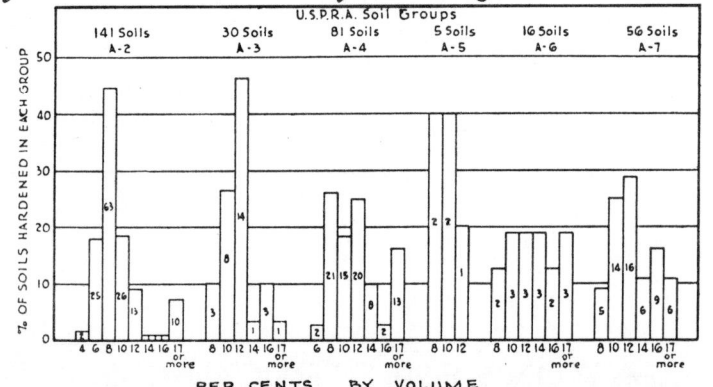

FIG. 59-RESULTS OF TESTS OF SOILS TO DETERMINE CEMENT REQUIRED FOR ADDITIONAL BINDING.**

BITUMINOUS STABILIZATION: *Soil should be selected or native granular materials A1 to A3 types. The usual depth of construction is 2½" to 4". Amount of bituminous material would vary according to size with maximum requirement for fine soils. An average would be ½ gal. per sq. yd. for each inch of stabilized depth.*
Bituminous materials usually used are cut-back asphalt MC2 or MC3, Road tars RT2 to RT5, Asphalt emulsion & slow curing liquid road oils.
RESIN STABILIZATION: *About ¼ of 1% by weight is required for normal application. The powdered resins (Vinsol, Stabinol, Pextite) are added to the soil in the same manner as Cement. Up to the present, 1949, resins have been used successfully only with acid soils.*
CALCIUM CHLORIDE STABILIZATION: *Current practice is to use ½ lb. per sq. yd. per inch of compacted depth with a maximum of 3 lb. per sq. yd. Valuable in reaching desired densities and in preventing frost action.*
LIST OF EQUIPMENT USED IN STABILIZATION: *Chisel tooth, spike tooth and offset disc harrows; disc plows; motor patrol graders, dozers & other spreading equipment; rubber tired tractors; wobbly wheel, rubber tired, sheepsfoot, tandem & 3 wheel rollers, special mixing equipment as premixing plants (Barber Greene type) & speed rotary tillers (Pulvi-mixers, Roto-Tillers).*

*Adapted from Aviation Eng. Manual, Apr. 1944 **Highway Research Bd. Wartime Road Problems Nº 7.

Atterberg Limits

Soils change from solid to plastic to liquid states, depending on the moisture content. The Atterberg limits are an attempt to define these points of transition in terms of moisture content. In general, the following characteristics of soils may be assumed from the values of these limits.

Low liquid limit indicates a coarse-grained soil—a reliable soil.

High plasticity index means fine grained to clay—an unreliable soil.

Low plasticity index means low compressibility and low shrinkage—a reliable soil.

These limits are also an aid in defining type of soils (P.R.A. classification in particular).

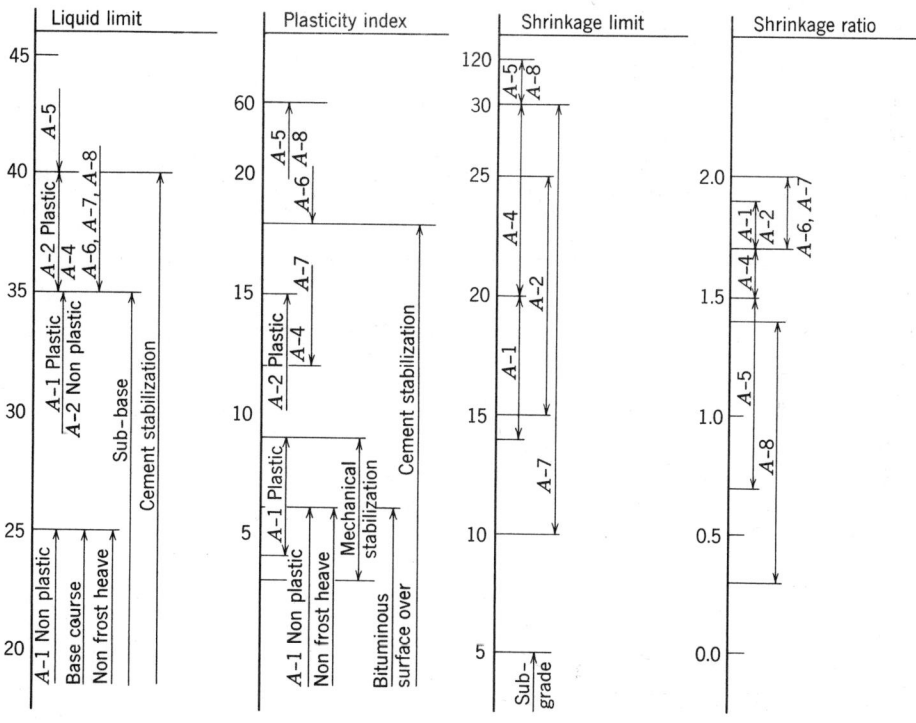

FIG. 60.   CORRELATION BETWEEN ATTERBERG LIMITS,
P.R.A. CLASSIFICATION, AND SOIL USES.

See also p. 53.

PURPOSE:

1. To classify soils into P.R.A., Casagrande, or C.A.A. groups.
2. To assign soils an approximate value as a foundation or construction material.
3. High values of liquid limit and plasticity index indicate high compressibility and low bearing capacity.
4. To determine soil suitability for road construction.

TABLE XIX LIMITING VALUES	BASE COURSE	SUBGRADE	SUB-BASE	STAB. SURF.	SOIL CEMENT	CEM. TREATED BASE
	No Shrinkage L.L.=25; P.I.=6 max	Lineal Shrinkage 3% to 5%	L.L.=35; P.I.=15 max.	P.I.=4 to 9	L.L.=40; P.I.=18 max.	L.L.=25 P.I.=6 to 9

The water content or moisture content is expressed as a percentage of the oven dried weight of the soil sample. These soil constants are determined from the soil fraction passing the No. 40 (420 micron) sieve.

The Liquid Limit (L.L.) of a soil is the water content at which the groove formed in a soil sample with a Std. grooving tool will just meet when the dish is held in one hand & tapped lightly 10 blows with the heel of the other hand. In the machine method the L.L. is the water content when the soil sample flows together for ½" along the groove with 25 shakes of the machine at 2 drops per sec. Diameter of brass cup or evaporating dish about 4½".

Size of sample: By hand 30 grams: By machine 100 grams. Several trials are made, the moisture content being gradually increased. Blows are plotted against water content and the Liquid Limit picked off from the curve as shown

or $L.L. = \dfrac{Weight\ of\ water}{weight\ of\ oven\ dried\ soil} \times 100.$

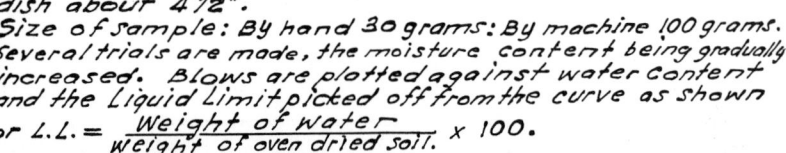

EXAMPLE OF FLOW CURVE.*

Crank & Cam device to produce 1 centimeter drop of Cup.   Grooving Tool.

CASAGRANDE LIQUID LIMIT MACHINE.

Soil Cake After Test

FIG.61- LIQUID LIMIT (L.L.) A.S.T.M. D 423, A.A.S.H.O., T-89.

The Plastic Limit (P.L.) is the lowest water content at which a thread of the soil can be just rolled to a diam. of ⅛" without cracking, crumbling or breaking into pieces.

$P.L. = \dfrac{Weight\ of\ water}{Wt.\ of\ oven\ dried\ soil} \times 100$

Size of soil sample is 15 grams.
Soil which cannot be rolled into a thread is recorded as Non-Plastic (N.P.)

SOIL THREAD ABOVE THE PLASTIC LIMIT.

CRUMBLING OF SOIL THREAD BELOW THE PLASTIC LIMIT.

FIG.62-PLASTIC LIMIT (P.L.) A.S.T.M. D 424, A.A.S.H.O., T-90.

PLASTICITY INDEX (P.I.): A.A.S.H.O., T-91. numerical difference between LIQUID LIMIT (L.L.) & PLASTIC LIMIT (P.L.) or P.I. = L.L.-P.L. Example: Given L.L.=28, P.L.=24, P.I.=4. Cohesionless soils are reported as Non-Plastic (N.P.). When Plastic Limit is equal to or greater than Liquid Limit the P.I. is reported as 0.

SHRINKAGE RATIO (R): = bulk specific gravity of the dried soil pat used in obtaining Shrinkage Limit. $R = \dfrac{Weight\ of\ oven\text{-}dried\ soil\ pat\ in\ grams}{Volume\ of\ oven\ dried\ soil\ pat\ in\ c.c.}$ or $\dfrac{W_o}{V_o}$

SHRINKAGE LIMIT (S): A.S.T.M., A.A.S.H.O. T-92. Water content at which there is no further decrease in Volume with additional drying of the soil but at which an increase in water content will cause an increase in volume.

$S = \left(\dfrac{1}{Shrinkage\ Ratio} - \dfrac{1}{Spec.\ Gravity}\right) \times 100.$ Size of sample 30 grams.

1¾" Dia. x ½" High Milkdish.

Wet Soil — BEFORE SHRINKAGE.
Dry soil — AFTER SHRINKAGE.

LINEAL SHRINKAGE: is the decrease in one dimension of the soil mass when the water content is reduced to the Shrinkage Limit or the % change in length occurring when a moist sample has dried out.

FIELD TESTS. Cigar Shaped   Shrinkage Soil   1"x1"x10" Mold   5"   Pins   Soil

14

Embankments and Pavements

The design of highways and airfields is essentially a foundation problem: that of carrying a highly concentrated wheel load down to the earth. It differs from a building foundation in two main respects. First, it does not have a heated, waterproof covering over it and therefore must by its own nature resist the frost and drainage problems. Second, it must by its very nature violate the cardinal rule of building foundations of not putting loads on disturbed earth. Therefore the problem of embankment design requires primary consideration.

EMBANKMENT DESIGN

Safe Slope

Embankments composed of granular materials have their slopes limited to the angle of repose (Table I) regardless of the height. Since the shearing resistance of cohesive soils does not vary with the load normal to the plane of shearing, the height as well as the cohesive strength governs the safe slope. For low heights the slope may be very steep, but for larger ones it may become very flat. Such slopes may be analyzed by the "Swedish method," Fig. 4, or one of the many similar ones. The nomograph, Fig. 1, has been arranged to give the relationship of height, weight, cohesion, and internal friction so as to enable the designer to select his slope quickly. All embankments must be protected against surface erosion. The presence of water in the soil adversely affects the safe slope of the embankment.

Safe Foundation

The foundation should safely resist the shears transmitted by the embankment. The easiest method of analysis is the sliding block, Fig. 2. For plastic foundations the Swedish method may be used, passing the circle through the foundation until the weakest one is found. The nomograph, Fig. 1, will give safe designs for plastic foundations of known depth. Where adverse foundation conditions are encountered, corrective measures may be taken by loading the toe or by using a berm part way up the slope. If the layer of soil is not very deep, the best method is to remove it and replace it with good material.

LIMITATIONS: *All slopes of cohesive material require flatter angles as the height is increased. This limiting height will vary with the degree of compaction, cohesive strength and angle of friction. It will also vary with the strength of the foundation on which it rests. Granular soils have no limiting heights.*

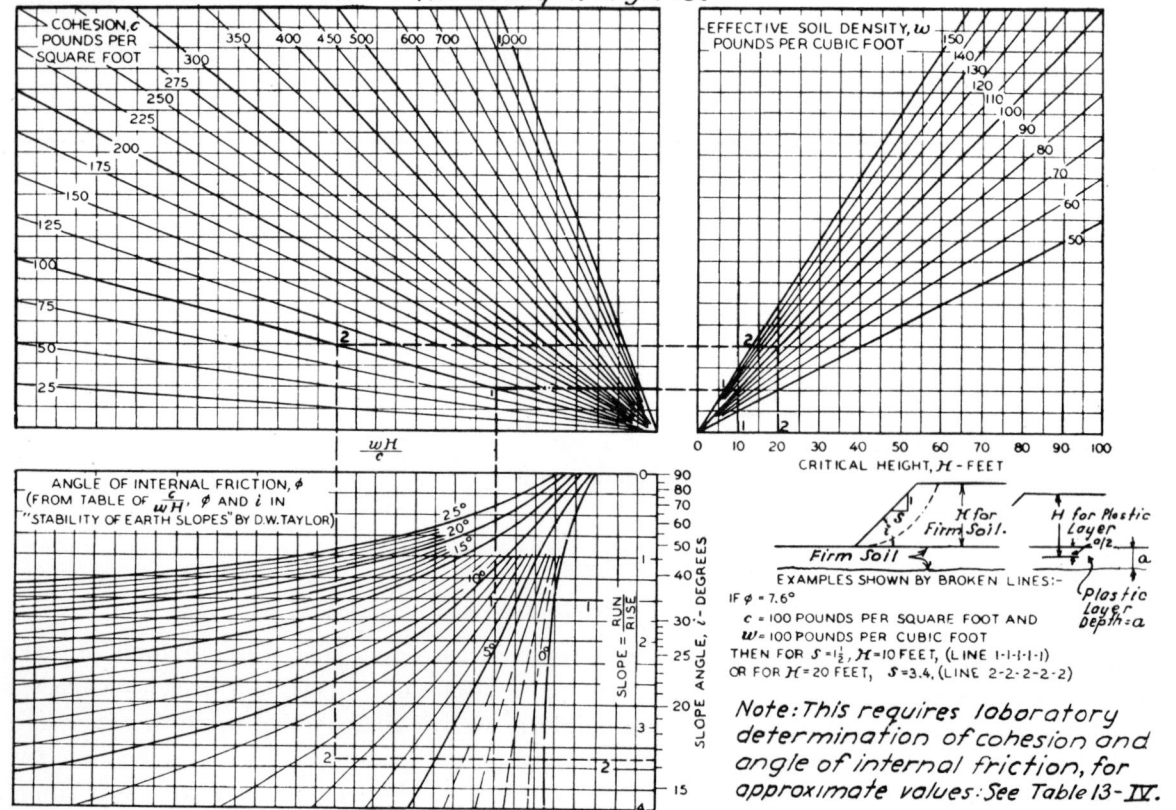

FIG. I. DETERMINATION OF EMBANKMENT SLOPES & HEIGHTS.

TABLE I

SAFE SLOPE OF BANK GRANULAR SOILS (ANGLE OF REPOSE)

Sand, clean	1 on 1.5
Sand, some clay	1 on 1.33
Gravel	1 on 1.33
Gravel with sand, some clay	1 on 1.5
Rotten rock	1 on 1
Bituminous cinders	1 on 1
Anthracite ashes	1 on 1.5 to 2.0

* By Taylor, adapted from *Eng. News-Record,* Vol. 128, No. 7, Feb. 12, 1942, article by P.R.A.

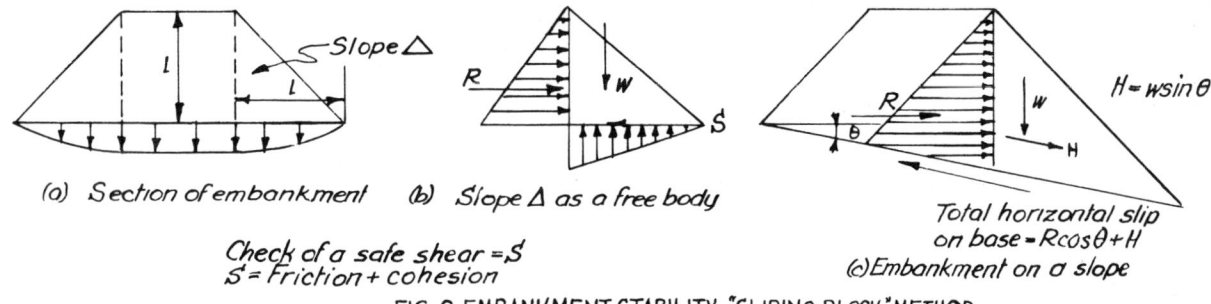

(a) Section of embankment   (b) Slope Δ as a free body

Check of a safe shear = S
S = friction + cohesion

Total horizontal slip
on base = R cos θ + H
(c) Embankment on a slope

FIG. 2. EMBANKMENT STABILITY- "SLIDING BLOCK" METHOD

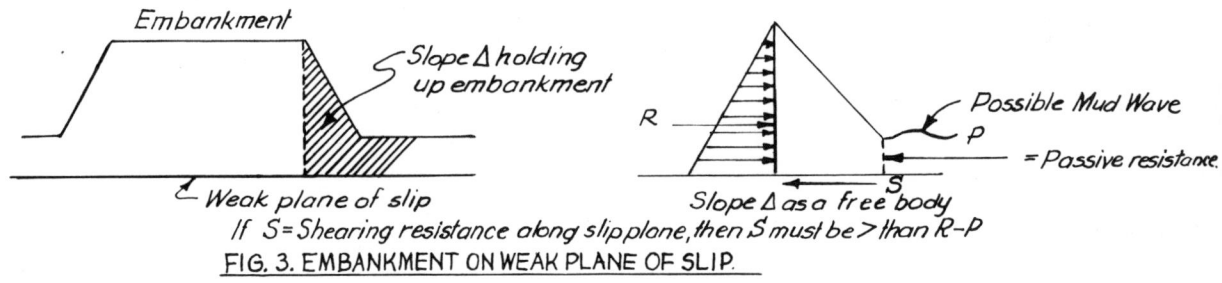

If S = Shearing resistance along slip plane, then S must be > than R-P
FIG. 3. EMBANKMENT ON WEAK PLANE OF SLIP.

For solution suggested by Jergensen, see p. 7–20.

Locate O for weakest
circle.   For suggested
values of α and β
see Table II.

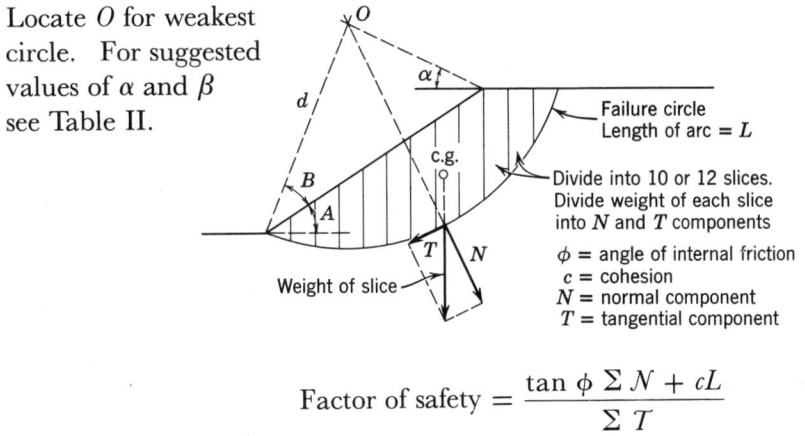

Failure circle
Length of arc = L

Divide into 10 or 12 slices.
Divide weight of each slice
into N and T components

ϕ = angle of internal friction
c = cohesion
N = normal component
T = tangential component

$$\text{Factor of safety} = \frac{\tan \phi \, \Sigma \, N + cL}{\Sigma \, T}$$

Recommended minimum value 1.25–1.5

FIG. 4.   ANALYZING SLOPE STABILITY BY SWEDISH METHOD.

TABLE II

For Location of Center of Failure Circle *

Slope	Slope angle A	α	β
1:0.58	60°	40°	29°
1:1	45°	37°	28°
1:1½	33°47′	35°	26°
1:2	26°24′	35°	25°
1:3	18°26′	35°	25°
1:5	11°19′	37°	25°

*After Fellinius, based upon observed locations of center of weakest circle of failure.

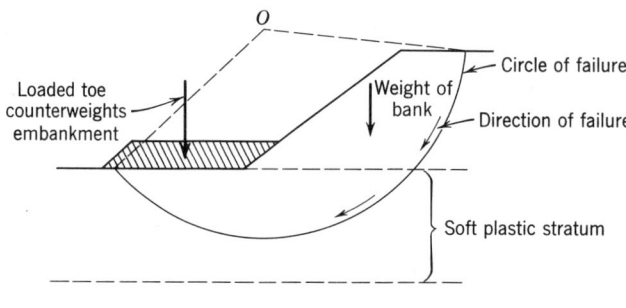

LOADING TOE

SAFETY BERM

FIG. 5.   STABILIZING EMBANKMENTS ON ADVERSE FOUNDATIONS.

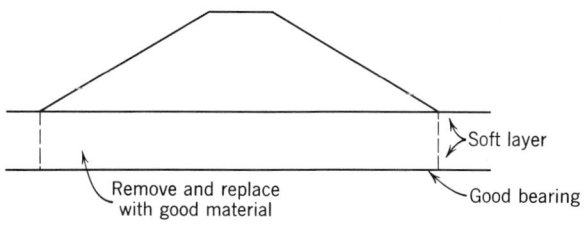

Soft layer

Remove and replace
with good material

Good bearing

REMOVAL OF POOR MATERIAL

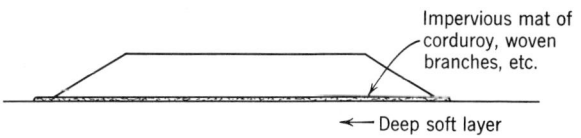

Impervious mat of
corduroy, woven
branches, etc.

← Deep soft layer

FLOATING EMBANKMENT

Embankment floated on soft soil to prevent
expense of consolidating or removing soft soil.
Mat distributes load and prevents break through.

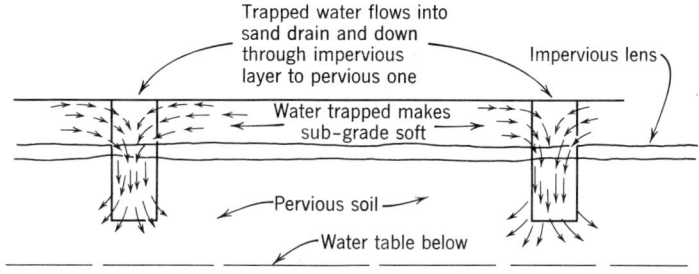

Trapped water flows into
sand drain and down
through impervious
layer to pervious one

Impervious lens

Water trapped makes
sub-grade soft

Pervious soil

Water table below

FOR LIGHT FILLS OVER INORGANIC SILTS.

FIG. 6. EMBANKMENT WHERE POOR SOIL EXISTS.

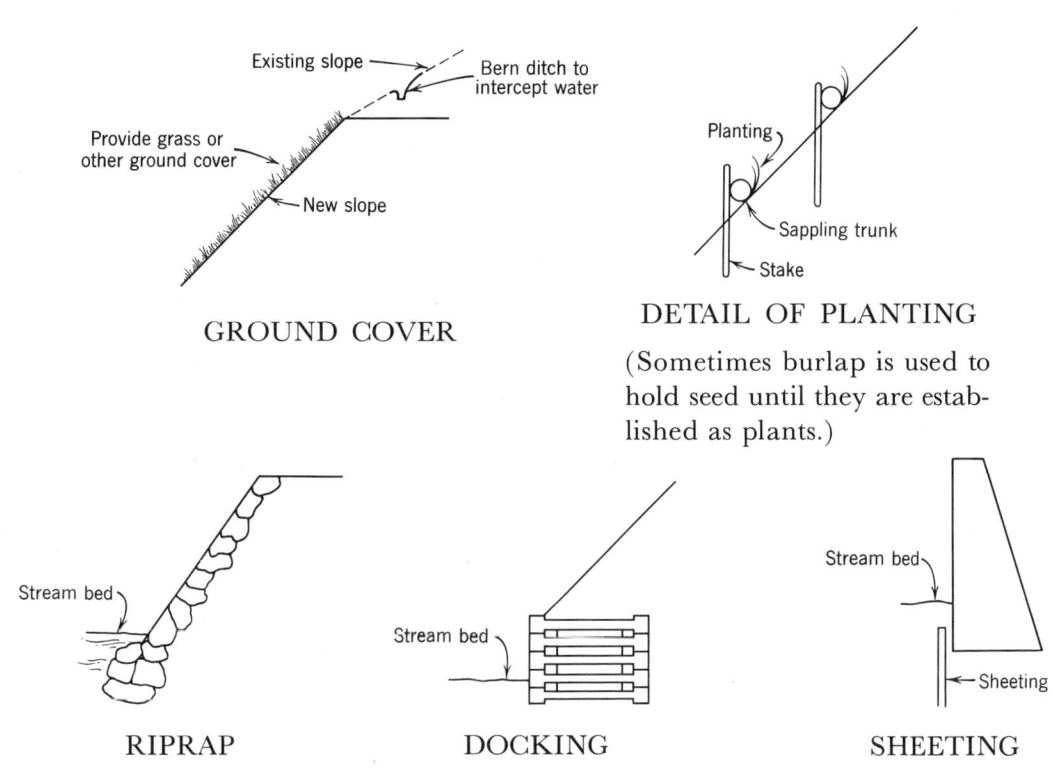

Existing slope

Bern ditch to
intercept water

Provide grass or
other ground cover

New slope

GROUND COVER

Planting

Sapling trunk

Stake

DETAIL OF PLANTING

(Sometimes burlap is used to
hold seed until they are established as plants.)

Stream bed

RIPRAP

Stream bed

DOCKING

Stream bed

Sheeting

SHEETING

Used for river banks (see bridges) and places where plantings cannot grow.
For size of riprap see p. 5–20.

FIG. 7. EROSION PROTECTION OF EMBANKMENTS.

Discussion

Geological Fills

Geological fills may be in strata or lenses, as for instance river till, where we find alternate strata or lenses of clay, silt, sand, or gravel.

A plastic deposit that has been overlain by a stratum which has been removed is called preloaded. Since it has been preconsolidated, i.e., the water has been forced out, the settlement liability has been reduced. The possibility of using this added stability depends upon tests; see p. 13–24 ff.

Embankment Compaction

Compaction consists usually in depositing in layers and rolling to a certain percentage of maximum density. Rolling may be done by rollers, by pneumatic-tired compactors, or by special construction equipment; see Chapter 15. Maximum density can be reached at a certain (optimum) moisture content, which is determined in the laboratory; see Chapter 13.

SETTLEMENT

Short-time settlements such as occur as the result of compression of granular soil under embankments generally present no problems as they are complete by time the embankment is finished. Long-time settlements due to the squeezing out the moisture can cause great difficulty with a roadway on the top of the embankment. Such settlement can be hastened by the use of sand drains. For computations of the time and amount of settlement see Fig. 8, also Chapter 13.

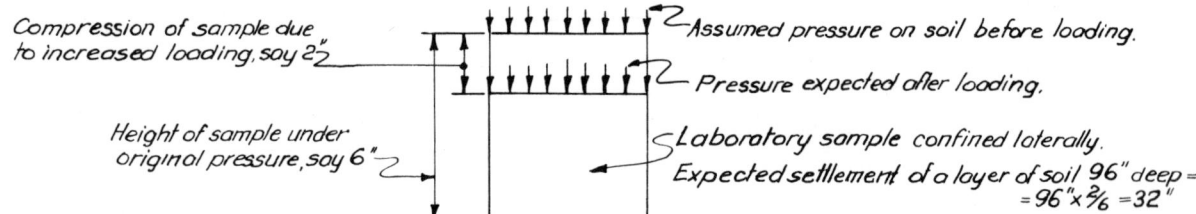

FIG. 8. PREDICTION OF SETTLEMENT OF COHESIVE SOILS DUE TO INCREASED PRESSURE FROM LAB. SAMPLE.

TIME OF SETTLEMENT: May vary as square of depth if water can flow out from top and bottom of stratum. If flow is from top or bottom only, time of settlement should be quadrupled.

Mud waves may occur when the weight of the fill overloads the shearing capacity of the soil. This condition is more likely to occur during or right after construction, as the shearing strength of the foundation soil is increased as it is consolidated by the fill. The possibility of mud waves may be checked by the method shown in Fig. 2, sliding block, or by the Swedish method, Fig. 4.

Sand-Drain Method

Excess pore water may be bled off from compressible subsoils by the construction of vertical columns of porous sand, called sand drains, or sand piles, which are placed at intervals through the material to be drained. The weight created by a gradually added cover of fill causes the pore water to flow from the holding subsoil into the sand drains and upward.

As there is little shearing strength in soil oversaturated with pore water, the weight of fill added must not exceed the load that the soil can bear at any stage of consolidation. Otherwise the shearing strength will be exceeded and a mud wave will result. The pore water pressure must be checked as the fill progresses to keep within the safe bearing capacity of the soil.

The effectiveness of sand drains depends upon the type of soil. In granular soils, they are not necessary, because pore water can be drained away in a short time when given a chance to escape.

Clayey soils are usually so impervious to the flow of any contained water that sand drains would have to be too close together for economy and the length of required time for the water to reach them would be excessive.

Sand drains are most applicable in highly compressible soils, such as silt and marsh muck and for draining lenses or perched water tables.

Laboratory control is advisable to determine the feasible use of sand drains as well as their spacing, the probable time required for subdrainage, and the maximum rate at which fill should be added.

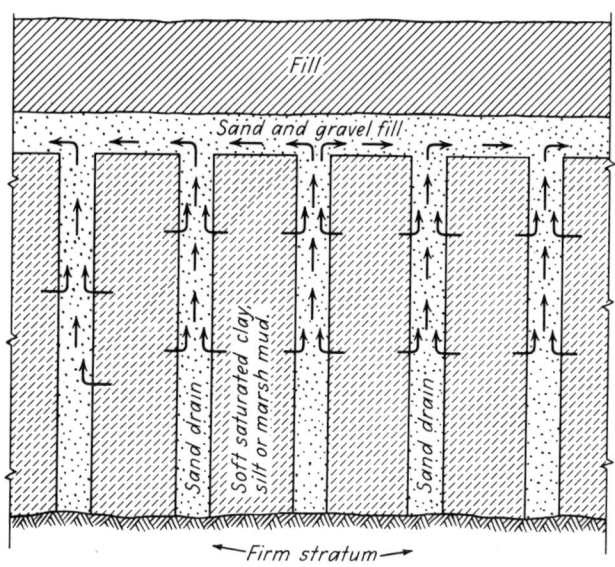

FIG. 9. SECTION OF AREA BEING DRAINED AND CONSOLIDATED BY SAND-DRAIN METHOD.

Sand Drains in New Jersey Turnpike

Mr. L. C. Urquhart of Porter, Urquhart & Beavin contributes the following:

"Sand drains, varying in length from 10 ft. to 100 ft. and spaced from 6 ft. to 14 ft., were driven over about two-thirds of the northern 18 miles of the New Jersey Turnpike under the direction of Porter, Urquhart, Associated. That stabilization has been obtained by this method has been proved after 3 years of operation. Some minor settlement requiring patching has occurred, mostly in the vicinity of some of the bridges. On the northern 4 miles, sand drains from 20 to 30 ft. in length were driven, although the depth of the mud is from 70 to 100 ft. In this area, the grade of this 'floating' portion of the road was raised from 1 to 3 ft. to allow for additional settlement over a period of years. Settlement from 4 to 12 in. has taken place over portions of this road, but differential settlement has been minor, and very little patching has been required."

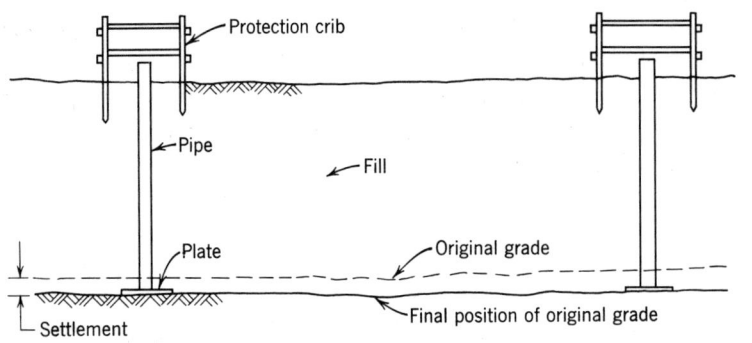

FIG. 10.   USE OF SETTLEMENT PLATES TO OBSERVE
GROUND SETTLEMENT UNDER FILLS.

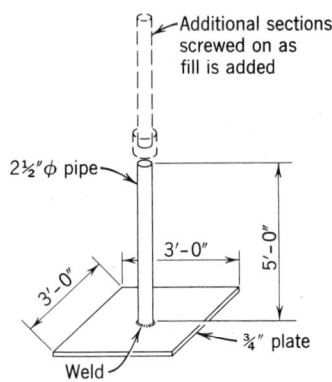

FIG. 11.   DETAIL OF
SETTLEMENT PLATE.

EMBANKMENT SHRINKAGE

The amount of cut required to produce an embankment is always greater in volume than that of the fill.   The excess volume is called *shrinkage* or sometimes *wastage*.

Case 1.   Yield of borrow in finished embankment.

$$\text{Volume} = \frac{\text{Weight}}{\text{Density}}: \text{Volume varies inversely as density.}$$

$$\text{Assume} \begin{cases} \text{borrow pit dry density} & = 110 \text{ lb. per cu. ft.} \\ \text{embankment dry density} = 125 \text{ lb. per cu. ft.} \end{cases}$$

Then 1 cu. yd. of borrow will yield 110/125 cu. yd. embankment.

Case 2.   Shrinkage after embankment compaction.   This will be zero if embankment is compacted to maximum density.   In ordinary practice, i.e., power equipment wheel compaction, no rollers, no moisture control, it may be taken as: Sand and gravel, 1 to 2% *; clay or loam, 2 to 3%.* Certain deposits such as expansive clays swell in embankments.

Case 3.   Loss by waste, of improper material such as top soil or muck, should be allowed for.

TABLE III

VOLUME OF BORROW REQUIRED FOR 1 CU. YD. OF EMBANKMENT.

(Empirical rules for use where densities are not obtainable.   Power equipment wheel compaction, not rolled.)

Gravel	1.09*	1.12†	Light sandy earth	1.14*	1.20†
Gravel and sand	1.10*	1.13†	Vegetable surface soil	1.18*	1.24†
Clay and clayey earth	1.11*	1.15†	Ledge rock		0.70†

---

* *American Civil Engineers' Handbook*, Merriman and Wiggin.

† In accordance with modern highway practice.

SUBGRADES

After the embankments have been designed, the subgrade should be investigated for drainage, frost action, and ability to support the pavement.

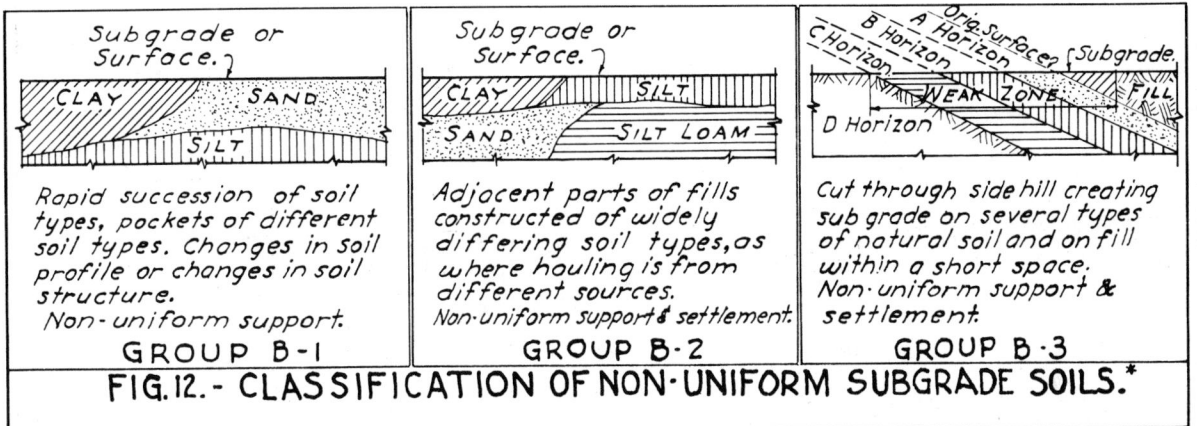

FIG. 12. — CLASSIFICATION OF NON-UNIFORM SUBGRADE SOILS.*

*Adopted from Public Roads Administration & Highway Research Board Publications.

Treatment for Non-Uniform Subgrades

B–1. Loosen, pulverize, mix, and recompact the soil to maximum density or remove to depth of 12 to 36 in. and substitute uniform base course material. Provide adequate subdrainage for water trapped in perches or porous pockets.

B–2. Avoid this condition if possible. If unavoidable, provide a uniform base of selected soil or thoroughly manipulate the soil for 12 to 24 in. depth and, recompact to maximum density.

B–3. Provide a uniform layer of base material 18 to 36 in. deep across the weak zone. Compact the fill to same density as adjacent bank. Provide outlet subdrainage for seepage that is following porous soil strata or moving between strata.

References. *Engineering Properties of Soil*, by C. A. Hogentogler; *Highway Subgrades*, by A. G. Bruce; *Public Roads*, Public Roads Administration; *Wartime Road Problems*, Highway Research Board.

Drainage

Adequate subdrainage should be provided for roads and embankments to:
Stabilize the subgrade.
Reduce frost damage by removing source of water.
Prevent formation of slippage planes by reduced cohesion.
Prevent slides by overloading the embankments with moisture.
Prevent accumulations of water and ice on pavement from side hill seepage.
Prevent "pumping" of the subgrade.
Subdrains may be used to draw down the water level under the road as shown in Fig. 13. Intercepting drains may be used to prevent slides caused by excess ground water; Fig. 14.

A base filter is used under pavements to drain the subgrade. It stabilizes the subgrade and removes the water to prevent frost action or pumping. See Fig. 20.

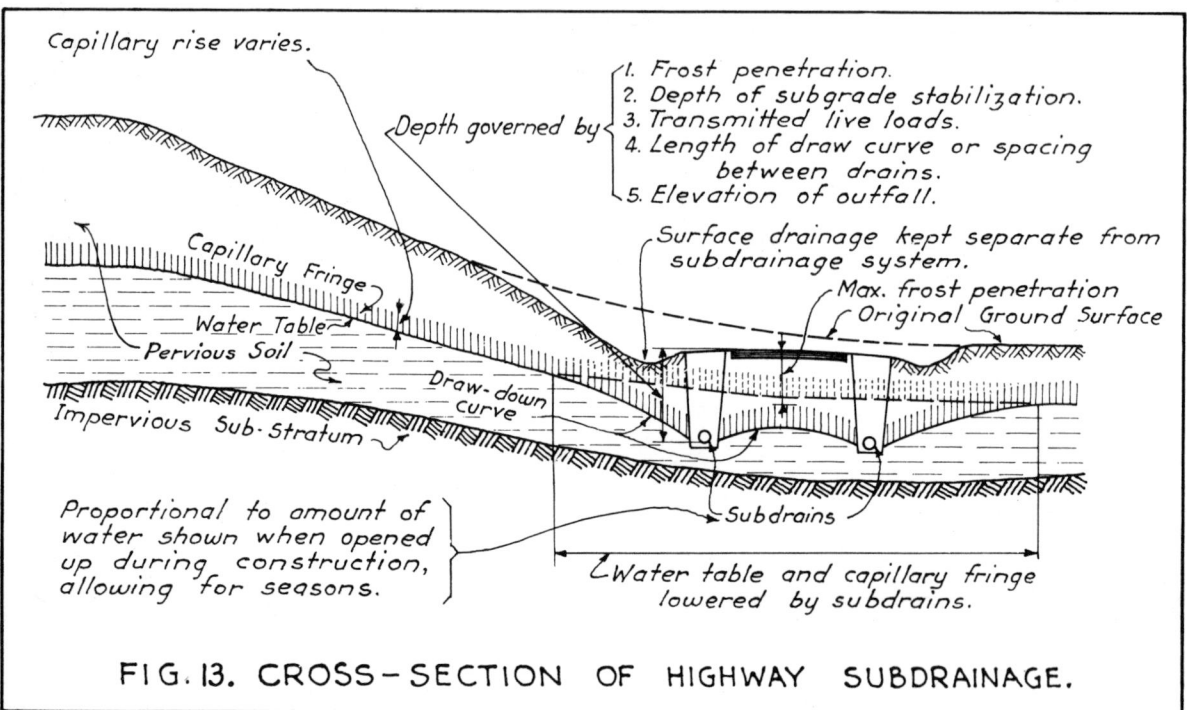

Capillary rise varies.

Depth governed by:
1. Frost penetration.
2. Depth of subgrade stabilization.
3. Transmitted live loads.
4. Length of draw curve or spacing between drains.
5. Elevation of outfall.

Capillary Fringe

Surface drainage kept separate from subdrainage system.
Max. frost penetration
Original Ground Surface

Water Table
Pervious Soil
Draw-down curve
Impervious Sub-Stratum

Proportional to amount of water shown when opened up during construction, allowing for seasons.

Subdrains

Water table and capillary fringe lowered by subdrains.

FIG. 13. CROSS—SECTION OF HIGHWAY SUBDRAINAGE.

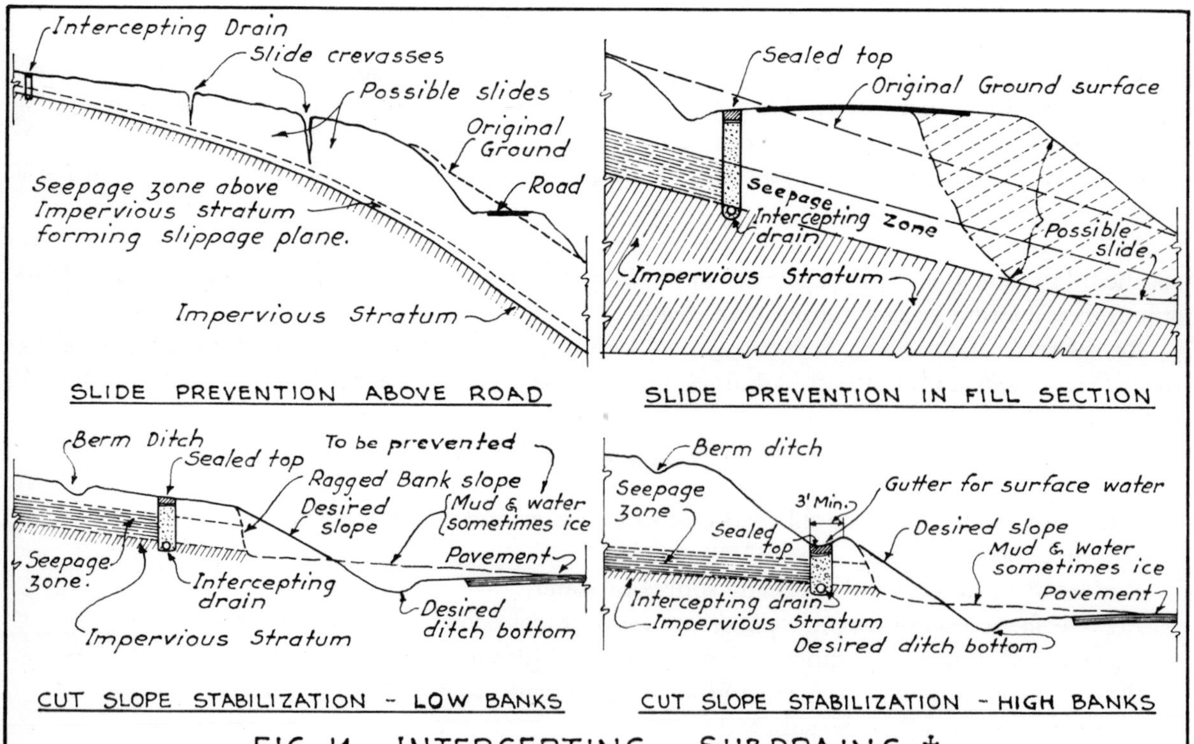

Intercepting Drain
Slide crevasses
Possible slides
Original Ground
Road
Seepage zone above Impervious stratum forming slippage plane.
Impervious Stratum

SLIDE PREVENTION ABOVE ROAD

Sealed top
Original Ground surface
Seepage zone
Intercepting drain
Impervious Stratum
Possible slide

SLIDE PREVENTION IN FILL SECTION

Berm Ditch
Sealed top
To be prevented
Ragged Bank slope
Desired slope
Mud & water sometimes ice
Pavement
Seepage zone.
Intercepting drain
Impervious Stratum
Desired ditch bottom

CUT SLOPE STABILIZATION - LOW BANKS

Berm ditch
Seepage zone
Sealed top
3' Min.
Gutter for surface water
Desired slope
Mud & water sometimes ice
Pavement
Intercepting drain
Impervious Stratum
Desired ditch bottom

CUT SLOPE STABILIZATION - HIGH BANKS

FIG. 14. INTERCEPTING SUBDRAINS.†

† Adapted from Handbook of Culvert & Drainage Practice, Armco Drainage and Metal Products.

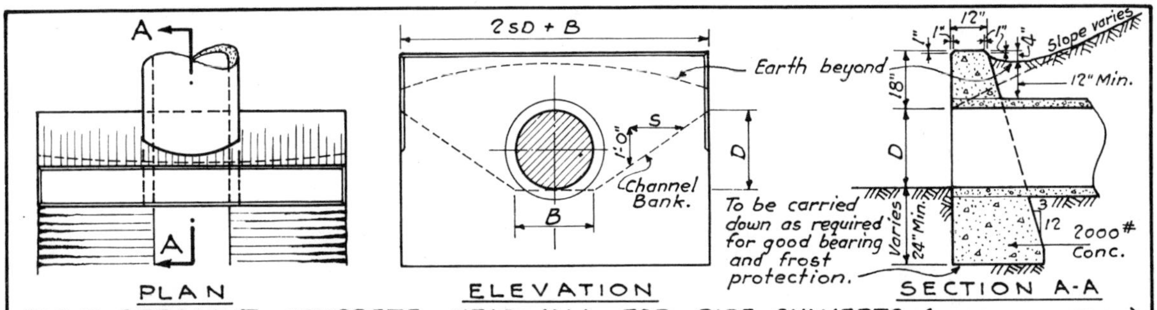
A
A
2sD + B
Earth beyond
1'-0"
S
D
Channel Bank.
B
To be carried down as required for good bearing and frost protection.
12"
1"
1"
1"
1/4"
Slope varies
12" Min.
18"
D
Varies
24" Min.
3
12
2000# Conc.
PLAN
ELEVATION
SECTION A-A

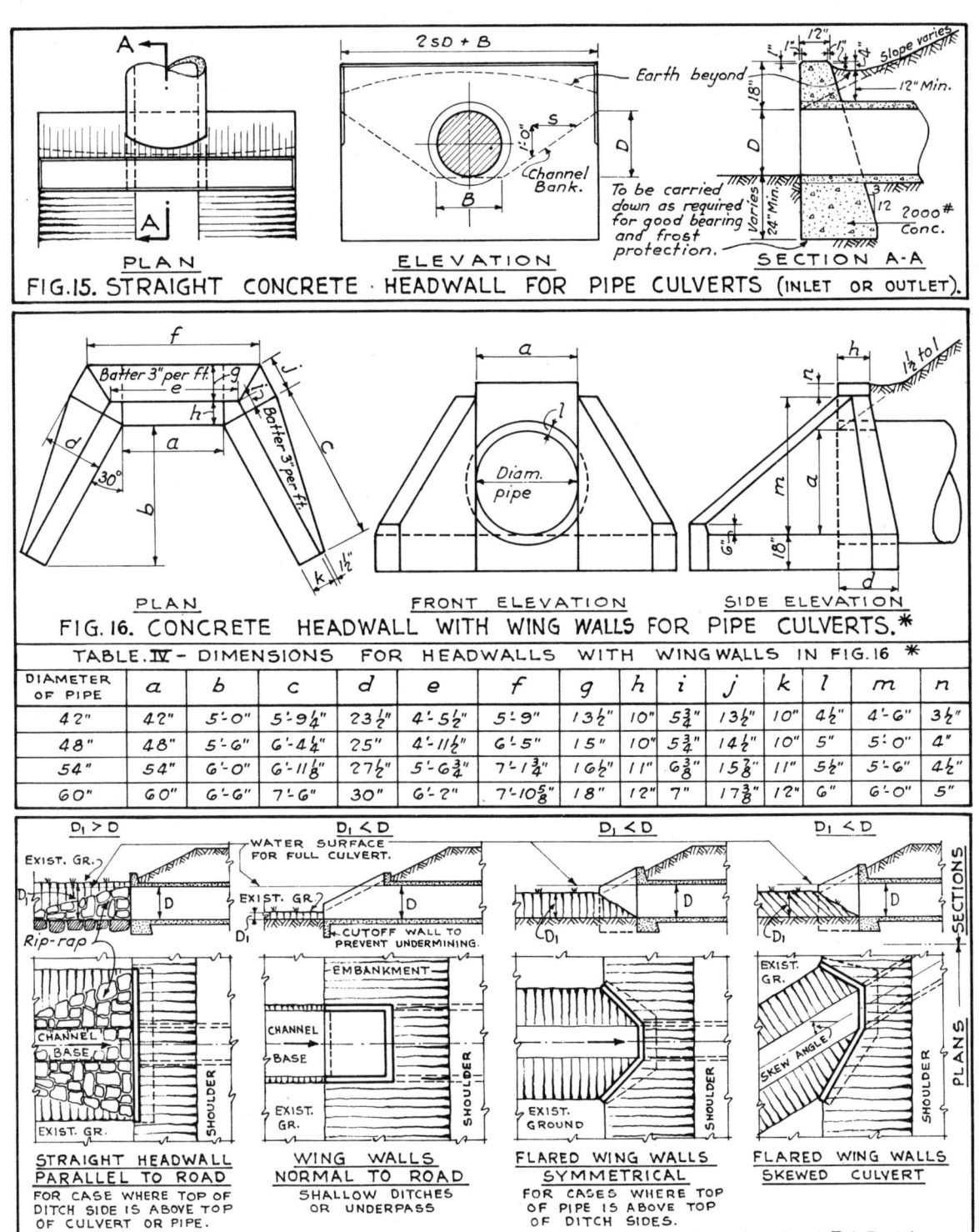

FIG. 15. STRAIGHT CONCRETE · HEADWALL FOR PIPE CULVERTS (INLET OR OUTLET).

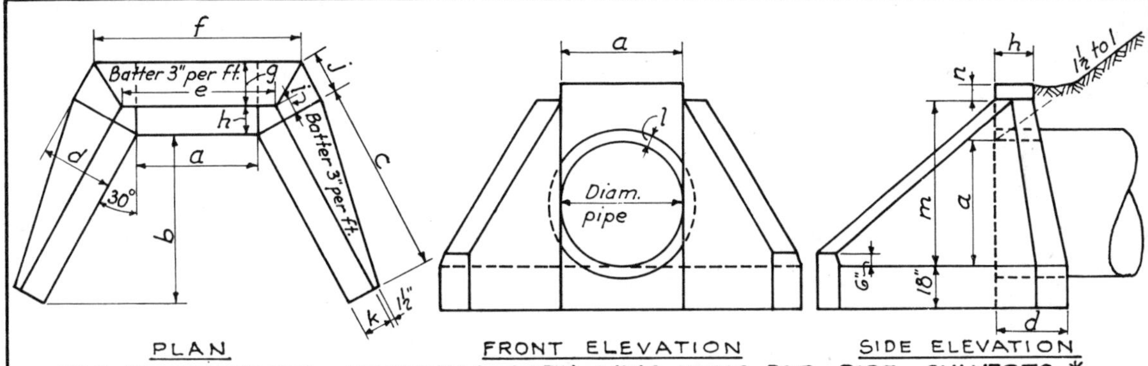
f
Batter 3" per ft.
g
e
h
j
i
Batter 3" per ft.
d
a
c
30°
b
k
1½"
a
l
Diam. pipe
h
1½ to 1
n
m
a
6"
18"
d
PLAN
FRONT ELEVATION
SIDE ELEVATION

FIG. 16. CONCRETE HEADWALL WITH WING WALLS FOR PIPE CULVERTS.*

TABLE. IV - DIMENSIONS FOR HEADWALLS WITH WINGWALLS IN FIG. 16 *

DIAMETER OF PIPE	a	b	c	d	e	f	g	h	i	j	k	l	m	n
42"	42"	5'-0"	5'-9¼"	23½"	4'-5½"	5'-9"	13½"	10"	5¾"	13½"	10"	4½"	4'-6"	3½"
48"	48"	5'-6"	6'-4¼"	25"	4'-11½"	6'-5"	15"	10"	5¾"	14½"	10"	5"	5'-0"	4"
54"	54"	6'-0"	6'-11⅛"	27½"	5'-6¾"	7'-1¾"	16½"	11"	6⅜"	15⅞"	11"	5½"	5'-6"	4½"
60"	60"	6'-6"	7'-6"	30"	6'-2"	7'-10⅝"	18"	12"	7"	17⅜"	12"	6"	6'-0"	5"

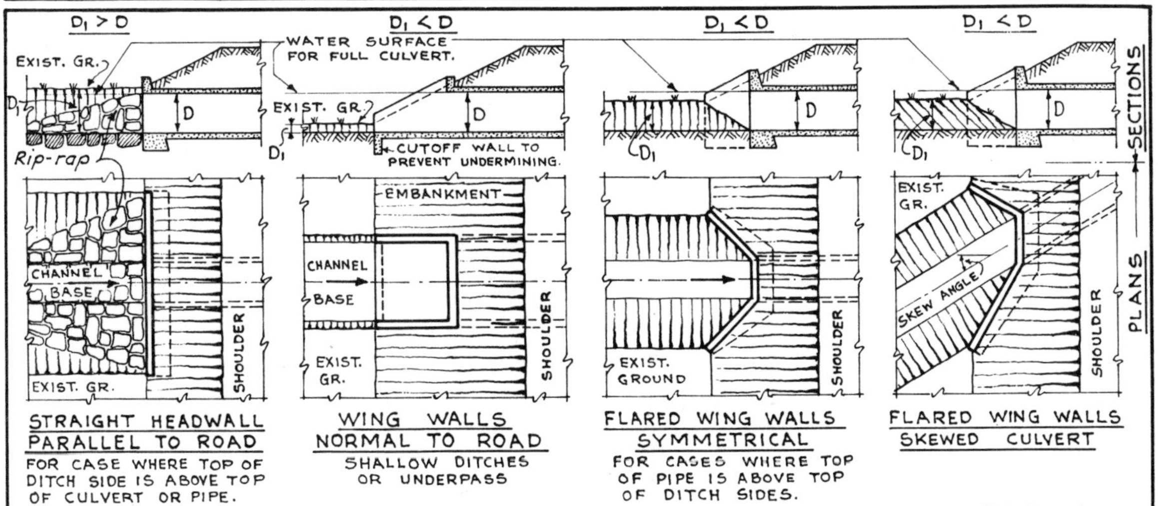
D1 > D
D1 < D
D1 < D
D1 < D
WATER SURFACE FOR FULL CULVERT.
EXIST. GR.
D1
D
Rip-rap
EXIST. GR.
D1
D
CUTOFF WALL TO PREVENT UNDERMINING.
D
D1
D
D1
SECTIONS
CHANNEL BASE
EXIST. GR.
SHOULDER
EMBANKMENT
CHANNEL
BASE
EXIST. GR.
SHOULDER
EXIST. GROUND
SHOULDER
EXIST. GR.
SKEW ANGLE
SHOULDER
PLANS
STRAIGHT HEADWALL PARALLEL TO ROAD
FOR CASE WHERE TOP OF DITCH SIDE IS ABOVE TOP OF CULVERT OR PIPE.
WING WALLS NORMAL TO ROAD
SHALLOW DITCHES OR UNDERPASS
FLARED WING WALLS SYMMETRICAL
FOR CASES WHERE TOP OF PIPE IS ABOVE TOP OF DITCH SIDES.
FLARED WING WALLS SKEWED CULVERT

FIG. 17. HEADWALL DESIGN AS CONTROLLED BY TOPOGRAPHY.

* Virginia Dept. of Highways, by permission from Urquhart, Civil Engineering Handbook, McGraw-Hill. Book Co., 1940.

SEE SECTION ON DAMS FOR DESIGN OF DAM FILTERS.

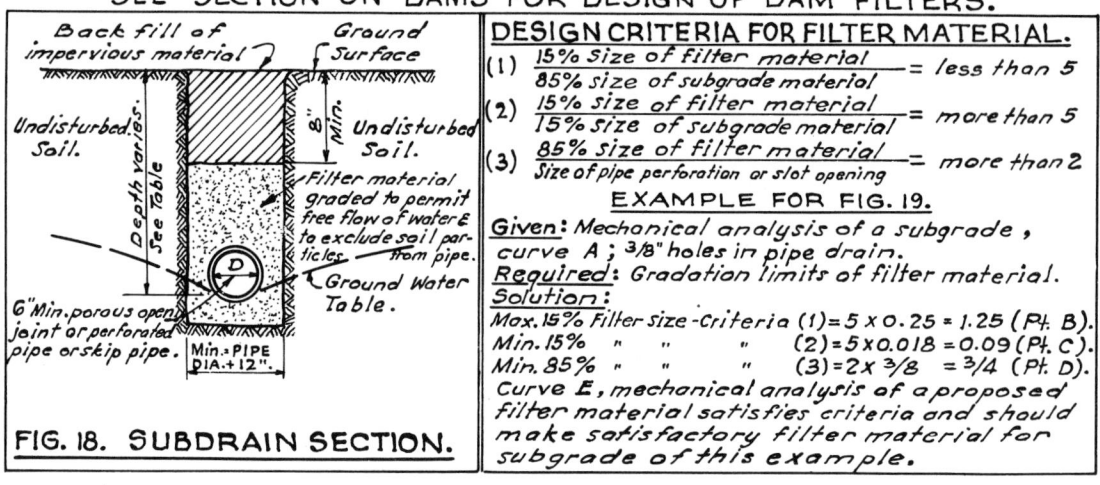

FIG. 18. SUBDRAIN SECTION.

DESIGN CRITERIA FOR FILTER MATERIAL.

(1) $\dfrac{15\% \text{ Size of filter material}}{85\% \text{ size of subgrade material}}$ = less than 5

(2) $\dfrac{15\% \text{ size of filter material}}{15\% \text{ size of subgrade material}}$ = more than 5

(3) $\dfrac{85\% \text{ size of filter material}}{\text{Size of pipe perforation or slot opening}}$ = more than 2

EXAMPLE FOR FIG. 19.

Given: Mechanical analysis of a subgrade, curve A ; 3/8" holes in pipe drain.

Required: Gradation limits of filter material.

Solution:

Max. 15% Filter size - Criteria (1) = 5 x 0.25 = 1.25 (Pt. B).

Min. 15%   "   "   "   (2) = 5 x 0.018 = 0.09 (Pt. C).

Min. 85%   "   "   "   (3) = 2 x 3/8 = 3/4 (Pt. D).

Curve E, mechanical analysis of a proposed filter material satisfies criteria and should make satisfactory filter material for subgrade of this example.

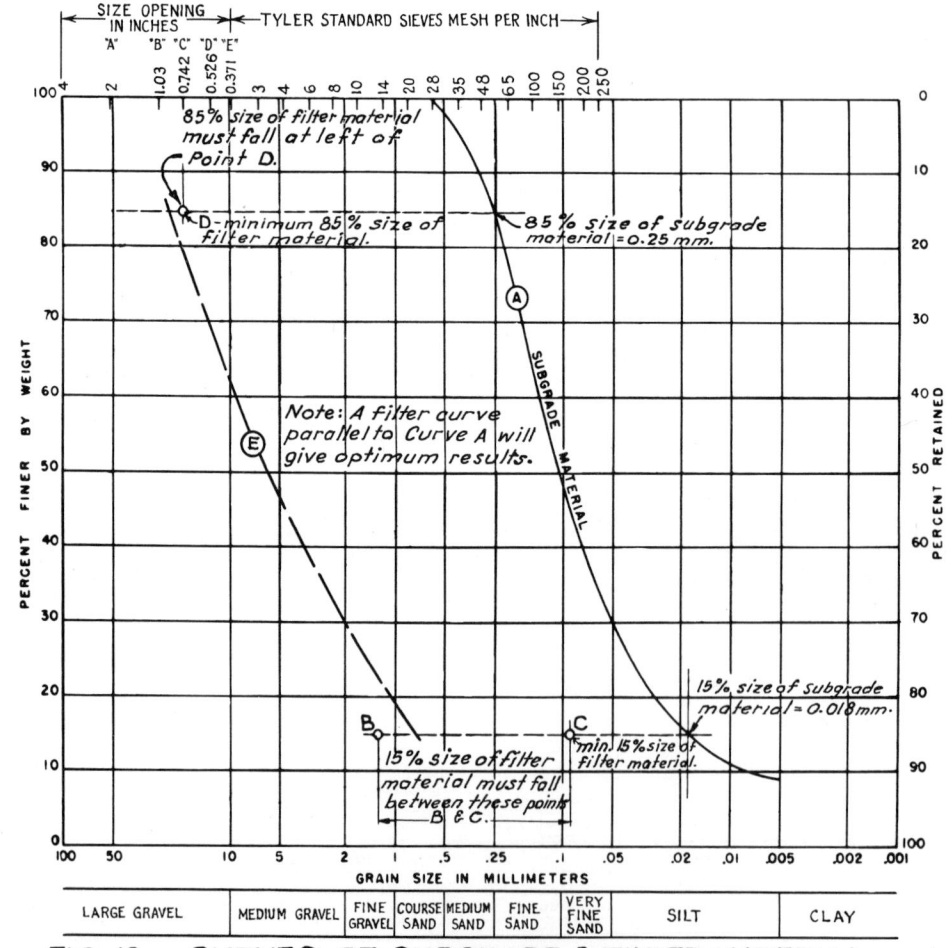

FIG. 19.   CURVES OF SUBGRADE & FILTER MATERIAL.

See Design Criteria and Example above.
After Dr. K. Terzaghi (1932) subsequently modified by U.S. Army Engineers
(Manual - Chapt. XX). Feb. 1943

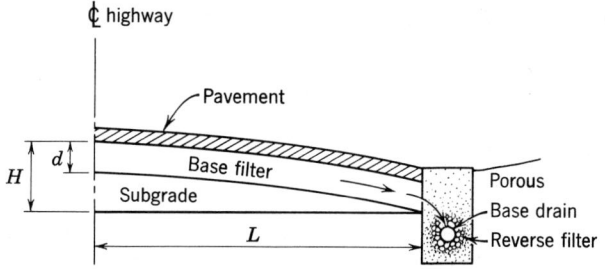

FIG. 20. DESIGN OF BASE FILTER.

Maximum discharge, cubic feet per second $= Kd \dfrac{H}{60L}$

where K = coefficient of permeability, p. 7–15; d, H, and L are in feet.

Base filters are designed to drain 50% of the filters within 10 days. The time t for 50% drainage is

$$t = \frac{L^2}{2KH^2} \times 10^{-5}$$

Where several materials are used in a base:

$$K = \frac{K_1 d_1 + K_2 d_2 + K_3 d_3}{d_1 + d_2 + d_3}$$

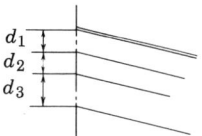

FIG. 21.

Prevention of Frost Damage

FROST ACTION SOILS: *Soils subject to frost action are well-graded soils containing more than 3 per cent by dry weight of particles less than 0.02mm. (0.0008 inch) in size, and uniformly graded soils containing more than 10 per cent of particles less than 0.02mm. in size. See Fig. 24.

GENERAL: To prevent frost damage, the combined thickness of pavement and non-frost action base should be equal to the average depth of frost penetration as shown in Fig. 23 except as limited by Table V below.
　　　Plasticity Index should be less than 6, preferably non plastic and liquid limit less than 25 if soils are not subject to frost damage.

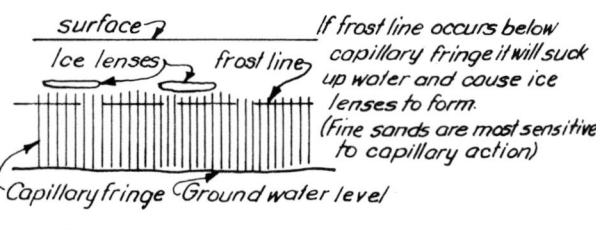

If frost line occurs below capillary fringe it will suck up water and cause ice lenses to form. (Fine sands are most sensitive to capillary action)

FIG. 22. RELATION OF CAPILLARY PROPERTIES TO FROST BOILS IN HIGHWAYS.

Melting ice lenses create water in subgrade which cannot drain because ground below is frozen.

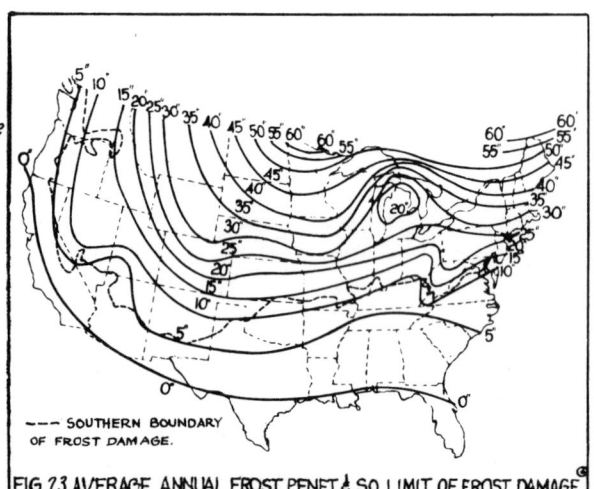

--- SOUTHERN BOUNDARY OF FROST DAMAGE.

FIG. 23. AVERAGE ANNUAL FROST PENET. & SO. LIMIT OF FROST DAMAGE USE FOR HIGHWAY SUBGRADE

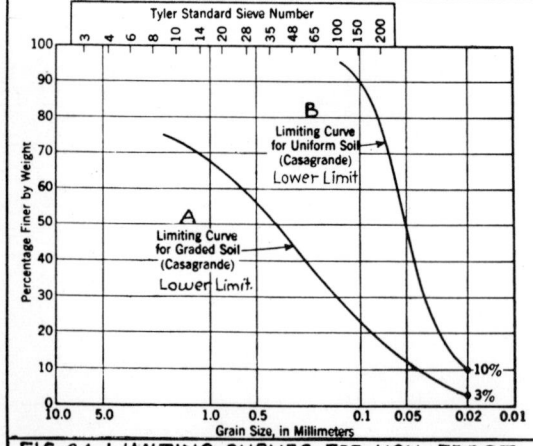

FIG. 24. LIMITING CURVES FOR NON-FROST HEAVING SOILS (AFTER CASAGRANDE). ‡

See explanation for use of chart at right.

TABLE V. MAXIMUM REQUIRED THICKNESS IN INCHES OF FLEXIBLE PAVEMENT AND NON-FROST ACTION BASE ®®

DESIGN WHEEL LOAD (POUNDS)	FINENESS OF SUBGRADE-% PASSING SIEVE NO. 200		
	OVER 25%	10 - 25%	UNDER 10%
15,000 and under	24 in.	20 in.	15 in.
40,000	38 "	26 ·	26 ·
60,000	46 ·	38 ·	32 ·
150,000	72 ·	60 ·	48 ·

USE OF FIG. 24.

Plot curve for soil in question on Fig. 24. If the curve is close to curve A, the 3% limit for dry weight of particles less than .02 mm. is to be used. If the curve is close to curve B, the 10% limit shall be used. The Highway Research Board recommends all soils containing more than 8% by weight of particles finer than 200 mesh be considered as soils subject to frost action.

* Adapted from: Aviation Engineers Manual, 1944. ** C.A.A. Design Manual *** Highway Research Board 1943 Proceedings, D.J. Belcher. ‡ Civil Engineering, Vol. 12. ® U.S. Weather Bureau, 1951. ®® War Deptm't. C.E.

Subgrade Pumping under Pavements

Subgrade pumping of a pavement under a moving load occurs in fine sands and silts which hold water but do not drain easily. Water enters through joints or cracks and produces an emulsion with the soil. The passage of traffic forces this emulsion out through the joints, leaving voids in the subgrade. The entire process is progressive, leading to destruction of the pavement. Correction by drainage is indicated.

Soils subject to pumping are often subject to frost action, and the two conditions may be compounded. Correction by removal and replacement of the soil with non-frost heaving material to a depth of frost penetration is indicated.

Red Lights

Do not figure the safe slope of high embankments of cohesive soils on the basis of observed slopes of low embankments.

The presence of ground water may affect the cohesion of soils. Heavy rains may reduce the cohesion.

In artesian condition, water trapped under a hydrostatic head by an overlying impervious layer will change the results of time consolidation calculations.

In consolidation by the sand-drain method, fill should not be placed so fast that the shearing strength of the soil is exceeded.

In cuts, water from the interception of sloping or water-bearing strata must be fought by intercepting drains and taken into account in design so as to prevent slides.

Avoid settlement due to squeezing out of water in deep layers of clay or plastic material caused by the excess weight of the structure imposed. This is more likely to occur under large fills of considerable area than it is under buildings where the added weight at lower depth may be inconsiderable because of distribution.

The overloading of foundation by an embankment of soft material or peat or dense silt matter will cause a flowout and rise, popularly known as a mud wave.

Residuary Hydraulic Pressure

In case of sudden low water such as tides or drawdowns in a reservoir the exposed surface embankments will be loaded with unbalanced pore water, and the strength will be reduced by irrigation so that a slide may occur.

Evaluating the Subgrade

In designing the pavement the designer assumes a value for the subgrade and checks this value in the field. The soil is generally classified by one of the recognized systems (see Chapter 13 for classification) and the C.B.R. or K value is read off from Fig. 25. This value is used in the pavement design which follows. The true K or C.B.R. value can be determined by field tests; see Chapter 15.

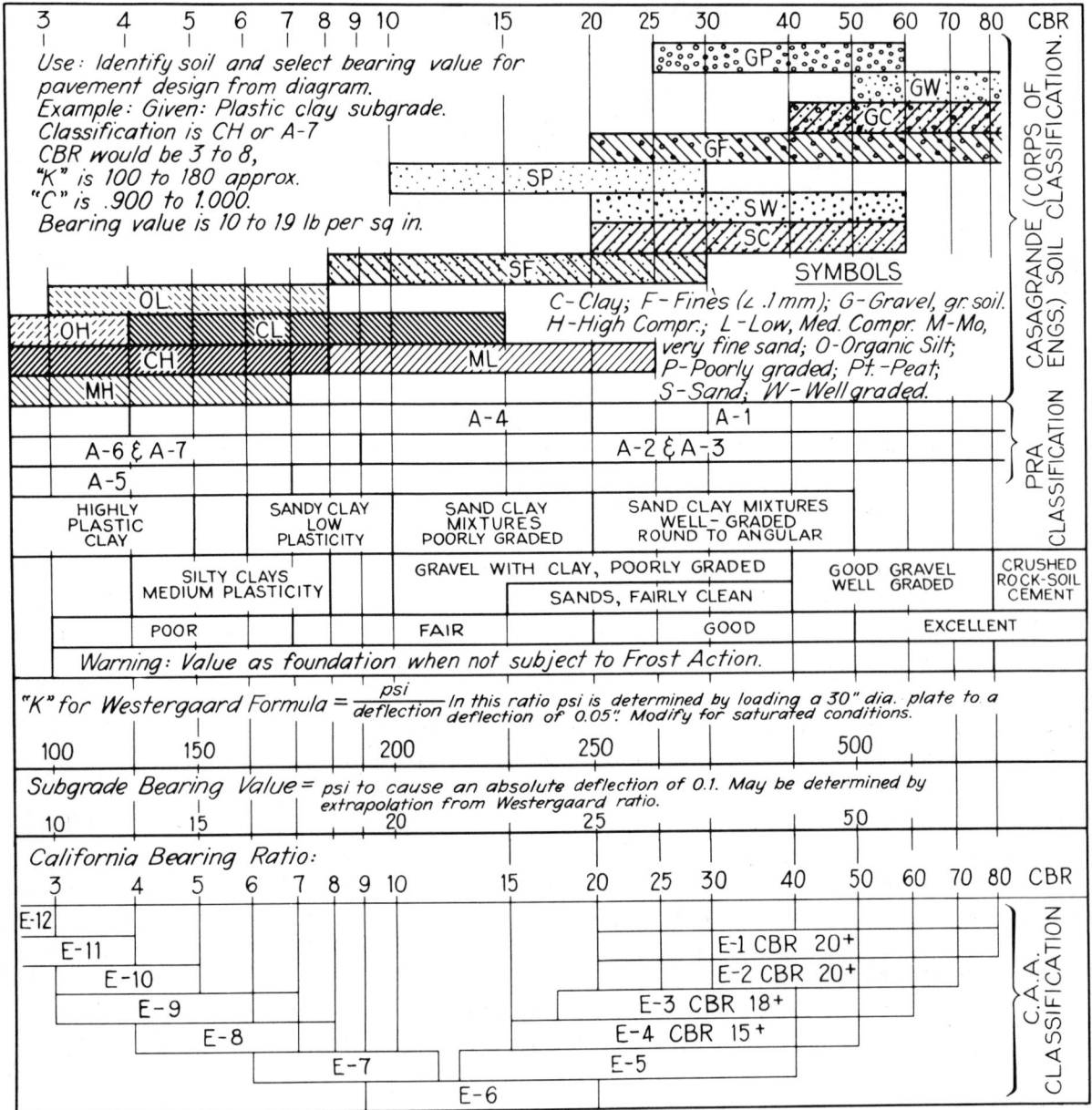

FIG. 25. SOIL BEARING VALUE & CLASSIFICATION DIAGRAM.

Notes:

Bearing values given are approximate and should not be used as a substitute for CBR or Field Load tests. This diagram is compiled from material in following references: Soil Tests for Design of Runway Pavements by Middlebrooks (U.S.E.D.) & Bertram (A.A.F.) Proceedings Highway Research Board. December 1942 Engineering News Record, Volume 130, No 4. Jan. 28, 1943. Design of Airport Runways, Office, Chief of Engineers, U.S. Army. Manual No. 3, U.S. Navy, Bureau Yards and Docks. Chapter XX. Eng. Manual, War Dept. Concrete Road Design by Frank T. Sheets. & C.A.A.

FOUNDATIONS OF PAVEMENTS FOR ROADS AND AIRFIELDS

Pavement

As the pavement section is part of the foundation, the design of the complete section is given below. Weak subgrades require thicker pavements than strong ones.

The theory of load distribution is shown in Fig. 26.

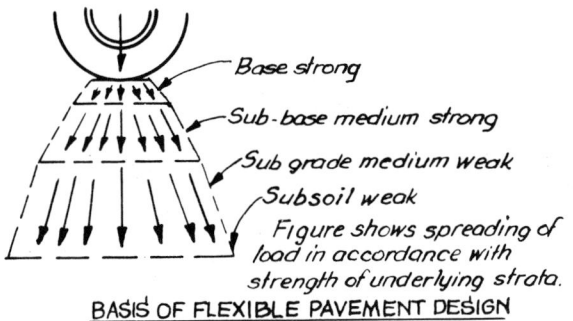

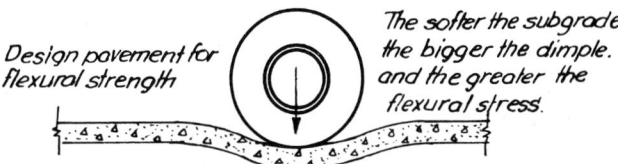

BASIS OF FLEXIBLE PAVEMENT DESIGN   BASIS OF RIGID PAVEMENT DESIGN.

FIG. 26. THEORY OF LOAD DISTRIBUTION THROUGH PAVEMENTS.

Approach to Design of Highway Pavement

First determine wheel load. See Table VI for suggested values.

TABLE VI

Wheel Loads for Pavement Design *

Type of Highway, Street, or Road	*Wheel Load (Static)*
Heavy-duty urban routes, downtown business streets, state and county trunk lines through cities and urban zones. Class AA, A, and B roads with T traffic abnormally high.	12,000 lb. (85 to 100 p.s.i.)
Heavily traveled rural routes, principal city streets, state and county trunk line roads in rural zones. Class AA, A, and B roads with P or M traffic.	10,000 lb. (80 to 90 p.s.i.)
Roads and streets carrying only occasional 8000-lb. wheel loads (A.A.S.H.O. and P.R.A. maximum and legal limit in many states) with moderate volume of mixed traffic. Class C and D roads with P or M traffic.	7000 lb. (70 to 85 p.s.i.)
Roads and streets carrying a light volume of passenger vehicle traffic with occasional light commercial vehicles. Class E or F roads with P or M traffic, private roads and drives.	4000 lb. (60 to 75 p.s.i.)

Wheel load selected should be based on local laws and regulations, and if possible on traffic studies of load intensity and frequency. Pavement design is based on the wheel load and not on the gross weight of vehicle. Rigid pavements are designed with a safety factor (usually 2) allowing practically unlimited stress repetitions caused by the design load. Thus an occasional overload up to as high as twice the design load will not be destructive. Flexible pavements, while not adapted to such exact analysis, will also carry occasional overloads if conservatively designed. Dual wheels are considered as one wheel load and one contact area if tires are within 3 ft. centers.

---

* The Design of Street Pavements, R–153, Portland Cement Assoc., Chicago, Ill., and Reinforced Concrete Pavements, R. D. Bradbury, Wire Reinf. Institute, Washington, D. C.

Flexible Pavements

Determine the thickness of pavement according to one of the following methods:

On the basis of soil classification. Classify the soil according to P.R.A. classification (see Chapter 13 for methods of classification), and select pavement from Table VII.

On the basis of the California Bearing Ratio (C.B.R.), design is made from the graph of Fig. 27. See Chapter 15 for the method of C.B.R. test.

TABLE VII

PRACTICAL DESIGN THICKNESS OF PAVEMENT BASE AND SUB-BASE *

Compiled by Highway Research Board from State Highway Experience based on 10,000-lb. wheel loads.

Major Divisions Subgrade Soils	Coarse-Grained Sandy and Gravelly Soils					Fine-Grained Silt and Clay Soils			
Classification Subgrade Soil (P.R.A.)	A-1-b Non-Plastic	A-1-a Plastic	A-2-a Non-Plastic	A-2-b Plastic	A-3	A-4 A-4-7	A-5 A-5-7	A-6	A-7
Pavement	2″	2″	2″	2″	2″	2″	2″	2″	2″
Base course	0″	5″	5″	6″	5″	8″	8″	8″	8″
Sub-base course	0″	0–12″	0″	0–12″	0″	2–14″	4–14″	0–14″	0–14″
Total thickness	2″	7–19″	7″	8–20″	7″	12–24″	14–24″	10–24″	10–24″

Pavement may be Surface Treatment, Road-Mix, Cold Plant Mix, Penetration or Central Plant Hot-Mix. When Surface Treatment is used the base thickness should be as shown plus 2″ in lieu of pavement. Base course thicknesses as shown are for gravel, crushed stone, slag, sandy clay, sand-clay-gravel, caliche & lime-rock. For Soil Cement Base use 5″ over A–1 plastic to A–3 and 6″ over A–4 to A–7 sub-grades. Sub-Base may be sand, gravel, cinders, slag, crusher-runstone, shale, screenings, stabilized local soil. The Plasticity Index of Base & Sub-base should not exceed 6 for any case.

---

*Adapted from *The Thickness of Flexible Pavements* by Highway Research Board.

Rigid Pavements

Determine the thickness from the graph of Fig. 29 on the basis of strength of concrete assumed and the modulus of subgrade reaction K. See Chapter 15 for the method of determining K in the field.

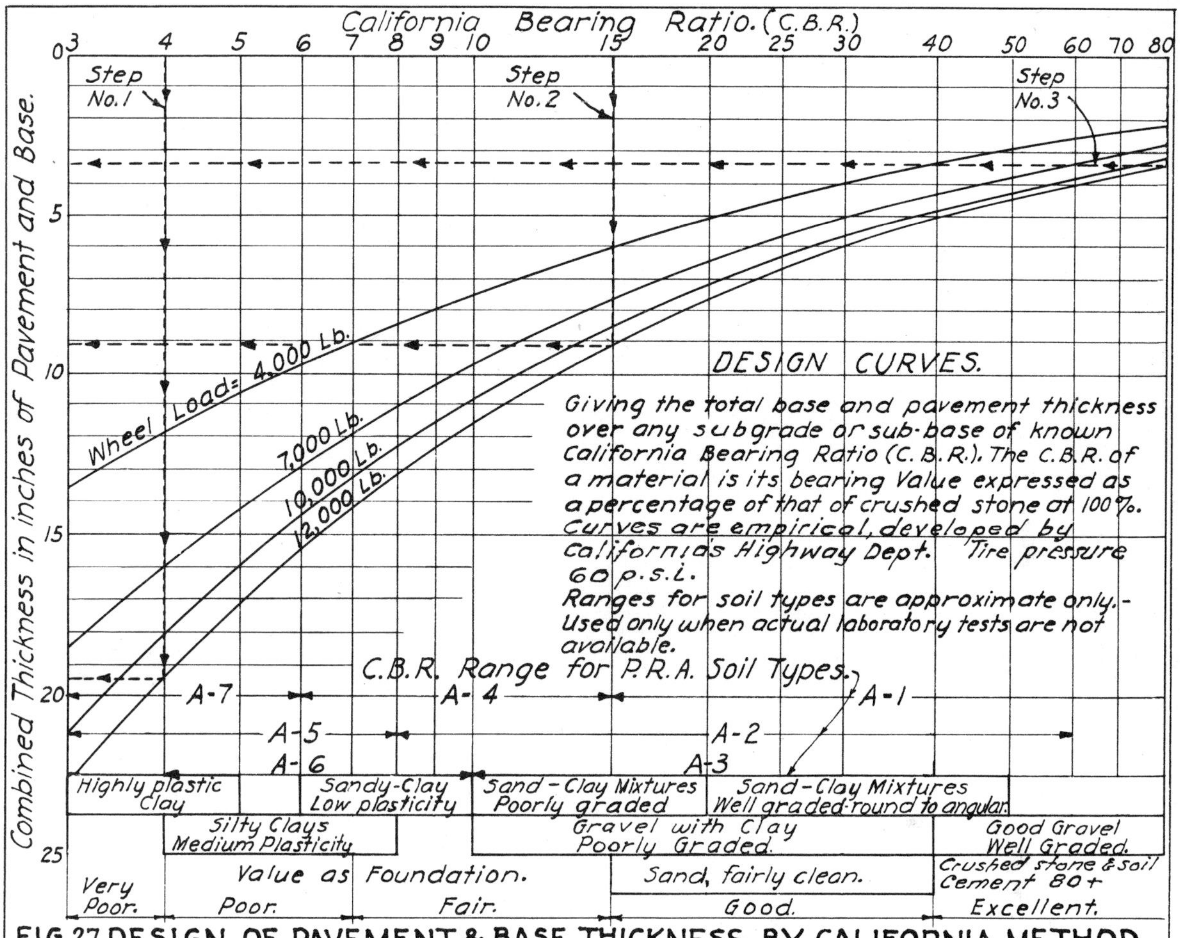

FIG.27. DESIGN OF PAVEMENT & BASE THICKNESS BY CALIFORNIA METHOD.

The chart shows *California Bearing Ratio (C.B.R.)* on the horizontal axis (3, 4, 5, 6, 7, 8, 9, 10, 15, 20, 25, 30, 40, 50, 60, 70, 80) and *Combined Thickness in inches of Pavement and Base* on the vertical axis (0, 5, 10, 15, 20, 25).

Steps: Step No.1, Step No.2, Step No.3.

Wheel Load curves: 4,000 Lb., 7,000 Lb., 10,000 Lb., 12,000 Lb.

DESIGN CURVES.

Giving the total base and pavement thickness over any subgrade or sub-base of known California Bearing Ratio (C.B.R.). The C.B.R. of a material is its bearing value expressed as a percentage of that of crushed stone at 100%. Curves are empirical, developed by California's Highway Dept. Tire pressure 60 p.s.i.
Ranges for soil types are approximate only.- Used only when actual laboratory tests are not available.

C.B.R. Range for P.R.A. Soil Types.

A-7   A-4   A-1
A-5   A-2
A-6   A-3

Highly plastic Clay	Sandy-Clay Low plasticity	Sand – Clay Mixtures Poorly graded
Silty Clays Medium Plasticity		Gravel with Clay Poorly Graded.

Sand – Clay Mixtures Well graded-round to angular.
Good Gravel Well Graded.
Sand, fairly clean.
Crushed stone & soil Cement 80+

Value as Foundation.

Very Poor.	Poor.	Fair.	Good.	Excellent.

NOTE: Using base material with a high C.B.R. for lower layers in place of material with a lower C.B.R. does not decrease the total base thickness, which is governed by the C.B.R. of the subgrade. In any case the combined thickness of pavement and non-frost action base material such as clean sand or gravel should be from ½ to full depth of frost penetration. The minimum C.B.R. of the upper base material for a depth of 5" to 8" beneath the pavement should be 80 for 10,000# and 12,000# wheel loads and 40 to 65 for 4,000# and 7,000# wheel loads.

Design Example:
Step1. Step2. Step3.

FIG. 28.

Pavement, Base Material Bearing Ratio = 80, Sub-Base Material Bearing Ratio = 15, Compacted Sub-grade Bearing Ratio = 4. Thickness required of each material.

Total thickness required above each layer of known C.B.R.

Given:- A heavy duty Class "A" highway, "T" traffic with up to 12,000# wheel loads, a plastic clay subgrade with a C.B.R. of 4. Available sandy borrow for sub-base with a C.B.R. of 15. Available base material with a C.B.R. of 80.

Required:- Thickness of sub-base, base and pavement.

Solution:- Step 1; from the 12,000# curve the required total thickness of base and pavement above the subgrade (C.B.R of 4 per cent) is 20 inches. Step 2; the minimum depth of more stable material (higher C.B.R.) above the sub-base (C.B.R. of 15 per cent) from the 12,000# curve is 9" very nearly. Step 3; The required thickness of pavement over the base (C.B.R of 80 per cent) is 3", say 2" of bit. concrete binder and 1" of bit. concrete wearing course.

References: A. Casagrande, O.J. Porter, Eng. Manual of U.S. Eng. Dept. 1941 to 1943 & Eng. News Record, Jan. 28 1943.

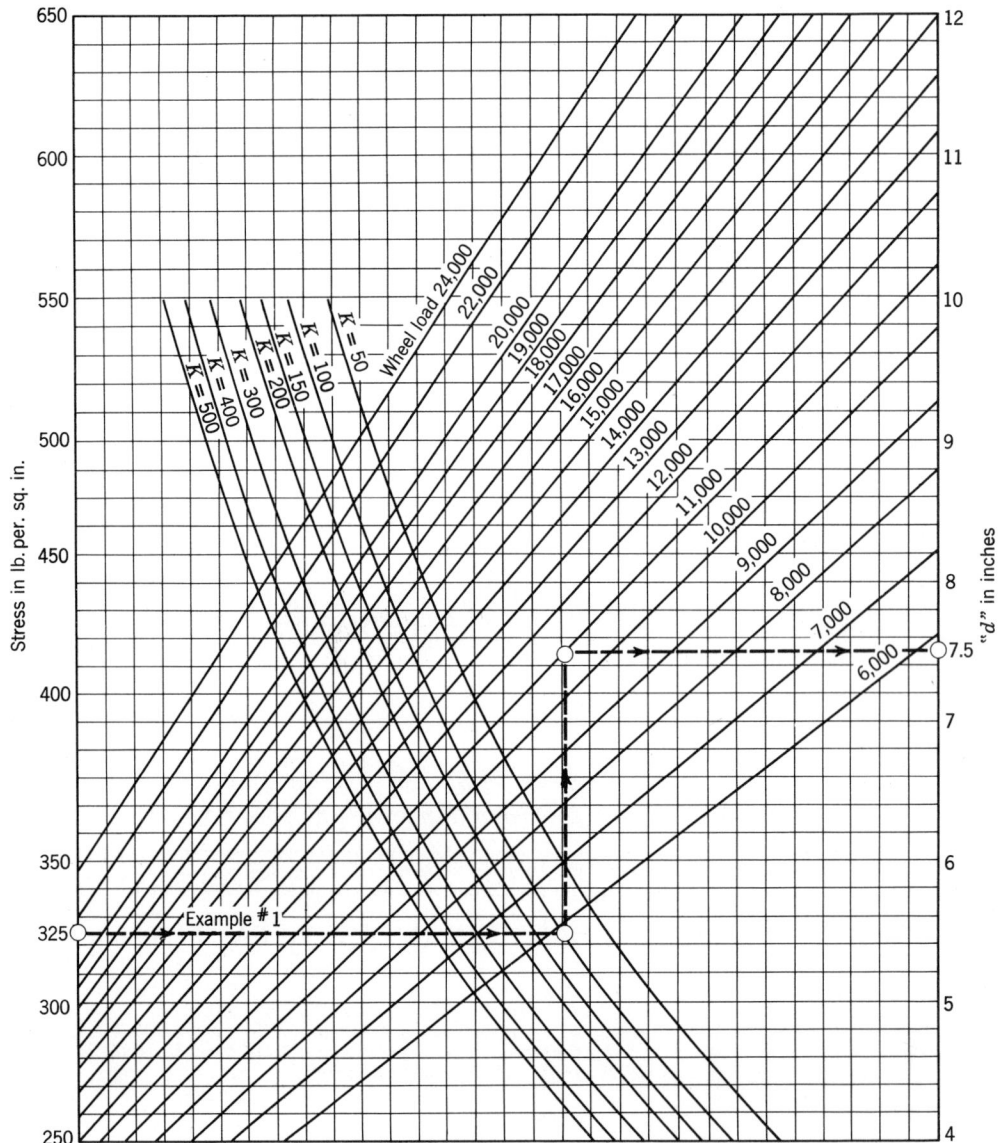

FIG. 29.   DESIGN CHART FOR PORTLAND CEMENT CONCRETE PAVEMENTS
HAVING PROTECTED CORNERS.*

Giving the interrelationship between: (1) pavement thickness, (2) wheel load, (3) subgrade support, (4) flexural stress in the concrete.

Wheel loads on dual tires.

_____

* From P.C.A.   Protected corners are those interlocked to adjacent slab by dowels.

Example 1

Given: Modulus of rupture = 650 p.s.i.

Modulus of subgrade reaction $K =$ 100

Wheel load   = 11,000 lb.

Safety factor of 2 (usual): 650/2 = 325.

To find: Thickness.   Enter table at left at 325 p.s.i. and go right to $K = 100$.   Go up to wheel load = 11,000 lb., then go right and read thickness = 7.5 in.

Modulus of rupture is about ⅐ the 28-day compressive strength of concrete.   For highways a design value of 500–550 is used; for airfields, 600–650.

Approach to Design of Airfield Pavements

Determine wheel load.   See Table VIII for suggested values if size of aircraft to use the airfield is not known.

Flexible Pavement

Determine thickness according to C.B.R. method.   See Fig. 30.

TABLE VIII

PAVEMENT LOADING PER WHEEL IN POUNDS

Air Carrier Service	Single Wheel	Dual Wheel Strut Load
Feeder	15,000	20,000
Trunk line	30,000	40,000
Express	45,000	60,000
Continental	60,000	80,000
Intercontinental	75,000	100,000
Intercontinental express	100,000	125,000

APPLICATION OF CALIFORNIA BEARING RATIO (CBR) METHOD OF DESIGN

COMBINED THICKNESS of pavement base and subbase taken from Fig. 30 when CBR of subgrade is known. Determination of CBR consists of testing a compacted sample of soil at optimum moisture content and maximum density in a 6" diameter cylinder with a 3 sq. inch area circular piston. Enough load is applied to deflect the sample at a rate of .05 inch per minute to a total deflection of .50 inch; the load is measured and stated in ratio to that supported by crushed stone under the same conditions. The same test is applied after the sample is allowed to soak for four days - the ratio obtained at the second test is the C.B.R. Approximate values of CBR are given in Fig. 25. Upper base usually 6" of crushed stone. If not economically available increase thickness of asphaltic concrete.

PROPORTIONING COMBINED THICKNESS INTO PAVEMENT BASE AND SUBBASE:

See example below for method. Where materials available for base course vary widely as to C.B.R. the selection of which materials to use may be based on a cost analysis of several alternate designs. The total thickness required over a given subgrade will always be the same wheel loads for design. Use ½ of recommended gross plane weight.

DESIGN EXAMPLE: **Given:** 40,000 lb. wheel load, Tire pressure single wheel = 100 p.s.i., Subgrade of CBR 4, Subbase material of CBR 15, lower base material of CBR 25 and upper base material of C.B.R. 80

Required: Thickness of pavement and base layers.

Solution: (See Fig. 30)

Step 1. - Thickness over subgrade of C.B.R. 4 is 33"

Step 2. - Thickness over base of C.B.R. 15 is 14"

Step 3. - Thickness over base of C.B.R. 25 is 9"

     6" of 80% base and 3" of Asphalt conc. pavement.

(Figure 31 — cross-section diagram)

| Pavement |
| CBR 80 Upper Base |
| CBR 25 Lower Base |
| Sub-base |
| CBR 15 |

Subgrade CBR 3

FIG. 31.

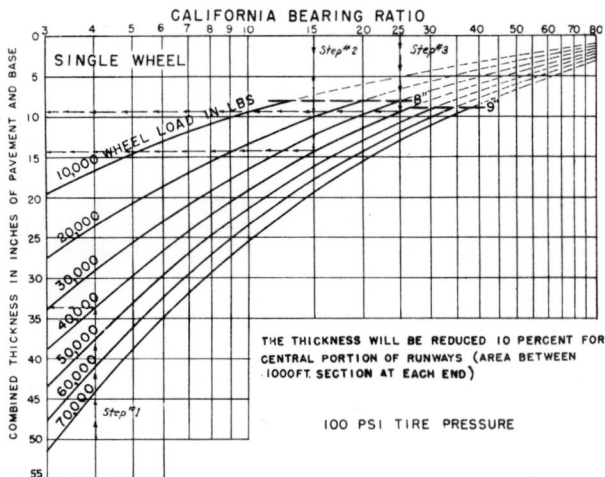

THE THICKNESS WILL BE REDUCED 10 PERCENT FOR CENTRAL PORTION OF RUNWAYS (AREA BETWEEN 1000 FT. SECTION AT EACH END)

100 PSI TIRE PRESSURE

FIG. 30

FLEXIBLE PAVEMENT DESIGN CURVES FOR TAXIWAYS ETC.

TABLE IX. MINIMUM ALLOWABLE CBR UPPER 6" OF BASE COURSE*	
WHEEL LOAD	MINIMUM CBR
15,000 lbs. or less	50
40,000 lbs.	65
70,000 lbs.	80
150,000 lbs.	**80

Tentatively established for use when CBR 80 material is not locally available and importation is impracticable. Base material of less than CBR 80 should not be used directly under a pavement when subgrade soil is plastic.
**This generally is crushed stone.

* Adapted from Engineering Manual of the War Department Part XII Chapter 2 Rev. Aug 11, 1950.

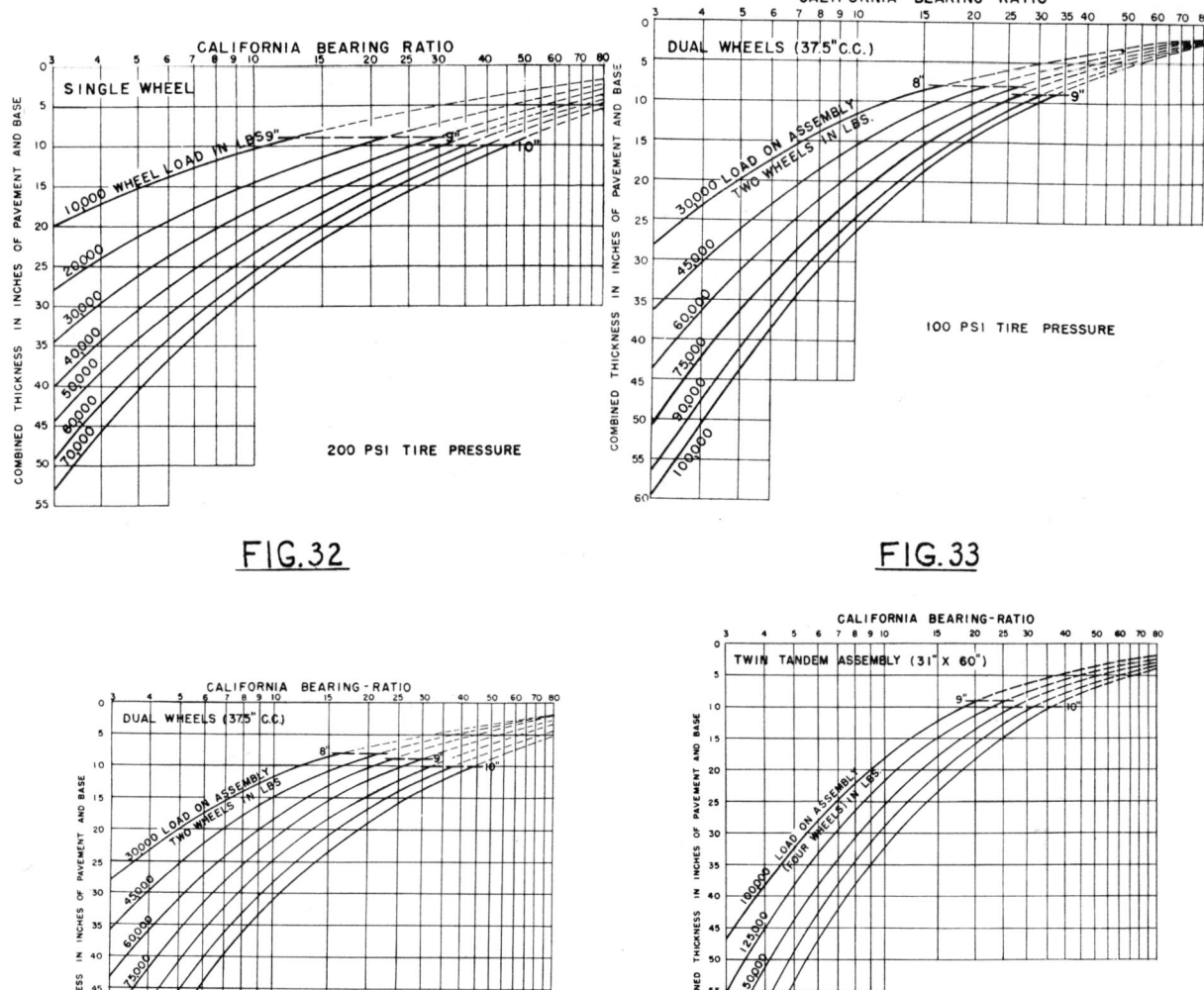

FIG. 32
FIG. 33
FIG. 34
FIG. 35

FLEXIBLE PAVEMENT DESIGN CURVES FOR TAXIWAYS ETC.*

NOTE: The thickness will be reduced 10 percent for central portion of runways (area between 1000 ft. section at each end).

* Adapted from Engineering Manual of the War Dept. Part XII Chap. 2 Rev. Aug. 11, 1950.

Rigid Pavement

Select a factor of safety from Table X.   Assume a strength of concrete and determine thickness from the graph of Fig. 36.

Example 2

Given: Modulus of rupture of concrete =   700 p.s.i.*
Modulus of subgrade reaction   =   200
Wheel load   = 75,000 lb.
Safety factor of 2:700/2   =   350

Enter table at left at 350 p.s.i. and go right to $K = 200$.   Go up to wheel load $= 75,000$ lb., then go right and read thickness 14.75 in.   Use 15 in. pavement.

TABLE X

FACTOR OF SAFETY FOR RIGID PAVEMENT DESIGN

Aprons, taxiways, hard-standings,
    runway ends, hangar floors   1.8–2.0

Runways (central portions)   1.3–1.5†

---

* Modulus of rupture, see Glossary.
† If taxiway crosses, use factor of safety 1.8–2.0 for area of intersection.

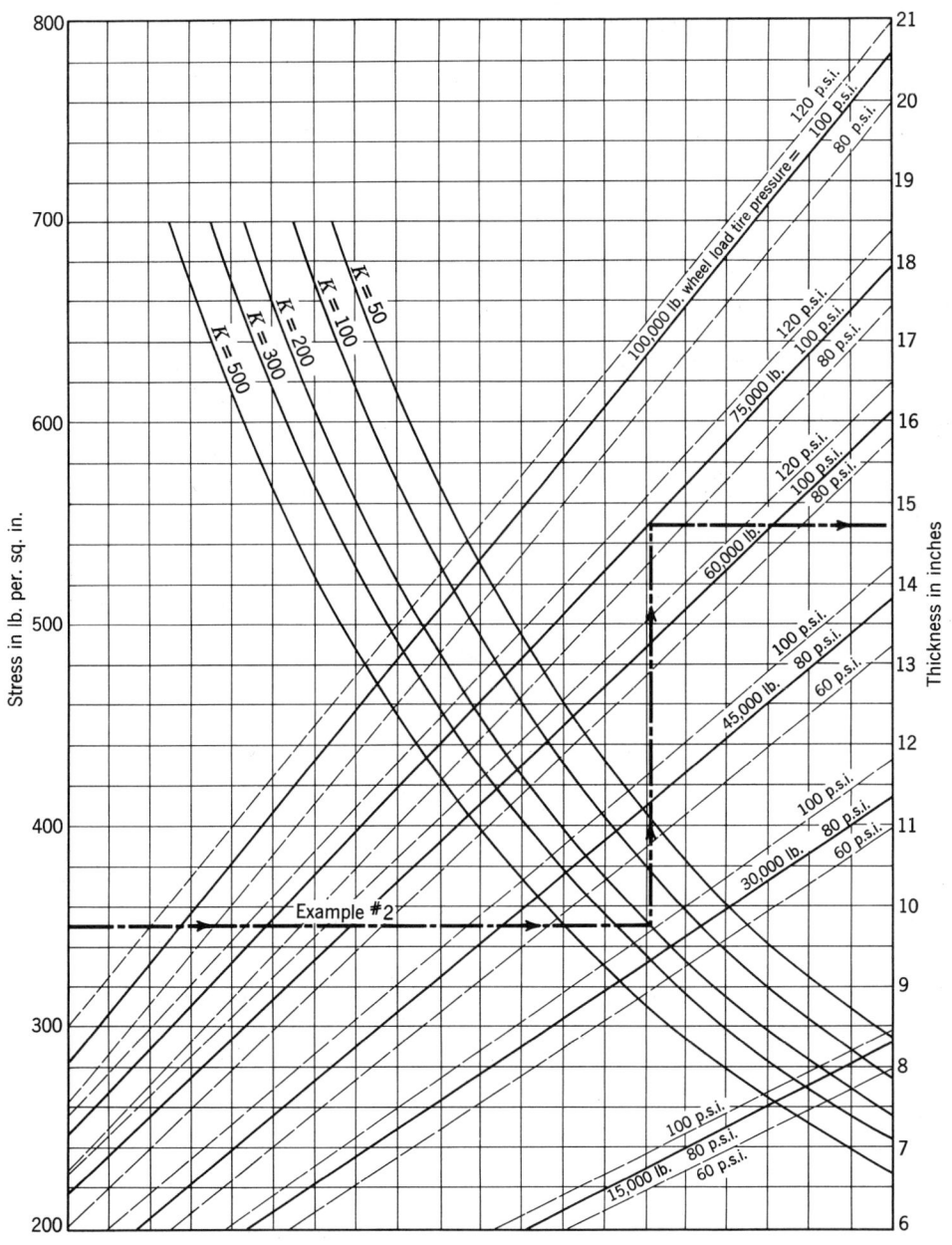

From P.C.A.

FIG. 36.   DESIGN CHART FOR CONCRETE AIRPORT PAVEMENT
FOR SINGLE WHEEL LOADS.

$E = 4,000,000$ p.s.i.; $\mu = 0.15.$*

_____

* μ = Poisson's ratio.

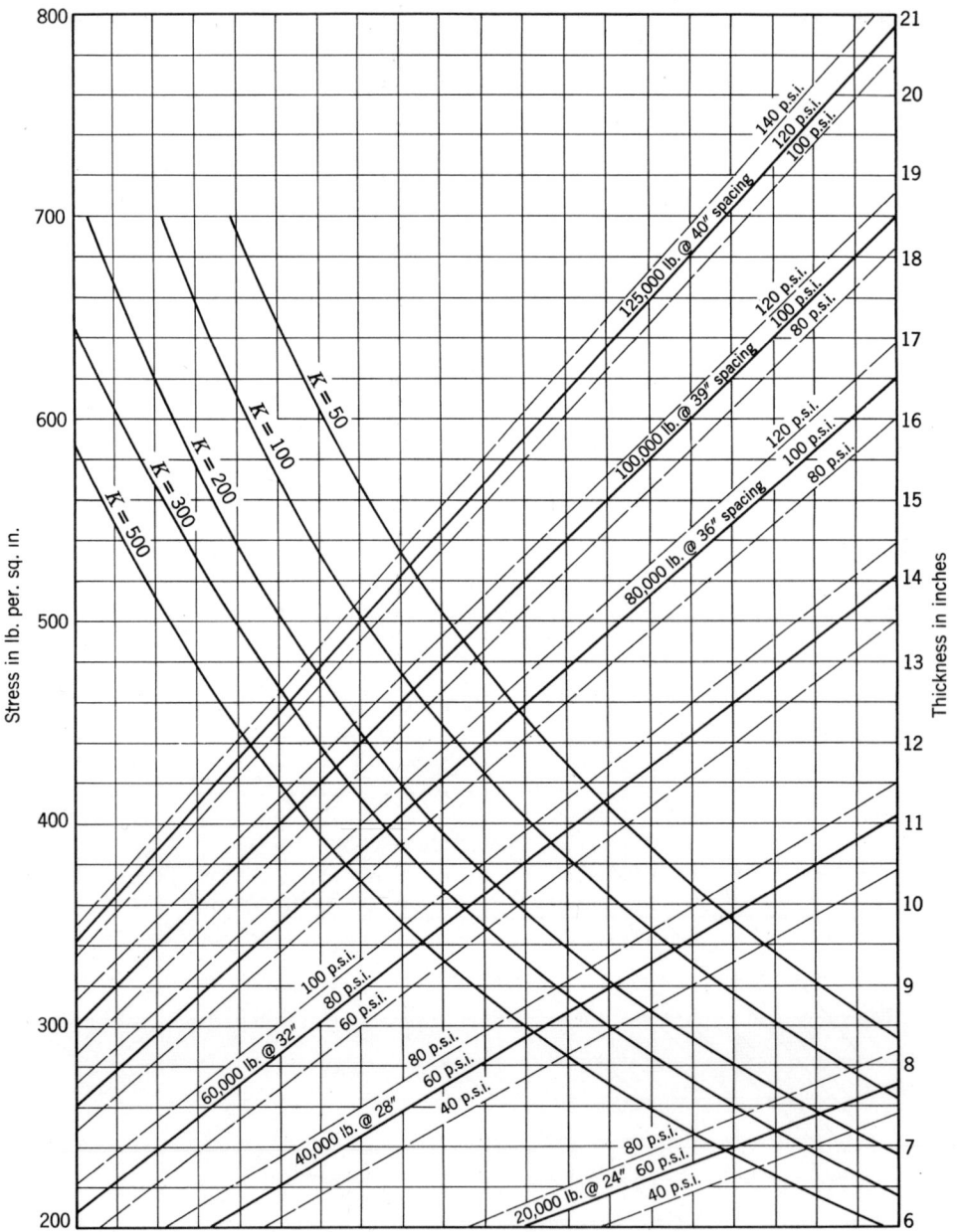

FIG. 37. DESIGN CHART FOR CONCRETE AIRPORT PAVEMENT
FOR DUAL WHEEL LOADS.

$E = 4,000,000$ p.s.i.; $\mu = 0.15$.*

---

*μ = Poisson's ratio.

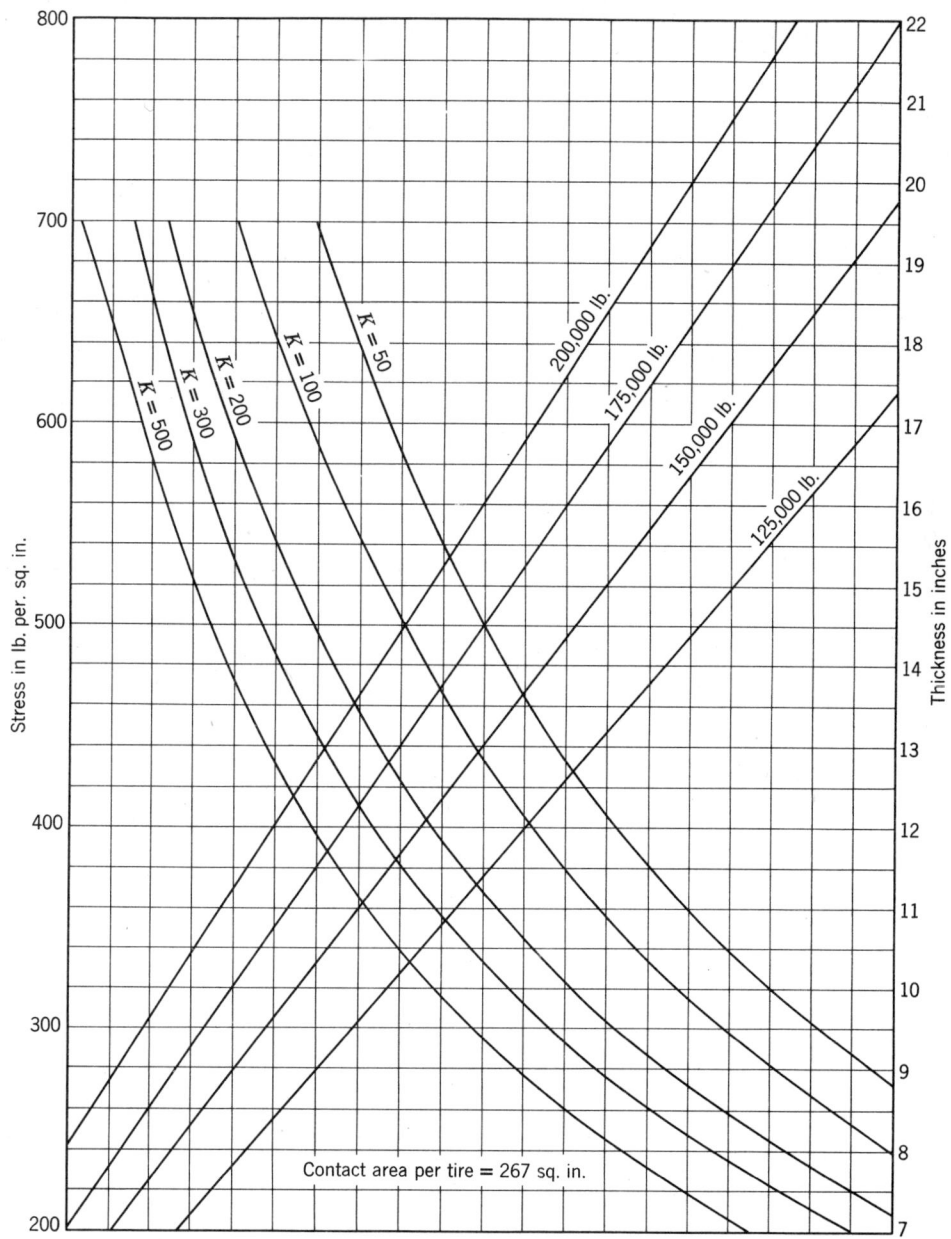

FIG. 38.   DESIGN CHART FOR CONCRETE AIRPORT PAVEMENT
FOR DUAL-TANDEM LANDING GEARS.

Spacing of wheels = 31.5 in. abreast, 62 in. tandem; $E = 4,000,000$ p.s.i.; $\mu = 0.15.$*

---

* μ = Poisson's ratio.

DESIGN OF PAVEMENTS

Discussion

Since the pavement distributes the wheel load to the subbase and thence to the subgrade, the design of any pavement is a problem in distributing a given wheel load to a safe soil bearing capacity. This capacity can be established either by soil classification or by load test in the field.

The soil classification method is the more convenient, but the field test, which is generally a plate load test, is more direct. Of course, it should take into account the varying conditions such as water level.

Some highway departments design rigid pavements by using a standard thickness throughout based upon an assumed minimum K value.* For instance, the New York Thruway uses a uniform 9-in. slab.

In addition there are other methods of design:

Asphalt Institute uses an assumed or measured subgrade bearing power and design curves based on tire pressure. Used for flexible pavements.

Gray's formula is based on a cone of pressure and an assumed or measured subgrade bearing pressure. Flexible pavements.

C.A.A. design is based upon assignment of the subgrade to arbitrary classifications and reading off the design from curves. Flexible and rigid pavements.

The Army uses plate load tests for rigid and C.B.R. values for flexible airfield pavements.

The Navy uses plate load tests for both flexible and rigid designs. The Navy design of flexible pavements is based on the performance of plate load tests on different thicknesses of base constructed in trial sections, which simulate the actual construction to be done on the airfield.

These test sections show the distribution effects of different thicknesses of base.

The Navy design limits the deflection to 0.2 in., using a plate load test of the same size and pressure intensity of the wheel that the airport is being designed for.

Wheel Loads

Pavements are designed for the predominant wheel load, which is the load that will be exceeded not more than 100,000 times during the life of the pavement. Therefore it should be arrived at by a study of the size and frequency of loading and by the established life of the pavement. Impact is not a factor for airport pavement since the planes do not track in lanes the way motor vehicles do. Also the center section between the ends of runways are designed thinner since the load is partially airborne.

---

* The K value is the subgrade reaction obtained from a plate load test.

INDUSTRIAL FLOORS ON GROUND

Because of the heavy loads balanced on single axles of lift trucks, floor design has the same order of importance and technique as pavement design.

Settlement

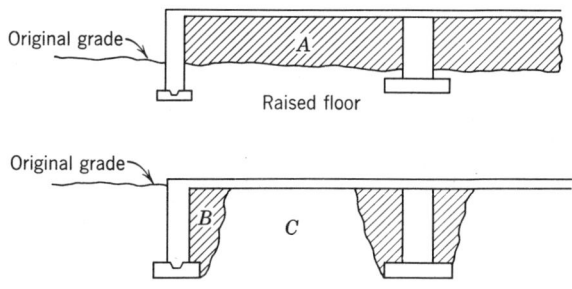

FIG. 39.   FLOOR ON GRADE.

Additional backfill *A* to be consolidated to a certain *K* (modulus of subgrade reaction), as for instance a 95% density for a sandy loam might give *K* of 250; see Fig. 25.

Deep backfill *B* might be subject to settlement.

Cracking

Floors are subject to cracking because of (*a*) spalling at the joints, (*b*) contraction, (*c*) expansion. (*d*) settlement of the subgrade.

Design of Floor Slab to Carry Lift Truck

Impact factor = 1.5.

1.5 × 12,000 = 18,000 lb. axle or 9000 lb. wheel load.

Note: Truck shown is frequently used.   Sometimes 10,000-lb.-capacity truck is used.

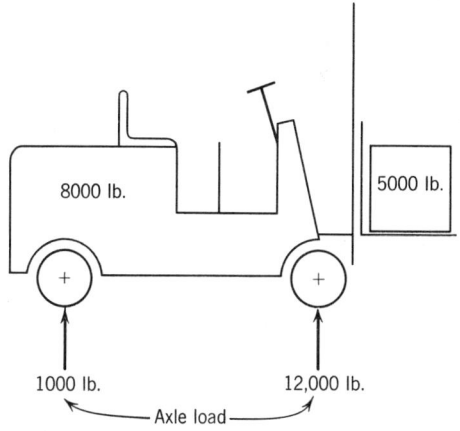

FIG. 40.   LOADING ON WAREHOUSE FLOORS.

Example 3.   Design of Warehouse Floor.

Given: Wheel load 6000 lb. (exclusive of impact).

Concrete modulus of rupture = 500 p.s.i.

Modulus of subgrade reaction *K* = 100.

Enter Fig. 41 at 500 and read off slab thickness of 7½ in. (Table provides for impact.)

Note: Value of *K* is established by test.

SUGGESTED FOR FACTORY FLOORS

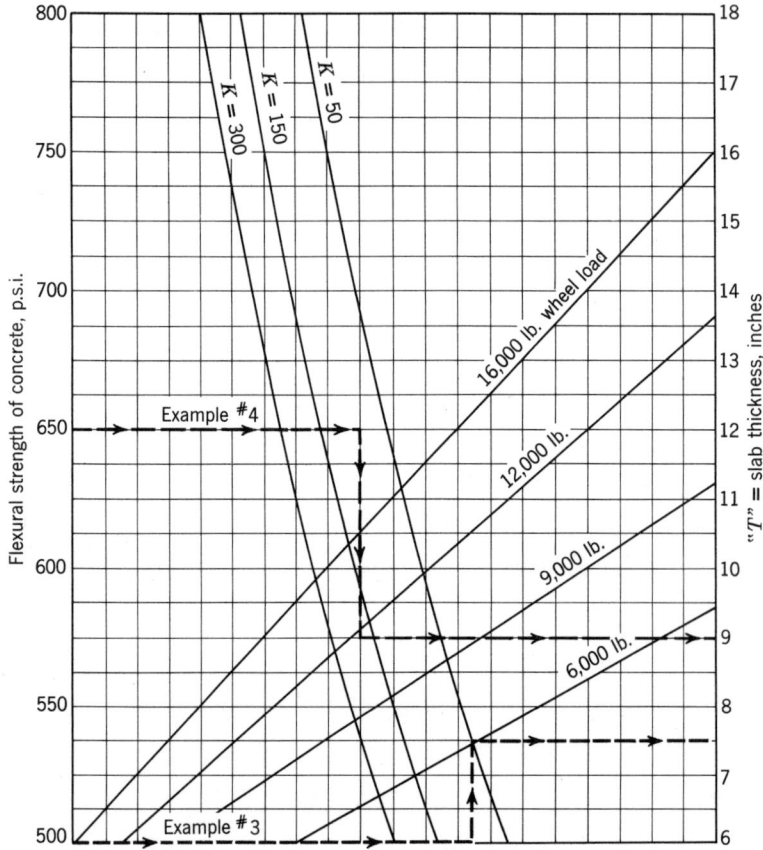

FIG. 41.   DESIGN CURVES FOR CONCRETE PAVEMENT THICKNESS (HIGHWAYS).*

Example 4

To determine slab thickness T.

Given:

Concrete p.s.i.	=	650
Subgrade Modulus K =		100
Wheel load	=	12,000 lb.

With above values follow dotted line on graph; then $T = 9$ in. (uniform).

* From War Dept. Corps of Engineers, Engineering Manual, April, 1947.

Discussion

Consideration of cracks and joints is of prime importance because of their tendency to ravel or spall off and enlarge under traffic. Small cracks are not so subject to this defect, and therefore sawn joints are to be preferred. Tooled joints have two objections: (1) the tooling of the edge weakens the concrete; and (2) the rounding of the edge increases the span of the gap at the surface and hence the wheel impact.

A great difficulty with floors on the ground is shrinkage. This may be reduced in different ways, such as:

1. Pouring panels in checkerboard order to allow the initial shrinkage to take place before the adjoining panels are poured.

2. The keyway suggested in Fig. 42.

3. Joints partly sawed through which will crack under shrinkage (they are sometimes called crack control joints).

The introduction of reinforcement serves to resist shrinkage. If reinforcement is placed in two surfaces it will produce a stronger slab in flexure and therefore permit the use of thinner slabs on subgrade of the same value. The tendency at present is to use concrete with a high flexural modulus and omit the steel, using shrinkage control as described above.

The use of concrete with a 28-day compressive strength of 3000 p.s.i. will correspond to a flexural strength of 500 p.s.i. on the design curve. This value may be increased to 550 p.s.i. if two layers of mesh are used.

Keys or other load transfer devices should be placed at the keyway joints. Sawed joints transfer load by aggregate interlock of the irregular line of rupture below the saw cut.

Expansion joints are to be avoided if at all possible except at the periphery of the building, as they take a severe beating from trucks. If necessary, a cover plate should be used. Ordinarily, expansion joints would seem to be superfluous as they would serve only to prevent buckling up of the slab under expansion. Inasmuch as the slab is set up under tension and bonded to the subgrade, it seems highly doubtful that expansion joints would be required except under exceptional conditions.

When the building is founded upon piles, another problem is encountered, namely, differential settlement. Either the floor must be designed as a framed slab supported on piles, or the slab must be separated from the building so as to settle uniformly. Where the ground is so poor as to indicate the possibility of differential settlement, often a flexible bituminous pavement is used.

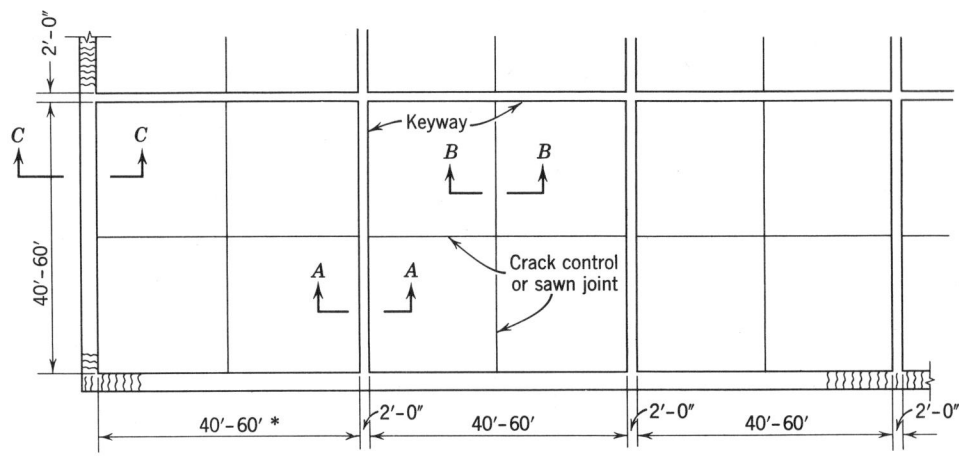

TYPICAL FLOOR PLAN

Note: With sawn joint keyway may be omitted.

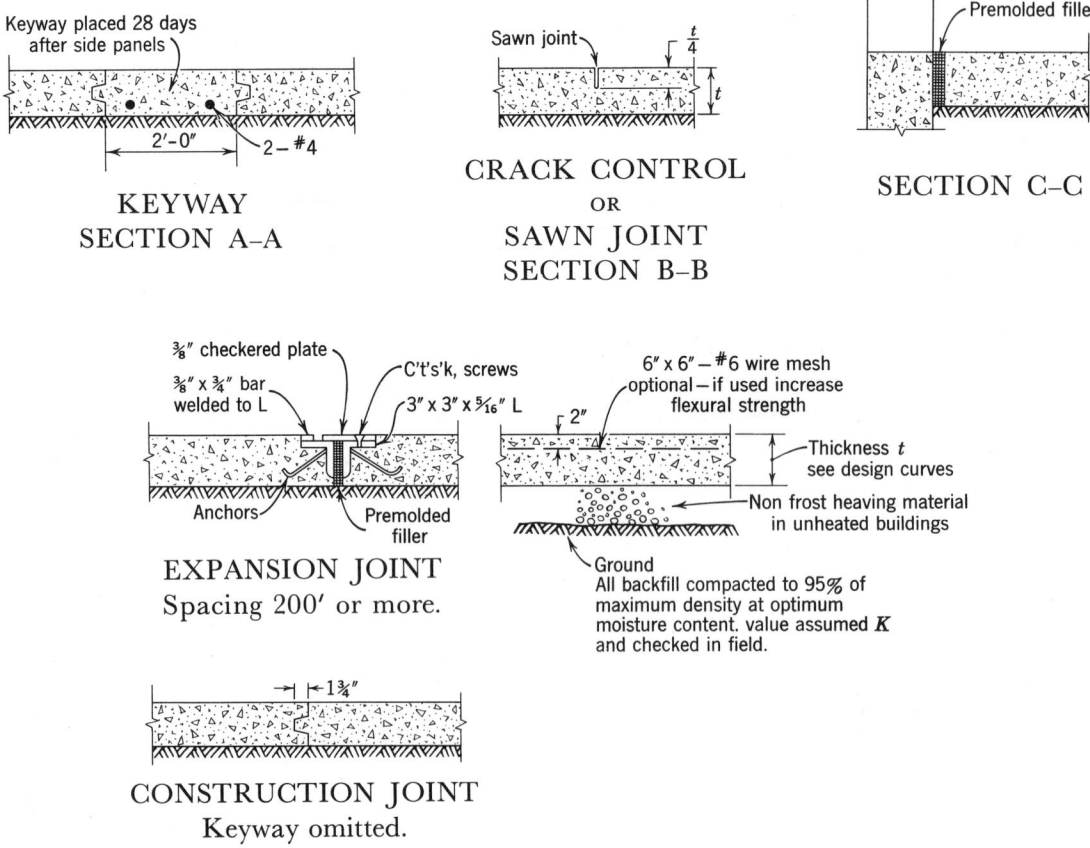

KEYWAY
SECTION A–A

CRACK CONTROL
OR
SAWN JOINT
SECTION B–B

SECTION C–C

EXPANSION JOINT
Spacing 200′ or more.

CONSTRUCTION JOINT
Keyway omitted.

*40′ max. recommended with no mesh.   60′ max. with mesh.

FIG. 42.   INDUSTRIAL FLOOR ON GROUND.

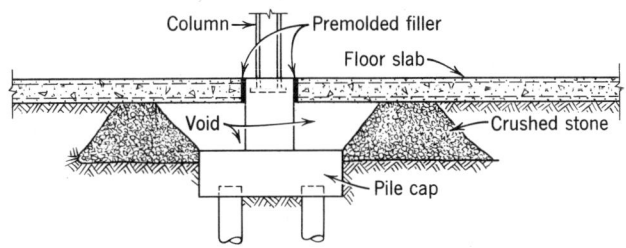

SLAB ON GROUND—BUILDING ON PILES—SLAB SEPARATED
FROM BUILDING TO PERMIT UNIFORM SETTLEMENT

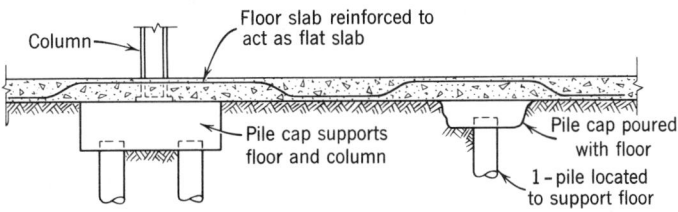

SLAB AND BUILDING SUPPORTED ON PILES

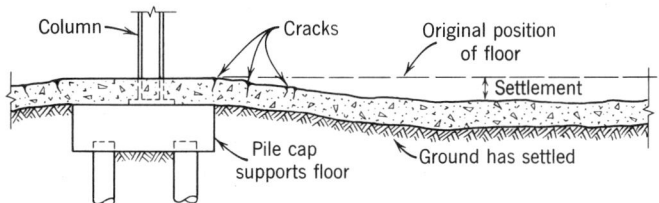

IMPROPER CONSTRUCTION

FIG. 43.   INDUSTRIAL FLOOR ON GROUND.

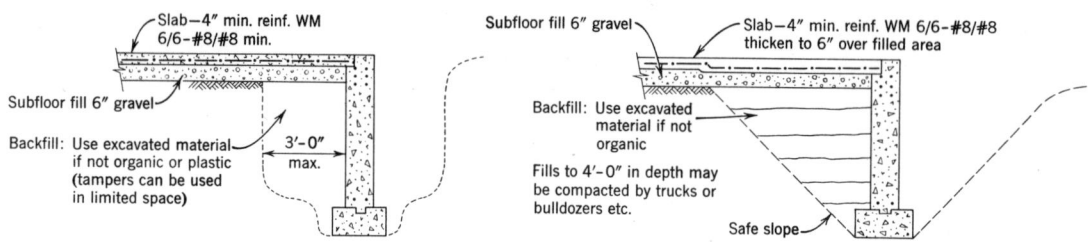

For cohesive and compacted soils that can hold a vertical bank.

For non-cohesive and non-compactable soils bank slopes 1 on 1 or flatter.

CASE I. FOOTINGS TO 6'-0" DEEP.

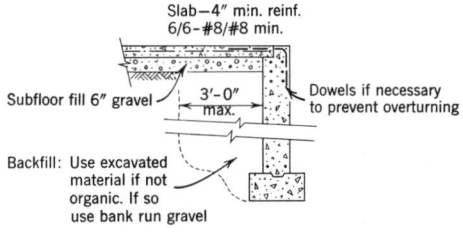

For cohesive and compact soils that can hold a vertical bank, such as hard-pans, gravel, gravel with some clay, sand with some clay, very stiff clay (materials with good compaction properties).

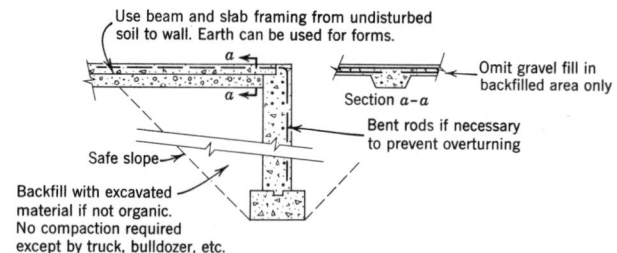

For non-cohesive and non-compactable soils, bank slopes 1 on 1 or flatter.

CASE II. FOOTINGS OVER 6'-0" DEEP.

CASE III. BUILDING ON PILES.

General Notes

1. All backfill to be placed in 12" layers and compacted to 90% of maximum density of optimum moisture content as measured by the modified A.A.S.H. method.

2. Walls must be checked for overturning, bending, and frost protection.

3. Brace walls to prevent overturning during compaction.

4. Case III is recommended for all conditions where greater settlement of slab than building is anticipated. Also recommended where entire slab is on backfill.

Warning. Where subgrade is a deep fill, or of poor material, frame the floor. Use of a flat slab, utilizing this fill for forms, may be economical. See Fig. 43.

FIG. 44. SLABS ON GROUND AT FOUNDATION WALLS.

Field Practice

Field practice embraces the inspection and sometimes supervision of construction of engineering works by a field man, who may have the background of an inspector, a designer, a clerk-of-the-works, a contractor's superintendent, or a surveyor. If the inspection and supervision are performed in accordance with modern practice, the field man merits the dignity that is implied by the title of field engineer.

Modern practice for field engineers comprises extensive technological advances, many of them made within the past two decades.

The purpose of this chapter is to enable the inspector or field engineer to brief himself as to the essentials in the inspection and supervision of the work which he is to undertake. To that end a checking list is provided for each type of work, such as piles or concrete footings, and each list is supplemented by a discussion.

LAYING PIPE LINES

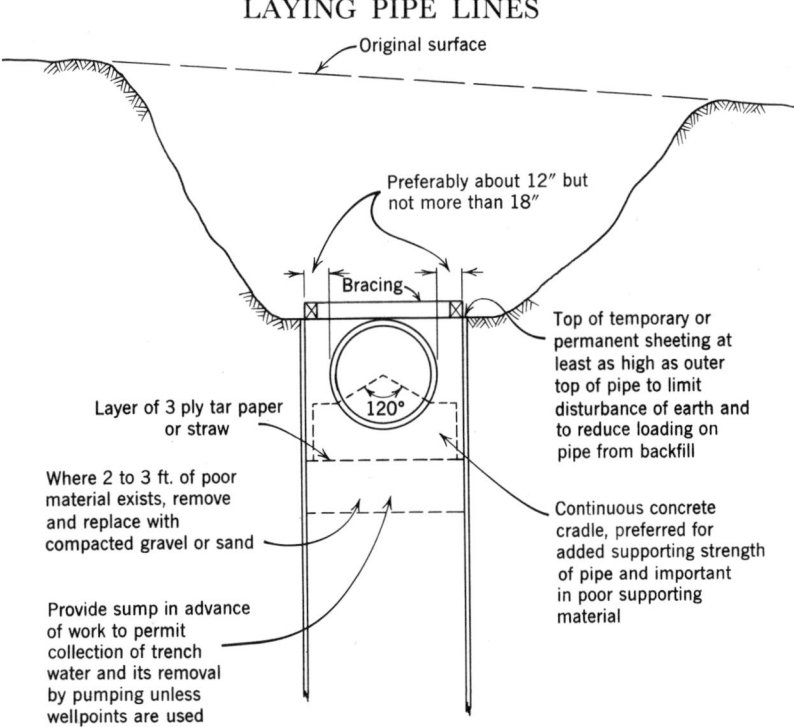

Pipe trench where open cut is feasible otherwise extend sheeting to surface of original ground.

FIG. 1. PRACTICAL INSTALLATION SECTION.

By F. C. Ziegler.

Discussion

For non-pressure gravity pipe lines such as for precast reinforced-concrete pipe or monolithic sections, leakage tests for reasonable water tightness can be made by bulkheading both ends of a section and filling the pipe with water to a height of 4 or 5 ft. above the inner top at the upstream end. This can be accomplished by means of a 6-in. standpipe leading from the bulkhead. Reasonable permissible leakage measured in the drop of water level in the standpipe would be ½ gal. per in. of pipe diameter per hour per 100 ft. of pipe during an 8-hour test. Such tests should be made in short sections before backfilling.

In pressure pipe lines, the joints should be tested for tightness by interior air or water. Soapy water applied to the joints will reveal leaks when under air pressure. An air test is more severe than a water test under the same pressure conditions.

When laying pipe lines do not permit backfilling over joints until they have been inspected and tested for leakage.

Backfill

In backfilling operations it is important to remove cross bracing and wales in sheeted trenches unless otherwise required by specifications, in order to obtain a solid fill free from pockets and later settlement.

In backfilling over pipes, care should be taken to remove boulders, which can be classified as rocks 10 in. or more in diameter. Nesting of stone should be prohibited.

Indiscriminate use of bulldozers for backfilling should not be permitted. Backfilling should be carefully regulated in order that the pipe will not be damaged by dropping material from a height. Instead, material should be placed in small layers and compacted by tamping or puddling as required by specifications.

Red Lights

When laying pipe lines in streets, check for possible obstructions and interferences from other pipe lines such as water mains, sanitary and storm sewers, gas mains, and electric conduits.

Special care should be taken to keep lines a safe distance from overhead electric and telephone pole lines. Such lines will interfere with cranes or other excavating and material-handling equipment; they also present a risk of electrocution of workmen caused by equipment coming in contact with live wires.

If pipe line is lower than existing nearby lines be sure that trench is sheeted and securely braced to prevent slippage of ground that would cause them to become displaced and damaged.

It is important to prevent loss of ground that will cause pavements, curbs, and sidewalks to settle, necessitating costly removal and replacement later.

Check basements and foundations of all buildings along the route of deep sewers and drains so that extra precautions can be taken to prevent damage thereto from slippage of ground.

Underpinning of bridge piers and abutments or heavily loaded buildings may be necessary. Neglect of such precautions may result in cancellation of public liability and property damage insurance, or exhorbitant premiums therefor.

Where damage to buildings is a possibility, an advance survey should be made. Notes should be made of buildings and structures detailing cracks and settlements in walls and foundations, etc., both exterior and interior, supplemented by photographs. Such record will be valuable evidence in the event of later claims and lawsuits.

Trenching and pipe-laying operations in a street require space for construction equipment, for pipe and other materials, and for temporary storage of excavated material. If traffic must be maintained, this frequently will be hazardous, and, except in a very wide street, excavated material cannot be stored thereon for backfilling and must be hauled away.

In sheeted trenches be sure to limit the excavated width between the vertical sides to the minimum necessary for accessibility to make up tight pipe joints. This should never exceed the outer diameter of pipe plus 2 to 3 ft. The dead load to be borne by the pipe can thereby be limited to its safe load-bearing strength.

Avoid floating of empty pipe lines due to dewatering failures or sudden flooding of trenches before backfilling. This could occur when pipe ends are bulkheaded or when water that fills a trench cannot also fill the pipe owing to barriers of earth or other obstructions.

FOOTING BOTTOMS

Check Lists

1. See that foundation pits are clear of water before placing concrete.
2. Lower water level to prevent boils.
3. Remove or skim off disturbed soil before placing concrete.
4. Check soil for type called for in specifications or on plans, such as sand, clay, gravel. Report deviations before permitting placing of concrete.
5. Remove decomposed rock down to type of rock called for, e.g., soft rock, medium rock, or hard rock.
6. Check size and reinforcement of footings against plans.
7. See that footings are free of frost. Check that foundations will remain free of frost until building is completed.

Discussion

The inspector should determine from plans the type of soil on which the foundation design is based and check against actual conditions.

Shallow pipe borings and/or auger borings should be made under each footing if there is a question about the underlying soils.

If there is any question in regard to soil bearing capacity, the inspector should notify the engineer, who may according to his judgment revise the size of footings or require footings to be carried deeper. A soil test may be required.

Soil is to be original strata and below loam or organic matter.

The bottom elevation of footing is to be at least the elevation called for on the plan. If necessary, owing to soil condition, the elevation may be lowered for suitable bearing. The engineer should be consulted.

A record of actual elevation of footing bottom installed should be kept.

The slope between footings should be checked when elevations differ from plans or when they are determined in the field. A common rule is that this slope should not be steeper than 1 vertical to 2 horizontal for soils, but it should be fixed by the engineer.

Conditions which may require sheeting where it is impossible to keep minimum slope should be watched.

Possible undermining of existing foundations should be checked.

The lowest footings should be placed first so that the levels below the upper footings are automatically exposed.

Evidences of filled ground should be reported. Fragments of brick, coal, wood, and peat indicate filled ground.

Red Lights

Dishonest Bottom

1. Do not allow the difficulty of inspection to weaken your duty to see that a good foundation of material called for is secured.

2. See that decomposed rock is removed and that sloping rock has a seat if called for or evidently required.

3. Report unusual rock conditions which may require seats or buttresses.

4. Respect the rules for not permitting concrete to be placed in water or on disturbed soil. Concrete footings should be laid in undisturbed soil. This may be accomplished by:

(*a*) Skinning off the disturbed material with a shovel just before placing the concrete.

(*b*) Lowering the water level for avoidance of quick conditions; see Chapter 11.

(*c*) Placing a thin layer of concrete on the surface to hold the ground until the bars and forms are in place ready for concrete.

(*d*) Placing lowest levels first.

5. Do not place concrete on frozen soil. Protect the soil under footings from freezing after footings are placed. Use salt, hay, or other means of protection.

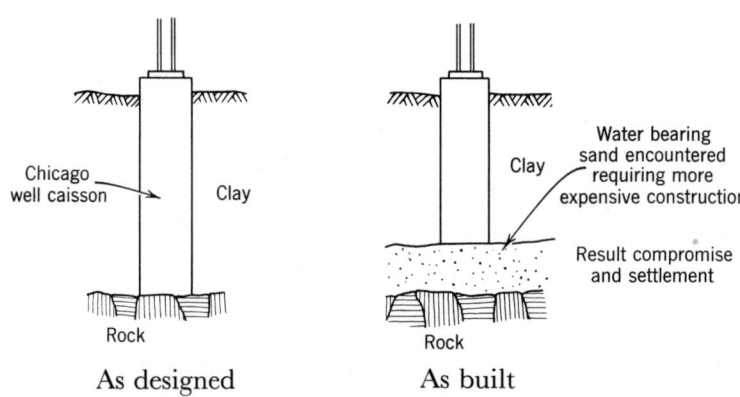

As designed   As built

FIG. 2.   ONE CASE OF DISHONEST BOTTOM.

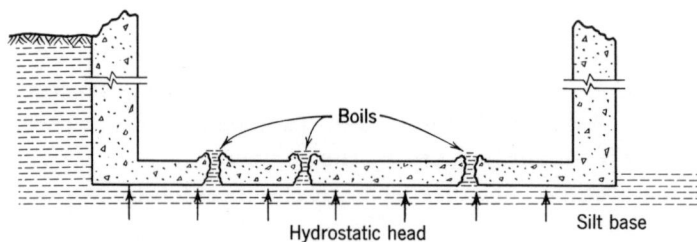

Silt boils, caused by not relieving the hydraulic head while concrete was still soft enough to permit water to boil up through the concrete mat.

Correction: lower the head by method given in Chapter 11.

FIG. 3.   REINFORCED CONCRETE WITH SAND BOILS AND CONSEQUENT LEAKS.

BACKFILL

Check List

Use only material specified.

Compact in thin layers (see specifications).

Compact by: (*a*) hand tampers; (*b*) vibrators; (*c*) rollers, in accordance with specifications.

Control moisture; see specifications and discussion below.

Discussion

Compaction of Backfills

For minimum shrinkage backfills should be made with the approximate moisture contents of:

Sand	8%
Silt	15%
Clay	15–20% *

These percentages correspond approximately to the moisture contents which permit maximum density.

Clays must be broken up free of lumps in order to be properly compacted. Rolled fills are generally compacted in layers of 3 in. to 12 in., 6 in. being most common. They are compacted to the specified per cent maximum density. For clays a sheepsfoot roller, Fig. 4, is generally used to break up the lumps. For sands a pneumatic roller, Fig. 5, is used. In places where rollers cannot be used, particularly around buildings, a tamper, Fig. 6, is used. Sands may be compacted by "puddling" (inundating and draining).

Red Lights

Caution must be used in clay fills to establish a sequence of operation which will provide drainage; otherwise operations will bog down during rainy periods as compaction cannot be accomplished when surface water is trapped at the working area.

Backfill tamping behind a wall may overturn it if it is not braced.

Certain plastic soils cannot be compacted. Rocks and decayed niggerheads may cause trouble.

FIG. 4. SHEEPSFOOT ROLLER.
Courtesy of LeTourneau—Westinghouse Co., Peoria, Ill.

* For development of job moisture content see Chapter 13.

FIG. 5. BROS STRAIGHT WHEEL GIANT MODEL ROLLER AND ALLIS-CHALMERS TRACTOR. (COMPACTION OF FILLS AND GRADES.)

Wm. Bros. Boiler and Manufacturing Co.

FIG. 6. TRIPLEX PNEUMATIC BACKFILL TAMPER.
Courtesy Chicago Pneumatic Tool Co.

SAFETY PROVISIONS

To be Looked Out for by the Inspector

The inspector should insist that the contractor provide adequate and accessible scaffolding when riveted or welded work is to be inspected, and safe and stable means of access between stories or different levels.

The safety of the men or work is primarily the contractor's responsibility, but the inspector should see that the contractor follows safe practices, including: not overloading steel or concrete framing with construction loads; allowing sufficient time before stripping forms; adequate bracing for sheet piling; safe scaffoldings and runways; barricades around openings; adequate guys or braces for wind during construction; shoring of rock faces to prevent shearing failures or caves.

In underpinning work, a stage plan showing the sequence of operations should be provided, which the inspector should check and see carried out.

The inspector should be on the lookout for operations tending to undermine or threaten adjacent foundations, or permitting pumping water or drainage to draw sand from adjacent footings.

In making load tests on floor slabs or beams, the inspector should see that shores are provided, or other provisions made, so that a failure of the slab being tested will not involve a failure of the slab below it or of other parts of the structure. *All load tests should be conducted on the assumption that, if the test area should fail, no one would be injured.*

The inspector should take no chances with ice in freezing weather.

Engineers should carry public liability and property damage insurance against injury caused by their inspectors or representatives.

CONCRETE—GENERAL

Check List for Inspectors

Inspectors' Equipment

Complete set of plans and specifications and approved set of reinforced-concrete working drawings.

Supply of required forms, sample tags, bags and boxes for samples.

Balance, capacity 2 kg., sensitive to 0.1 gram.

Set of square-mesh sieves of specified aggregate sizes and cleaning brush.

Fruit jar pycnometer or hot plate and pan for moisture content of aggregates.

12-oz. graduate bottle and 1 lb. of sodium hydroxide (caustic soda) for colorimetric test.

Pint milk bottle for silt and clay test.

6 in. by 12 in. metal or paraffined cardboard molds for concrete test cylinders, shipping boxes for same, and scoop for filling.

Slump cone, ⅝ in. by 24 in. tamping rod, and mason's trowel.

⅓ or ½ cu. ft. calibrated bucket and scale for unit weight tests, when specified.

Thermometer similar to Weston All-Metal type, 0 to 180° F. for cold-weather concreting.

6-ft. rule and 50-ft. steel tape.

Plumb bob and marking keel.

Field book and pencils for records and diary.

Pressure meter for measuring air.

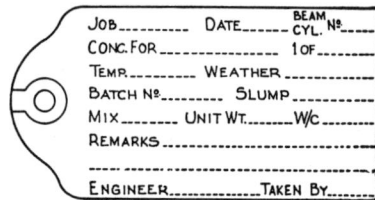

FIG. 7. CLOTH TAG FOR ATTACHING TO CONCRETE TEST BEAMS OR CYLINDERS.

Procedure in Inspection

Tested and Approved Materials.   Cement, aggregates, reinforcing steel, and water tested and source approved before use.

Schedule of required field tests adhered to.

Prompt shipment of samples of materials delivered at site.

Prompt reporting of field tests.

Accurate and complete daily reports and records.

Removal of rejected materials from site of work.

Storage and Handling of Materials.   Aggregates stockpiled in 2-ft. to 4-ft. layers on mats or planking.

Aggregate segregation avoided; see Fig. 8.

Cement protected from moisture and weather.

Cement handled to avoid loss by blowing or leakage, see Fig. 8.

Reinforcing steel protected from rusting, bending, or distortion and kept free from oil or grease.

Batch Plant Inspection

Batching Plant.   Inspected and approved before use.

Daily check of weighing scales, accurate to tolerance of 0.004.

Use ten 50-lb. weights, check in 500-lb. increments to greatest batch weight *or* have scales checked and sealed by certified scale master.

Adequate visibility of weighing and batching.

Telltale dial or balance indicator for correct quantities in hoppers.

Positive shut-off for bulk cement.

Prompt removal of excess material in hoppers.

Protection for weighing equipment from dust or damage.

Oscillating beams normally horizontal with equal play.

Beam scale for each aggregate usually required.

Control of Concrete.   Determine percentage of surface moisture in aggregates; also gradation.

Check at least 3 times daily, or more often when slump of concrete or condition of aggregate changes.   Reject any segregated concrete.

Translate the design into batch weights.

Run trial batch to check on slump and unit weight of mixture.

Check on cement factor during operations to detect bulking due to voids, air entrainment, or batching inaccuracies.

Adjust batch weights to produce required cement content per cubic yard and yield of concrete per batch.

Check actual amount of cement used to concrete laid each day as check on dimensions of concrete and accuracy of batching.

Note. The inspector should not vary the approved design mix without authority from the project or resident engineer.

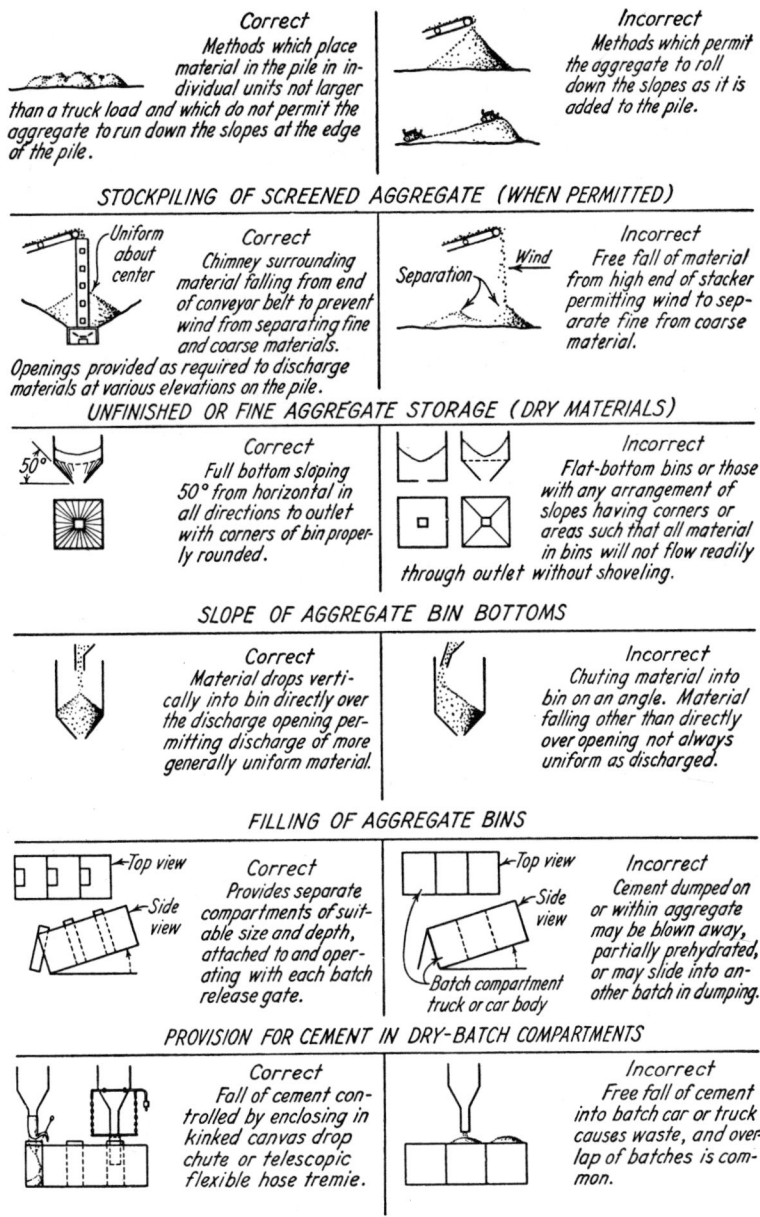

STOCKPILING OF SCREENED AGGREGATE (WHEN PERMITTED)

Correct
Methods which place material in the pile in individual units not larger than a truck load and which do not permit the aggregate to run down the slopes at the edge of the pile.

Incorrect
Methods which permit the aggregate to roll down the slopes as it is added to the pile.

UNFINISHED OR FINE AGGREGATE STORAGE (DRY MATERIALS)

Correct
Uniform about center
Chimney surrounding material falling from end of conveyor belt to prevent wind from separating fine and coarse materials.
Openings provided as required to discharge materials at various elevations on the pile.

Incorrect
Separation   Wind
Free fall of material from high end of stacker permitting wind to separate fine from coarse material.

SLOPE OF AGGREGATE BIN BOTTOMS

Correct
50°
Full bottom sloping 50° from horizontal in all directions to outlet with corners of bin properly rounded.

Incorrect
Flat-bottom bins or those with any arrangement of slopes having corners or areas such that all material in bins will not flow readily through outlet without shoveling.

FILLING OF AGGREGATE BINS

Correct
Material drops vertically into bin directly over the discharge opening permitting discharge of more generally uniform material.

Incorrect
Chuting material into bin on an angle. Material falling other than directly over opening not always uniform as discharged.

PROVISION FOR CEMENT IN DRY-BATCH COMPARTMENTS

Correct
Top view
Side view
Provides separate compartments of suitable size and depth, attached to and operating with each batch release gate.

Incorrect
Top view
Side view
Cement dumped on or within aggregate may be blown away, partially prehydrated, or may slide into another batch in dumping.
Batch compartment truck or car body

LOADING CEMENT FROM BATCHER

Correct
Fall of cement controlled by enclosing in kinked canvas drop chute or telescopic flexible hose tremie.

Incorrect
Free fall of cement into batch car or truck causes waste, and overlap of batches is common.

FIG. 8.   STORAGE AND HANDLING OF AGGREGATES AND CEMENT.

From *Concrete Manual*, U. S. Bureau of Reclamation.

Transporting Materials. Record of batch weights and number of batches dispatched; check with mixer inspector daily.

Tight truck partitions high enough to prevent intermingling of aggregates and loss of cement. Separate cement partitions, when specified.

Required amount of cement placed in batch partitions.

Covers for batch trucks provided.

Cement carried in sacks if specified.

Field Inspection. Drawings approved and up to date.

Forms. Check surfaces of forms against specifications. Where surfaces are in view or exposed to weather, form ties shall be no closer to the surface than 1 in., and no wire or snap ties shall be allowed because of eventual rust stain. Check correct alignment and elevation.

Centering true and rigid with horizontal and diagonal bracing.

Tight enough to prevent mortar leakage.

Columns plumb, true, and cross braced.

Floor and beam centering crowned ¼ in. per 16 ft. of span.

Beveled chamfer strips at angles and corners when specified.

Inside of forms oiled or wetted. Oil applied before placing of reinforcing.

Check installation of bolts, sleeves, inserts, and embedded items against plan details. These items must not infringe on structural items.

Check cleaning and removal of debris through temporary openings.

Check slab depths, beam and column sizes.

Provide temporary relief of hydrostatic pressure on walls and slabs by relief holes, drainage, or other means, and maintain relief until engineer in charge approves otherwise.

Removal of Forms and Shoring. Record of date forms poured and date forms removed. See Table I.

Forms not removed until concrete is set, should ring under a hammer blow; follow job specifications.

Reshores placed after forms removed—generally reshore for 2 floors. Use 4 x 4 braced at middle or 6 x 6 unbraced for conventional heights. If in doubt, check with superiors.

Inspect surface at once after form removal. Notify superior of serious defects. Follow specifications for removal of defective concrete.

Removal of Forms.* No safe rules can be given for the time of removal of forms unless cylinders are taken and tested. The suggestions in Table I are subject to the approval of the engineer in each case.

TABLE I

Temperature (Fahrenheit)

	Over 95° †	70°–95°	60°–70°	50°–60°	Below 50°
Walls	5 days	1½ days	2 days	3 days	Do not remove until
Columns	7 days	2 days	3 days	4 days	site-cured test cyl-
Beams	10 days	4 days	5 days	6 days	inder develops 50%
Slabs	10 days	5 days	6 days	7 days	of 28-day strength

* New York City Housing Authority.

† Where exposed surfaces of concrete can be effectively sealed to prevent loss of water, these times may be reduced to the 70°–95° times.

Remove forms carefully and avoid damage to green concrete.

Repair surface defects immediately upon removal of forms. Avoid feather edges in making patches. Fill bolt holes completely. Cut back tie wires where permitted an inch from surface and patch.

Patching. All tie holes, voids, stone pockets, or other minor defective areas shall be patched on removal of forms. Defective areas shall be chipped away with all edges perpendicular to the surface. Patched and adjoining areas shall be kept moist for several hours before patching. Patches on exposed work shall be carefully matched to adjoining work by the addition of white cement if necessary. All patches shall be cured in the same manner as adjoining surfaces.

Reinforcing Steel. Clean and free of scale, oil, and defects. Can be rubbed down with burlap sacks or wire brushes.

Accurately fabricated to plan dimensions.

Supports rigid, metal preferable; do not allow use of rocks, brickbats, old concrete fragments, etc., to support steel.

Check minimum clear spacing between bars; 1½ diameters for round bars and 2 times side dimension for square bars.

2-in. cover for steel in exposed exterior surfaces or as specified or detailed.

Check, from approved working drawings, the quantity, size, placing, bending, splicing, and location of reinforcing.

Check prebent steel against bending schedule upon delivery.

Mixing Concrete. Mixer in good condition and kept clean of hardened concrete.

Mixer blades not worn, and drum watertight.

Check drum speed, usually 200 to 225 peripheral ft. per min.

Check mixing time frequently; should be 1½ minutes minimum.

No retempering of concrete. Mixer completely emptied before starting new batch.

Adherence to specified water content. Amount of mix water based on moisture content of aggregates obtained from batch plant inspector and correct amount added at mixer.

Check consistency; make slump test at least 2 or 3 times daily.

Check for full cement content in each batch if cement is batched at mixer.

Ready-Mixed Concrete, Transit Mixers. Strict adherence to job specifications.

Calibration of water-discharge mechanism plainly marked.

Error in water measurement should not exceed 1%.

No leakage in valves; should be tight when closed.

Drums should be watertight. Check specified revolutions, usually 50 to 150 allowed for mixing.

Number, arrangement, and dimensions of mixer blades checked against manufacturer's statement. Blades not worn more than 15% of stated width.

Main water tank provided against loss by leakage or surging. To discharge full volume for mixing in not more than 5 minutes.

Volume of concrete mixed not more than 58% gross volume of drum. (If concrete is central mixed and only transported in truck mixers, 80% of volume is usually allowed.)

All truck mixers inspected and approved.

Complete removal of wash water or remaining concrete after each mixer discharge.

Wash water transported in auxiliary tank with gage and watertight valve.

Adherence to specified mixing time and any restrictions on mixing en route.

Drum to be revolved during transfer of water into drum.

Adherence to correct amount of water. Inspector should approve adding additional water. If necessary to add water to discharge, dry cement should be added at required W/C ratio.

Concrete containing air-entraining agent not to be mixed en route.

For transit trucks, the concrete shall be mixed not less than 50 revolutions of the drum at the manufacturer's specified speed.

Placing of Concrete. Forms inspected and approved before concreting.

Steel reinforcing in place and inspected.

Earth under footings to be undisturbed, original soil.

Rock or ledge should be well cleaned off and washed; dirt and loose rock fragments should be removed. Sloping rock stepped or benched for level bearing.

Concrete shall not be placed in running water. Accumulated water to be removed where possible; where impossible, concrete to be placed by tremie as directed by engineer.

Segregation, rehandling, or flowing to be avoided.

Check concrete especially when placing in subsurface structures to avoid segregation of aggregates, excessive water, accumulation of laitance, batches over or under sanded. (Sometimes caused by sand spilling over the bin barrier into the stone, or vice versa.)

Each unit to be placed continuously between construction joints as approved by engineer.

Spading and vibrating to maximum subsidence without segregation and next to forms and joints. Avoid excessive internal vibration. Internal vibrators should operate at a speed of not less than 5000 vibrations per minute.

Reinforcing bars shaken to insure bond with concrete, but excessive vibration and manipulation to be avoided.

In thin high sections avoid having concrete stick and harden on steel and forms above placing level.

Mold required number of test cylinders each day.

See that wood form spreaders are removed and not buried as concrete is placed.

Concrete placed as close to final position as possible in continuous horizontal layers.

Embedments. Pipe, conduit, and castings in concrete shall be embedded at least 3 in., except, in thin floor slabs, place on top of lower reinforcement. See that inserts and other fixtures are set as called for and that pipe sleeves on different floors are so aligned as not to require pipe offsets. Excessive size or number of embedments should be reported.

Construction Joints. Avoid if possible, except as detailed on plans.

If necessary at end of day's pour, install plumb, at right angles to plane of stress and in area of minimum shear.

When concreting is resumed at a construction joint, hardened concrete shall be cleaned and wetted and a thin layer of mortar spread over it.

Check on placing of dowels, keys, waterstops, and other details as shown on plans.

Floors. Check and remove laitance when concrete reaches required level. If excessive, cut down on mix water or overworking of concrete.

Finish floor as specified.

Pumping and Conveying. Only if approved or specified.

Equipment cleaned before and after pouring.

Continuous flow of concrete; no segregation.

Exposed Surfaces. Retain original surface film and form marks; do not rub, except as specified.

Fins and projections removed.

Small voids filled with 1:2 mortar.

Construction joints only as detailed on plans.

To match color, use trial pats with white cement added to mix.

Metal ties, chairs and spacers covered with 1½ in. of concrete.

Curing Concrete. Kept moist for 1 week minimum or sprayed with approved colorless liquid sealing compound.

Continuous saturation by sprays or wet fabric is preferred to intermittent sprinkling by hand. On vertical surfaces see that wet fabric is kept in contact with concrete.

Prompt application of curing materials as soon as possible after finishing concrete. Check that they are on hand ready for use.

Cold-Weather Concreting. Do not heat cement. Aggregates and water heated to not over 165° F. No snow or frozen lumps in aggregate.

Check temperature of concrete as placed, not less than 60° F. nor more than 100° F. Use immersion thermometer inserted in concrete near forms or surface.

Remove ice and snow from forms or other place of deposit and from reinforcement before placing concrete.

Do not allow placing of concrete on frozen ground.

Frost Protection. Provided by full enclosure of concrete and temperature of not less than 60° F. maintained for 7 days or as specified. Keep humidity high in enclosure.

Check that heating units will not harm concrete or damage surface for applied finishes.

Or, by consent of engineer, frost protection, provided by protecting surface with straw, hay, or fabric for 7 days. In buildings enclose story below and heat to 50° F. for 7 days.

Temperature protection gradually removed to prevent sudden temperature shock to concrete; 15° in 24 hours recommended.

Accelerating Admixtures (Calcium Chloride). Use only if specified. Tested before use.

Delivered in moisture-proof bags or airtight drums.

Quantity used not over 2 lb. per sack of cement.

Dissolve 1 lb. per quart of water, and add not more than 2 qt. per sack of cement to mixing water. Subtract amount of solution from normal quantity of mixing water.

Dry calcium chloride not to be added to aggregate in mixer skip or placed in contact with dry cement.

For cold-weather placing and curing, provide same precautions as for plain cement.

High-Early-Strength Cement. Use only if specified. Mixing and placing same as standard cement.

Prompt finishing (delay will ruin finish).

Curing temperature maintained as specified (usually 70° F. for 2 days or 60° F. for 3 days). Must be kept moist for at least 3 days.

Load Tests. May be required for faulty workmanship, violation of specification, or concrete suspected of having been frozen.

Notify superiors if necessary.

Pay Items

Accurate record kept of all pay items in contract, such as:

Volume of concrete placed and batches wasted.

Volume of openings or embedded structures if payment for such is not made.

Amount of reinforcing steel in pounds or tons actually placed.

Number and length of extra dowels and dowel holes drilled.

Embedded items or structures.

Any other contract pay items.

Field Testing

Slump Test for Consistency, A.S.T.M. C–143. Use a standard slump cone made of No. 16 gage galvanized metal in the form of a frustum of a cone with the base 8 in. in diameter, the top 4 in. in diameter, and the altitude 12 in. Provide mold with foot pieces and handles.

Take 5 samples of concrete, and thoroughly mix to form test specimen. Sample from discharge stream of mixer, starting at beginning of discharge and repeating until batch is discharged. For paving concrete, samples may be taken from the batch deposited on the subgrade. Before placing concrete, dampen the cone and place on a flat, moist, non-absorbent surface. In placing each scoopful of concrete move the scoop around the top edge of the cone as the concrete slides from it, in order to insure symmetrical distribution of concrete within the cone. Fill the mold in 3 equal layers, rodding each layer with 25 strokes of a ⅝-in. φ rod 24 in. in length, bullet pointed at the lower end. Distribute the strokes in a uniform manner over the cross section of the cone and penetrate into the underlying layer. Rod the bottom layer throughout its depth. After the top layer has been rodded strike off the surface of the concrete with a trowel or board so that the cone is exactly filled. Immediately remove the cone from the concrete by raising it carefully in a vertical direction. Then measure the slump immediately by laying the 24-in. rod across the top of the cone and measuring down to the top of the sample. This is known as the slump, which is equal to 12 in. minus the height in inches, after subsidence, of the concrete specimen. The slump test should be made frequently, at least 3 or 4 times a day.

Unit Weight of Plastic Concrete, A.S.T.M. C–138. Use a calibrated bucket of minimum No. 11 gage metal, a ⅝-in. by 24-in. bullet-pointed rod, and a scale accurate to 0.5% of total weight tested. Capacity of bucket should be ¹⁄₁₀ cu. ft. for ½-in. maximum aggregate; ½ or ⅓ cu. ft. for 2-in. maximum aggregate, and 1 cu. ft. for 4-in. maximum aggregate. Place a representative sample (selected as described for slump test above) in the bucket in 3 equal layers, rodding each layer 25 strokes as described for slump test. Vibrated concrete shall be compacted in the measure by vibration. Strike off surface, taking care that measure is just level full. Weigh to nearest 0.1 lb., subtract weight of bucket, and compute net weight of concrete in pounds per cubic foot.

Notes. 1. It is suggested that the inspector carefully sample about 1 cu. ft. or more of concrete and run slump test, unit weight test, and mold cylinders and beams in one sequence of operations. Complete data will then be obtained.

2. Concrete sample should not be taken from a chute, where partial segregation will be present.

Organic Impurities in Fine Aggregate (Colorimetric Test), A.S.T.M. C–40

This method of test covers the procedure for an approximate determination of the presence of injurious organic compounds in natural sands which are to be used in cement mortar or concrete. The principal value of the test is to furnish a warning that further tests of the sands are necessary before they are approved for use.

A representative test sample of sand weighing about 1 lb. shall be obtained by quartering or by the use of a sampler.

Fill a 12-oz. graduated prescription bottle to the 4½-oz. mark with the sample to be tested. Add a 3% solution of caustic soda, known as sodium hydroxide, until the volume of sand and solution after shaking reaches the 7-oz. mark. Let the bottle stand for 24 hr., then observe the color of the liquid above the sand. If colorless or light amber color, the sand may be considered satisfactory. If it is light brown or darker, the sand should be sent to laboratory for additional tests.

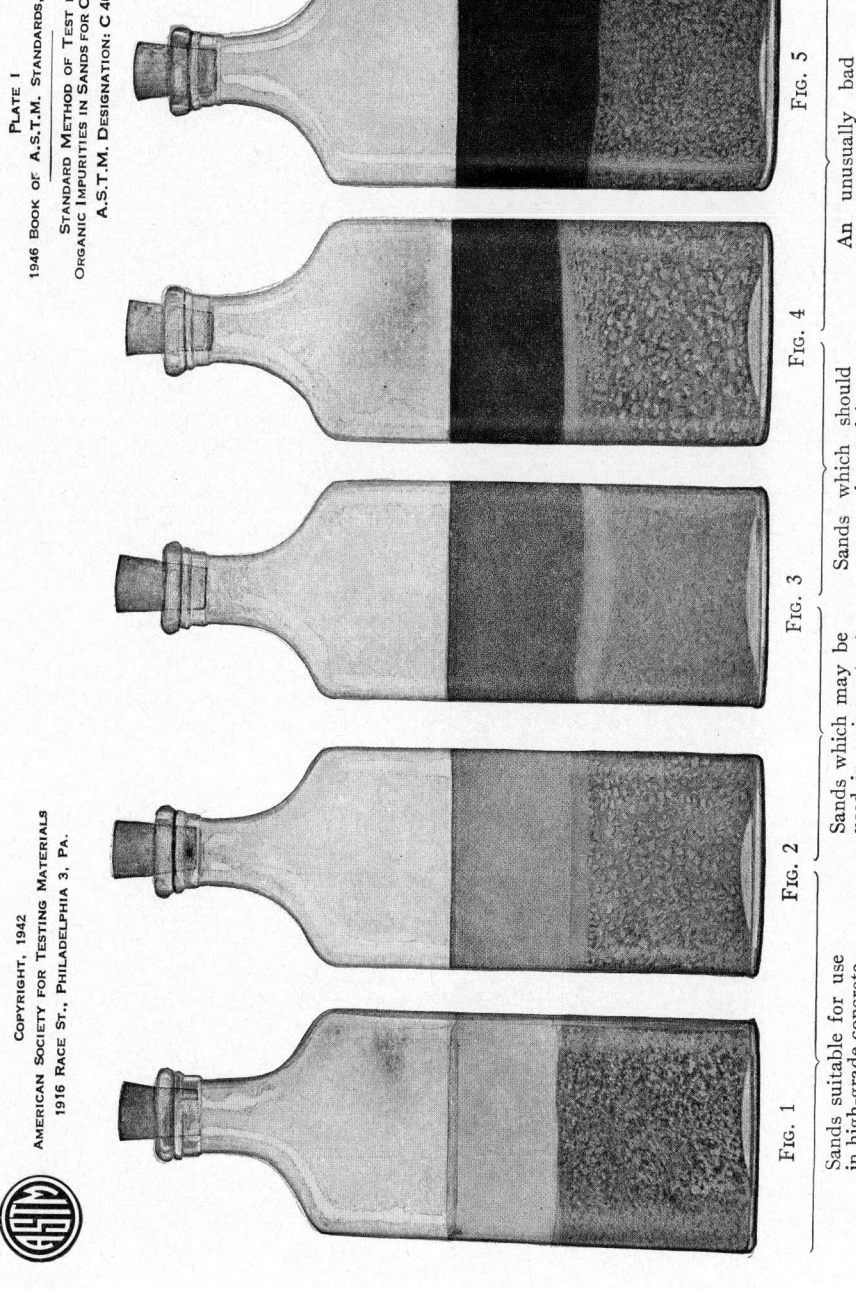

FIG. 1	FIG. 2	FIG. 3	FIG. 4	FIG. 5
Sands suitable for use in high-grade concrete.	Sands which may be used in unimportant concrete work.	Sands which should never be used in concrete.		An unusually bad sand, soil, or loam.

FIG. 9.   Colors of treated sands with suggested ranges of application.

Red Lights

Cracks due to misplaced or omitted reinforcing.
Voids due to failure to place concrete correctly.
Excess water—weak concrete.
Changes in aggregate supply that may produce weak cylinders.
Settlement cracks due to concreting on poor footing bottoms.
Bulged concrete—weak forms.
Frozen concrete—inadequate frost protection.

DISINTEGRATION OF MASS CONCRETE

Discussion

Disintegration of concrete, particularly mass concrete, has often occurred. Some reasons are:
Weathering caused by thawing and freezing of moisture in the concrete.
Use of unsound aggregates.
Presence of clay, organic, or other deleterious material in the aggregates.
Segregation of the concrete in the pouring of the concrete.
Expansion of rust on reinforcing steel.
Percolation of water leaching out the cement.
Defective cement.
These causes may be overcome by:
Using dense concrete mixtures.
Using a low water-cement ratio.
Using tested aggregates.
Proper placing of concrete.
Using air-entrained concrete.
The density and durability of concrete are helped by using graded aggregates and a low water-cement ratio. Mass concrete usually has low stresses, and often the concrete is designed for these low stresses without regard for durability. The water cement ratio generally should be limited to six (6) gallons per sack. Well-graded aggregates make the concrete dense, and this density, combined with a low water-cement ratio, reduces the amount of moisture that can enter the concrete.

Aggregates should be tested for soundness. Alternate cycles of thawing and freezing or the equivalent magnesium sulfate test will determine the distintegration of the aggregate. As a general rule, aggregates from igneous sources such as traprock are more likely to be sound than those from sedimentary sources such as limestone. Observation of concrete made from the aggregates to be considered can be of help in determining tendencies to disintegrate or spall. Some aggregates react with the sodium oxide (alkali) in the cement to form new compounds which expand. Such expansion takes place over a period of time. The best practice is to avoid such aggregates. When it is essential to use them, the alkali content of the cement is generally limited to 0.6%.

Proper placing of the concrete, including rigid control of the water, is essential. Excess water can cause segregation and porous concrete. Reinforcing steel should be kept back at least 2 in. from the face to protect it from moisture and the consequent exploding off of the concrete by expansion of the corroding bars. Construction joints can be a point of water entry; see p. 3–37.

Concrete having entrained air (3 to 6%) has greater resistance to frost damage. Furthermore, the lubricating effect of the air bubbles permits the use of a lower water-cement ratio with increased workability.

For check list and construction methods required to produce sound concrete see *Data Book for Civil Engineers,* Vol. 3.

CONSTRUCTION STAKEOUTS

Stakeout for Structures

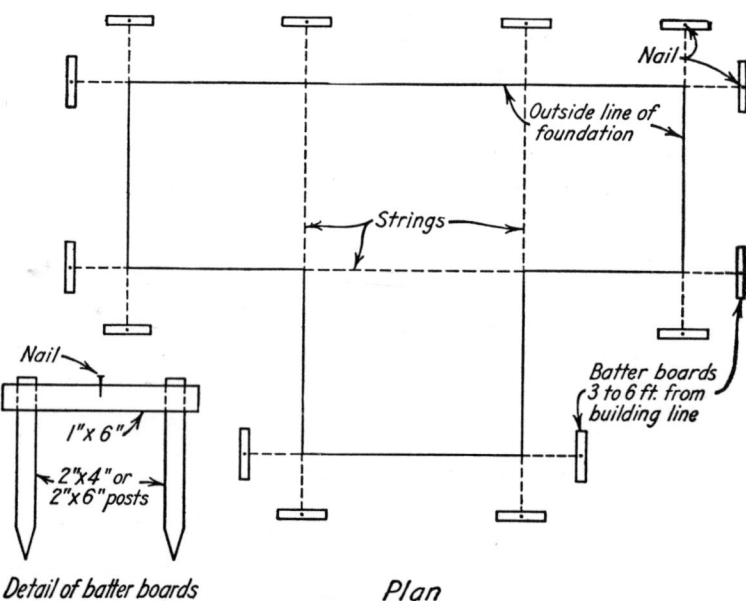

FIG. 10.   BATTER BOARDS FOR STRUCTURES.

Batter boards as illustrated are set on, or parallel to, the building or structure lines either before or after the rough excavation is completed.   When set before excavating, the batter boards should be checked upon completion of the rough excavation.   Points on the batter boards may be set on the outside foundation line or sometimes on the center line of columns.   It is preferable to set the top of each batter board to some definite grade, such as the first-floor elevation or else some even foot above or below a working grade.

Before setting the batter boards a base line should be established and referenced in with ties. Targets may also be set on the base line projected.   Angles turned from the base line should be established by the method of repetition, as an error of 1 minute in 300 ft. will throw the building line off 1 in.

From time to time during construction, the batter boards should be checked for disturbance or movement.

Highway Construction Stakeout

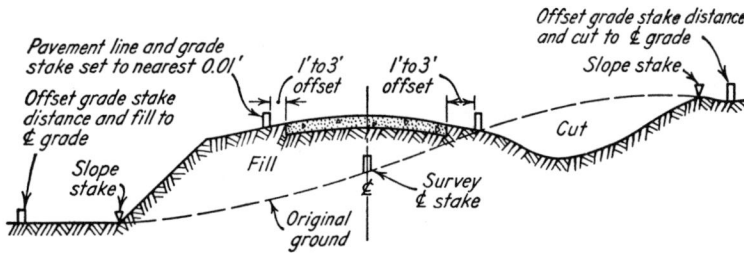

FIG. 11. HIGHWAY CONSTRUCTION STAKEOUT.

Before work begins, the construction centerline is staked out, usually on 50-ft. stations. Hubs are set at P.C.'s, P.T.'s, P.I.'s, and transit points. These hubs are tied in or offset, and the ties are recorded in the field book.

Offset grade stakes are set on 50-ft. stations far enough out to escape disturbance during operations where possible. Elevations of these stake tops are taken with a level, and the cut or fill to finish center-line grade is computed and marked on each stake. The distance to the toe or top of slope is marked on the offset grade stake or else the actual location of the toe or top of slope is marked with a slope stake. The station and the distance from the offset stake to center line are marked on the face of the offset stake. The superelevation plus or minus to edge of pavement and any pavement widening or curves are also marked on the offset stakes.

After rough grading is completed, blue tops or fine grade stakes are set every 50 ft. minimum. Blue tops are stakes set to fine grade and the top marked blue. Allowance for settlement or subsidence is sometimes made in setting these grades, or it may be made the contractor's responsibility, the engineer in the latter case setting the stakes to the grades shown on plan.

For concrete pavement, stakes are set usually every 50 ft. on tangents and straight grades and every 25 ft. on horizontal and vertical curves. These stakes are carefully aligned with a transit and tacks set on line. Either the tops are set to exact grade or the cut or fill is marked to finish grade.

Pavement stakes are set with a sufficient offset to allow room for the flanged bases of the forms, the offset usually being about 18 in. or 2 ft. from the edge of pavement. After the initial lane is placed, additional stakes may be set for other lanes or the forms may be set by leveling over with a line level.

For asphaltic pavements stakes are usually not set when the base has been constructed true to grade as the paving machines can be set for the required thickness. If the base is variable, steel pins for line and grade are usually set at 50- or 25-ft. intervals and offset enough to allow the machines to work. A 1-ft. offset is usually sufficient.

The amount of stakeout done for highway construction depends on the value and importance of the work, and judgement is required. For example, on cheap tertiary road construction only center-line stakes might be set at 100-ft. stations and a list of cuts and fill given to the foreman. The line and grade may then be transferred by the foreman, using a tape and hand level, to convenient trees, offset stakes, etc.

Through wooded country, stakes or marks are usually set at the clearing and grubbing limits. Trees to be saved are indicated by markings or signs.

In addition to line and grade stakes, right-of-way stakes may be necessary, also project markers and stakes set at intersection of right-of-way and adjoining property lines.

Railroad Construction Stakeout

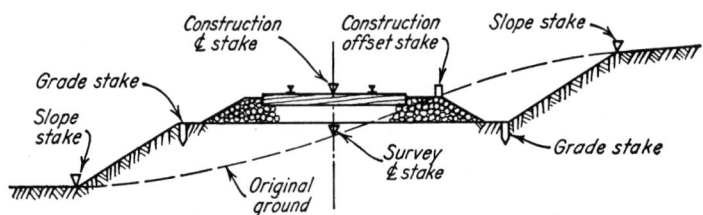

FIG. 12.   RAILROAD CONSTRUCTION STAKEOUT.

Stakeout for the grading work is similar to highway stakeout.

After grading is finished, and the ballast, ties, and rails are being installed, stakes for exact alignment and grade of rails are set.   These stakes are tacked for line and may be set on center line or offset about 2 ft. from one rail.   The grade marked is usually finish grade to the near rail, super-elevation being set for the other rail by using a track level.

Airfield Construction Stakeout

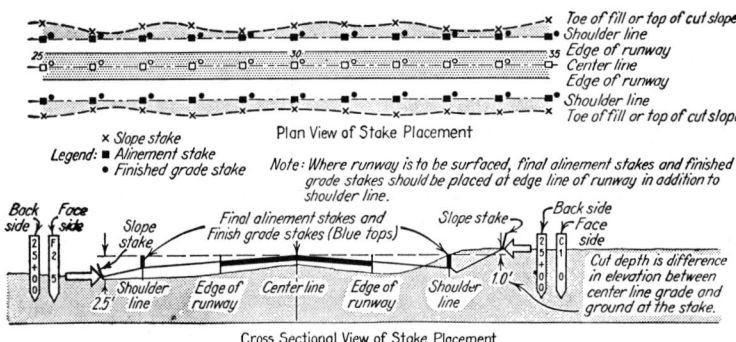

FIG. 13.   AIRPORT STAKEOUT.

The stakeout required differs from highway work in that the widths of runways and taxiways, together with their shoulders and graded areas, are so great that it is not practicable to set offset stakes to serve during construction.

The construction center line is staked out at 50-ft. stations and well referenced and tied in, and targets are set on the line extended.   During grading operations stakes are set continually day by day, at least one party usually being required at all times for each runway under construction.

For rough grading stakes at 50-ft. intervals both longitudinally and transversely are sufficient, but for fine grading stakes should be set at 25-ft. intervals.

Concrete pavement stakes are set exactly the same as for highways, but owing to the widths of runways and aprons it is not desirable to depend on a string level to transfer the grades for more than 2 or 3 lanes.   Additional stake lines should be run in at intervals of 25 or 30 ft. transversely.

Stakeout for asphaltic pavements is the same as for highways.

Stakes for grading interior areas are usually set on 50- to 100-ft. grids and marked for cut and fill.

Pipe-Line Stakeout *

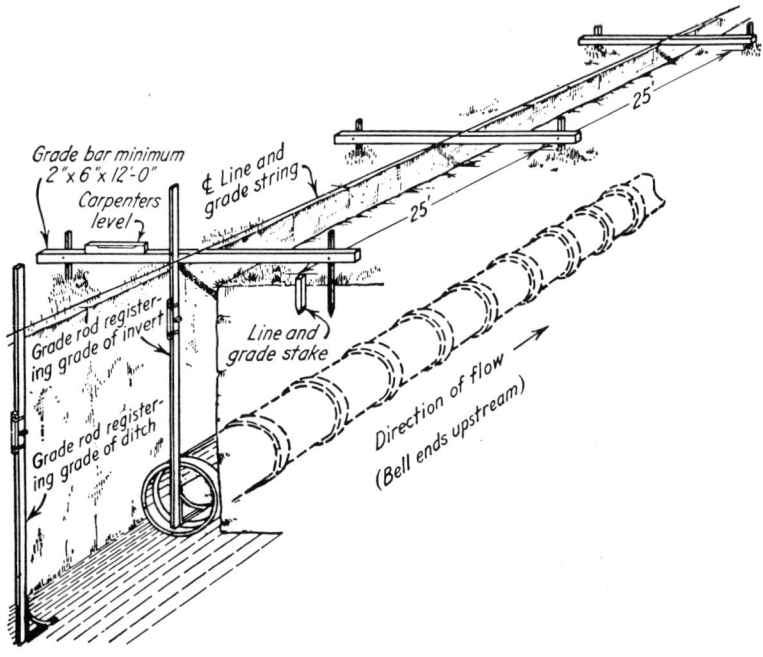

FIG. 14.   PIPE-LINE STAKEOUT.

Before beginning the excavation, stakes should be set 25 ft. apart parallel to and offset from the center line of the drain on the side opposite to that on which earth will be thrown.   Elevations of tops of stakes should be taken with a level and depth of cut marked on each.   These stakes will serve as guides for the rough excavation.

Excavation should be begun at the outlet.

After the excavation is approximately to grade, batter boards should be placed across the trench opposite each stake with the top of each board at the same distance above the grade of the flow line. About 6.5 or 7 ft. above grade is good practice.   The center line is then marked on the batter boards, and a string connecting these points will be directly above and parallel to the grade line.   The center line at any point may then be obtained by dropping a plumb bob from the string, and the grade determined by measuring down from the string with a pole of proper length.

Laying of pipe should begin at the outlet and proceed upstream.

GRADING

Check List for Inspectors

Inspectors' Equipment

Complete set of approved plans and specifications.

Surveying instruments if required.

* From *Principles of Highway Construction Applied to Airports, Flight Strips and Other Landing Areas for Aircraft,* Public Roads Administration.

100-ft. tape and 6-ft. rule.
Line level and line.
Equipment for sampling and testing soils as required.

Procedure in Inspection

Preparation of Site. Check against specifications for:
Stripping.
Storage of topsoil.
Removal of obstructions.
Clearing and grubbing.
Protection of trees.
Removal of peat, muck, humus, sod.
Removal or resetting of poles.
Resetting or installation of culverts.
Drains, sewers, water pipes, utilities.
Cavities and trenches to be backfilled and tamped.
Stake grades and slopes.
Cross-section borrow pits.
Cross-section rock as exposed before excavating.

Selection of Material. Follow specifications in selecting material such as placing granular material under paved areas.
Broken rocks on slopes and in marshy foundations.
Wasting peat, muck, frozen clods, organic matter.

Soil Compaction. Check specification requirements such as:
Weight of equipment and number of passes. Eight to twelve passes with sheepsfoot roller are customary. Three-wheel roller, 8 to 12 tons for final rolling of each layer and on the subgrade beneath base course. Caterpillar tractors may be used for granular soils when sheepsfoot or three-wheel rollers are not effective.
Thicknesses of layers rolled (usually 4 in. to 12 in.).
Harrows, rotary tillers, reduction of moisture and soil mixture.
Provision of water distribution in dry weather.
Provision of uniform travel for construction equipment.
Do not permit end dumping over face of high fills.
Stable slopes may be obtained by filling beyond final grade and subsequently excavating to that grade.
Protection of pipes from injury by equipment during construction.

PILE DRIVING

Check List for Inspectors and Data

Procedure in Inspection

Inspector should first determine from specifications the type of pile to be used, should familiarize himself with specifications, and should have approved drawings for his use in field.
Check steam or compressor capacity against pile hammer manufacturer's rating.
Condition and lengths of pile or pile shells before driving.

Type of pile hammer and size. Weight of striking part or ram and stroke (see Tables II, III, IV, and V) or energy per blow and rated strokes per minute.

Plumbing of pile or mandrel before driving.

Lateral tolerance of pile; limit 3 in. from horizontal location.

Plumbness of pile; limit 2% of pile length.

Inspect pile shell just before concrete is poured, by lowering a drop-light or large flashlight to observe collapse or tearing of shell or the pressence of sand, mud, or water.

Inspector to plot lengths of piles below cutoff.

Inspector to check boring record to assure that the ends of piles are in solid material and that there is no compressible soil stratum below them.

Check concrete mix from specifications or drawings.

Protection of concrete against freezing.

Pile caps not laid on frozen ground.

Piles cut off at the proper elevation.

After tops of bearing piles have been cut off see that the heads are brush painted twice with hot creosote oil and then heavily coated with asphalt roofing cement.

Check diameters of points and cutoffs of timber piles against specifications.

If untreated piles are partly above water lines call your superior's attention to it.

Check nearby structures for damage from vibration.

Heave

The first pile in each group shall be checked for heave due to driving of adjoining piles. If heave has occurred, all piles in group shall be redriven. For cast-in-place piles, check the point elevation.

Driving Control

The *Engineering News* formulas for allowable bearing loads where piles are driven to practical refusal are:

(a) Drop hammer: $P = \dfrac{2WH}{S + 1}$

(b) Single-acting power hammer: $P = \dfrac{2WH}{S + 0.1}$ *

(c) Double-acting hammer: $P = \dfrac{2E}{S + 0.1}$ *

where P = allowable load, in pounds; W = weight of ram, in pounds; H = height of fall or stroke, in feet; and S = average penetration per blow under last 5 blows, in inches.†

The reason for the difference in the formulas (a) and (b) or (c) is the extra speed of the power hammer, which affects the time of consolidation of earth between blows. Both (a) and (b) are gravity-type hammers, while (c) is steam or air driven.

---

* The trend of engineering thought is that the application of the *Engineering News* formula for steam hammers is not on the side of safety for small penetrations per blow (less than ¼ in.). Hence, recommended values are suggested in Tables II, III, and V, based on a modification of the formula, in which the dividing factor is changed from $S + 0.1$ to $S + 0.3$.

The weight of the ram should be substantially greater than the weight of the pile.

† Five blows is commonly specified, but because of the high speed of a power hammer it is suggested that the average penetration per blow during the last 20 seconds of driving is more practicable.

Examples. Given $W = 2000$ lb., $H = 15$ ft. 0 in., $S = 0.5$ in.   Required P, using drop hammer.

$$P = \frac{2 \times 2000 \times 15}{0.5 + 1} = 40,000 \text{ lb.}$$

Given $W = 5000$ lb., $H = 3$ ft. 0 in., $S = 0.4$ in.   Required P, using single-acting steam hammer.

$$P = \frac{2 \times 5000 \times 3}{0.4 + 0.1} \quad * = 60,000 \text{ lb.}$$

Comments.   The field engineer's checking criterion is the number of strokes per minute, to supplement the steam pressure, and also penetration.   If steam pressure falls off, the number of blows per minute cannot be delivered and the penetration falls off.   Therefore, time the driving speed of steam hammers to be sure that the manufacturer's rated speed in strokes per minute is maintained at all times to attain allowable bearing loads indicated by formulas.   See that sufficient steam or air capacity is provided.

Load Tests

Conduct as follows.   A suitable balanced platform shall be built on top of pile which has been in place for at least 2 days.   If it is a concrete pile, the concrete should be thoroughly hardened. Place initial load equal to the proposed pile load using heavy material such as pig iron.   Increase this load 25% after 12 hours, and 25% after 24 hours; thus the total load is 150% of proposed load.

Allow final load to remain at least 48 hours.   Take readings before and after placing of each load and 12 and 24 hours after placing final load.

The total net settlement deducting rebound after removing load should not be more than 0.01 in. per ton of total test load.

---

* See footnotes on p. 15–21.

TABLE II
SINGLE-ACTING POWER HAMMERS—VULCAN IRON WORKS
(Allowable loads by formula (b) and recommended values)

Loads in 1000 Pounds

Hammer Size	Weight of Ram	Stroke, ft.	Blows per Minute	0.1	0.2	0.3	0.4	0.5	0.6	0.7	0.8	0.9	1.0
								Penetration per Blow in Inches					
2	3000	2.42	70	73	48	36	29	24	20	18	16	14	13
1	5000	3.00	60	150	100	75	60	50	43	37	33	30	27
0	8000	3.05	50	244	162	122	97	81	69	60	54	48	44
OK	9300	3.25	50	302	202	152	121	101	86	75	67	60	55
Recommended values *				50%	60%	66.5%	71.5%	75%	78%	80%	82%	83.5%	84.5%

TABLE III
SINGLE-ACTING POWER HAMMERS—McKIERNAN-TERRY
(Allowable loads by formula (b) and recommended values)

Loads in 1000 Pounds

Hammer Size	Weight of Ram	Stroke, ft.	Blows per Minute	0.1	0.2	0.3	0.4	0.5	0.6	0.7	0.8	0.9	1.0
								Penetration per Blow in Inches					
S-3	3000	3.00	65	90	60	45	36	30	26	22	20	18	16
S-5	5000	3.25	60	162	108	81	65	54	46	41	36	32	30
S-8	8000	3.25	55	260	173	130	104	87	74	65	58	52	47
S-10	10000	3.25	55	325	217	162	130	108	93	81	72	65	59
S-14	14000	2.67	60	375	250	187	150	125	107	94	83	75	68
Recommended values *				50%	60%	66.5%	71.5%	75%	78%	80%	82%	83.5%	84.5%

* See footnotes on p. 15-21.

TABLE IV

VALUES OF E FOR McKIERNAN-TERRY DOUBLE-ACTING PILE HAMMERS *

Size of Hammer	Ft-Lb. Blow at Given Strokes per Minute		Size of Hammer	Ft-Lb. Blow at Given Strokes per Minute	
	Strokes per Min.	Ft-Lb. per Blow = E		Strokes per Min.	Ft-Lb. per Blow = E
7	225	4,150	9B2	100	3,700
	195	3,720		105	4,200
	170	3,280		110	4,750
				115	5,350
9B3	145	8,750		120	5,940
	140	8,100		130	7,000
	135	7,500		140	8,200
	130	6,800			
			10B2	100	10,700
10B3	105	13,100		105	12,000
	100	12,000		110	13,500
	95	10,900		115	15,000
	90	9,550			
			11B2	100	15,600
11B3	95	19,150		105	17,250
	90	18,300		110	18,900
	85	17,500		115	20,500
	80	16,700		120	22,000

*E = energy of ram for various driving speeds.

TABLE V

ALLOWABLE LOADS ON PILES IN THOUSANDS OF POUNDS USING MAXIMUM E (DOUBLE-ACTING HAMMER)

Penetration per Blow, In.	Recommended Values, %	Size of Hammer						
		7	9B3	10B3	11B3	9B2	10B2	11B2
0.1	50	41.5	87.5	131.0	191.5	82.0	150.0	220.8
0.2	60	27.6	58.3	87.3	127.6	54.6	100.0	147.2
0.3	66.5	20.7	43.7	65.5	95.7	41.0	75.0	110.4
0.4	71.5	16.6	35.0	52.4	76.6	32.8	60.0	88.3
0.5	75	13.8	29.1	43.6	63.8	27.3	50.0	73.6
0.6	78	11.8	25.0	37.4	54.7	23.4	42.9	63.2
0.7	80	10.3	21.8	32.7	47.8	20.5	37.5	55.3
0.8	82	9.2	19.4	29.1	42.5	18.2	33.3	49.1
0.9	83.5	8.3	17.5	26.2	38.3	16.4	30.0	44.1
1.0	84.5	7.5	15.9	23.8	34.8	14.9	27.3	40.1

Sheet Piling

Purpose: To support the sides of an excavation and prevent loss of ground.

Types: 1. Wood sheeting.
2. Reinforced-concrete sheeting.
3. Interlocking steel sheeting.

Wood sheeting may be tongue and groove, splined, or Wakefield sheeting, made with three planks bolted together with the center one offset to form a tongue and groove. Wood sheeting is limited to about 20 ft., but the excavation can be made deeper than this by driving a second set of sheeting planks within the first set.

Reinforced concrete is used where it is to be left in place as part of the permanent structure.

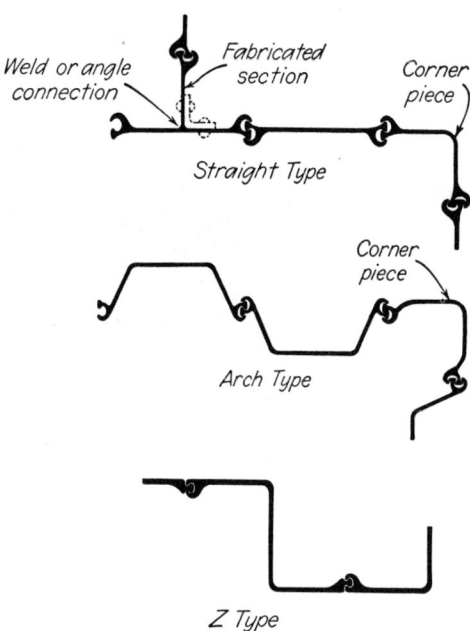

FIG. 15. STEEL SHEETING.

Steel sheeting can be driven in lengths up to about 50 ft. Sheeting of all types should be driven progressively in stages around the excavation to minimize the danger of breaking the lock between sheets. Driving should be stopped at once if the sheet meets an obstruction, especially in the case of wood sheeting.

See that sheet piling is driven straight and to the required lines and grade, with penetrations to firm subsoil.

Steel sheet piling along excavations to be carefully interlocked and timber sheeting tightly closed to prevent loss of ground.

Soldier-beam and timber-lagged sheeting should be watched to avoid ground slippage.

Vertical sheeting permits little water to pass through it; consequently the difference in hydrostatic pressure may cause boils in the bottom of the excavation. If steel sheeting can be driven into an impervious stratum to cut off the water, it will prevent boils. Sheeting should be held in place with wales and braces or shores. In excavations of more than a few feet the braces or shores should be prestressed with wedges or otherwise to prevent movement.

Small pits may be carried to great depths with horizontal sheeting because the earth arches around them. Great care must be taken, however, not to loosen ground, as that may break the arch and cause a collapse. On long excavations, horizontal sheeting has been used successfully between vertical H beams called "soldier beams."

Spud Piles

Where it is found difficult to drive a pile of the type that is being used on the job on account of boulders or other obstructions, a so-called "spud pile" will sometimes solve the difficulty. This is a rugged steel mandrel, strong enough to break up or push aside the obstructions. The mandrel, in driving, may be forced sideways or "weaved," to push obstructions out of the way, but such forcing, if carried to extremes, can break or bend the mandrel.

Red Lights

Buckling and heaving of cast-in-place piles is caused by bulking of the soil due to driving closely spaced piles in a group. The shells for an entire group are commonly driven before any are filled, and buckling can be detected by inspection. The practice of driving an inner shell to correct a buckling should not be allowed. A buckled shell should be withdrawn. A successful method for avoiding buckling is called "pre-excavation." An open-end pipe, somewhat smaller than the pile, is first driven and the soil in it is removed by compressed air or other means. The pipe is then withdrawn and the pile is driven down in the hole. If the shell has been filled before the adjoining shell is driven, a rise of the wet concrete in the shell indicates buckling, and the pile should be replaced if the rise is significant.

Heaving, or lifting of a filled pile out of the ground, may result from the same cause. Unless the heaving is very slight, the pile should be rejected.

Injury to wood piles. Crushing or brooming of pile head or, in precast concrete piles, the cracking or disintegrating of concrete makes it impossible to drive piles properly as this dissipates the energy of the blow of hammer.

Possible telescoping or crushing of the middle of wooden piles is indicated by sudden loss of resistance.

Possible deflection of the foot of pile. This happens when a pile hits a slanting surface of rock and then drives easier as the result of the splitting or sliding of the bottom.

A sudden change from hard to easy driving in wood piles should be regarded with great suspicion. If withdrawn, the pile is usually found to be shattered. Excavations have disclosed many old wood piles shattered or sheared by overdriving.

Hard driving, and especially hammering down the concrete in a pipe pile to form a "pedestal," causes vibration that may be dangerous to surrounding structures.

In driving open-end pipes through sand, the sand tends to arch in the pipe and form a solid plug which makes the pipe drive like a closed-end pipe or solid pipe and greatly adds to the difficulty of driving. The sand should therefore be blown or dippered out frequently.

Water jetting of piles should be prohibited (1) where there is a risk of undermining a nearby structure; (2) where clayey and silty soils would be disturbed; (3) where piles depend on friction in such soils. Sometimes it is impossible to drive piles in sand except by jetting.

Borings should be inspected for soft strata below the level where piles fetch up, as reliance in pile-driving formulas for allowable loads may be unsafe.

Occasionally in plastic soils piles will bulk; that is, the ground will rise between piles or the piles will tend to pop out. Corrections include: (*a*) the use of a steel pile which has low displacement; (*b*) redriving the piles that tend to rise; (*c*) use of open-end steel pipe piles; see p. 1–10.

_____

Engineer

REPORT ON PILE DRIVING

FIELD INSPECTION

Report No. _____

Job _____ Date _____

Reported to _____

Hammer data _____

Foot-ing No.	Pile No.	Pene-tration	No. Blows Last In.	No. Strokes per Min.	Bearing Capacity	Ap-proved	Re-jected	Re-marks

See field drawing No. _____ for field location of piles in this report _____

_____

Inspector

SOIL SAMPLING *

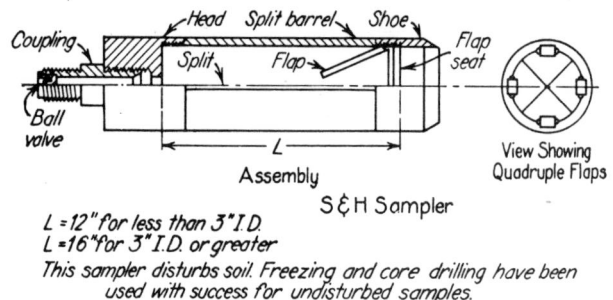

L = 12" for less than 3" I.D.
L = 16" for 3" I.D. or greater
This sampler disturbs soil. Freezing and core drilling have been used with success for undisturbed samples.

FIG. 16.   DEEP SAMPLER, COHESIONLESS SOIL.

By permission, from *Soil Mechanics,* by Krynine, McGraw-Hill Book Co., 1941.

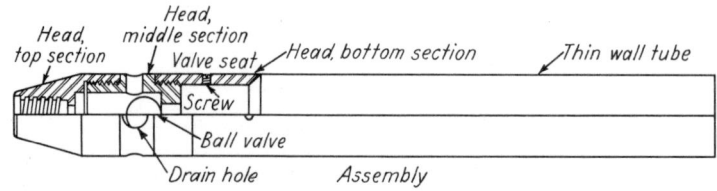

FIG. 17.   "SHELBY-TUBE" SAMPLER.

Sprague and Henwood, Inc., Scranton, Pa.

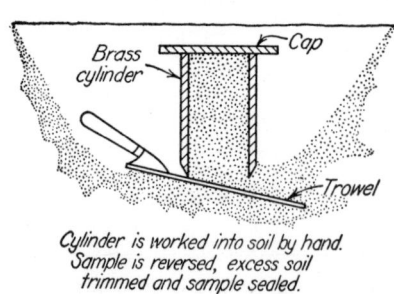

Cylinder is worked into soil by hand. Sample is reversed, excess soil trimmed and sample sealed.

FIG. 18.   SHALLOW SAMPLING, COHESIONLESS SOIL (SAND).

By permission, from *Soil Mechanics,* by Krynine, McGraw-Hill Book Co., 1941.

* See also Chapter 8.

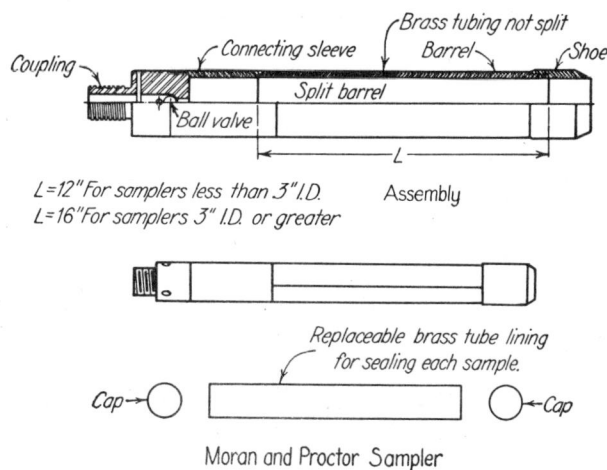

FIG. 19.   DEEP SAMPLER, COHESIVE SOILS.

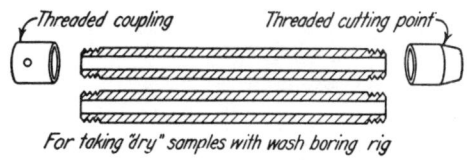

FIG. 20.   SPLIT SPOON SAMPLER.

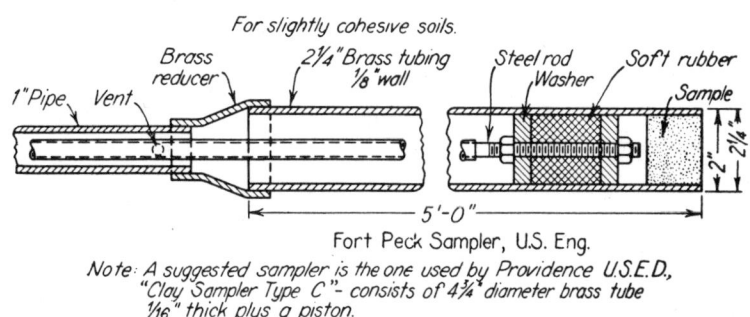

FIG. 21.   PISTON-TYPE SAMPLER, COHESIVE SOILS.

Red Light

Do not miss layers of peat or soft soil by taking samples too far apart, say every 5 ft. instead of every foot.

Undisturbed Samples

For undisturbed samples from test pits see Fig. 22.   For undisturbed samples taken with Shelby tube see Fig 17.

To obtain a chunk sample from a sub-grade or other level surface such as the bottom of a test pit:

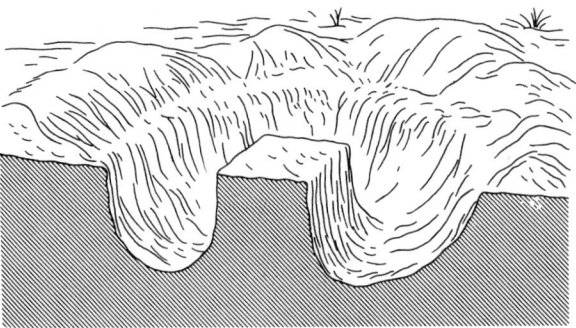

1. Smooth ground surface and mark outline of chunk.
2. Excavate trench around chunk.

3. Deepen excavation and trim sides of chunk with butcher knife.

FIG. 22.*

---

* From *Soil Tests for Military Construction*, by Major G. E. Bertram, American Road Builders Association.

LOAD TEST

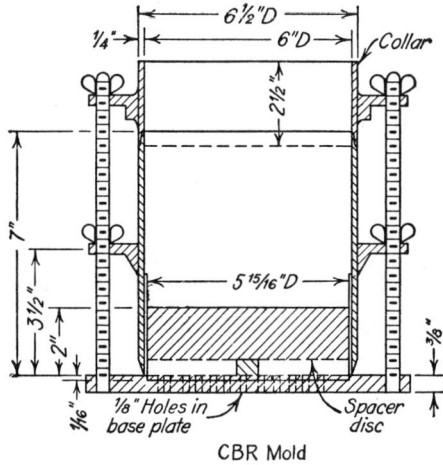

CBR Mold

FIG. 23.   APPARATUS.

California Bearing Ratio

Purpose is to obtain relative resistance of a soil in place or soil to be placed and compacted to a specified degree to a standard broken-stone layer.   The resistance of the standard layer is 1000 p.s.i. at 0.10 in. and 1500 p.s.i. at 0.20 in. of penetration.

For soil in place, apply a 3 sq. in. end area piston at a constant rate of penetration of 0.05 in. per min. to a total penetration of 0.5 in.   The penetration force required per square inch at the values is recorded and stated as a ratio of the corresponding values of the standard layer; usually the values for 0.1-in. deflection are used.

Laboratory determination is made by remolding the sample of the soil until it has the specified density using the A.S.T.M. or A.A.S.H.O. methods, p. 14–22, except that 55 blows of the rammer are used instead of 25 and material is passed through a ¾-in. sieve instead of a No. 4 sieve.   These samples are then loaded by means of the same piston and recorded as given above for the field test.

For the purpose of determining the effect of saturating conditions on the soil, tests may be made on soaked samples.

Plate Load Test to Obtain Modulus of Subgrade Reaction

The thickness of a concrete pavement depends upon the strength of the subgrade.   This strength may be measured by the plate load test.

Load is applied to a steel or aluminum plate 30 in. in diameter and 2 in. thick, and the settlement is measured by Ames deflection gages symmetrically placed on the plate.   A convenient method of loading is by means of a jack reacting against a steel beam bearing against the bottom of two loaded trucks.   The load in pounds per square inch between the plate and the soil that causes a settlement of 0.05 in. is the value k used in the formulas for determining concrete slab thickness; see p. 14–20.

The equipment should be capable of applying a load up to 50,000 lb.   The plate must be set level with 100% bearing; plaster of paris bedding should be used when testing clay soils or old pavements.

Weather is not an important factor in making this test.

In *sandy soils,* no correction for moisture need be made.

In *plastic soil* a correction must be made if the moisture content at the time of the test is less than the maximum which may be anticipated in operation.   In such a case, determine k for the soil as it is and also make unconfined compression tests on samples of the soil having the same moisture content as present in the field and also on samples having the maximum anticipated moisture content.   Should the latter figure be unknown, use the saturated moisture content.   The ratio between these unconfined compression tests applied to the k value found by the plate test will give the corrected k value to use in the pavement formulas.

An Army method of correction is to use the ratio of the deformation of samples at the two moisture contents under a unit load of 10 p.s.i. in a consolidation test.

Check List for Inspector for Plate Test

Plate level and properly bedded.

Angle iron supports for dials anchored and bearing on ground at least 8 ft. away from the test plate or truck wheels.

Dials vertical and mounted on heavy angle-iron frame.

Dials set so that they have ½-in. travel.

Settlement and load readings made at such intervals and loads as specified.

Density and moisture of subgrade adjacent to area being tested checked.

Steel ball between jack and I beams to insure vertical loading.

Dials protected from rain.

Angle-iron supports and all testing equipment protected from wind.

Area graded to drain away from test location.

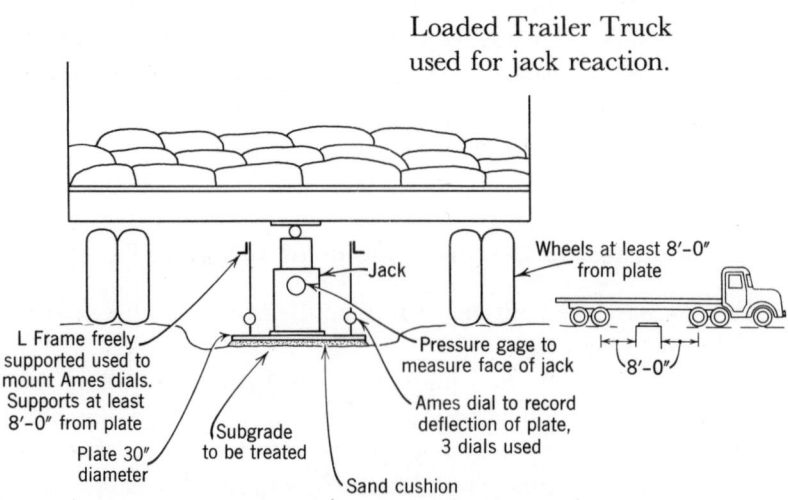

FIG. 24.   PLATE LOAD TEST TO OBTAIN MODULUS OF SUBGRADE REACTION k.

16

Costs

Knowledge of costs is essential to a designer. For selection of the most appropriate type of foundation, cost studies are required. A cost study includes a tentative design of the most promising solutions, a material takeoff, and the pricing. Examples of such studies occur throughout the book.

Cost data should include:

Costs of elements, such as different types of excavations, piles of all classes, concrete in place, and waterproofing.

Costs of construction, such as sheeting, pumping, shoring.

Overall costs, such as costs of excavating per cubic yard, taking into account type of soil, sheeting, pumping.

Degree of Accuracy Required

Relative accuracy is more important than absolute accuracy for comparative cost estimates. Such studies will give the correct choice although the total cost is wrong.

Cost index enables the engineer to adjust dated cost data to the time of the project by a slide-rule operation. The dates and cost indices are given for all costs given here. In many cases absolute costs are needed for checking contractor's estimates or budget estimates.

Cultural knowledge based on a current source of cost knowledge is as important to an engineer as a general familiarity of English literature is to an educated man.

Use of Judgment

Costs are data and as such should be used with judgment. Costs are never absolute but subject to the vacillations of any market. Between certain limits the index will bring them up to date. The costs given here are for so-called "average" conditions. Bear in mind that intricate forming problems, lack of good local aggregates, poor site accessibility, and other such considerations will have an effect upon the costs which can be evaluated only by exercising judgment.

The Engineering News-Record Construction and Building Cost Indexes reflect wage rate and material price trends. They do not adjust for labor efficiency, materials availability, competitive conditions, management, mechanization or other "intangibles" affecting construction costs.

A hypothetical cube of construction requiring 6 bbl. of cement, 1,088 M ft. bm. of lumber, 2,500 lb. of steel, and 200 hours of common labor is used to measure the trend of the cost of heavy engineering construction.

The building cost index is based on a similar hypothetical cube using the same quantities of materials, but 68.38 hours of skilled labor.

This simple structure was adopted to facilitate prompt reporting of changes due to price and wage rate movements, both as to direction and degree.

Both indexes have proved, over the years, infallible as to direction and in normal times remarkably accurate as to degree. Under abnormal conditions of increasing or decreasing job productivity, allowance for the "intangibles" listed above should be made in measuring the degree of change in overall completion costs.

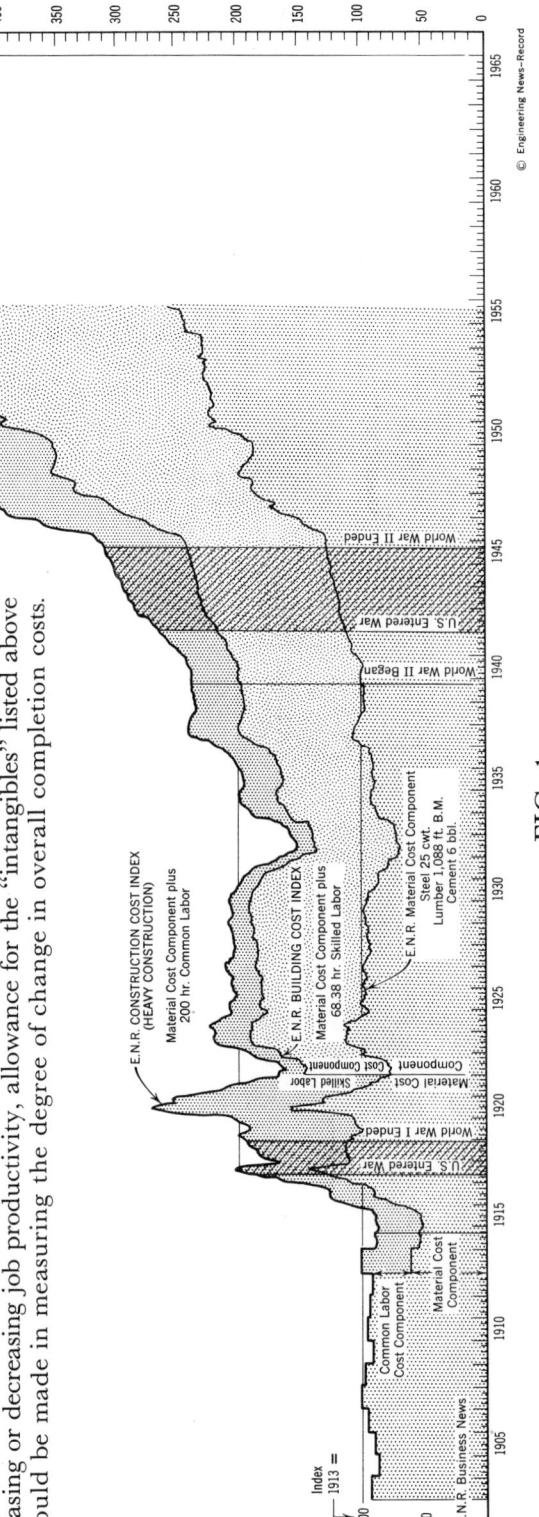

FIG. 1.

Use of chart: To find cost when E.N.R. index number varies from that given on following pages, multiply given cost

by $\dfrac{\text{E.N.R. index for time desired}}{\text{E.N.R. index given}}$ and extend curve

for each 3-month period.

Adapted from *Engineering News-Record*, copyright 1955, McGraw-Hill Publishing Co.

CONCRETE

Foundation concrete cost may run about $65 per cubic yard. A cubic yard may require about 33 sq. ft. of forms and 80 lb. of steel. A more accurate estimate can generally be made on the following basis:

Concrete, transit mix delivered 3000 lb.	$20.00 per cu. yd.
Placing of concrete	7.00 per cu. yd.
Forms footing	0.65 per sq. ft.
Pile cap	0.55 per sq. ft.
Walls	0.80 per sq. ft.
· Piers	0.80 per sq. ft.
Reinforcing steel	0.15 per lb.

Notes: Prices are for New York City. Job overhead and job profit but no general contractor's profit included, three uses of form lumber anticipated. ENR Building Cost Index 454, September, 1954.

GENERAL EXCAVATION

Excavation costs may vary widely. Those given in the following pages are approximate averages for Middle Atlantic states, ENR Building Cost Index 454, September, 1954. Overhead and job profit have been figured but not a general contractor's profit. It has been assumed that excavated material can be dumped on the site. Backfill costs assume no borrow.

The costs of sheeting and pumping should be figured separately as shown on pp. 16-5, 16-9.

Trucking cost, if required, $0.25 per ton mile.

TRENCH EXCAVATION

Earth trench excavation less than 10 ft. deep by machine will generally cost for open sites in long trenches about as follows:

Dry sand	$0.75 per cu. yd.
Wet sand	1.50 per cu. yd.
Gravel	0.75 per cu. yd.
Clay	1.00 per cu. yd.

For cramped sites and short runs the cost runs up to $3.00 per cu. yd. for all types.

Rock trench excavation for open sites costs about as follows:

Shale and hardpan	$10.00 per cu. yd.
Limestone	15.00 per cu. yd.
Gneiss, granite, trap	20.00 per cu. yd.

Tamped backfill, $1.40 per cu. yd.

Sheeting extra; see p. 16-5.

FOUNDATION EXCAVATION

Earth foundation excavation up to 10 ft. deep in open sites by machine generally costs about:

Dry sand	$0.50 per cu. yd.
Wet sand	1.50 per cu. yd.
Gravel	1.00 per cu. yd.
Clay	1.50 per cu. yd.

For cramped sites, costs may be as much as $2.00 per cu. yd. For small deep excavations such as piers, costs may run $5.00 to $6.00 per cu. yd.

Rock excavation costs about as follows:

Shale	$ 5.00 per cu. yd.
Hardpan	6.00 per cu. yd.
Limestone	8.00 per cu. yd.
Gneiss	10.00 per cu. yd.
Granite, trap	12.00 per cu. yd.

For confined excavation such as piers, costs may run $25 per cu. yd., or even up to $200 or $400 for meticulous, confined hand work.

Backfill cost $1.50 per cu. yd. except that backfill around footings which can be placed by bulldozing costs $0.50.

Hand excavation under good conditions costs about $5.00 per cu. yd.

HEAVY EXCAVATION

Heavy earth excavation for airports, highways, etc., up to 20 ft. deep costs about:

Sand and gravel	$0.60 per cu. yd.
Clay	0.75 per cu. yd.

For exceptionally large easy jobs the cost may be as low as $0.40 per cu. yd. For site work in building areas it may be as high as $1.25. Finish grading costs about $0.04 per sq. ft.

Rock excavation costs about as follows:

Shale and hardpan	$1.00 per cu. yd.
Limestone	4.75 per cu. yd.
Gneiss	5.00 per cu. yd.
Granite or trap	6.00 per cu. yd.

COFFERDAM EXCAVATIONS FOR BUILDINGS

Cofferdam excavation costs vary greatly. The following are estimated average values for the excavation only, sheeting and pumping omitted:

Sand and gravel	$ 1.50 per cu. yd.
Clay	2.00 per cu. yd.
Shale	5.00 per cu. yd.
Hardpan	6.00 per cu. yd.
Limestone	15.00 per cu. yd.
Gneiss, granite, trap	20.00 per cu. yd.

See pp. 16–5, 16–9 for sheeting and pumping.

TUNNELS

Rock tunnel excavation costs exclusive of pumping and lining are estimated as:

	Tunnel Diameter	
	Less than 10 ft.	More than 10 ft.
Soft rock	$50.00	$24.00
Medium rock	50.00	24.00
Hard rock	65.00	36.00

Timber crib cofferdams

Timber		$250 per ft. b.m.
Fill		$2–$4 per cu. yd.

SHEET PILING

Sheet piling costs run about $200 a ton for steel sheet piling and $375 MBF for timber exclusive of bracing which costs about $400 MBF. For pit work, including bracing, costs per square foot are:

	Timber	*Steel*
12 ft. deep	$2.00–2.50	$3.50–4.00
18 ft. deep	2.50–3.00	3.50–4.50
24 ft. deep	3.50–4.50	4.50–5.50

One-third savings might be allowed for salvage.

Notes: Costs are for Middle Atlantic States, overhead and job profit included, but not general contractor's profit. ENR Building Cost index 454, September 1954.

PILES

Pile costs vary considerably with the difficulty of driving. As a rule, under 35 ft. piles cost about:

Timber 25 ton untreated	$ 1.50 per lin. ft.
Timber 25 ton treated	2.00 per lin. ft.
Timber 25 ton treated long piles *	2.50 per lin. ft.
Concrete 30 ton precast	6.00 per lin. ft.
Concrete 30 ton cast in place	4.50 per lin. ft.
Concrete, Franki 60 ton	13.00 per lin. ft.
Steel H piles 30 ton	6.00 per lin. ft.
Open end steel pipe, 10¾ in. ϕ	7.50 per lin. ft.
12¾ in. ϕ	8.50 per lin. ft.
15 in. ϕ	10.00 per lin. ft.
16 in. ϕ	11.50 per lin. ft.
18 in. ϕ	14.00 per lin. ft.

* West coast pile 60–70 ft. long.

The cost of the heavy piles, steel H column, and open-end pipe can be figured better thus:

Pile	$ 0.065 per lb.
Stiff driving and handling	2.25 per lin. ft.
Concrete fill (steel pipe)	22.50 per cu. yd.
Pipe clean out	75.00 per cu. yd.

Notes: Prices are for Middle Atlantic States, overhead and job profit, but no general contractor's profit included, ENR Building Cost index 454, September 1954.

Note further that for long precast concrete piles handling costs increase.   For small jobs the price will be higher because of the high on and off cost of the pile driver.

UNDERPINNING

Timber spur shores in place	$350 per ft. b.m.
Underpinning by approach method	
Excavation	$ 35
Concrete	$ 60
	$ 95 per cu. yd.
Steel underpinning cylinders	$ 35–$40 per lin. ft.

WELDING COSTS

Cost of field (fillet) welds per linear foot of weld:

¼ in., flat	$1.50
¼ in., overhead and vertical	$1.75
⁵⁄₁₆ in., flat	$1.50
⁵⁄₁₆ in., overhead and vertical	$1.75
⅜ in., flat	$2.25
⅜ in., overhead and vertical	$2.50

Note: Cost of butt welding runs about 15–20% higher than fillet welding.   All prices apply to New York City area only.

DRILLING AND BLASTING

All cost prices include powder, equipment, insurance, drilling, blasting mats, etc.

Open cut, soft rock, less than 2500 cu. yd.	$ 5.00	per cu. yd.
Open cut, soft rock, over 2500 cu. yd.	$ 3.60	per cu. yd.
Open cut, medium rock, less than 2500 cu. yd.	$ 6.00	per cu. yd.
Open cut, medium rock, over 2500 cu. yd.	$ 3.75	per cu. yd.
Open cut, hard rock, less than 2500 cu. yd.	$10–$50	per cu. yd.
Open cut, hard rock, over 2500 cu. yd.	$ 4.00	per cu. yd.
Cost of powder: 40% gelatin $43.50 per 100 lb.		
60% gelatin $48.50 per 100 lb.		
Line drilling per lin. ft. of hole.	$ 0.60	
Excavation excluded.		

WATERPROOFING

For medium size jobs hydrolithic waterproofing costs about:

Floors	$0.60 per sq. ft.
Walls	1.20 per sq. ft.
Columns	1.50 per sq. ft.
Pits (walls and floors)	1.50 or $100 minimum

Costs include raking of floor slab and chipping of walls to provide bond, ⅝ in. finish on walls and 1 in. finish on floors, scaffolding, overhead, and job profit. Because of the highly specialized nature of the work, jobs located away from the contractors home office cost 5–15% more for expenses of supervising personnel.

Membrane waterproofing for the membrane *alone* costs about:

Tar and felt	$0.25 per sq. ft.
Pitch and fabric	0.50 per sq. ft.

However, the other factors such as false walls and floors on which to apply waterproofing and extra excavation for the side walls increase the cost to about 25% more than that for a hydrolithic waterproofing job.

DOCK WORK

Cost figures given below are approximate and include a nominal cost for equipment, transportation, plant and set up, accessibility, contingencies, etc. These factors usually vary with each type of job.

Timber pier per sq. ft., about $15 plus $50 per lin. ft. for the fender system each side of pier.

Concrete pier per sq. ft., approximately same as above.

Pier sheds cost about $3 per sq. ft. or more.

Quays cost approximately $500 per lin. ft.

Creosoted piles, $80 per lin. ft. of groin.

Creosoted wales, $450 per MBF.

Timber sheet piles, $375 per MBF.

Steel sheet piles, $200 per ton.

Timber work and fastenings, about $600 per MBF.

Structural shortleaf yellow pine plus fastenings, $525 per MBF; timbershoring, $700 per MBF.

Piles per linear foot in place:

Up to 60 lin. ft.	$1.50 per lin. ft.
Up to 75 lin. ft. (over 60 ft.)	$1.65 per lin. ft.
Over 75 lin. ft.	$2.00 per lin. ft.

Cost of creosoting of piles, $0.03 per lb. treatment.

Soft driving, $0.40 per lin. ft.

READY-MIXED CONCRETE AND BASIC MATERIALS UNIT PRICES

All prices are for the New York City area only.

2000 lb. concrete, 1:7 mix,	$13.45 per cu. yd.
2500 lb. concrete, 1:6 mix,	$14.05 per cu. yd.
3000 lb. concrete, 1:5 mix,	$14.75 per cu. yd.
3750 lb. concrete, 1:4½ mix,	$15.75 per cu. yd.
1:7 cinder concrete,	$13.45 per cu. yd.
Sand	$3.30 per cu. yd.
Gravel or stone (¾ in. or 1½ in.)	$4.75 per cu. yd.
Grit	$4.75 per cu. yd.
Cinders	$3.75 per cu. yd.

Cost delivered.   Overhead and job profit not included.

WELL-POINT COSTS *

I. Open Excavation

Job No.	Depth below Water Table, ft.	Header Perimeter, ft.	Total Cost,† $	Cost per Foot of Header Perimeter, $	No. of Pumping Days	Cost per Diem after Required Pumping Days, $
1	7‡	1300	44,741.68	34.42	120	215.66
2	12	400	17,220.98	43.05	60	181.45
3	20‡	800	41,214.94	51.52	110	195.72
4	23‡	1000§	30,392.64	30.39	25	214.37

II. Trench Excavation

Job No.	Depth below Water Table, ft.	Length of Trench, ft.	Total Cost,† $	Cost per Foot Length of Trench, $	No. of Pumping Days	Cost per Diem after Required Pumping Days, $
1	5	30,000¶	111,067.28	3.70	150	178.32
2	11	6,000	95,919.62	15.99	150	145.81
3	15‡	15,000	189,262.70	30.39	150	233.60

* Courtesy Griffin Wellpoint Corp.
† Total cost includes 5% overhead and 6% profit.
‡ With sand filter.
§ Two-stage header system.
¶ Single pipe header.

PUMPING COSTS PER DAY

Condition	Item	1 Shift	Continuous: 3 Shifts: 1 Day, 2 Nights	Continuous: Saturday or Sunday: 3 Shifts
Clear water	Engineer *	$36.20	$108.60	$217.20
Minimum	2-in. pump †	4.00	4.00	4.00
equipment	Total cost	$40.20	$112.60	$221.20
	Quantity pumped ‡	80,000 gal.	240,000 gal.	240,000 gal.
Clear water	Engineer	$36.20	$108.60	$217.20
Maximum	3–4 in. pumps †	20.00	20.00	20.00
equipment	Total cost	$56.20	$128.60	$237.20
	Quantity pumped ‡	960,000 gal.	2,880,000 gal.	2,880,000 gal.
Muddy water	Engineer	$36.20	$108.60	$217.20
Minimum	3-in. pump §	4.80	4.80	4.80
equipment	Total cost	$41.00	$113.40	$222.00
	Quantity pumped	32,000 gal.	96,000 gal.	96,000 gal.
Muddy water	Engineer	$36.20	$108.60	$217.20
Maximum	3–4 in. pumps §	20.00	20.00	20.00
equipment	Total cost	$56.20	$128.60	$237.20
	Quantity pumped ‡	216,000 gal.	648,000 gal.	648,000 gal.

Notes: 1. Not included are: set up, moving, gasoline, profit.

2. In a number of instances centrifugal pumps may be substituted for the pumping of muddy water with an increase in the quantity pumped.

* Engineers' rate $3.65 plus fringe benefits of 8% and overhead of 16%. Double time for Saturdays and Sundays. Maximum 3 pumps per engineer.

† Centrifugal pump, 10 ft. suction hose, 50 ft. discharge hose, rental basis.

‡ Assumed head, 20 ft.

§ Diaphragm pump, 10 ft. suction hose, 50 ft.

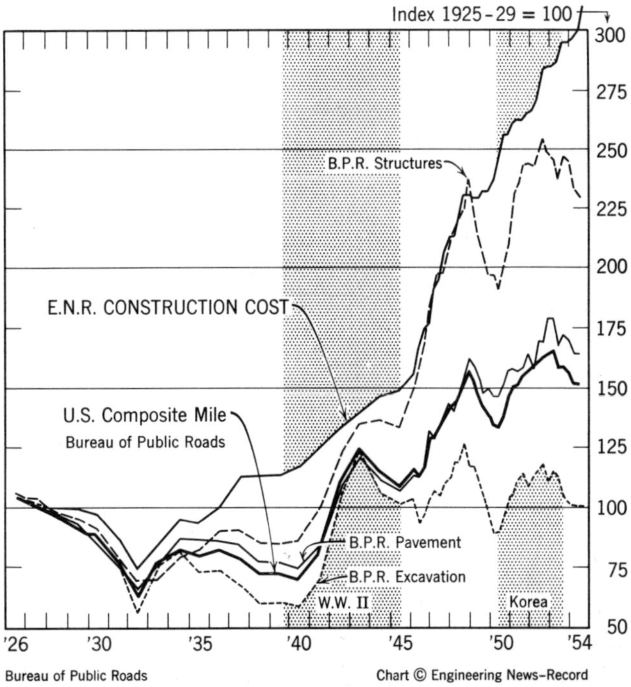

FIG. 2.

HIGHWAY PRICE INDEX-COMPOSITE STANDARD MILE.

Bureau of Public Roads

Chart © Engineering News–Record

HIGHWAY PRICE INDEX—COMPOSITE STANDARD MILE

U. S. Bureau of Public Roads, 1925–29 = 100

Year	Excavation[1] 17,491 cu. yd.* Bid price[3]	Excavation Sub-index	Surfacing[2] 3,726 sq. yd.* Bid price[3]	Surfacing Sub-index	Reinf. steel 16,000* lb. Bid price[3]	Struct. steel 4,325* lb. Bid price[3]	Struct. concr. 68* cu. yd. Bid price[3]	Comb. Sub-index	Com-posite mile index
Base									
25–'29 = 100	$0.35†	100.0	$2.22†	100.0	$0.052†	$0.067†	$22.15†	100.0	100.0
1926............	.36	103.7	2.29	103.1	.053	.074	22.76	103.7	103.4
1930............	.30	86.3	1.86	84.1	.045	.061	20.08	89.4	85.7
1932............	.18	55.0	1.44	64.8	.034	.046	15.33	68.0	61.0
1939............	.21	59.8	1.73	77.8	.044	.059	19.13	85.9	72.6
1940............	.21	59.2	1.68	75.6	.045	.063	19.17	87.6	71.6
1941............	.24	69.2	1.87	84.1	.054	.076	21.44	100.8	81.4
1942............	.37	104.1	2.39	107.9	.065	.090	26.16	122.3	108.8
1943............	.44	124.0	2.71	122.3	.067	.095	30.19	134.4	124.9
1944............	.37	106.6	2.45	110.6	.064	.089	31.94	136.5	113.1
1945............	.36	101.6	2.38	107.4	.062	.077	31.62	132.5	109.0
1946............	.35	99.1	2.65	119.3	.075	.113	38.79	164.7	119.0
1947............	.38	108.4	3.01	135.5	.093	.132	45.84	196.9	135.0
1948............	.42	119.3	3.37	151.9	.108	.158	51.00	223.9	151.2
1949............	.38	107.4	3.40	153.1	.104	.146	47.36	210.3	145.8
1950............	.33	94.5	3.32	149.8	.100	.139	44.62	199.4	137.7
1951............	.39	110.0	3.54	159.5	.120	.180	52.07	237.8	153.7
1952............	.40	114.2	3.80	171.3	.124	.186	54.50	247.8	162.5
1953............	.38	108.6	3.82	172.0	.122	.186	53.53	243.8	160.2
1954............	.35	100.9	3.63	163.6	.116	.167	50.91	229.9	151.2
1955;									
1st quarter.....	.36	101.1	3.67	165.5	.113	.157	51.14	227.3	151.8
2nd quarter....	.35	100.9	3.60	162.3	.112	.152	50.09	223.3	149.4

[1] Common excav. plus other excav. items expressed as equivalent common excav.

[2] Portland-cmt. concr. plus other surfacing expressed as equivalent portland-cmt. concr.

[3] Calculated to one more decimal place than shown in this table.

* Fixed quantities used for establishing composite mile for price trend.

† Prices used for establishing composite mile index bases.

Comparative Costs of Concrete and Asphalt Road Surfaces

		Rigid Concrete			*Flexible Asphalt*								
		Design	*Cost **		*Design*				*Cost **				
CBR	*K*	*Total Thick.*	*Cents per sq. yd.*	*Total $ per sq. yd.*	*Total Thick.*	*Pavement*	*Base*	*Subbase*	*Pavement*	*Base*	*Subbase*	*Total $ per sq. yd.*	*Total Cost per sq. yd. if prime and/or tack coats are applied.*
Case I—Wheel Load 16,000 lb.													
5	140	8½″	.236	4.01	21″	3	3	15	1.51	.58	1.04	3.13	3.27
15	230	8¼″	.229	3.89	10½″	3	3	4½	1.51	.58	.31	2.40	2.54
25	280	8″	.222	3.77	7″	3	4	—	1.51	.77	—	2.28	2.42
50	500	7½″	.208	3.54	6″	3	3	—	1.51	.58	—	2.09	2.23
Case II—Wheel Load 12,000 lb.													
5	140	7½″	.208	3.54	18″	2½	3	12½	1.26	.58	.87	2.71	2.85
15	230	7¼″	.201	3.42	9″	2½	3	3½	1.26	.58	.24	2.08	2.22
25	280	7″	.194	3.30	6½″	2½	4	—	1.26	.77	—	2.03	2.17
50	500	6½″	.181	3.08	5½″	2½	3	—	1.26	.58	—	1.84	1.98
Case III—Wheel Load 8,000 lb.													
5	140	6″	.167	2.84	15½″	1½	3	11	.76	.58	.77	2.11	2.21
15	230	5¾″	.160	2.72	8″	1½	3	3½	.76	.58	.24	1.58	1.68
25	280	5½″	.153	2.60	5½″	1½	4	—	.76	.77	—	1.53	1.63
50	500	5¼″	.146	2.48	4½″	1½	3	—	.76	.58	—	1.34	1.44

* *Unit Prices:*

Concrete @ $17.00 per cu. yd.
Asphaltic concrete @ $9.00 per ton.
Stone base @ $7.00 per cu. yd.
Subbase @ $2.50 per cu. yd.
Asphalt prime coat:0.5 gal. per sq. yd. @ $.20 per gal.
Asphalt tack coat: 0.2 gal per sq. yd. @ $.20 per gal.

Assumptions:

Modulus of rupture of concrete = 700 p.s.i.
Allowable flexural stress of concrete = 350 p.s.i.
CBR of base material = 80
CBR of subbase material = 50
Design is based on dual wheel loadings.

Building Trades Wage Rates, August 1, 1955

Quoted in $/hr., 8-hr. day; time and one-half for overtime after 40 hr.

Compiled by ENR City and State	Carpenters	Bricklayers	Struct. Irwkrs.	Reinf. Irwkrs.	Labor, Bldg.	Labor, Hvy. Const.	Stonemasons	Mason's Helpers	Plasterers	Mosaic & Terrazzo	Tile Layers	Cement Finishers Finishers
Atlanta, Ga.........	2.60	3.25	2.95	2.80	1.38	1.38	3.25	1.50	2.88	3.25	3.25	2.65
Austin, Tex..........	2.50	3.50	2.93	2.65	1.25	1.35	3.50	1.30	3.18	3.00	3.00	2.50
Baltimore, Md......	2.75	3.20	3.33	3.08	1.68	1.68	3.28	1.83	3.08	2.95	2.83	3.08
Birmingham, Ala.....	2.60	3.25	2.93	2.93	1.38	1.48	3.25	1.38	2.82	2.90	2.90	2.68
Bismarck, N.D......	2.20	3.00	2.70	2.60	1.50	1.50	3.00	1.70	2.75	—	3.00	2.25
Boston, Mass........	2.93	3.35	3.48	3.48	2.22	2.22	3.35	2.22	3.45	3.25	3.25	3.39
Buffalo, N. Y........	3.11	3.45	3.27	3.27	2.36	2.36	3.45	—	3.37	3.13	3.13	3.09
Chicago, Ill.........	3.30	3.55	3.50	3.50	2.50	2.50	3.55	2.50	3.63	3.30	3.38	3.30
Cleveland, Ohio.....	3.40	3.45	3.40	3.40	2.65	2.65	3.18	2.63	3.40	3.15	3.23	3.40
Concord, N. H.......	2.38	3.25	3.20	3.20	2.00	2.00	3.25	2.00	3.25	3.25	3.25	3.25
Denver, Colo........	2.98	3.50	2.93	2.93	1.93	1.93	3.50	2.35	3.38	3.20	2.80	2.90
Detroit, Mich........	3.32	3.58	3.48	3.07	2.55	2.55	3.58	2.55	3.49	3.31	3.31	3.17
Helena, Mont........	2.60	3.00	2.75	2.75	1.90	1.90	3.13	2.08	3.00	3.13	3.13	3.00
Jackson, Miss........	2.43	3.00	2.80	2.55	1.20	1.20	—	—	2.63	—	—	2.55
Jacksonville, Fla......	2.55	3.05	2.81	2.55	1.00	1.00	3.05	1.10	2.80	2.63	2.63	2.23
Los Angeles, Calif....	2.96	3.60	3.33	3.08	2.24	2.24	3.60	2.58	3.75	3.18	3.18	2.89
Milwaukee, Wis......	3.06	3.32	3.02	3.02	2.30	—	3.32	2.41	3.12	3.25	3.14	2.82
Minneapolis, Minn...	2.90	3.33	3.07	3.07	2.15	2.15	3.33	2.47	3.13	2.83	2.78	3.00
Nashville, Tenn......	2.43	3.15	2.75	2.60	1.20	1.60	3.15	1.35	2.75	2.93	2.93	2.25
New Orleans, La.....	2.60	3.18	2.98	2.67	1.48	1.48	3.18	1.43	2.80	2.76	2.76	2.55
New York, N. Y......	3.73	4.15	4.08	3.83	2.59	2.59	—	—	4.35	3.56	3.73	3.73
Newark, N. J........	3.61	3.86	3.98	—	2.80	—	—	—	3.86	—	—	3.86
Philadelphia, Pa.....	3.30	3.92	3.73	3.38	2.03	2.33	3.35	2.03	3.65	3.33	3.38	3.30
Portland, Ore.	2.75	3.50	3.07	2.87	2.23	2.23	3.50	2.60	3.25	2.90	3.05	2.80
Providence, R. I.....	3.63	3.23	3.15	3.15	1.98	1.98	3.15	2.83	3.20	2.88	2.88	2.83
St. Louis, Mo........	3.23	3.63	3.23	3.23	2.28	2.28	3.63	2.73	3.50	3.30	3.08	3.25
Salt Lake City......	2.60	3.13	2.88	2.88	1.88	1.88	3.13	2.30	3.13	2.63	2.63	2.60
San Francisco, Calif..	3.16	3.75	3.35	2.93	2.28	2.28	3.75	—	3.66	3.08	3.18	2.95
Seattle, Wash........	2.76	3.50	3.07	2.87	2.35	2.35	3.50	2.65	3.25	3.10	3.15	2.72
Toledo, Ohio........	3.25	3.46	3.35	3.22	2.47	2.47	3.46	2.60	3.35	3.46	3.46	3.35

Lathers	Electrns. (Inside)	Painters	Glaziers	Plumbers	Steam-fitters	Roofers	Water-proofers	Sht. Met. Workers	Welders	Hoist Eng. 1-Drum	Hoist Eng. 2-Drum	Tract. Op. (30 hp +)	Shovel Operator	Truck Dr. (1½T +)
2.88	3.00	2.50	2.35	3.15	3.15	1.85	1.85	2.73	*	2.35	2.70	2.43	2.95	1.50
3.18	3.00	2.25	2.25	2.93	2.93	1.65	1.65	2.75	*	2.55	2.90	2.90	2.90	1.25
3.08	3.08	2.60	2.55	3.08	3.08	2.25	2.25	3.08	*	2.55	3.25	2.85	3.25	1.83
2.25	3.08	2.60	2.45	3.13	3.13	2.36	2.36	2.88	*	2.32	2.60	2.46	2.60	1.85
1.75	2.35	2.05	2.05	2.37	2.37	2.00	2.00	2.25	*	2.00	2.15	2.00	2.25	1.50
3.45	3.12	2.70	2.74	3.22	3.22	2.98	3.39	3.11	3.11	3.40	3.40	3.03	3.40	2.20
3.30	3.30	3.00	—	3.30	3.23	3.06	—	3.23	—	3.26	3.26	—	—	—
3.63	3.53	3.20	3.52	3.44	3.44	3.45	3.45	3.36	3.44	3.15	3.15	2.90	3.50	2.12
3.40	3.43	3.23	3.33	3.40	3.40	3.40	3.40	3.33	3.15	3.28	3.28	3.15	3.40	2.42
3.25	2.40	1.80	2.00	2.45	2.45	2.00	—	2.00	—	2.85	2.85	2.40	2.85	—
3.38	3.00	2.85	2.63	3.20	3.20	2.85	2.85	3.02	*	2.66	2.38	2.66	2.83	2.05
3.58	3.62	3.08	2.83	3.40	3.37	3.35	3.11	3.47	*	3.30	3.30	3.30	3.30	2.35
3.00	2.75	2.50	2.35	2.90	2.90	2.65	—	2.65	—	2.28	2.50	2.50	2.50	2.00
2.50	2.75	2.25	—	2.96	—	1.90	1.90	2.65	—	2.35	2.35	2.35	2.60	1.55
2.80	3.10	2.33	2.37	3.10	3.10	2.30	2.30	2.50	*	2.50	2.50	2.09	2.50	1.50
3.75	3.25	2.99	2.78	3.44	3.44	2.94	2.94	3.21	*	2.79	2.79	2.87	3.10	2.34
3.19	3.06	2.67	—	3.12	3.12	2.70	2.69	2.92	3.04	2.92	2.92	3.08	3.25	2.24
3.13	3.29	2.75	2.61	3.08	3.08	2.75	2.75	2.98	*	2.85	2.85	2.53	2.97	2.15
2.88	2.85	2.35	2.18	2.93	2.93	2.15	2.15	2.60	—	2.10	2.35	2.10	2.55	1.50
2.65	3.10	2.28	2.50	3.10	3.10	2.61	—	2.78	2.78	2.80	2.80	2.15	2.80	1.58
3.73	3.66	3.29	3.83	4.09	3.98	3.83	—	3.94	—	3.99	3.99	3.33	4.25	2.12
3.60	3.80	3.71	—	3.71	3.71	3.58	—	3.60	—	—	—	—	—	—
3.50	3.81	2.80	3.00	3.62	3.62	3.15	3.15	3.61	*	3.07	3.07	3.07	3.07	2.33
3.15	3.05	2.63	2.73	3.15	3.05	2.83	2.83	2.99	*	2.58	2.88	—	—	2.23
3.15	2.75	2.36	2.63	2.90	3.00	2.60	3.00	2.80	2.80	3.40	3.40	—	—	2.07
3.25	3.60	3.03	3.35	3.50	3.50	3.10	3.10	3.50	*	2.68	3.23	3.23	3.23	2.88
3.13	2.88	2.59	2.35	2.96	2.96	2.50	2.50	2.73	3.20	2.43	2.65	2.60	2.75	1.93
3.51	3.35	3.01	2.83	3.56	3.56	2.90	2.90	3.24	3.33	2.96	3.02	3.07	3.23	2.38
3.15	3.14	2.71	2.57	3.31	3.31	2.75	2.75	3.13	3.20	3.00	3.00	2.95	3.30	2.60
3.35	3.35	2.97	2.70	3.35	3.35	3.15	3.15	3.15	3.35	3.14	3.14	3.00	3.28	2.17

Adapted from *Engineering News-Record,* copyright 1955, McGraw-Hill Publishing Co.

TESTING COSTS

Following is a schedule of cost prices for the most common tests:

Soil Surveys

Sounding rod (machine driven), $2.00 per lin. ft.
Auger holes, $2.00 per lin. ft.
Undisturbed earth samples (3-in. casing), $10.00 each.
Rock borings, 1�5⁄16-in. core, $7.50 per ft.
Soil borings and dry spoon sample, $4.00 per ft.

Concrete Design and Tests

Mix design, New York City controlled concrete (4 mix), $150 each.
Mix design, ordinary, 1 mix, $40 each.
Compression test, 6-in. diameter cylinder, $2.00 each, plus delivery cost.
Beam test, flexural strength (2 breaks), $6.00 per beam.
Concrete slab cores, per inch of depth, $2.00 per in.
Concrete core compression test, $5.00 each.
Reinforcing rods, tensile and bending tests, according to diameter.

Size	Cost per Tensile Test	Cost per Bend, Test	Determination of Weight per Lin. Foot
Below ¾ in.	$ 5.00	$3.00	$3.00
¾ in. to ⅞ in.	$ 8.00	$4.00	$3.00
1 in. to 1½ in.	$10.00	$5.00	$3.00

Engineering control and inspection of concrete, $2.00 per cu. yd. (*Note:* This figure is highly variable, depending on the size of job on hand.)

17

Specifications

GENERAL CONDITIONS

General conditions may be included in contract if the foundation contractor is a prime contractor, or the general conditions of the main contract may be made a part of the foundation contract by reference.

For copies of general conditions see *Data Book for Civil Engineers*, Vol. 2, John Wiley & Sons, or *A.I.A. Standard General Conditions;* copies are available in bookstores.

SPECIAL CONDITIONS

Index

1. Surveys, Lines, and Grades.*
2. Responsibility Regarding Existing Utilities and Structures.
3. Tools, Plant, and Equipment.
4. Accidents.
5. Stage Plans.
6. Contractor's Office.
7. Field Office for Owner and Engineer.
8. Telephone.
9. Measurement of Quantities.
10. Shop Drawings.
11. Cost Breakdown.
12. Borings and Subsurface Information Not Guaranteed.
13. Field Measurements.
14. Reference to Other Specifications.
15. Cofferdams.
16. Pumping. Loss of Material.
17. Subcontractor.

Article 1. Surveys, Lines, and Grades.*   The Owner will furnish only basic reference lines and bench marks from which the Contractor shall establish such other points as he may need, unless otherwise specified,

Or the Contractor will make his own surveys and establish his own grades after the Engineer furnishes the basic reference lines and bench marks.

On heavy construction work such as railroads, dams, bridges, etc., it is common practice for the Engineer to establish all lines and grades. On grading work such as airports and highways, it is advised that the Engineer establish reference lines and grade stakes at the beginning of the work and specify that all grade stakes, reference lines, etc., destroyed by the Contractor during the progress of his work be replaced at the Contractor's expense.

Article 2. Responsibility regarding Existing Utilities and Structures.   The existence and location of underground utilities indicated on the plans are not guaranteed and shall be investigated and verified in the field by the Contractor before starting work. Excavation in the vicinity of existing structures and utilities shall be carefully done by hand.

---

* If used, will supersede paragraph in "General Conditions."

The Contractor shall be held responsible for any damage to, and for maintenance and protection of, existing utilities and structures.

Insert the following clause on jobs requiring blasting or pile driving close to adjacent structures. (Often a separate contract between Owner and Engineer.)

For the protection of both himself and the Owner, the Contractor shall make a survey of adjacent properties before commencing operations. Such survey shall locate all existing cracks and damage to the existing structures by means of drawings and photographs. Telltales shall be placed as directed by the Engineer. A copy of this report shall be filed with the Engineer. Any refusal of owners of adjacent property to permit entry for purpose of inspections shall be noted in the report.

Note: This survey may be made by the Owner's engineer or by the insurance company's engineer.

Article 3. Tools, Plant, and Equipment. If, at any time before the commencement or during the progress of the work, tools, plant, or equipment appear to the Engineer to be insufficient, inefficient, or inappropriate to secure the quality of the work required or the proper rate of progress, the Engineer may order the Contractor to increase their efficiency, to improve their character, to augment their number, or to substitute new tools, plant, or equipment as the case may be, and the Contractor must conform to such order; but the failure of the Engineer to demand such increase of efficiency, number, or improvement shall not relieve the Contractor of his obligation to secure the quality of work and the rate of progress necessary to complete the work within the time required by the Contract to the satisfaction of the Owner.

Article 4. Accidents. The Contractor shall provide, at the site, such equipment and medical facilities as are necessary to supply first-aid service to anyone who may be injured in connection with the work.

The Contractor must promptly report in writing to the Engineer all accidents whatsoever arising out of, or in connection with, the performance of the work, whether on, or adjacent to, the site, which caused death, personal injury, or property damages, giving full details and statements of witnesses. In addition, if death or serious injuries or serious damages are caused, the accident shall be reported immediately by telephone or messenger to both the Engineer and the Owner.

If any claim is made by anyone against the Contractor or any subcontractor on account of any accident, the Contractor shall promptly report the facts in writing to the Engineer, giving full details of the claim.

Article 5. Stage Plans. Stage plans of structural alterations, cofferdams, _____, furnished or approved by the Engineer, shall be adhered to unless objected to in writing by the Contractor, but the submission or approval of such stage plans by the Engineer shall not relieve the Contractor of full responsibility for the safety of the work.

Article 6. Contractor's Office. The Contractor shall provide and locate where directed a temporary, weather-tight job office for his own use complete with facilities for filing, drawings, specifications, correspondence, etc., and other appurtenances necessary for the proper operation of the work. Same shall be removed on completion of the work.

Article 7. Field Office for Owner and Engineer. The Contractor shall construct at his own expense _____ field office(s) for the Owner and Engineer.

The office shall be approximately _____ ft. by _____ ft. in size by 8 ft. minimum ceiling height and shall be of weathertight construction. The inside shall be lined with approved lining. The office shall have _____ windows, _____ doors, and a tight floor 8 in. off the ground.

The office shall be supplied with cylinder locks which can be opened by the same key. Six keys shall be furnished.

The office shall be provided with watchman and janitor service; a toilet, sink, running water, and sewer connections; heating equipment; electric wiring and fixtures and telephone service with ____ extensions.

- ____ ( ) suitable office desk with drawers and locks.
- ____ ( ) tables (not less than ____ ft. by ____ ft.).
- ____ ( ) office chairs.
- ____ ( ) swivel chairs.
- ____ ( ) supply cabinets with not less than ____ sq. ft. of shelves.
- ____ ( ) coat racks or closets.
- ____ ( ) drafting tables ____ ft. by ____ ft. with stools.
- ____ ( ) lockers, 1 ft. 6 in. by 2 ft. 0 in. by 6 ft. 0 in.
- ____ ( ) racks to hold plans.
- ____ ( ) tripod racks for ____ tripods.

The field office shall be built in the location as directed and shall be removed at the conclusion of the work or as directed. The Contractor shall submit a sketch of this building for approval.

Article 8. Telephone. The Contractor shall provide, pay for, and maintain in the job office a telephone. A coin box telephone shall be installed for the use of the subcontractors.

Article 9. Measurement of Quantities. The quantities of work performed will be computed by the Engineer on the basis of measurements taken by the Engineer or his assistants, and these measurements shall be final and binding.

All work computed under the Contract shall be measured by the Engineer according to the United States Standard Measurements and Weights.

Specification should state which items are to be measured along actual or slope surface and which horizontally. It should state which items are measured according to neat lines, or axially along center line, or any other detailed pertinent requirements.

Article 10. Shop Drawings. *See individual specifications.*

Article 11. Cost Breakdown. The Contractor shall within five days after the execution of the Contract submit in a form acceptable to the Engineer a schedule showing the subdivision of his contract consideration into its various parts, stating quantities and prices, to be made a basis for checking or computing monthly estimates. The prices shall include all costs of each item. No payments will be made to the Contractor until such schedule has been submitted to and approved by the Engineer.

Article 12. Borings and Subsurface Information Not Guaranteed. (*Use either clause a or clause b.*)

(*a*) Quantities and different classes of excavation shall be determined by cross sectioning. Borings and subsurface information shown is for the general information of the bidder and is not guaranteed.

(*b*) The contract price is based on subsurface conditions, approximately as shown by the borings and other subsurface information.

Article 13. Field Measurements. Where called for on the plans and specifications, or required for accuracy and fit with existing work, the Contractor shall make his own field measurements to verify any dimensions shown on the plans.

Article 14. Reference to Other Specifications. Where reference is made to specifications such as A.S.T.M. or A.A.S.H.O., the latest edition shall be used.

Article 15. *Draw a clause which will insure adequate cofferdams around a building excavation; for instance,* the Contractor will provide tight steel sheet pile cofferdam, cross braced, or otherwise supported, method to be submitted by the Contractor and approved by the Engineer. The Engineer's approval to the Contractor of the Contractor's construction method, including cofferdams, shoring, pumping, and underpinning, does not relieve the Contractor of his responsibility for carrying out the work without damage.

Steel sheet piling shall include corner sections. All pits shall be sheet-piled with corner bracing and caulking. Sheet piling to be driven to firm soil or rock or 3 ft. in advance of excavations. *Specify weight of hammer for sheet pile driving, say 4000 ft.-lb. energy.*

Article 16. Pumping. Loss of Material. Contractor will not be permitted to dewater excavation by methods which result in boiling and loss of material within a 20:1 slope of any existing masonry footings at a higher level. Sheet pile driven to rock under these conditions shall be seated to prevent loss of material.

Article 17. Subcontractor. If the Contractor is subletting any portion of this foundation work it shall be to experienced specialists approved by the Engineer.

Check List

1. Removal and disposal of existing structures and obstructions.
2. Rights in the use of materials found on the work.
3. Submission of weekly pay rolls and affidavits.
4. Work in freezing weather. *Specify whether: (a) work shall cease; (b) work must continue; (c) work many continue with specified protection.*
5. Protection of trees, plants, and shrubs.
6. Sanitary provisions and facilities, toilets, locker rooms, etc., for construction force.
7. Commissaries, lodging, bunk houses.
8. Watchmen—Contractor to furnish, etc.
9. Project signs, warning signs, barricades, emergency lighting, temporary heat, sidewalk bridges.
10. Coordination with others; Contractor may not be in total possession of site, etc.
11. Field or plant laboratory—Contractor to provide.
12. Restoration of site and access.
13. Explosives: use, handling, storage, and transportation.
14. Materials furnished by Owner: under what conditions, etc.
15. Federal participation; any special provisions required by participating agency.
16. Freight and waybills—Contractor to furnish.
17. Records of materials purchased—Contractor to furnish.
18. Property lines and monuments—Contractor to protect, reference and reset if disturbed.
19. Disposal of surplus material.
20. Storage of materials.
21. Detours: maintenance of, location, restoration, etc.
22. Shoring or underpinning of adjacent properties.
23. Guaranty against defective work. *List particular bonds required, such as for roofing or waterproofing guarantees.*
24. Fire: fire protection, restrictions, season, etc.

25. Cooperation of this Contractor with other contractors. *In this space should be enumerated the other contractors and instructions as to how this Contractor will be expected to cooperate with them.*

26. Schedule of minimum wage rates, posting of same, etc.

27. Deductions for Social Security, Workmen's Compensation, Unemployment Insurance, etc.

28. No deductions from wages except as authorized or required by law.

29. Payment of wages, weekly or otherwise, by cash or by check on solvent bank; arrangements to cash checks.

30. Preference in employment: local residents, citizens, veterans, etc. Employment source: agencies, hiring halls, etc.

31. Qualifications for employment: minors, union labor, convict labor, aliens, etc.

32. Hours of work.

33. Non-discrimination against race, creed, or color.

34. Transportation of employees for isolated work.

35. "Kick-Back" Statute (Copeland Act 48, Statute 948).

36. Access to site, restrictions, restoration.

37. Priorities or preference rating assigned to work—Owner will *or will not* assist in obtaining.

38. Engineer's preliminary cost and quantity estimate, usually included in unit price contracts.

39. Materials: preference shown domestic materials, restrictions on materials manufactured by convict or prison labor, etc.

40. Contractor's use of premises: restrictions, etc.

41. No personal liability of public officials (*for public works*).

42. Equipment and safety guards: Contractor and manufacturers to comply with local and state laws.

43. Restoration of sidewalks and pavement.

SITE INVESTIGATION

Ground Surveying

This is designed as a specification to cover the survey contract, whether let by Owner, Engineer, Architect, or Contractor.

I. Scope of Work.

Work Included.

Work Not Included.

II. Surveyor.

The survey must be made by a licensed surveyor. *In vicinities where licenses are not required by state law, a surveyor of high repute should be employed.* Surveyor is to be furnished with a legal description of the property taken from the deed and is to clarify any discrepancies in making the map.

III. Maps.

Specify applicable size, etc.

The surveyor shall furnish one large and one small map of the survey made on tracing cloth in ink. The large map is to be made in one of the following three sizes: 18 in. by 24 in., 22 in. by 30 in., or 22 in. by 38 in., and drawn to a scale of 1 in. = 10 ft., unless otherwise directed to use a smaller scale such as 1 in. = 20 ft., 1 in. = 30 ft., 1 in. = 40 ft., 1 in. = 50 ft., for exceptionally large property. However, in no case shall map exceed 22 in. by 38 in. The small map is to be made size 8½ in. by 13 in. of appropriate scale to show outline of property, buildings, etc. One blueprint or white print shall accompany each map.

IV. Corners and Bench Mark.

The surveyor shall place a 3-in. diameter by 4 ft. 0 in. long extra-heavy steel pipe filled with concrete at each corner of the lot or property surveyed. The surveyor shall furnish a permanent bench mark on the property.

V. Survey Data.

The large map shall show the following: *Specify as desired.*

1. A definite point of beginning, properly referenced and tied in to permanent reference points such as intersections of center lines of streets, permanent monuments, etc. Indicate whether survey is based on magnetic or true north.

2. Each boundary line of the lot located by metes and bounds with bearings on points of compass given. Give street numbers and lot and block numbers.

3. A written description of survey which must agree with the measurements and courses given on the plot; this description must read clockwise and must be signed and dated as of the date of the plot. There must be incorporated a statement that markers have been placed as called for.

4. Names of streets and parties owning property bounding the lot, with indication as to the limits of others' property on the boundary line.

5. Elevation of floors, drives, and abrupt changes in grade. Elevations to be referred to bench mark, cut in curb, or other suitable location, with location and elevation designated on drawing. Datum for elevations to be clearly indicated on map. At all waterfront properties this datum to be Federal, City, or Port Authority datum, the one being chosen that is most used in that locality.

6. Location and kind of buildings on property. Locate any underground tanks, footways, easements, roadways, or right-of-way on property. Locate all subsurface structures.

7. Isolated trees, with indication of size, also boundary line of wooded sections. Show shrubs, hedges, retaining walls, and any other permanent features.

8. Encroachments of every character, including buildings, fences, hedges, etc., with exact measurements.

9. Obstructions on street, such as catch basins, manholes, telephone, telegraph and electric poles, fire hydrants, etc., including elevations.

10. Width of streets and pavements, how paved, and location of curb and sidewalk lines. Give legal building lines.

11. Location, size, and depth of ditches, drains, and cesspools on or near property.

12. Location, elevation, and size of wells, water, gas, and sewer lines on or near property; indicate whether sanitary, stormwater, or combined sewer. Give available water pressure.

13. Nature of ground and possibilities of rock near surface. Give indication as to whether ground is suitable for ordinary building foundations without the use of piling.

14. Location of railroad tracks, if any, in street, and distance from near rail to property line.

15. For paved streets, curb and sidewalk legal grades, or difference between existing and legal grades. The legal grades of unpaved streets and the elevations of the existing ground.

16. Elevation of railroad siding or main line.

17. Elevations on the corners of 20-ft. squares carried out to show existing sidewalk, curb, gutter, and center-of-street elevations.

18. Elevation of maximum high and low water of adjacent water courses.

19. Width of navigable water adjoining property. Give depth of channel, show harbor, pier head, bulkhead, and channel lines. Show status of riparian rights.

20. If sewer is not available, permission and practicality of entering adjacent waterways with private sewer.

21. Location of available power, light, and telephone lines with names of utility companies owning same. Give current characteristics.

22. If ground is filled, show depth of fill if known. Give possibility of water and depth below surface as far as is known.

VI. Basis of Payment.

Specify lump sum payment for work as per Contract.

Exploration

I. Scope of Work.

Work Included.   Test pits.

Work Not Included.   Borings, pipe soundings.

II. Test Pits

Test pits shall be as shown on the drawings as to size, location, and elevation.

1. Sheeting.   Sheeting shall be installed as shown on the drawings.   If it is not shown on the drawings, the Contractor shall install adequate sheeting and be responsible for same; if such sheeting fails the Contractor shall dig a new test pit adjacent to the pit where the sheeting failed at no expense to the Owner.   Sheeting shall be installed so that there will be convenient access to the bottom of the pit.

2. Cover over Pits.   The Contractor shall install a roof over the test pits as shown on the drawings.   Where it is not shown on the drawings, the Contractor shall install a roof over the pits which will keep out all rain; the roof shall be approved by the Engineer.

3. Basis of Payment.   *Specify Contractor to be paid at contract price for each test pit.   If pits vary greatly in depth, specify various depth pits to be paid for at different unit prices.*

III. Test Holes by Clam Shell or Back Hoe.

Contractor shall provide a suitable movable crane or back hoe to dig pits where requested by the Engineer.

1. Basis of Payment.   *Specify Contractor to be paid at ____ rate per half day, which rate shall include moving equipment to and from the site for back-hoe or clam shell.*

BORINGS FOR STRUCTURES *

I. Scope of Work.

Work Included: This section shall include the making of all borings at points shown on plot plans and as specified herein. Obtaining the elevation of the ground surface and location of the borings shall be included.

Work Not Included: Test pits.

II. Workmanship and Methods.

Borings shall be located by the Contractor approximately as shown on the drawings.
Show starting point, angles, benches on drawings, or specify Owner will establish these in the field.

The Contractor shall send a copy of the daily boring log to the Engineer's office each day. This is to be sent directly from the field to the office of the Engineer.

Depth of borings shall be _____ ft. except that boring No. _____ shall be carried down _____ ft. If rock is encountered before reaching either of above depths, core borings as directed by the Engineer shall be made at least 5 ft. 0 in. into rock and further until 50% of a 5 ft. 0 in. core is recovered, or until the hole has been drilled a total of 15 ft. into rock.

The casing shall not be driven until the soil has been washed out below the casing, for the depth that the casing is to be driven.

For limestone regions and other regions where large boulders may occur, 10 ft. to 15 ft. into rock should be specified.

Boring through earth shall be made with a 2½-in. extra-heavy casing in 5-ft. lengths. Earth shall be removed by jetting or blowing, and all samples shall be taken by driving an approved 2-in. sample spoon 24 in. long with 140-lb. weight and 30-in. drop of weight. The sample spoon shall be driven below the bottom of the casing a minimum of 16 in.

Sample spoons shall be changed if necessary to obtain proper samples.

Boring in hard strata or rock shall be made by double-tube diamond-drill method to produce cores not less than 1⅛ in. in diameter. If material is soft rock, or where directed by the Engineer, a series M † double-tube core barrel of such construction that the drilling water is fed to the bit without coming in contact with the core shall be used.

A series M type of core barrel shall be on the site at all times. *Include when soft rock is expected.*

III. Samples.

Include continuous sampling when in a new area.

In all borings, continuous samples shall be taken to a depth of 15 ft. At other depths, samples of earth shall be taken every 5 ft. 0 in. and at any point where material changes in character.

First sample must be taken at 2½ ft. from surface, and a sample spoon used. *Include when continuous sampling is not called for.*

Samples of earth shall be sealed in watertight containers approximately 2 in. in diameter, 8-oz. size, and shipped to the office of the Engineer. They shall have labels giving the following information: number of boring, elevations of sample, and description of material.

---

* See Chapter 8 for description of boring equipment.

† Manufactured by Sprague and Henwood. Specially designed to prevent erosion of rock by wash water.

Samples of rock shall be placed in core boxes; boxes shall all be same size and not too large for one man to handle. Boxes shall have five (5) troughs for 1⅛ cores. Boxes shall have hinged covers and secure fastenings and shall be labeled with job name, boring number, box number, total number of boxes for boring number. Troughs shall be marked with top and bottom elevation for each core pull.

IV. Undisturbed Samples.

A 2-in. Shelby tube shall be used where directed by the Engineer to obtain undisturbed samples. The tube shall be forced, not driven, into the ground below the casing. The Contractor shall have 3 Shelby tubes on the job at all times.

V. Preparation of Samples for Shipment.

After the sample is taken, it must be shipped to the laboratory in such a manner as to prevent its disturbance or loss of moisture. Tube samples should have the ends filled with paraffin and sealed with metal caps. Chunk samples should be wrapped in many layers of burlap, each layer being saturated with paraffin. Samples taken in cans or pails should have all voids between the sample and the container filled with paraffin and the top sealed with paraffin.

The prepared sample is then packed in excelsior and crated to be shipped. It is of utmost importance that the sample be protected against shock or loss of moisture during shipment.

VI. Ground Water.

Records of ground water shall be kept for all holes. The casing shall be pulled up 1 ft. at night and left in the soil overnight, and a reading of ground water shall be taken the following morning. Where directed by the Engineer, an approved well point shall be attached to 1-in. pipe, and the pipe and point shall be placed inside the casing to the depth directed by the Engineer and left in the ground when the casing is pulled. The pipe may not be withdrawn. The 1½-in. pipe shall be perforated every 2½ ft. Readings shall be taken every day while borings are being made.

VII. Drawings.

The Contractor shall furnish a boring plan showing location elevation and number of holes, and he shall plot vertical sections showing material encountered referred to datum, number of blows for casing and spoon per linear foot, diameter and weight of casing, weight of hammer and drop of hammer on casing and spoon, and ground-water level for all holes when encountered. This information shall be provided in blueprint form.

VIII. Basis of Payment.

The Contractor shall be paid according to unit price per linear foot of hole measured from surface of ground to bottom of hole.

The Contractor shall state in his bid the following:

Unit price per linear foot for boring through any material not rock. (Maximum 150 blows per foot on sample spoon.)

Unit price per linear foot for using double tube for rock borings.

Unit price for rock boring using series M core barrel. *Include when soft rock is expected.*

Unit price for undisturbed samples.

Unit price for placing well points.

Specify how low bidder is to be determined; give quantities to which unit prices can be applied.

PIPE SOUNDINGS

Usually used for exploring individual footing bottom.

I. Scope of Work.

Work Included.   Pipe soundings.

Work Not Included.   Borings, test pits.

II. Workmanship and Methods.

The Contractor shall locate the soundings approximately as shown on the plot plan.

The soundings shall be taken by driving a 2-in. open pipe with a maul to a depth of not over 10 ft.   Pipe shall be withdrawn and the cores removed by rodding inside the pipe.   Cores shall be saved for an inspection by the Engineer.

III. Basis of Payment.

Specify the Contractor be paid at unit price per foot of sounding.

ROD SOUNDINGS

I. Scope of Work.

    Work Included.   Rod soundings.

    Work Not Included.   Test pits, borings, and pipe soundings.

II. Workmanship and Methods.

    Location of soundings shall be approximately as shown on the plot plan.

    Manual soundings shall be taken with a ¾-in. rod and a _____ lb. sledge hammer. The rod shall be driven to refusal. Where refusal occurs at a high point, another sounding shall be made 10 ft. away when directed by the Engineer. The number of blows shall be recorded.

    When a mechanical-type hammer is used in place of a sledge, the weight* and type of the mechanical hammer shall be reported and also the time for each foot driven and the number of blows.

III. Report.

    A report shall be made which shall give the information required above. The report shall also give the location of any additional or relocated soundings.

IV. Basis of Payment.

    Specify that Contractor be paid at unit price per foot of sounding.

---

* For example: 140 lb. hammer 30″ drop.

SOILS ANALYSIS

I. Scope of Work.

Work Included.

Work Not Included.

II. Tests.

A soils laboratory approved by the Engineer shall make the following tests in accordance with the method noted.*

Angle of internal friction †‡	A.S.T.M. Procedures for Testing Soils
Capillary rise§	C.A.A.
C.B.R. soaked and unsoaked §	U. S. Engineers Manual, Chapter XX.
Cohesion †‡	A.S.T.M. Procedures for Testing Soils.
Consolidation ‡§¶	A.S.T.M. Procedures for Testing Soils.
Direct shear †‡	A.S.T.M. Procedures for Testing Soils.
Effective size ‡	A.S.T.M. D–653.
Field moisture equivalent §	A.S.T.M. D–426; A.A.S.H.O. T–93.
Hydrometer analysis ‡¶	A.S.T.M. D–422; A.A.S.H.O. T–88.
Liquid limit ‡§¶	A.S.T.M. D–423; A.A.S.H.O. T–89.
Moisture density relations ‡§	A.S.T.M. D–698; A.A.S.H.O. T–99.
Modified Proctor test ‡§	See "Data Book—Field Practice," p. 119.
Natural density †‡§¶	A.S.T.M. Procedures for Testing Soils.
Plastic limit†‡§	A.S.T.M. D–424; A.A.S.H.O. T–90.
Plasticity index †‡§	A.S.T.M. D–424; A.A.S.H.O. T–91.
Proctor test ‡§	A.S.T.M. D–698; A.A.S.H.O. T–99.
Shrinkage factors ‡§	A.S.T.M. D–427; A.A.S.H.O. T–92.
Sieve analysis †‡§	A.S.T.M. C–136 and C–117; A.A.S.II.O. T–88.
Specific gravity ‡§¶	A.S.T.M. D–584; A.A.S.H.O. T–100.
Triaxial shear †‡	A.S.T.M. Procedures for Testing Soils.
Uniformity coefficient ‡	A.S.T.M. D–653.
Volumetric change at field moisture equivalent ‡§	A.S.T.M. D–427; A.A.S.H.O. T–92.

† Usually required for foundations.
‡ Usually required for embankments, retaining walls, earth dams.
§ Usually required for subgrades for roads and runways.
¶ Usually required for time-settlement.

III. Report.

The soils laboratory shall submit reports on forms previously approved by the Engineer. *See "Data Book, Vol. 3, Field Practice."* Where there are any instructions, drawings, or specifications of materials to be complied with, the report shall include a statement that the material tested complies or does not comply with the instruction, drawing, or specification.

IV. Basis of Payment.

Secure quotation by letter for lump sum for each test desired. Letter should state who moves samples from field to laboratory if soils laboratory is not doing the field work of securing samples or the transportation of samples is included in some other contract.

---

* See Chapter 13 for a description of these tests.

SOIL LOAD TEST

I. Scope of Work.

> **Work Included.** Soil load test.

> **Work Not Included.** Test pits, borings, and pipe or rod soundings.

II. Location.

The number, location, and elevation of the load tests shall be as shown on the drawings.

III. Fixed Load Method. *Generally specify for buildings. See p. 8–8.*

IV. Calibrated Jack Method. *Generally specified for modulus of subgrade reactions for Roads and Airports. See also p. 15–32.*

Load shall be applied with a calibrated hydraulic jack on a plate _____ in. thick and _____ in. in diameter. *For ordinary soils, roads, and buildings, specify 1½ in. thick by 24-in. diameter. For airports use 1½ in. thick by 30 in. in diameter. Rigid plates from 1 sq. ft. to 4 sq. ft. in area have been used by various engineers. New York City requires 4 sq. ft.*

Loads shall be applied in increments of 1000 lb. per sq. ft., and each load shall be maintained until the soil has adjusted itself to equilibrium before another increment is applied. The soil shall be loaded to failure. Settlements shall be determined by using three extensometers reading to 0.001 in., suspended from a beam independent of the jacking apparatus and resting on supports located outside the area of influence of the load.

The reaction against uplift for the jack shall be as approved by the Engineer; the entire assembled apparatus shall be approved by the Engineer before loading.

If the soil does not fail under maximum loading of _____ lb. per sq. ft. with the approved equipment, the load shall be removed by 1000 lb. per sq. ft. decrements and readings shall be taken at each decrement.

V. Report.

A curve shall be plotted showing deflection for various loads and recovery data if obtained, and report shall be given to the Engineer.

VI. Basis of Payment.

Specify lump sum for each load test or cost plus fee.

BEARING PILE LOAD TEST

This test complies with New York City Building Code, 1949.

I. Scope of Work.

Work Included. Bearing pile load test.

Work Not Included. Soil load test.

II. Equipment for Testing.

Before any load test is made, the proposed apparatus and structure to be used in making the load test shall be approved by the Engineer. *Superintendent in New York City.* All load tests shall be made under the supervision of the Engineer. *Superintendent or his representative in New York City.*

III. Location and Method of Testing.

The Contractor shall make a load test on each pile shown on the drawings. *See Notes for New York City after this paragraph.* The total test load shall be twice the proposed load value of the pile. The test load shall be applied in seven increments equal to ½, ¾, 1, 1¼, 1½, 1¾, and 2 times the proposed working load. Readings of settlements and rebounds shall be referred to a constant elevation bench mark and shall be recorded to 0.001 ft. for each increment or decrement of load. After the proposed working load has been applied, and for each increment thereafter, the test load shall remain in place until there is no settlement in a 2-hr. period. The total test load shall remain in place until settlement does not exceed 0.001 ft. in 48 hr. The total load shall be removed in decrements not exceeding one-fourth of the total test load with intervals of not less than 1 hr. The rebound shall be recorded after each decrement is removed, and the final rebound shall be recorded 24 hr. after the entire test load has been removed.

Notes for New York City. Number of piles to be load-tested depends on subsurface conditions previously determined by borings or test pits, one for each 2500 sq. ft. Three piles are then driven distributed over each area of similar subsurface conditions. If the driving records of piles vary between each other or from what may be expected from analysis of borings, or where 30-ton piles or over 30-ton piles are to be installed in soil underlaid by weaker bearing soil, additional piles may be requested. Ordinarily, then, one of the three piles is tested but not less than two piles for the entire site nor less than one pile for each 15,000 sq. ft. of building area.

IV. Reports.

Complete records of driving and load test shall be given to the Engineer. *Superintendent in New York City.* The pile-driving record shall show the make and type of hammer and the number of blows per foot to drive the pile for its full length.

V. Basis of Payment.

Specify payment by lump sum for each load test and per linear foot for pile for each pile driven.

PREPARATION OF SITE

I. Scope of Work.

Work Included.

Work Not Included.

II. Relocation or Demolition of Existing Buildings or Structures.

Specification relative to this type of work must state precisely the nature of the work, safeguards to be observed, the disposition of debris as well as of salvageable material, if any, and such other provisions as apply to the specific project.

III. Clearing and Grubbing.

The area within limits shown on the drawings shall be cleared of fences, trees, logs, stumps, brush, vegetation, rubbish, and other perishable or objectionable matter. Stumps and roots between slope stakes in cuts and in embankments 3 ft. or less in depth shall be removed to a depth of 18 in. below subgrade. Outside of slope limits and under embankments more than 3 ft. deep, all trees, stumps, brush, etc., shall be cut off approximately level with surface, except growth designated for preservation.

Spoiled material shall be burned or removed to approved disposal areas. *Specify location, or show on drawings.* Ashes shall be spread *or removed.*

Specify storage or use of merchantable timber, firewood, etc.

IV. Basis of Payment.

Specify that Contractor be paid at unit or lump sum price called for in the Contract.

Give method of measurement for unit price contract.

If unit price contract, state approximate quantities for each item to be used.

If lump sum contract, require submittal of unit prices applicable to any change in contract quantities.

EXCAVATION AND GRADING FOR STRUCTURES

I. Scope of Work.

Work Included. Excavation and grading for structures, pits, trenches, and all work as shown on plans.

Work Not Included. *Specify other sections such as "Preparation of Site," "Excavation, Trenching, Backfilling for Utility Systems," and items included in mechanical specification.*

II. Borings and Test and Exploration Pits.

Boring and subsurface data shown on drawings shall be for general information only, and variation therefrom shall not affect the terms of the Contract.

III. Stripping of Topsoil, Seeding, Sodding, etc.

Specify as required for jobs. See applicable portions of specification for "Grading for Roads, Airports, Railroads."

IV. Excavation.

Excavation Limits for Structures. Excavation and shoring shall be kept within 2 ft. of the neat lines of structure foundations. *Specify banks to be sloped at a safe angle or shored according to conditions.*

Excavation below Elevations Shown on the Drawings. If filling is not authorized by the Engineer, the undercut shall be filled with 1:3:6 stone concrete by the Contractor without cost to the Owner.

Drainage of Excavated Areas. Grading in vicinity of structures shall be controlled to prevent surface water running into excavated areas. *Specify drainage and maintenance as required. Include dewatering and pumping.*

Protection of Adjacent Buildings and Existing Structures. Excavations shall not be carried below existing building foundations until underpinning and shoring to be performed by others *or* by this Contractor *specify one* have been completed. All existing structures, pipes, and foundations which are to be incorporated into the final work shall be adequately protected or replaced by the Contractor without cost to the Owner.

Stockpiles. Excavated material to be used for backfill shall be stockpiled. *Specify how to stockpile.*

Waste. Excess material from excavation not suitable or required for backfill or filling shall be wasted. *Specify how to waste excess material.*

Rock Excavation. Blasting shall be done in accordance with local ordinances by skilled operators, and precautions shall be taken to avoid damage. Rock shall be removed by line drilling where called for on drawings and where directed by the Engineer. *(See basis for payment.)*

V. Existing Utilities.

Specify what the contractor is to do about existing utilities, e.g., cut off and cap, relocate, etc.

VI. Classification of Excavated Materials.

All excavated materials shall be classified as earth or rock.

Earth = all excavation except rock, as follows:

Rock = ledge rock, concrete or masonry structures which require drilling or blasting, and boulders larger than ⅓ cu. yd. in volume.

VII. Grading.

Specify as required. See applicable portions of specification, "Grading for Roads, Airports, and Railroads."

VIII. Base for Slabs on Fill.

Fill to support paving may *or may not* be made from excavated material. *Specify gravel, crushed stone, sand, or cinders, if excavated material is not to be used. Soil containing organic matter is unsuitable.* Fill shall be compacted in 8-in. layers with a 5-ton roller. Hand *or* mechanical tampers shall be used for places inaccessible to roller. All walls likely to be disturbed by tamping or rolling shall be shored.

IX. Backfilling.

All timber shall be removed and all trash shall be cleaned out from the excavation. Backfill shall be excavated material or _____. *Specify material to be used.* Backfill shall be placed in 8-in. layers and compacted by mechanical tamping. Backfill containing less than 10% clay may be puddled instead of tamped. Surface of backfill shall be left 6 in. above final grade to allow for settlement. After 3 months the Contractor shall return and fill low spots.

X. Protection of Pipes.

Pipes laid on original ground should be protected with a minimum of 4 ft. of tamped fill over the top of the pipes before heavy equipment is allowed to pass over. Pipes resting in fill shall be excavated for after the compacted fill is in place.

XI. Clean-Up.

All trash shall be removed. All excavated area shall be raked clean.

XII. Basis of Payment.

Specify payment by lump sum agreed upon in Contract. Provide clauses for payment of rock excavation per cubic yard as an extra. Measure rock excavation at 1 ft. 6 in. outside neat lines of foundations. Provide clauses for payment by time and material or unit price per cubic yard for excavation carried below elevations shown on drawings if such excavation is authorized by the Engineer. Provide clause for payment at unit price per linear foot for auger or pipe holes required by the Engineer to further explore subsurface conditions below elevation of foundations shown on drawings. Provide clause for payment at unit price or time and material for pumping and dewatering not specified. Provide clause for payment at unit price for underpinning not shown on drawings or specified. Provide clause for payment for lineholing at unit price per linear foot.

BEARING PILES

I. Scope of Work.

Work Included.   This section shall include the furnishing and driving of all piles shown on drawings.

Work Not Included.   Pile caps.

II. Type of Piles.

Omit type not included.   For selection of type see p. 1–10 to p. 1–12.

Cast-in-Place Concrete Piles.   Type A.   These piles shall be formed by driving a shell to the required bearing, leaving the shell permanently in place, and filling it with concrete.   Shells shall have sufficient strength and rigidity to permit their being driven and not to be distorted by soil pressure or the driving of adjacent piles; they shall be sufficiently watertight to exclude water during placing of concrete.   Piles may be tapered or cylindrical.   If tapered they shall increase uniformly in diameter or the diameter shall increase in uniform steps.   The minimum diameter of tapered piles shall be 8 in. at the point and 14 in. at the head.   The average diameter shall not be less than 11 in.   The minimum diameter of cylindrical piles shall be 12⅜ in.   No concrete is to be placed until all piles in a cluster have been driven and approved.

Cast-in-Place Concrete Piles.   Type B.   These piles shall be placed by driving a heavy steel pipe casing with an interior core or point to the required depth, removing the core and inserting a permanent steel shell, filling it with concrete, and then withdrawing the driving casing.   Shells shall have sufficient strength and rigidity not to be distorted by soil pressure or the driving of adjacent piles, and they shall be sufficiently watertight to exclude water during placing of concrete.   Shells shall be cylindrical with a minimum diameter of 12⅜ in.   No driving pipe shall be withdrawn until all piles within 10 ft., center to center, have been driven.

Cast-in-Place Concrete Piles.   Type C.   These piles shall be placed by driving a heavy steel pipe casing with an interior core or point to the required depth, removing the core, and filling the driving casing with concrete while withdrawing same.   The inside of the driving pipe shall be at least 14 in. in diameter, and no driving pipe shall be withdrawn until all piles within 10 ft., center to center, have been driven.

Steel Pipe Piles Filled with Concrete.   Steel pipe piles shall conform to the A.S.T.M. A–252. Piles shall have a minimum inside diameter of 10 in. and a minimum shell thickness of ⅜ in. except that the 10-in. and 12-in. piles may have a shell of 5⁄16 in.   They shall be driven without point but with open end *or* with cast-steel point.   Piles up to 20 ft. in length shall be in one piece.   *Piles from 20 ft. to 40 ft. shall have not more than one splice.   For longer piles, splices shall not be closer together than 20 ft.*

Specify open ends for piles to rock or hardpan, and point for friction piles, except that piles may have to be driven with open ends for predetermined distance in order not to disturb adjoining foundations, cleaned out, filled with concrete, and then driven to required resistance.

Precast Concrete Piles shall be of size and detail shown on drawings. *Specify strength of concrete 4000 lb., control, ingredients.*

No high-early-strength cement shall be used. Forms must be tight and rigid. Piles shall be marked with casting date and shall be cured for 30 days without handling or moving and at minimum temperature of 50° F.

The Contractor shall drive enough test piles to determine the length of pile required to secure the specified bearing and to determine required penetrations in the various areas of the work. These tests shall be made sufficiently in advance of the pile driving to prevent delay in the progress of work and so that the Contractor will have on hand, at all times, piles of proper length to meet any conditions that may arise.

Composite Piles shall consist of a concrete section from the cut-off to 1 ft. 0 in. below permanent water level superimposed upon a wood pile. Details of splice and dimensions of pile shall be in accordance with drawings.

Wood Piles shall be _____. *See "Suggested Grades and Species for Timber Specifications," p. 17–39.* They shall be sound, free from sharp crooks or bends or decay, and sufficiently straight so that a line drawn from the center of the head to the point will be wholly within the pile. The diameter at the point shall not be less than 7 in. for piles up to 40 ft. in length and not less than 6 in. for piles longer than 40 ft. At a point 2 ft. 0 in. from butt, piles less than 25 ft. 0 in. long shall have a minimum diameter of 10 in.; piles over 25 ft. 0 in. long shall have a minimum diameter of 12 in. All measurements shall be made under bark. *Specify A, B, or C; see "Résumé of A.S.T.M. D–25," p. 17–43.*

Treated Piles. *If to be treated, specify as per "Wood Preservation," p. 17–39.*

Steel H Piles. Material shall conform to A.S.T.M. A–7. Piles shall be structural steel sections as shown on drawings *including protective covering*. Paint: primer, zinc chromate; finish, bitumastic.*

III. Lines and Levels.

The Contractor shall establish and locate all lines and levels and be responsible for the correct location of all piles.

IV. Concrete.

Specify strength of concrete for cast-in-place piles 3000 lb. maximum, control, ingredients, slump 3 in. maximum. See applicable portion of "Structural Concrete" specifications. Concrete shall be placed in the dry in piles well cleaned of material and water by blowing or other methods. After cleaning pile shells, if water remains, concrete shall be placed by bottom-dump buckets or tremies.

V. Records.

The Contractor shall keep a record of each pile driven and shall furnish signed typewritten copies daily.

The records shall give the diameter, length, location, type, calculated safe load, penetration under the last five blows of the hammer, and the result of any tests.

VI. Drawings.

The Contractor shall submit for approval, before the award of the contract, complete detail drawings and specifications of the different type of piles estimated upon and a written statement describing equipment to be used.

VII. Driving.

Piles shall be driven with a drop hammer or with a single-acting steam hammer of Vulcan type, the weight of whose striking part times its fall is at least 15,000 ft.-lb., to a safe bearing value

---

* See *Data Book for Civil Engineers, Vol. II,* suggestions for specifying paint.

of _____ tons, or to refusal for piles driven to rock or hardpan. The double-acting steam hammer of the Standard McKiernan-Terry type may be used when driving piles to refusal but shall not be used for other piles except with special permission of the Engineer.

The ratio of the weight of pile F and the weight of the striking part of the hammer W shall be between the following limits: $\dfrac{F}{W} = \dfrac{1}{10}$ minimum to $\dfrac{F}{W} = 10$ maximum.

The safe value of piles shall be determined by the following formula:

$$P = \frac{2WH}{S+1} \text{ for drop hammer}$$

$$P = \frac{2WH}{S+0.3} \text{ for single-acting steam hammer *}$$

$$P = \frac{2(W+Ap)H}{S+0.1} \text{ for double-acting steam hammer}$$

where P = safe load in pounds, W = weight of the striking part of the hammer in pounds, H = the fall in feet of the striking part of the hammer or stroke, S = average penetration per blow in inches under the last five blows, A = area of piston in square inches, and p = mean effective steam pressure.

Note. Where piles are driven to refusal on rock or hardpan, the allowable load should be based on values given in table shown on p. 3–8, or as determined from required code.

Driving shall be done with fixed leads which will hold the pile firmly in position and alignment and in axial alignment with the hammer. Suitable anvils or cushions, depending on the type of pile, shall be used to prevent undue damage of the pile butts.

Driving of all piles shall be continuous without intermission until the pile has been driven to final resistance. The tops of piles shall be cut off true and level at the elevations indicated on the drawings. All portions battered, split, warped or buckled, or damaged or imperfect in any way shall be removed.

Shells and casings shall have sufficient excess length to allow the complete removal of working tops. *Omit for wood piles.*

After each group of casings is driven to the required resistance, all water and other material shall be removed and the shell shall be inspected with a light. The casings shall be free from water when the concrete is being placed. No piles in a cluster shall be filled until all the piles in the cluster are driven. *Omit for wood piles and steel H piles.* Piles shall not be jetted except with the approval of the Engineer. After jetting, piles shall be driven to the required resistance.

VIII. Redriving (Heaved Piles).

Observations and measurements shall be made in the field during the process of driving piles, by any suitable method satisfactory to both the Contractor and the Engineer, to determine whether a driven pile has been lifted from its original seat during the operation of driving adjacent piles. The Contractor shall provide the necessary tools, such as telltale pipes, and instruments, to make these measurements. Such measurements shall be properly corrected for any temperature variations that might exist in the pile shell or instrumentation.

Where such observations or measurements indicate that a pile has been unseated, it shall be

* See note, p. 15–21.

redriven to the resistance specified under "Driving." The Contractor shall be reimbursed on a per pile basis for such redriving. *See basis for payment.*

IX. Damaged and Misdriven Piles.

Broken or shattered piles will not be accepted.

Tolerances. Piles shall not be more than 2% out of plumb and not more than 3 in. out of place.

Should any pile be damaged by overdriving or not conform to the tolerances of the specification, an extra pile or piles shall be driven in its place, at the Contractor's expense unless in the opinion of the Engineer the pile is out of place or plumb as the result of an underground obstruction.

Piles rejected after driving may remain in the ground at the discretion of the Engineer, be filled with concrete, and be cut off as directed. When rejected piling is withdrawn, the space, if another pile is not driven into it, shall be filled solid with gravel or broken stone without payment therefor.

X. Obstructions.

Where boulders or other obstructions make it impossible to drive certain piles in the location shown and to the proper bearing strata, the Contractor shall resort to all usual methods to install piles as required, including spudding, jetting, or other feasible means. If, in the judgment of the Engineer, the Contractor is unable to complete properly any pile by resorting to such methods, the Engineer may order an additional pile or piles driven for which the Contractor will be paid in accordance with unit prices in the Contract. Piles abandoned because of obstructions encountered before reaching the accepted bearing strata shall be filled with concrete and be paid for as completed piles for the length driven.

Where directed by the Engineer, excavation operations shall be conducted to remove obstructions at the Owner's expense as covered in Section XII, "Basis of Payment."

XI. Tests.

Laboratory Tests. Tests of cement, concrete, and aggregates shall conform to applicable portions of specifications for "Structural Concrete."

		Number of Tests
Steel pipe piles	A.S.T.M. 252	One tension test on one length of each lot of 200 or less.

Field Tests. One load test will be included in this contract. It shall be conducted as follows: *See specification "Bearing Pile Load Test," p. 17-15.*

For piles subject to corrosion, erosion, decay, or frost acids, see p. 17-15.

XII. Basis of Payment. *Specify that:*

The Contractor is to be paid for work within limits shown on the drawings by lump sum or unit costs given in Contract.

This Contract shall be based on an average length of piles of two ft. as shown on the drawings.

The Contractor shall include in his bid unit prices for the following:

Both increase and decrease of total length of piling shown on drawings quoting a price per linear foot for each.

Specify piles to be paid for at point of cutoff, and payment to be based on the length measured in feet and inches.

Use of pile driver for extra work such as spudding, jetting, etc., quoting a price per hour.

Where obstructions require excavation or use of different type of piles, the Contractor shall do the work on a time and material basis as agreed upon in the Contract.

The Contractor is not to be paid for damaged or misdriven piles. See Section IX.

FOUNDATIONS

I. Scope.

Work Included.

Work Not Included.

II. Inspection of Soil.

The Contractor shall notify the Engineer when the excavating is completed, and no concrete shall be poured until the Engineer has approved the soil for each individual footing.

The Engineer may require the Contractor to bore not more than 8 ft. 0 in. under each footing with a pipe or auger without additional expense to the Owner.

III. Load Tests. *See specification "Soil Load Test," p. 17–14.*

IV. Ground-Water Level.

If ground-water level is found to be above the lowest pits, or if springs are encountered, the Contractor shall advise the Engineer and shall not proceed with the foundation work until the Engineer has issued instructions as to a method of taking care of this condition.

V. Pumping and Cofferdams.

The Contractor shall keep the site clear of water at all times until 30 days after completion of foundation contract. To this end the Contractor shall provide cofferdams and pumping as required without cost to the Owner.

VI. Underpinning.

The Contractor shall submit the plan of underpinning and shoring for the approval of the Engineer.

VII. Difference in Level of Foundations.

Any difference in level of foundations which violates safe slopes of material shall, where shown on plans, be taken care of by stccl sheet piling or carefully placed breast boards, all work to be performed by specialists and with plans approved by the Engineer.

Include in this general specification any other items such as: exploratory drilling of rock; channeling rock and omitting blasting.

Include specifications for piling, general excavation, waterproofing, concrete, masonry, etc., as required.

VIII. Basis of Payment.

Specify that Contractor be paid at the unit or lump sum price called for in the Contract.

If unit price, itemize price units. Specify a price per diem or time and material for additional pumping if ordered.

WATERPROOFING OF CONCRETE AND MASONRY FOR HYDROSTATIC PRESSURE

Hydrolithic

I. Scope.

Work Included. This section shall include all waterproofing by the plaster-coat or iron-coat method shown on the plans.

Work Not Included. This section shall not include membrane waterproofing, integral waterproofing, or dampproofing.

II. Materials.

Plaster-Coat Method. The cement mortar shall consist of waterproofing compound, cement, and sand mixed in strict accordance with manufacturer's specifications. The waterproofing compound shall be of a type approved by the Engineer.

Iron-Coat Method. The iron shall be clean, finely ground, and 98% pure iron. Chemicals may be added to accelerate the oxidation of the iron particles. The iron shall be approved by the Engineer.

III. Workmanship and Application.

Preparation of Surfaces. All surfaces to be waterproofed shall be examined by the Contractor before the work is started. The Engineer shall be notified of any defects in them. All surfaces to which waterproofing is applied shall first be thoroughly chipped and wire brushed, and then washed, first with diluted acid water and then with clear water, to present a new, fresh, and clean surface to which waterproofing will bond. For brick walls the Contractor shall rake out all joints to insure this bond further.

Hydrostatic Pressure shall be eliminated, while the waterproofing coat is being applied and until set, by means of sumps, pumping, or relief holes.

Plaster-Coat Method. The waterproofing coat for floors shall consist of a plaster coat 1 in. thick, which shall be screeded and floated to a smooth, true, even surface, free from imperfections. The waterproofing coat for walls and ceilings shall consist of two coats. The scratch and finish coats shall be wood floated and steel troweled to a smooth, true, even surface, free from imperfections. The joints between the floor waterproofing and wall waterproofing shall be made at least 6 in. above the floor line, and to this end the scratch coat on the walls shall be carried down to floor level, and the finish coat shall be stopped approximately 6 in. above floor level, so that, where the floor waterproofing is applied, it shall be turned up with a cove base of at least 2-in. radius and 6 in. high. Interior columns and interior walls extending through floor slabs shall be waterproofed to a minimum height of 3 ft. 0 in. above floor level.

Iron-Coat Method. All surfaces shall receive as many brush coats of iron mixture as are required, but not less than two; proper time for complete oxidation shall be allowed between coats.

Floors shall be finished with a 1-in.-thick wearing surface of cement, sand, and iron, screeded, floated, and steel troweled to a smooth, even surface, free from imperfections. A cove shall be formed at the intersection of floors and walls. Walls shall receive a slush coat of iron, sand, and cement, followed by a scratch and a finish plaster coat.

IV. Cement Base Paint.

Where cement base paint is to be applied for the purpose of resisting hydraulic head, it shall be 10% hydrated lime and 90% portland cement made into a paste or heavy cream, or an approved proprietary base paint such as Aquella.

Paint to be applied with a stiff bristle brush until thoroughly impregnated with the material and then maintained in moist conditions for 72 hr.

V. Repairs.

If any leaks appear within a period of 5 years after the work is done, the Contractor shall be obligated, at his own expense, to repair them by removing the coat at the point of leakage, roughing the concrete, and applying a new coat. The Contractor shall relieve the pressure while making repairs. The Contractor shall not be responsible for any defects caused by settling or other structural causes.

VI. The Contractor.

This work shall be performed by a firm or individual corporation which has made a specialty of this kind of waterproofing for at least 5 years and which can show at least three similar installations which have proved successful. *It is best to limit this work to about three firms well known for their qualifications in this line.*

VII. The Bond.

The Contractor shall furnish a bond, which shall be agreed upon in the Contract, to insure the successful performance of the Contract, and he shall agree that there is nothing in the above specification which will prevent such successful performance. The bond shall be for a period of 5 years.

VIII. Tests.

The waterproofing job shall be subjected to a test of head, equal to that specified on the design drawings, and this head shall be obtained by natural or artificial means in order to effect a test of the qualities of the waterproofing. The cost of this test shall be borne by the Contractor.

IX. Basis of Payment.

Specify that Contractor be paid at unit or lump sum price called for in the Contract.

Membrane *

I. Scope.

Work Included. This section shall include all waterproofing by membrane.

Work Not Included. This section shall not include plaster-coat, iron-coat, or integral waterproofing or dampproofing.

II. Materials.

Membrane waterproofing shall consist of _____ plies of tarred felt weighing 15 lb. per 100 sq. ft. and _____ moppings of waterproofing pitch.

III. Workmanship and Application.

Preparation of surfaces. All surfaces on which the waterproofing is to be applied shall be firm, smooth, dry, and free from loose materials.

Hydrostatic pressure shall be eliminated, while the waterproofing coat is being applied and until structural slab or wall is in place, by means of sumps, pumping, or relief holes.

Application of Membrane Waterproofing. 1. Coat the entire surfaces on which the waterproofing is to be applied with waterproofing pitch into which, while hot, embed a layer of tarred felt, as specified, following this with alternating moppings of pitch and layers of felt until _____ moppings of pitch and _____ layers of felt have been applied. Each layer of felt shall be thoroughly rubbed into the hot pitch, and the entire surface shall be immediately mopped with pitch to insure thorough embedding of the felt. The felt shall be laid without wrinkles or buckles, and the finished membrane shall be free from pockets or blisters.

2. Not less than _____ lb. of waterproofing pitch shall be used for constructed each 100 sq. ft. of completed waterproofing, and the pitch shall not be heated above 350° F.

3. At wall angles and footings and places where the waterproofing may be subjected to unusual strain, there shall be applied not less than two extra reinforcing layers of felt and alternating moppings of pitch.

4. Where laps are left to be connected, they shall be not less than 10 in. wide, and shall be temporarily protected by ½-in. troweled course of portland cement mortar. When connections with laps are made, laps shall be carefully cleaned, dry, and mopped with pitch before proceeding with the work.

5. Care shall be taken not to injure the waterproofing membrane either during application or after completion, and all finished work shall be approved before construction of permanent protective finish or wall.

6. The waterproofing shall be immediately protected by tile, brick, concrete, or similar material as specified.

---

* Courtesy Barrett Division, Allied Chemical and Dye Corporation.

Engineer's Note.

For five-ply construction six alternating moppings of pitch shall be required, and not less than 180 lb. of waterproofing pitch shall be used for constructing each 100 sq. ft. of completed waterproofing.

For four-ply construction five alternating moppings of pitch shall be required, and not less than 150 lb. of waterproofing pitch shall be used for constructing each 100 sq. ft. of completed waterproofing.

For three-ply construction four alternating moppings of pitch shall be required, and not less than 120 lb. of waterproofing pitch shall be used for constructing each 100 sq. ft. of completed waterproofing.

IV. The Contractor.

This work shall be performed by a firm or individual corporation which has made a specialty of this kind of waterproofing for at least 5 years and which can show at least three similar installations which have proved successful.

It is best to limit this work to about three firms well known for their qualifications in this line.

V. The Bond.

The Contractor shall furnish a bond, which shall be agreed upon in the Contract, to insure the successful performance of the Contract, and he shall agree that there is nothing in the above specification which will prevent such successful performance. The bond shall be for a period of 5 years.

VI. Basis of Payment.

Specify that Contractor be paid at unit or lump sum price called for in the Contract.

GRADING FOR ROADS, AIRPORTS, AND RAILROADS

I. Scope of Work.

Work Included.

Work Not Included.

II. Stripping and Spreading of Topsoil.

All topsoil shall be stripped from areas to be paved, excavated, or filled, and from other areas as shown on drawings. *If possible, specify depth of topsoil to be stripped.* Topsoil shall be stored in stockpiles, the location of which shall be as shown on drawings or as approved by the Engineer.

On areas shown on drawings to receive topsoil, the subgrade shall be scarified to a depth of 2 in. for the bonding of the topsoil with the subsoil. Grading and hand raking will be required, followed by rolling with one pass of a light roller weighing not more than 100 lb. per lin. ft. and not less than 25 lb. per lin. ft. On slopes steeper than 4:1 the topsoil shall be rammed or tamped in place as directed by the Engineer.

Areas to be sodded shall receive 3 in. of topsoil; areas to be seeded shall receive 4 in. of topsoil. *Increase up to 12 in. if material below is permeable.*

The cost of rehandling, storage, scarifying, and other items specified above shall be included in the price per cubic yard paid for stripping and spreading topsoil.

III. Excavation.

Excavation shall conform to limits indicated on the drawings or specified herein.

Excavation shall not be made below grade except where boulders or stone masonry is encountered or removal of unstable material is directed by the Engineer.

Material removed below grade shall be replaced with approved material thoroughly compacted or as otherwise directed by the Engineer.

Where excavated material is required for construction of embankments and the material encountered in the excavation consists of earth, soft rock, and hard rock, the Contractor shall construct the bottom of the fills with the hard rock, following this with the soft rock and finally the earth fill, care being exercised throughout to provide a well-compacted and void-free embankment. The cost of all work in connection therewith, including stockpiling and rehandling if required, shall be included in the unit price bid for excavation.

Borrow. Where additional material is required to complete the embankment or fill, the Contractor shall provide it. This borrow material shall be inorganic matter of P.R.A. Classification between A1 and A4 inclusive and approved by the Engineer. Location of suitable borrow pits is shown on the drawings. The Contractor shall give the Engineer at least 10 days' notice to permit cross-sectioning before removing borrow material from any approved borrow pit.

Rock Excavation. Rock excavation shall include removal of ledge rock, concrete or masonry structures which require drilling or blasting, and boulders larger than ____ cu. yd. (*varies with size of equipment used*) in volume.

Ledge rock, boulders, concrete or masonry structures shall be removed to a minimum depth of _____ in. below subgrade and backfilled with approved material thoroughly compacted.

Rock excavation shall be conserved if required for purposes shown on the drawings or for any other purpose, as the Engineer may direct.

Drainage. Spring or seepage water encountered shall be reported to the Engineer if drainage is not provided for by the drawings. The Contractor shall keep the excavation free from water at all times by pumping or otherwise.

Excess or Disapproved Excavated Material shall be disposed of as shown on the drawings. *Make sure that location of disposal is shown or specified.*

IV. Embankment and Fills.

Fills shall not be started until the area has been inspected and approved by the Engineer.

Embankment and fill material shall be free from frost, stumps, trees, roots, sod, or muck. Only approved material from excavation or borrow pits shall be used. Material shall not be placed on frozen ground.

Preparing Ground Surface. Sloped surfaces steeper than 4:1 shall be scarified or stepped and compacted to provide bond with new material.

When existing roadways are to be covered with less than 1 ft. of fill the surface shall be scarified and recompacted to the same density as specified for fills.

When fill is to be placed over wet ground that will not support the weight of trucks or other equipment, the lower part of the fill shall be made with coarse sand, gravel, or other selected material deposited in a blanket layer no deeper than necessary to support the operating equipment. Top 9 in. of blanket layer shall be compacted to required density before subsequent layers are placed.

Construction Methods. Excavated material shall be so handled, conserved, stored, and placed as to have the least desirable material at the bottom of embankments, grading up to the best material at the top.

Sandy soils shall be placed in 4-in. to 6-in. layers and compacted with caterpillar tractor, tamping roller, smooth-wheel roller weighing 8 to 10 tons, or approved pneumatic roller.

Clay soils shall be placed in 8-in. maximum layers and compacted with light tamping roller.

Glacial till shall be placed in 8-in. maximum layers and compacted with heavy tamping roller. The Contractor may use other equipment if approved.

Places inaccessible to roller shall be compacted with mechanical or hand tampers.

Final rolling of top layer shall be with a smooth-wheel power roller weighing 8 to 10 tons or approved pneumatic roller.

Stones in earth fill shall be well distributed. No stones over 4 in. in diameter shall be left within 12 in. of finished subgrade.

Each layer shall be free of ruts and shall meet compaction requirements before succeeding layer is placed. Layers shall be maintained with crown or slope to provide drainage and prevent erosion.

At least the top 6 in. of pavement subgrade shall be of selected granular material.

Rock Fill. In embankments or fills, rock may be any maximum size if uniform gradation. All voids shall be completely filled with fine material and compacted to form a dense mass.

The fill for a thickness of at least 2 ft. below the finished subgrade shall be selected earth material placed and compacted in layers to the degree specified below.

Operation of equipment shall be distributed to avoid rutting and unequal compaction.

Protection of Structures. Culverts, headwalls, and other structures shall be constructed before fill is placed. Fill around culverts, headwalls, or other structures shall be carefully and symmetrically placed in 6-in. to 8-in. layers and shall be compacted to the degree specified below. Where drainage pipes are to be built in fill, the fill shall be constructed to 1 ft. above the top of the pipe and then excavated for the pipe. *If not included elsewhere, insert here applicable paragraphs from "Excavation, Grading, and Backfilling for Utility Systems," p. 17–36.*

V. Compaction Requirements. *Specify one of the following.*

Test-Controlled Compaction. *Use for large or important projects.* In construction of embankments and preparation of subgrades, all soils shall be compacted to 90% of maximum density at optimum moisture as determined by Mod. A.A.S.H.O. T–99, except that soils for a depth of 9 in. below pavement subgrades in both cuts and embankments shall be compacted to not less than 95%.

Soils which have maximum density less than 100 lb. per cu. ft. as determined by Mod. A.A.S.H.O. T–99 shall be wasted or mixed with heavier soils to obtain the required weight.

When material varies from optimum moisture content, it shall be treated as follows:

When wet it shall be drained or worked until optimum moisture content is attained; when dry, shall be watered.

Practical Control. *Use only where test control is not warranted by size or importance of project.* In construction of embankments and preparation of subgrades the soil shall be compacted with approved equipment. The soil shall be treated and worked so as to be damp but not wet.

Compaction must be such that no creeping or weaving appear ahead of the roller.

Non-Compactible Subgrades in Cut Areas. In cut areas where the Contractor is required to achieve compaction of 95% as called for above, the Contractor will undercut material which is not compactible and replace with granular material of P.R.A. Classification A1 to A4 inclusive. Material will be deemed not compactible if the required compaction percentage cannot be attained by the use of 25 passes by the specified compaction equipment. To attain specified compaction, Contractor shall use tamping rollers, vibro-tampers, smooth rollers, or construction equipment as called for by the Engineer.

VI. Subgrade Preparation. *Specify one of the following.*

In cut areas the subgrade shall be scarified and compacted to 95% of maximum unit weight at optimum moisture for a depth of at least 6 in. See Article V above.

Rough subgrades shall be formed and compacted in accordance with the drawings to within a tolerance of 1½ in.

Soft areas in subgrade shall be removed and replaced with crushed stone, gravel, Telford, or as directed by the Engineer. These areas shall be drained as directed by the Engineer.

Rough subgrades, including slopes and ditches, shall be formed and maintained to provide proper drainage.

VII. Fine Grading of Subgrade. *This item may be included as part of the Contract covering the constitution of the base course or pavement.*

Rough subgrade shall be cleaned of all loose or foreign material and reshaped if rutted. Approved material shall be added to meet required grade. Shaping and compacting shall be done with blade graders and a 3-wheel power roller weighing 8 to 10 tons or pneumatic roller. Soft spots shall be eliminated and drained as specified in Article VI above.

Tolerances. Finished surface shall be smooth and even and shall not vary more than ⅜ in. in 10 ft. from true profile and cross section or more than ½ in. from true elevation.

VIII. Shoulder Construction.

Shoulder material shall be placed in uniform layers for full width and thickness. Each layer shall be compacted by rolling. Roller shall overlap shoulder when rolling both base course and pavement. Finished shoulder shall be firm against pavement.

Drainage shall be provided for pavement subgrade at low points.

Where trench method of construction is to be used for pavement, sides shall be cut to vertical face at proposed edge of pavement; roller cannot overlap shoulders.

IX. Finishing Slopes and Surfaces.

All areas shall be finished to smooth, compact surfaces in conformity with the plans.

Slopes. Blade grader or scraper finish will *or will not* be allowed. Hand shovel finish will *or will not* be required.

Shoulders, Ditches, and Gutters. Hand shovel and raking finish will *or will not* be required.

Maintenance. Finished work shall be drained and maintained in accordance with the plans until final acceptance.

X. Tests. *For test-controlled compaction see Article V above.*

The Contractor shall provide labor, material, and transportation for the following tests and sampling. The Engineer shall provide expert services and testing and sampling equipment.

Sampling. The Engineer shall follow A.S.T.M. methods of sampling. *See "Data Book, Vol. 3, Field Practice."*

Laboratory Tests. Methods of test shall be the latest revision of the following:

		Number of Tests
Dry weights when compacted at optimum moisture of various types of soil	Mod. A.A.S.H.O. T–99	As required to provide a control for moisture and density field tests.

Field Tests. *See Chapter 15.*

	Number of Tests
Moisture content	At least one for every 500 sq. yd. on each layer, or sufficient number of tests to insure thorough
Dry weight of compacted soil	and uniform compaction. Additional tests if soil or moisture conditions change.

Auger borings shall be made as directed by the Engineer when there are indications of poor material underlying subgrade.

XI. Protection of Pipes.

Pipes laid on original ground shall be protected with a minimum of 4 ft. of tamped fill over the top of the pipes before heavy equipment is allowed to pass over. Piles resting in fill shall be excavated for after the compacted fill is in place.

XII. Basis of Payment. *Specify that the Contractor be paid at unit or lump sum price called for in the Contract.*

Give work included and excluded under this price or *give method of measurement.*

If unit price, itemize price units.

If lump sum, itemize basis of payment for extra work including the following items:

Price per cubic yard for earth excavation.

Price per cubic yard for rock excavation.

Price per cubic yard for borrow.

Price per cubic yard per 100-ft. station for overhaul.

Price per cubic yard for placing topsoil.

DAMS

It is assumed that the Engineer has designed the dam of either earth fill or concrete, or both, and that the embankment requirements may be met from local borrow pits.

I. Scope.

Work Included.

Work Not Included.

II. Shop Drawings.

Shop drawings based on the design drawings for reinforced concrete, structural steel, ashlar, masonry, and all equipment such as gates, valves, and piping shall be submitted to the Engineer for his approval.

III. Cofferdams and Unwatering.

The Contractor shall construct and maintain all necessary cofferdams, channels, flumes, and/or other temporary diversion and protective works; shall furnish all materials required therefor; and shall furnish, install, maintain, and operate all necessary pumping and other equipment for unwatering the various parts of the work, and for maintaining the foundation, cut-off trenches, and other parts of the work free from water as required for constructing each part of the work. Locations of cofferdams are shown on the drawings. Drawings for cofferdams and other diversion works showing type and sequence of construction, elevations, etc., and any proposed changes in location shall be submitted to the Engineer for approval. River discharge curves and diversion works capacity curves are shown on the drawings solely for the purpose of aiding the Contractor to time his construction operations to prepare for such flood storage and/or bypass such flow as may be necessary. The reliability or accuracy of any of these curves is not guaranteed. After having served their purpose, all cofferdams and other temporary protective works downstream from the dam shall be removed from the river channel or leveled to give a sightly appearance, so as not to interfere in any way with the operation or usefulness of the reservoir. All cofferdams or other temporary protective works shall be removed to the extent required to prevent obstruction in any degree whatever of the flow of water to the intake or outlet works.

IV. Preparation of Foundation.

Foundation for Earth Fill. After all necessary stripping and excavation have been completed, the foundation area shall be unwatered and the foundation for the earth fill shall be so prepared by scraping and rolling that the surface materials of the foundation are as compact and well bonded with the first layer of the fill as is specified for the subsequent layers of the earth fill.

Note. Specifications for the preparation of foundations for rock-fill dams and for concrete structures on formations other than rock are determined by local conditions.

Foundation on Rock for Concrete. The surfaces of all rock foundations upon or against which concrete is to be placed shall be prepared to provide adequate bond between the rock and the concrete by roughening and cleaning the rock surfaces. All loose rock fragments, spalls, dirt, gravel, grout, and other objectionable materials shall be removed from the rock surfaces. Immediately before concrete is placed upon or against any rock surface, the surface shall be thoroughly cleaned by means of stiff brooms, hammers, picks, jets of water and air applied at high velocity, wet sand-blasting, or other effective means satisfactory to the Engineer. After cleaning and before concrete is placed, all water shall be removed from depressions so as to permit thorough inspection and proper bond of concrete with the foundation rock.

Stripping for Embankment. The entire areas of the dam and dike sites, including the areas over cut-off trenches, shall be stripped or excavated to a sufficient depth to remove all materials not suitable, as determined by the Engineer, for the foundations. The unsuitable materials to be removed shall include top soil, all rubbish, vegetable matter of every kind, roots, and all other perishable or objectionable materials which might interfere with the proper compacting of the materials in the embankments or be otherwise objectionable. The stripped materials shall be wasted *or* saved for landscaping. *Specify location of disposal areas.*

V. Embankment.

Embankment Construction, General. The term "embankment" shall include the earth-fill portion of the dam and the riprap on the upstream face of the dam. The embankment shall be constructed to the lines and grades shown on the drawings. The Contractor shall allow for _____ % of shrinkage and include this amount in his bid. No brush, roots, sod, or other perishable or unsuitable materials shall be placed in the embankment. The suitability of each part of the foundation for placing embankment materials thereon, and of all materials for use in the embankment construction, will be determined by the Engineer. No material shall be placed in the embankment when either the material or the foundation or embankment on which it would be placed is frozen.

Earth Fill in Embankment. The earth-fill portions of the dam, including the fill in the cut-off trench shall consist of a soil with the physical characteristics given below. While in general this gradation fits local sources, it is contemplated that it will be necessary to improve the natural borrow by selection and mixing as described below. A scientific control covering moisture determination, grain-size analysis, and density measurement is contemplated, and the Contractor will be expected to conduct his operations accordingly.

No materials shall be placed in the earth-fill portion of the dam until after the diversion of the river has been accomplished, except as may be approved by the Engineer. No earth-fill material shall be placed until the foundation therefor has been unwatered and suitably prepared. The distribution and gradation of materials throughout the earth-fill portions of the dam shall be such that the earth embankment will be free from lenses, pockets, streaks, or layers of material differing materially in texture or gradation from the surrounding material.

The mixture of clay, sand, and gravel, bank run or pre-mix, shall be placed in the earth embankment in continuous, approximately horizontal, layers not more than 6 in. in thickness after rolling. Tamping rollers having staggered, uniformly spaced knobs and equipped with suitable cleaners shall be used for compacting the earth fill. The projected face area of each knob and the number and spacing of the knobs shall be such that the total weight in pounds of the roller and ballast, if distributed over the equivalent area of one row of knobs parallel to the axis, shall not be less than 250 lb. per sq. in.

The material in each layer while being compacted by rolling shall contain optimum moisture for maximum density for compacting purposes within practicable limits, and this optimum water content shall be uniformly distributed throughout the layer. The application of water to material for this purpose shall be done at the site of excavation as far as practicable and shall be supplemented as required by sprinkling on the embankment. Harrowing or other working of the material may be required to produce uniformity of water content. While in the above-described condition, each layer of material shall be compacted by passing the specified roller over the entire surface the number of times required as follows: Finished embankment shall be compacted to not less than 95% of the dry densities which correspond to optimum moisture for the soil and as determined by the Engineer.

All portions of test-pit and cut-off trench excavation within the area to be covered by the embankment and below the required stripping lines for the embankment foundation shall be filled with compacted embankment material as herein specified for the earth fill. The earth fill on each side of the core walls shall be kept at approximately the same level as the placing of the earth fill progresses, and the walls shall be carefully protected against displacement or other damage. Portions of the earth fill between projections on the dam abutments, near the core walls, which cannot be properly compacted by means of rolling equipment, shall be thoroughly compacted by means of hand-operated mechanical tampers. The degree of compaction for such portions of the earth fill shall be equivalent to that obtained by moistening and rolling as specified for other portions of the earth fill. The upstream face of the earth fill shall be reasonably true to line and grade, and all projections of more than 6 in. outside the neat lines of the earth fill shall be removed before the rock riprap is placed. The upper 12 in. of the crest of the dam embankment shall be constructed of selected gravelly material or selected fine-rock material as shown on the drawings.

Embankment Material Including Core. *Specify gradation limits, i.e., effective size and uniformity coefficient limit, for different sections of embankment. See Chapters 7 and 13.*

Non-Plastic Material. Where the material as deposited in 6-in. layers does not fulfill the above requirements, finer or coarser material as required shall be added and thoroughly mixed with the layer below by harrows, blade graders, rotary tillers, or by other means, to the satisfaction of the Engineer.

Plastic Material. Where plastic material is required to be added or where granular material is required to be added to plastic material, it shall be spread in thin layers not over 3 in. and mixed with a sheepsfoot roller, plus blade-grading and harrowing.

Reverse Filter shall be constructed as shown on the drawings. It shall consist of three 12-in. layers of progressively coarser material compacted by rolling and graded as follows:

> First layer shall be fine sand with a 15% size of _____.
> Second layer shall be coarse sand with a 15% size of _____.
> Third layer shall be gravel with a 15% size of _____.

Note. For guidance in specifying the 15% size, see p. 7–10.

VI. Cement Grouting.

Pervious rock foundation under dams and above dams should be grouted to prevent the flow of water.

Where directed by the Engineer, rock shall be grouted.

The location of grout holes and depths shall be as directed by the Engineer.

Grout shall be placed at pressures up to 200 lb. per sq. in. as required.

Grout shall be composed of cement and water, except that for very open seams sand shall be introduced into the mixture.

Grouting machinery used shall be subject to the approval of the Engineer.

VII. Rock Fill.

The rock fill shall consist of a suitable free-draining mixture of rock fragments, boulders, or cobbles. The largest rock in the rock fill shall be not more than 1 cu. yd. in volume. The inclusion of gravel or rock spalls in the mass in an amount not in excess of that required to fill the voids in the coarser material shall be required. The larger stones shall be placed on the downstream slope and the smaller stones next to the upstream blanket. The rock fill shall be placed in approximately horizontal layers not exceeding 3 ft. in thickness but well bonded between layers, and during the placing of each layer the fine material shall be sluiced into the voids in the rock by a stream of water having sufficient force to move the material in place. The materials need not be hand placed, but there shall be no unfilled spaces within the fill.

VIII. Blanket for Rock Fill.

Specify impervious earth fill or blanket of timber or concrete as shown on the drawings.

IX. Basis of Payment.

Specify that Contractor be paid at unit or lump sum price called for in Contract.
Give unit prices for extra earth and rock excavation and embankment below lines shown on drawings.
Rock grouting per cubic foot; wagon drilling and core drilling per linear foot.
Extra steel and/or wood sheath piling, per square foot.
Extra pumping, on basis of time and material.
Measure quantities for earth dams in place.

DRAINAGE, SEWERS, SEWAGE TREATMENT, AND WATER SUPPLY

Excavation, Trenching, and Backfilling for Utility Systems

I. Scope of Work.

Work Included.

Work under this section shall consist in furnishing all materials, equipment, and labor for excavation, trenching, and backfilling for utility systems. "Utility systems" shall include underground piping and appurtenances for gas, gasoline, oil, and water distribution systems, storm water drains, and sewage collection systems.

Work Not Included.

II. Stripping of Topsoil, Seeding, Sodding, etc.:

Specify as required for job. See applicable portions of specification for "Grading for Roads, Airports, and Railroads."

III. Excavation.

General. The Contractor shall do all excavation of whatever substances encountered to depth shown on drawings. Excavated materials not required for fill or backfill shall be removed from site as directed by the Engineer and disposed of by the Contractor.

Excavation for manholes and other accessories to have 12-in. minimum and 24-in. maximum clearance on all sides.

Excavation shall not be carried below the required level.

Excess excavation below required level shall be backfilled at the Contractor's expense with earth, sand, gravel, or concrete, as directed by the Engineer, and thoroughly tamped.

Unstable soil shall be removed and replaced with gravel, crushed stone, or crushed slag, which shall be thoroughly tamped. The Engineer shall determine the depth of removal of unstable soil. *Specify that the Contractor will* or will not *be paid extra for removing unstable soil and replacing with gravel.*

Ground adjacent to all excavations shall be graded to prevent water running in.

The Contractor shall remove, by pumping or other means approved by the Engineer, any water accumulated in excavation, and shall keep trench unwatered until the bedding is complete. *Specify pumping to be* or not to be *paid for extra.*

Trench Excavation. Banks of trenches shall be vertical *or as shown on drawings.*

Width of trench shall be 6 in. minimum, 8 in. maximum, on each side of the pipe bell. The bottom of trench for sewers and culverts shall be rounded so that an arc of the circumference equal to 0.6 of the outside diameter of the pipe rests on undisturbed soil or on a concrete cradle as shown on drawings.

Material such as peat or other soft material shall be reported to the Engineer.

Where required by the engineer, pipe shall be placed on straw or other mattress.

Bell holes shall be excavated accurately to size by hand.

In rock, excavations shall be carried 8 in. below bottom of pipe. Granular earth or gravel shall be used for backfill, tamped thoroughly, and rounded to receive pipe as above.

Rock excavation shall include removal of boulders larger than ⅓ cu. yd. in volume and of ledge rock, concrete, or masonry structures that require drilling or blasting.

Bracing and Shoring. The Contractor shall do all bracing, sheathing, and shoring necessary to perform and protect all excavations as indicated on the plans, as required for safety, as directed by the Engineer, or to conform to governing laws.

Specify that bracing and shoring are to be or are not to be *paid for extra.*

Temporary Bridges or crossings shall be built by the Contractor where required to maintain traffic. Where pipes are laid on top of existing soil, bridges shall be constructed to protect pipe from construction equipment wheels.

IV. Tests.

Tests for workmanship on utility lines shall be conducted in accordance with the applicable utility specification before backfilling.

V. Backfilling.

After pipes have been tested and approved, backfilling shall be done with approved material free from large clods or stones.

Trenches. Backfill material shall be placed evenly and carefully around and over pipe in 6-in. maximum layers. Each layer shall be thoroughly and carefully rammed until 1 ft. of cover exists over pipe.

The remainder of backfill material shall be placed, moistened, and compacted.

Water settling will not be permitted in clay soils. It may be required at the option of the Engineer in sandy soils.

Trench under Roadway and Areas to Be Paved. Material shall be placed in 8-in. maximum layers after filling 1 ft. above pipe as previously described. Each layer shall be compacted to density equal to that of adjacent original material so that pavement can be placed immediately.*

Manholes and Other Structures. All forms, trash, and debris shall be removed and cleared away. Approved backfill material may be from excavation or borrow; it shall be free from rock, lumber, or debris. Backfill material shall be placed symmetrically on all sides in 8-in. maximum layers. Each layer shall be moistened and compacted with mechanical or hand tampers.

In roadway or area to be paved, each layer shall be compacted to density equal to that of adjacent original material so that pavement can be placed immediately.

Pipes and Culverts in Fill Section or Projecting into Fill Section. Foundation support shall be as shown on the drawings. Where pipe is not structurally supported, unstable material shall be removed. A pipe bed and embankment, if required, shall be constructed of selected material and compacted. Selected material shall be placed symmetrically on each side of pipe in 6-in. maximum layers.

Material shall be compacted as outlined under grading (*or include here; see p. 17–30*).

Layers shall be placed and compacted until a berm is formed at least one pipe diameter on each side of pipe and 12 in. minimum fill over pipe.

Maintenance. The Contractor shall refill for settlement all backfilled areas.

---

* Camber may be specified.

VI. Replacing Pavements.

Subgrades shall be compacted with a mechanical tamper.

The minimum width of replaced concrete pavements shall be 4 ft. except 6 ft. shall be replaced at joints. (*Avoid cutting pavements at joints; if unavoidable, reconstruct same as original joint.*) Depth shall be 1.3 times original thickness. Existing pavement edges shall be cut vertical. *Use 1:2:3 mix, water-cement ratio 5 gal.; use high-early-strength cement if road is to be opened in less than 3 days.*

The minimum width of replaced bituminous pavements shall be 3 ft. with base of same depth as original pavements; surface course shall be cold-patch mixture. The existing pavement shall be cut vertically and horizontally to a straight line. Edge of existing pavement shall be painted with RC–3 or RC–4. The patch shall be rolled in both directions with a 5-ton roller.

VII. Clean-Up.

The Contractor shall clean up and dispose of all excess material, trash, wood forms, and other debris.

VIII. Basis of Payment.

Specify that the Contractor be paid at unit or lump sum price called for in the Contract.

Give work included and/or excluded under this price.

Give method of measurement; make certain trench pay lines horizontal and vertical are shown or specified. Give depth classifications where required.

If unit price, itemize price units.

If lump sum, itemize basis of payment for extra work including the following items:

> *Price per F.B.M. for sheathing, shoring, and bracing, installed and removed.*
>
> *Price per F.B.M. for sheathing, shoring, and bracing, installed and not removed.*
>
> *Price per day for pumping.*
>
> *Price per cubic yard for rock excavation.*
>
> *Price per cubic yard for removal of soft material and replacing with gravel.*
>
> *Price per square yard for replacing pavement.*

CATHODIC PROTECTION

Impressed Current.   A protective current applied to auxiliary anodes such as graphite, duriron, from an outside driving source (rectifier or motor generator).

Electrical Bond

State that the steel structure shall be electrically bonded by this contractor or that the steel structure has been electrically bonded in the design.

Required Current Flow

The protective current shall be regulated in order to obtain the protective potential at the metal surface. This protective potential is −.085 volt measured between the structure and a copper sulfate reference electrode placed close to the steel surface.

The current required will vary according to the coating used, velocity of the water, salinity of the water, and temperature. In general, something between 5 and 10 milliamperes will be required between mud line and high water, and between 1 and 4 milliamperes below the mud line or on soil contacting surfaces.

Test

After the completion of the structure, the installation shall be checked by an approved engineer for the above requirements.   If it is found inadequate, this contractor shall, at his own expense, increase the protective current capacity.

Galvanic Anode Protection Alternate.   A protective current applied from galvanic anodes, such as magnesium or zinc, which have an innate voltage difference with the structure causing protective current flow.

The Contractor shall state the cost of substituting galvanic anode protection for the impressed current covered in his base bid, together with an estimate of the annual cost of replacement of the sacrificial blocks.

Qualified Subcontractor

This work shall be installed by a contractor qualified by experience in this line and equipped to make designs and checks on the operation of this installation.   This subcontractor shall be approved by the engineer.

Overall Guarantee

The Contractor shall be responsible for the design being adequate to provide the protective potential specified above.

WOOD PRESERVATION

I. Scope

Work Included. This contract includes the pressure preservative treatment of wood as shown on plans *or* as specified to be treated.

Work Not Included.

II. Material

Wood. *Specify species, dimensions, and class of piles to be treated.*
Specify species and grade of timber and lumber to be treated.
Specify type of preservative to be used.

Preservatives

(*a*) Coal tar creosote and creosote coal tar solutions shall comply with Standards Numbers P1 and P2 of the American Wood Preservers Association or U. S. Federal Specifications TT–W–556 and TT–W–566, respectively.

(*b*) Water-borne salt preservatives shall meet the requirements of the American Wood Preservers Associations Standard P5 as follows:

	Federal Spec.
Chromated zinc chloride	TT–W–551
Tanalith (Wolman salts)	TT–W–573
Acid copper chromate (Celcure)	TT–W–546
Ammoniacal copper arsenate (Chemonite)	TT–W–549
Chromated copper arsenate (Greensalt or Erdalith)	
Chromated zinc arsenate (Boliden salt)	TT–W–538
Copperized chromated zinc chloride	TT–W–562

(*c*) Oil-borne preservatives shall meet the requirements of A.W.P.A. Standard Specification No. P8 as follows:

Pentachlorophenol	Federal Spec. TT–W–570
Copper napthanate	

They shall be dissolved in petroleum oil complying with A.W.P.A. Standard P9.

III. Treatment Processes and Retention of Preservatives

A. Piles. All piles shall be pressure treated with *creosote or creosote coal tar* solutions by A.W.P.A. Treatment Standards as follows:

For *Foundations, Land* or *Fresh Water*.
Southern pine piles—12 lb., empty cell
Douglas fir piles   —12 lb., empty cell
Norway pine piles —12 lb., empty cell
Red oak piles   —12 lb., empty cell

For *Salt Water* Subject to *Marine Borers*.
20 lb.—full cell
14 lb.—full cell

B. Timber and Lumber. *Creosote.*

	Land or Fresh Water	Marine Water
Southern pine	10–12 lb., empty cell	20 lb.—full cell
Douglas fir	8–10 lb., empty cell	14 lb.—full cell
Red oak	8–10 lb., empty cell	lb.—full cell

Timber and Lumber. *Salt Treatments.* For use where wood is to be painted or in the natural state.

Retentions of dry salt

	Moderate Leaching Conditions	Not in Ground or Water
Chromated zinc chloride	1.00 lb.	0.75
Tanalith (Wolman salts)	0.5	0.35
Acid copper chromate (Celcure)	0.75	0.50
(Chemonite)	0.45	0.30
(Greensalt)	0.75	0.35
(Boliden)	1.0	0.5
Copperized chromated zinc chloride	1.0	0.75

Timber and Lumber. *Oil-Borne Preservatives.*

Retentions, lb. of preservative per cu. ft. of wood.

	Ground Contact	Not in Ground or Water
Pentachlorophenol	0.5 lb.	0.3 lb.
Copper napthanate	0.5	0.3

Note: Federal Specification TT–W–571, for "Wood Preservative; Recommended Treating Practice," is recommended as an excellent guide for choice of preservative and retentions essential, with regard to varying conditions of exposure where treated wood is used.

IV. Pressure Treatment Specifications. (American Wood Preservers' Association Standards:)

Piles   C1 and C3
Poles   C1 and C4
Posts   C1 and C5

Railway ties   C1 and C6
Lumber and timbers C1 and C2

V. Protection of Cut Surfaces and Pile Cut-offs.

Field cuts in treated material shall have 2 coats of hot creosote or 2 coats of concentrated solution of other preservative applied in accordance with A.W.P.A. Standard M4. Holes bored in treated wood shall be protected also by methods specified in A.W.P.A. Standard M4.

Plank Ends—no recommendation (R.H.M.)

Pile cut-offs shall have 2 successive coats of hot creosote followed with 30/70 creosote pitch compound or by other means as recommended in A.W.P.A. Standard M4.

RIP RAP

I. Scope of Work.

Work Included. *Specify areas and thicknesses as shown on plan, also whether it is to be hand-placed or dumped.*

Work Not Included.

II. Rip Rap, Hand-Placed.

Hand-placed rip rap (*specify for bank facing*) shall consist of rough unhewn quarry stones, approximately rectangular, placed directly on the specified slopes or surfaces. It shall be so laid that the weight of the large stones is carried by the soil rather than by adjacent stones. Stones shall weigh between 50 and 150 lb. each, and at least 60% of them shall weigh more than 100 lb. each.

III. Preparation for Hand-Placed Rip Rap.

Before any rip rap is placed, the surface to be covered shall be fully compacted and graded to the required slope. Rip rap on slopes shall commence in a trench below the toe of the slope and shall progress upward, each stone being laid by hand perpendicular to the slope with the long dimension vertical, firmly bedded against the slope and against the adjoining stone, with ends in contact, and with well-broken joints. Similar methods shall be used when laying rip rap on stream beds, in ditches and on level surfaces.

The finished surface of the rip rap shall present an even, tight surface, not less than 12 in. thick, measured perpendicular to the slope.

The stones weighing more than 100 lb. shall be well dispersed throughout the area with the 50–100 lb. stones laid between them in such a manner that all stones will be in close contact. The remaining voids shall be filled with spalls of suitable size and well tamped to produce a firm and compact revetment.

IV. Rip Rap, Dumped.

(*Specify for current and wave protection.*)

The rip rap shall consist of rough unhewn quarry stone placed directly in the locations and to the contours shown on the plans by dumping in final position as nearly as practicable.

The stones shall weigh from 50 lb. to 300 lb. and shall vary more or less uniformly in size. The exposed surface shall have a preponderance of the smaller stone placed so that the surface conforms closely to the slopes shown on the plans or as directed by the Engineer. *For heavy wave exposure specify stones up to 1000 to 3000 lb. or over. Give quality of stone (specify sound rock of granite, sandstone, limestone, etc., as available).*

V. Basis of Payment.

Hand-placed rip rap shall be paid for by the square yard.

Dumped rip rap shall be paid for by the cubic yard.

The quantity to be paid for shall be the actual number of square yards or cubic yards of rip rap deposited to the satisfaction of the Engineer. The stone shall be measured in the vehicle or vessel transporting it to the site of the work.

The unit price shall include the cost of furnishing and placing the rip rap, labor, equipment, and incidentals necessary to complete the work.

RÉSUMÉ OF A.S.T.M. STANDARD SPECIFICATIONS FOR ROUND TIMBER PILES, D–25–55

Scope

1. Round timber piles to be used untreated, or treated with standard preservatives.

(*a*) For sawn timber as sheet piling, see "Grade Use Guide," National Lumber Manufacturers Association.

Species of Wood

2. Specify species of wood desired and type of treatment desired. Commonly used species include cedars, cypress, Douglas fir, elm, hemlock, western larch, maple, oaks, pines, spruces, and tamarack.

Use Classification

3. There are three classes of timber piles, A, B, and C.

(*a*) *Class A*. Heavy railway bridges and trestles, etc. Minimum diameter of butt to carry 14-in.-wide caps.

(*b*) *Class B*. Docks, wharves, highway, and general construction. When timber is to be capped, butts must accommodate caps 12 in. wide.

(*c*) *Class C*. Cofferdams, in foundations completely submerged, false work, and temporary uses.

Requirements for All Classes of Piles

Quality

4. Free from decay, red heart, or insect attack. (*For exceptions see ASTM D-25–55 Article 4.*)

Lengths

5. Individual piles may vary from specified length by ±1 ft. for piles less than 40 ft. and ±2 ft. for piles 40 ft. or longer.

Circumferences and Diameters

6. (*a*) Circumferences shall be measured under the bark and shall have minimum and maximum dimensions according to ASTM D–25–55 Table I, except that 10% of the piles in any shipment may have circumferences 2-in. less than called for in above table.

(*b*) The ratio between maximum to the minimum diameter at the butt of any pile shall not exceed 1.2.

Heartwood

7. Heartwood content in untreated piles shall be not less than 8 tenths of the diameter at the butt, and shall be specified if required.

Sapwood

8. Wood piles for preservative treatment shall have not less than 1-in. of sapwood at the butt end.

Cutting and Trimming

9. (*a*) Butts and tips of piles shall be sawed square with axis of pile.

(*b*) All knots and limbs shall be trimmed or smoothly cut flush with the pile surface.

Peeling

10. Piles are classified according to extent of bark removal, as clean-peeled, rough-peeled, or unpeeled.

(*a*) Clean-peeled piles require the removal of all outer bark and at least 80% of inner bark. No strips of inner bark wider than ½ in. shall remain.

(*b*) Rough-peeled piles require the removal of all outer bark.

(*c*) Unpeeled piles require no bark removal.

Requirements for Class-A or B Piles Straightness

11. (*a*) A straight line from center of butt to center of tip shall lie entirely within the body of the pile.

(*b*) Piles shall be free from crooks that exceed 2½ in. in any 5-ft. length.

Twist of Grain

12. Twist of spiral in any 20-ft. length shall not exceed 180°.

Knots

13. Sound knots shall be no larger than 4 in. or ⅓ of the diameter at which they occur for piles 50 ft. or less and in ¾ of the length from the butt. Sound knots in the remaining quarter of length for piles over 50 ft. shall be no larger than 5 in. or ½ the diameter at which they occur. Cluster knots are prohibited. The sum size of all knots in any foot of length shall not exceed twice the size of the largest permitted single knot.

Holes

14. Holes less than ½ in. in diameter shall be permitted, providing the sum of the diameters do not exceed 1½ in. for any square foot of pile surface.

Splits and Shakes

15. (*a*) Splits shall not be longer than the butt diameter.

(*b*) The length of any shake or combination of shakes in the outer half of the radius of the butt of the pile shall not exceed ⅓ of the circumference of the butt of the pile.

Requirements for Class-C Piles Straightness

16. (*a*) A straight line from the center of the butt to the center of the tip may lie partly outside the body of the pile. The maximum distance between the line and the pile shall not exceed ½% of the length of the pile or 3 in.

(*b*) Piles shall be free from crooks that exceed 2½ in. in any 5-ft. length.

Twist of Grain

17. Twist of spiral in any 20-ft. length shall not exceed 180°.

Knots

18. Sound knots shall be no larger than 5 in. or ½ the diameter at which they occur. Cluster knots are prohibited. The sum of sizes of all knots in any foot of length shall not exceed twice the size of the largest permitted knot.

Holes

19. Holes less than ½ in. in diameter shall be permitted, provided the sum of diameters of all holes in any square foot of pile surface does not exceed 3 in.

Splits and Shakes

20. (*a*) Splits shall be no longer than 1½ times the butt diameter.

(*b*) The length of any shake or combination of shakes in the outer half of the radius of the butt of the pile shall not exceed ½ the circumference of the butt of the pile.

Red Lights

The following anecdotes may serve as warnings:

1. The Engineer bound together in one specification the general construction and mechanical trades, intending that the Contractor's bid should include the sum of all the trades. The Contractor contended that inasmuch as in that particular state it was necessary to let public work for the mechanical trades separately, he had only included the general construction in his bid.

2. A specification called for excavated material ordered rehandled by the Engineer to be paid for double. (The Engineer intended this to cover stockpiling of topsoil.)

The entire embankment was to be made up with the fines on top and the coarser material toward the bottom. This was in reverse of the way it would normally be excavated, from the borrow.

The Contractor made a claim for rehandling charge on the bulk of the excavation.

3. Gumbo subgrade under a western airfield was specified to be consolidated to a certain percentage of optimum moisture. This consolidation was to be performed by specified equipment, and, when it was found that it was impossible to obtain this compaction with a large number of passes, it was necessary to remove the soft material.

The resident engineer's position was that the Contractor should continue compaction, but the Contractor won the arbitration in this case.

4. Specification pumping to dewater an excavation for the purpose of placing foundations was stretched into requiring the Contractor to keep the foundation unwatered during a period of substantial delay in the placing of the footings. The Contractor won this arbitration.

5. The Engineer specified an overall clause requiring the Contractor to build foundations which would not settle, although at the same time the Engineer designed the foundations. The Contractor won that one.

6. In a deep foundation operation the Engineer showed the caissons extending below water to the extent that the air pressure required in the caissons would be greater than the legal air pressure allowed for workmen, and the Contractor won this one.

If, however, the Engineer had shown the caissons at this depth, without specifying that they be placed by a given pneumatic process, the contractor would have had to build the caissons. An example of overspecification of Contractor's method.

7. In another case, the Engineer specified bridge piers to be made by pouring concrete inside of steel cylinders, and concrete could be placed by tremie. Before the concrete was set the cylinders were to be unbolted and raised for reuse. This left an unsatisfactory surface, exposed to cold and ice. The Contractor won this—another instance of overspecification of Contractor's method.

8. In a large number of cases, the Engineer specified piles which could not be readily driven, owing to obstacles such as boulders or old cribs. This is usually due to writing specifications with inadequate soil investigation.

9. The specifications called for gate contractor to verify dimensions of steel fittings to install movable gates in a dam. The Engineer, for some unknown reason, added a set of field dimensions of his own to this part of the specification. The dimensions that he added were incorrect, which tended to vitiate the strength of the clause.

General Comments

Do not specify piles without mentioning the grade. See p. 17–39.

Claims by contractors arise from inadequate borings shown on plans.

Always specify the date of completion on which the Contractor is to base his bid.

Specify that the Contractor shall verify all clearances and elevations of existing work before fabricating _____ and shall be responsible for the proper installation and operation of _____.

Specify by tolerances rather than general adjectives. For example, insert percentages rather than use the terms "well compacted" or "adequate bearing."

Designers should review all specifications.

The best bids will be obtained from specifications which eliminate as much as possible of the gamble that the Contractor has to take.

Specification of work included is of great importance. No loophole should be left in the specifications to allow any uncertainty as to just what is to be included in the bids. These loopholes are sometimes big enough to allow the Contractor to drive the proverbial team of horses through them.

18

Exercising Engineering Judgment

Every engineer is called upon to make decisions as to foundations based on subsoil data.

This points to the importance of thorough subsoil exploration and emphasizes the saving to owners through such thorough exploration.

Relative Economy

Some of the decisions which he has to make relate to whether or not the use of one type is more advantageous than another, such as spread footings vs. a pile footing. Cost studies may be indicated. This particular problem is discussed in Chapter 3.

Assumption of Soil Bearing Capacity

The assumption of a safe soil bearing capacity has been treated in Chapter 8. This is an important assumption, and information as to density is not always at hand on small scattered jobs. We have these further approaches:

Shearing Strengths

Shearing strengths are of importance in the checking of stability of embankments or cut slopes and also in the study of slides and their application to walls and dams or building excavations. See p. 13–18.

In addition, the tables on p. 13–12, which give bearing strength of soil, are a very useful check on Table 3–I.

The use of a power shovel to explore foundations down to a limited depth is valuable, as it exposes foundation conditions much better than borings and enables the inspector to take undisturbed samples with facility.

Subaqueous Excavation

In Chapter 11, some data are given on practical subaqueous excavation. This may give the designer a chance to exercise his judgment as to the cost of deep excavations, which may possibly be avoided. For instance, the raising of a boilerroom floor in spite of the fact that it may occupy valuable space higher up may save a great deal of money in the cost of foundations.

Another point here would be the design of thin foundations in order to avoid excavation below water level. The device of using steel billet between the column and the foundations as against the use of a reinforced-concrete pedestal or grillage is an example.

Underpinning Adjoining Buildings

Consideration should be given to the problems of underpinning adjoining buildings. If it is necessary to go deeper than the adjoining building, it may be possible to so locate the deep portions of the basement that they will not affect the footings of the adjoining building.

Building Relocation

A building may be relocated to avoid bridging an underground structure such as a trunk sewer.

Water-Level Assumptions

Assumptions of water level should be conservative both ways. Assuming too low a head might cause water to break through or seep into low areas; assuming too high a head might result in using wood piles subject to rot.

In the case of an hydraulic head there is the question of whether a mat is required or whether the water can be taken care of by gravity drainage or underfloor drains to a sump.

Also, a comparative cost study may indicate whether the expensive hydrolithic waterproofing work on a basement is necessary or whether the reinforced-concrete walls may be placed with the joints being caulked and the small resulting seepage collected in a sump and ejected.

An engineer may have the choice of membrane or hydrolithic waterproofing. Possibly it may be desirable to use membrane for roof and hydrolithic for a head of water. See Chapter 9.

Raising a Building

An attempt to raise a building which has settled may be far more expensive that the objective is worth. In other words, it may be more practical to underpin the settled building without raising it. Raising a building may cause serious cracks and damage.

Calling in Engineers Too Late

A point that is usually overlooked is that of bringing in the engineer too late to advise on the selection of a site. A client may make a very unfortunate selection of a site, without the advice of his engineer, and having already purchased it, will be stuck with expensive foundations. In other words, a client should have his engineer make subsurface investigations and exploration before the property is purchased, or at least inquire into the probable type of foundation that a certain site may require.

In the case of bridge piers in an alluvial plain, subject to erosion, borings may often disclose submerged ledges which may indicate an economical and safe location for a bridge.

Corrosion and Decay

The question of whether wood piles may be subjected to decay due to possible future lowering of water level is important.

An item to be considered is that steel piles driven through fill containing ashes or garbage may rapidly corrode.

The problem of electrolysis must also be kept in mind. Outside of what we commonly think of as corrosion, there are problems in electrolysis. A difference in potential between a building and the ground might induce a current to flow from exposed steel in the footings to moisture in the ground, with a resultant corrosion of the steel.

Salt Water for Concrete

Use of brackish or sea water for concrete has been known to destroy entire large reinforced-concrete installations.

Recognition of Artificial Fill

Distinguishing between an old fill and a geological fill is important. The engineer should look for the occurrence of fragments of coal, peat, wood, or organic matter which could occur only in artificial fill. It is to be remembered that borings may miss pockets of organic deposits or other unfavorable soil. The occurrence of old standing trees gives a lead on whether or not the soil is a recent fill.

Difficulties in Using Piles

Sometimes rock will occur in such a condition that piles will slide off the inclined surfaces Under these circumstances, the possibility of selecting open caissons or spread footings might make sense.

There may be a bed of boulders lying on a submerged former water-course bed through which piles cannot be driven successfully. Knowledge of this condition again may point to some other form of foundation.

Forecasting Length and Type of Piles

In modern practice, judging soil resistance by the number of blows on the spoon may indicate the necessity for the use of very deep piles. It might be well to reconsider the possibility of spread footings or mats, especially taking advantage of the weight of soil removed in deep basements. A comparative cost study may be indicated.

Usually the foundation engineer is subordinate to the architect, but he will be doing the architect a favor if he calls attention to an architectural design which causes especially great expense, such as a very deep basement under high hydraulic head.

An engineer may very well profit by discussing the probable conditions on a site with an experienced foundation contractor, but he must be on his guard against being advised by companies with proprietary interests. For instance, an engineer might greatly benefit by consulting a worldwide pile company with a subsidiary boring service; this company may have a knowledge of foundation conditions in the vicinity which may be very valuable.

Adjoining Buildings Give a Reading

In investigating types of foundations, an engineer should remember that buildings in the immediate vicinity are in many respects a full-size test indicating liability of settlement and extreme water-level conditions. Of course, it is necessary to know the history of the foundations of the adjoining buildings, as sometimes an engineer makes the mistake of assuming that an old building was put on spread footings when actually it rests on piles. In this event, the engineer's incorrect assumption leads to a very dangerous conclusion. Also an adjoining building may stand on inadequate or decayed piles.

Heaving of Piles

Certain soils are not sufficiently compressible to permit the driving of piles without heave or excessive rebound. In this case, the use of a certain amount of open-end piles may relieve the situation. The soils referred to are clay, saturated silts, and fine sands. This type of soil may also cause the cave-in of thin shells for cast-in-place piles.

Decomposed Rock

It may be a question of judgment as to whether a pocket of decomposed rock should be removed or a spread footing used, or whether piles should be driven. In the author's experience, a pipe pile with a point is satisfactory to go through decomposed rock. A comparative cost study of each method may be necessary.

Office Engineering

An engineer should not form opinions on important structures sitting in his office without having inspected the site.

Confidence in Your Opinion

Courage, derived from a background of experience and knowledge, will sometimes enable an engineer to make great savings over the dictates of play-safe policy based on ignorance.

19

Factual Data and Appendix

TABLE A -"H"-BEARING PILES   DIMENSIONS & PROPERTIES FOR DESIGNING

Section Number and Nominal Size	Weight per Foot	Area of Section A	Depth of Section d	FLANGE Width b	FLANGE Thickness t	Web Thickness W	AXIS X-X I	AXIS X-X S	AXIS X-X r	AXIS Y-Y I'	AXIS Y-Y S'	AXIS Y-Y r'
	lb.	in.²	in.	in.	in.	in.	in.⁴	in.³	in.	in.⁴	in.³	in.
BP 14 14×14½	117	34.44	14.234	14.885	.805	.805	1228.5	172.6	5.97	443.1	59.5	3.59
	102	30.01	14.032	14.784	.704	.704	1055.1	150.4	5.93	379.6	51.3	3.56
	89	26.19	13.856	14.696	.616	.616	909.1	131.2	5.89	326.2	44.4	3.53
	73	21.46	13.636	14.586	.506	.506	733.1	107.5	5.85	261.9	35.9	3.49
BP 12 12×12	74	21.76	12.122	12.217	.607	.607	566.5	93.5	5.10	184.7	30.2	2.91
	53	15.58	11.780	12.046	.436	.436	394.8	67.0	5.03	127.3	21.2	2.86
BP 10 10×10	57	16.76	10.012	10.224	.564	.564	294.7	58.9	4.19	100.6	19.7	2.45
	42	12.35	9.720	10.076	.418	.418	210.8	43.4	4.13	71.4	14.2	2.40
BP 8 8×8	36	10.60	8.026	8.158	.446	.446	119.8	29.9	3.36	40.4	9.9	1.95

TABLE B—STEEL SHEET PILING

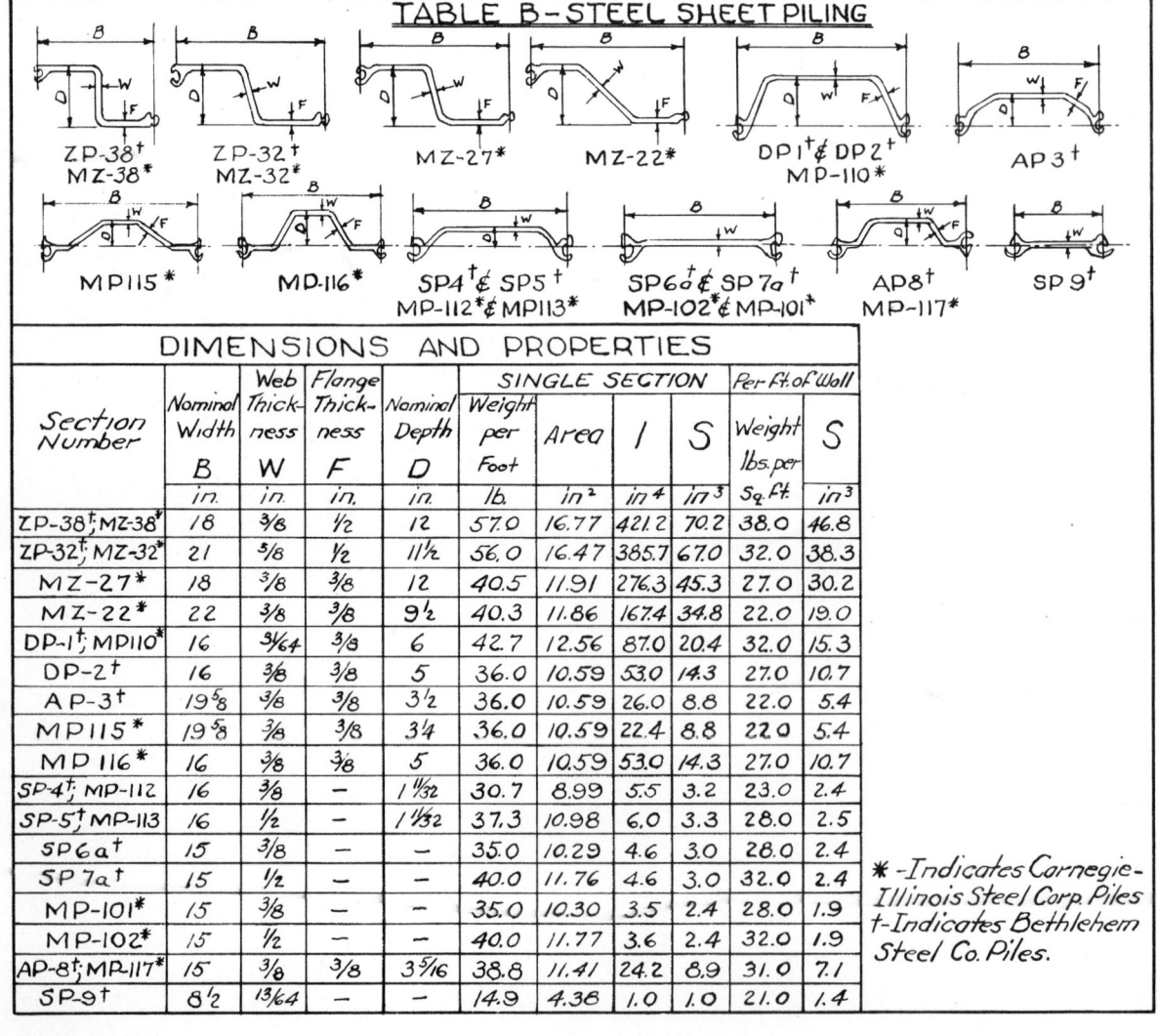

ZP-38† MZ-38*   ZP-32† MZ-32*   MZ-27*   MZ-22*   DP1† & DP2† MP-110*   AP3†

MP115*   MD-116*   SP4† & SP5† MP-112* & MP113*   SP6a† & SP7a† MP-102* & MP-101†   AP8† MP-117*   SP 9†

DIMENSIONS AND PROPERTIES

Section Number	Nominal Width B	Web Thickness W	Flange Thickness F	Nominal Depth D	SINGLE SECTION Weight per Foot	SINGLE SECTION Area	SINGLE SECTION I	SINGLE SECTION S	Per ft. of Wall Weight lbs. per Sq. Ft.	Per ft. of Wall S
	in.	in.	in.	in.	lb.	in.²	in.⁴	in.³		in.³
ZP-38†, MZ-38*	18	3/8	1/2	12	57.0	16.77	421.2	70.2	38.0	46.8
ZP-32†, MZ-32*	21	5/8	1/2	11½	56.0	16.47	385.7	67.0	32.0	38.3
MZ-27*	18	3/8	3/8	12	40.5	11.91	276.3	45.3	27.0	30.2
MZ-22*	22	3/8	3/8	9½	40.3	11.86	167.4	34.8	22.0	19.0
DP-1†, MP110*	16	3/64	3/8	6	42.7	12.56	87.0	20.4	32.0	15.3
DP-2†	16	3/8	3/8	5	36.0	10.59	53.0	14.3	27.0	10.7
AP-3†	19⅝	3/8	3/8	3½	36.0	10.59	26.0	8.8	22.0	5.4
MP115*	19⅝	3/8	3/8	3¼	36.0	10.59	22.4	8.8	22.0	5.4
MP116*	16	3/8	3/8	5	36.0	10.59	53.0	14.3	27.0	10.7
SP-4†, MP-112	16	3/8	—	1 11/32	30.7	8.99	5.5	3.2	23.0	2.4
SP-5† MP-113	16	1/2	—	1 11/32	37.3	10.98	6.0	3.3	28.0	2.5
SP6a†	15	3/8	—	—	35.0	10.29	4.6	3.0	28.0	2.4
SP7a†	15	1/2	—	—	40.0	11.76	4.6	3.0	32.0	2.4
MP-101*	15	3/8	—	—	35.0	10.30	3.5	2.4	28.0	1.9
MP-102*	15	1/2	—	—	40.0	11.77	3.6	2.4	32.0	1.9
AP-8†, MP-117*	15	3/8	3/8	3 5/16	38.8	11.41	24.2	8.9	31.0	7.1
SP-9†	8½	13/64	—	—	14.9	4.38	1.0	1.0	21.0	1.4

* -Indicates Carnegie-Illinois Steel Corp. Piles
† -Indicates Bethlehem Steel Co. Piles.

PLATE I.

TABLE A – ALLOWABLE WORKING STRESSES IN CONCRETE			
	BASED ON ULTIMATE STRENGTH = fc.		
DESCRIPTION	ALLOWABLE WORKING STRESSES		
	N.Y.C 1948	A.C.I. 1947	A.C.I. 1951
FLEXURE:			
Extreme fiber stress in compression.	$0.40 f'_c$	$0.45 f'_c$	$0.45 f_c$
Extreme fiber stress in compression adjacent to supports of continuous or fixed beams, or slabs, or of rigid frames.	$0.45 f'_c$	$0.45 f'_c$	$0.45 f_c$
Tension in plain concrete footings.	$0.03 f'^*_c$	$0.03 f'_c$	$0.03 f'_c$
SHEAR:			No special anchorage
Beams with no web reinforcement and without special anchorage of longitudinal steel.	$0.02 f'_c$	$0.02 f'_c$	$0.03 f'_c$
Beams with no web reinforcement, but with special anchorage of longitudinal steel.	$0.03 f'_c$		
Beams with properly designed web reinforcement but without special anchorage of longitudinal steel.	$0.06 f'_c$	$0.06 f'_c$	$0.12 f'_c$
Beams with properly designed web reinforcement and with special anchorage of longitudinal steel.	$0.09 f'_c$	$0.12 f'_c$	
Flat slabs at distance "d"[3] from edge of column cap or drop panel.			
(a) When at least 50% of total neg. reinf. passes over the column cap.	$0.03 f'_c$	$0.03 f'_c$	$0.03 f'_c$
(b) When 25% or less of total neg. reinf. passes over the column cap.	$0.024 f'_c$	$0.025 f'_c$	$0.025 f'_c$
(c) For intermediate percentages, use intermediate values.			
Footings where longitudinal bars are without special anchorage.	$0.02 f'_c$	f'^{2}_c	$0.03 f'^{2}_c$
Footings where longitudinal bars have special anchorage.	$0.03 f'_c$	$0.03 f'_c$	
[2] Not to exceed 75 lbs. per sq. in.			
[3] "d" being the distance equivalent to the thickness of slab without drop panels minus 1½", or the thickness of flat slab through the drop panels (where such are used) minus 1½", or thickness of flat slab (with drop panels) at points outside the drop panel minus 1½".			
BOND:[6] Top bars with 12" or more concrete below (a) Plain (b) Deformed			$0.03 f'_c$ / $0.07 f'_c$
Beams, slabs & one-way footings: (a) Plain bars or struct. shapes.	$0.04 f'_c$	$0.04 f'^{4}_c$	$0.45 f'_c$
(b) Deformed bars.	$0.05 f'_c$	$0.05 f'^{5}_c$	$0.10 f'_c$
In two-way footings: (a) Plain bars or structural shapes.	$0.03 f'_c$	$0.045 f'^{4-7}_c$	$0.36 f'_c$
(b) Deformed bars.	$0.0375 f'_c$	$0.056 f'^{5-7}_c$	$0.08 f'_c$
[4] Not to exceed 160 lbs. per sq. in. [5] Not to exceed 200 lbs. per sq. in. [6] Bars not conforming to ASTM designation A 305 shall be treated as plain bars. Plain bars must have hooks. [7] Values for two-way footings include allowance for special anchor. [8] Except top bars with over 12" of concrete below.			
BEARING:			
Direct bearing on full area.	$0.25 f'_c$	$0.25 f'_c$	$0.25 f'_c$
Direct bearing on one-third full area or less.	$0.375 f'_c$	$0.375 f'_c$	$0.375 f'_c$
The allowable bearing stress on an area greater than one-third but less than the full area shall be interpolated.			
AXIAL COMPRESSION:			
In columns with lateral ties.	$0.25 f'_c$		
In pedestals.	$0.25 f'_c$	$0.25 f'_c$	$0.25 f_c$
For E see page 19-4.	$n = \dfrac{30,000}{f'_c}$	$\dfrac{30,000}{f'_c}$	

TABLE B – REINFORCEMENT (Values in lbs. per sq. in.).	
Structural grade billet steel – Tension = 18,000	Web reinforcement Tension N.Y.C. = 16,000
Intermediate grade billet steel. " = 20,000	A.C.I. = 20,000
Rail steel, straight or machine bent" = 20,000	Cold drawn steel wire Tension = 20,000

*For N.Y. City code requirements add 4" to depth of footing.

PLATE II.

TABLE A - ALLOWABLE WORKING STRESSES IN STEEL (IN LBS. PER SQUARE INCH)

	A.I.S.C.-1951	N.Y. CITY-1948	OTHER LOCALITIES
TENSION			
Structural steel section	20,000	20,000	
Rivets - on area based on nominal diameter - tension only	20,000	20,000	
Rivets - tension combined with shear	not given	15,000	
Bolts and other threaded parts - on area at root of thread	20,000	15,000	
COMPRESSION [1]			
Structural rolled steel on short lengths - lateral deflection prevented	not given	20,000	
Columns - gross section axially loaded main member $L/r < 120$	$17,000 - 0.485 \frac{L^2}{r^2}$	Same as A.I.S.C.	
secondary member $L/r = 120$ to 200	$\frac{18,000}{1 + L^2/18,000 r^2}$		
Plate girder stiffeners - gross section	20,000	not given	
Webs of rolled section at toe of fillet	24,000	not given	
BENDING (FLEXURE) [2]			
Rolled sections and built up members - extreme fiber			
Tension on net section except no deduction for rivet holes $< 15\%$ flange area	20,000	20,000	
Compression $\frac{Ld}{bt} < 600$ (L for cantilever unstayed at outer end = two times length of compression flange)	20,000	Same as A.I.S.C.	
$\frac{Ld}{bt} > 600$	$\frac{12,000,000}{\frac{Ld}{bt}}$		
Rolled beam encased in stone concrete (Not more than 1:5$\frac{1}{2}$ mix) as follows: 1$\frac{1}{2}$" min., continuous concrete slab - each side, 2" min. protection	not given	22,000	
Pins - extreme fiber	30,000	30,000	
SHEARING			
Rivets - power driven, Pins and Turned bolts in reamed or drilled holes	15,000	15,000	
Unfinished bolts	10,000	10,000	
Webs of beams and plate girders, gross section	13,000	13,000	
BEARING	Double Shear / Single Shear	Double Shear / Single Shear	
Rivets and turned bolts in reamed or drilled holes	40,000 / 32,000	40,000 / 32,000	
Unfinished bolts	25,000 / 20,000	25,000 / 20,000	
Pins	32,000	32,000	
Contact area - milled stiffeners and other milled surfaces, fitted stiffeners			
Expansion rollers and rockers (lbs. per linear inch)	600 diam.	600 diam.	
CAST STEEL			
Tension Note: for A.I.S.C.: Compression and bearing same as for structural	See note at left	16,000	
Compression steel, other unit stresses 75% of those for structural steel		16,000	
CAST IRON			
Tension, Shear		3,000	
Bending - extreme fiber - Compression side	not given	16,000	
Tension side		3,000	
Compression on columns - maximum $L/r = 70$		$9,000 - 40 \frac{L}{r}$	
WELDED JOINTS			
Compression on section through throat	20,000	20,000 [3]	
Tension " " " "	20,000	20,000 [3]	
Shear " " " " of fillet weld	13,600	13,500	
Shear " " " " of butt weld	13,000	13,500	
Bending - Fiber stresses shall not exceed values given above for compression and tension respectively			

Notation: in table "A"
L = unbraced length in inches
r = radius of gyration in inches
b = width of compression flange in ins.
t = thickness of compression flange in ins.
d = depth in inches.

1. A.I.S.C. allows main members with L/r from 120 to 200 if not subject to shock or vibrating loads - allowable stress $= \frac{18,000}{1 + L^2/18,000 r^2} \times \left(1.6 - \frac{L}{200 r}\right)$

For main compression members 120 - For bracing and other secondary members in compression 200
For main tension members 240 - For bracing and other secondary members in tension 300

2. A.I.S.C. only: Use 20% higher stress for negative moments at supports in continuous beams provided that section is not less than that required by maximum positive moments and compression flange is figured as unsupported from point of contraflexure to support   3. Butt weld only.

PLATE III.

TABLE A – WORKING STRESSES – MASONRY (In p.s.i.)

KIND OF MASONRY	COMPRESSION – GROSS AREA OF CROSS SECTION				KIND OF MASONRY	COMPRESSION – GROSS AREA OF CROSS SECTION			
	New York City 1948		Dept. of Commerce 1924			New York City 1948		Dept. of Commerce 1924	
	Cem. Lime[2] Mortar	Cement[3] Mortar	Cem. Lime[2] Mortar	Cement[3] Mortar		Cem. Lime[2] Mortar	Cement[3] Mortar	Cem. Lime[2] Mortar	Cement[3] Mortar
Granite	640	800	640	800	Brick - Solid	250	325	130[1]	170[1]
Gneiss	600	750	—	—	Brick - Hollow Wall	125	150	70	80
Limestone	400	500	400	500	Struct Clay Tile-Cells Vert.	100	125	70	80
Marble	400	500	400	500	Struct Clay Tile-Cells Hor.	60	70	70	80
Sandstone	250	300	320	400	Conc. Block or Tile	60	70	70	80
Bluestone	300	400	—	—	Solid Conc. Units	125	150	—	—
Natural Stone Cut	110	140	—	—	Plain Conc.[4] 1:7 Mix	400			
Natural Stone Uncut	110	140	—	—	Plain Conc. 1:8 Mix			400	

[1] May be increased 50% for local concentrated loads or eccentric loading.

[2] Cement lime mortar: A mortar composed of 1 part Portland cement, 1 part hydrated lime to not more than 6 parts of sand - proportioned by volume.

[3] Cement mortar: A mortar composed of 1 part Portland cement to not more than 3 parts of sand, proportioned by volume, with an allowable addition of hydrated lime or lime putty not to exceed 15% of the cement by volume.

[4] For greater strength concrete use 25% of the ultimate stress.

TABLE B – PROPERTIES OF STRUCTURAL MATERIALS

SUBSTANCE	SPECIFIC GRAVITY.	ULTIMATE STRESS. In Lb. per Sq.In.	ELASTIC LIMIT. In Lb. per Sq.In.	MODULUS OF ELASTICITY. In Lb. per Sq.In.	COEFFICIENT OF LINEAR EXPANSION. For 1°F.
Aluminum, Structural 14S-T4	2.79	62,000 Ten.	41,000 {Ten. Comp.	10,600,000	.0000121
Iron, Cast, Gray	7.2	25,000-33000 Bend 18,000-74,000 Ten.		12,000,000	.0000059
Iron, Wrought	7.75	48,000 Ten.	26,000 Ten.	28,000,000	.0000067
Steel, Structural	7.85	60,000 - 72,000	33,000 Ten.	29,000,000	.0000067
Steel, Intermediate Grade Reinf. Bars	7.85	70,000 - 90,000	40,000	29,000,000	.0000067
Steel, Hard Grade Reinf. Bars	7.85	80,000	50,000	29,000,000	.0000070
Steel, Structural nickel (3.25% Ni).		85,000 - 100,000	50,000	29,000,000	
Glass (common)	2.4 - 2.6	2,000-3000 - Ten. 6,000-12,000 - Comp.		10,000,000	.0000047
Clay Brick (common)	1.92	4,000 COMP. 200 TENSION 600 BENDING		2,000,000	.0000031
Concrete - 3,000# f'c [1]	2.3			3,000,000	.0000079
Stone - Granite	2.7	12,000 COMP. 1,200 TENSION 1,600 BENDING		7,000,000	.0000047
" Limestone	2.5	8,000 COMP. 800 TENSION 1,500 BENDING		7,000,000	.0000044
" Marble	2.7	8,000 COMP. 800 TENSION 1300 BENDING		7,000,000	.0000056
" Sandstone	2.3	5,000 COMP. 150 TENSION 1,200 BENDING		3,000,000	.0000061
Wood - Douglas Fir (Rocky Mt. Region)	.48	6,400 - 9,600 Bending.		1,200,000	.000002 1 - With grain .000032 - Across "
" - Pine Southern S.L. Yellow	.58	7,300 - 12,800 Bending.		1,600,000	.000003 - With grain .000019 - Across "

[1] E for 2,000# f'c = 2,000,000;
for 2,500# f'c = 2,500,000;
for 3,750# f'c = 3,750,000

PLATE IV.

TABLE I

TENSION IN MASONRY

	Case A	*Case B*
Cement mortar	20 p.s.i.	60 p.s.i.
Cement lime mortar	15 p.s.i.	45 p.s.i.

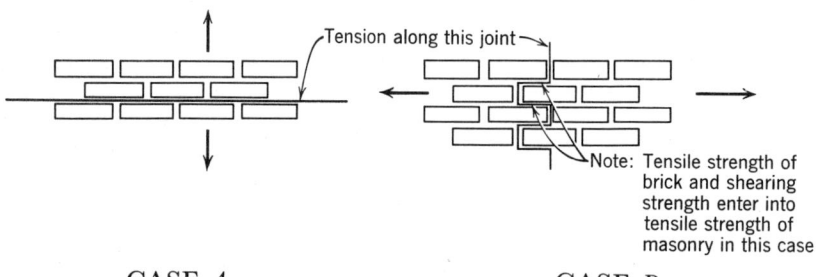

CASE *A*   CASE *B*

FIG. 1.

MASONRY WALLS & PARTITIONS

DEAD LOAD WITHOUT PLASTER TYPE OR SUBSTANCE	LBS. PER SQ. FT.	LBS. PER CU. FT.
EXTERIOR WALLS		
Solid brickwork		120
Concrete, stone		144
Granite, blue stone, marble		168
Limestone		156
Sandstone		144
4" brick + 6" hollow block backup	75	
4" " " 8" " " "		80
Hollow stone concrete block		62
Hollow cinder " "		48
Solid " " "		87
INTERIOR WALLS & PARTITIONS		
2" T.C. or cinder block (non-bearing)	14	
3" " " " " " "	18	
4" " " " " " "	20	
6" " " " " " "	27	
8" " " " " " "	34	
10" " " " " " "	40	
4" load bearing T.C. or cinder block	22	Increase ⅔ for conc. block (gravel or stone aggreg)
6" " " " " " "	31	
8" " " " " "	36	
10" " " " " "	42	
12" " " " " "	52	
2" solid gypsum	9½	
3" " "	13	
3" hollow "	10	
4" " "	12	
6" " "	17	
3⅞" Glass Block	20	

ROOFING & PLASTER OR CEILING FINISHES

TYPE OR SUBSTANCE	LBS. PER SQ. FT.
Wood shingles	2
Asphalt "	3-4
Flat clay tile and cement shingles	16
Clay tile shingles	9
Asbestos shingles or siding	3
2" book tile	12
3" " "	20
Sheet metal roofing	2
Corrugated roofing (No. 20)	2
Corrugated asbestos	3-4
Wood rafters or sheathing	3
Slag roofing	5
5 ply-felt tar and gravel roofing	6
4 " " " " " "	5
3 " " " " " "	4
3 " composition roofing	1
Slate roofing laid) 3/16 and ¼" thickness	7-9½
in place with } 3/8" thickness	14½
3" double lap) ½" "	19½
Skylight-frame and glass	10
Plate glass per inch thickness	14
Hung ceiling-met. lath & Port. cem. plaster	10
" " lime or gypsum plaster	8
Lime or gypsum plaster on walls (direct)	5
" " " " slabs "	6
2 x 4 studs plastered each side	14
Channel studs, met. lath & cem. plaster-2" thick	20

FLOORING & FLOOR SLABS

TYPE OR SUBSTANCE	LBS. PER SQ. FT.
Cinder fill per inch of thickness	5
Cement finish per inch of thickness	12
Terrazzo, 1½" thick	18
Tile and setting bed	15-23
Marble and " "	25-30
Asphalt mastic flooring-1½" thick	18
Linoleum or asphalt finish	2
Hardwood flooring-⅞" thick	4
Soft wood sub " ⅞" "	3
2 x 4 sleepers and fill	10
Oak & longleaf yel. pine in lbs. per cu. ft.	48
Spruce, fir, hemlock, white pine-lbs. per c.f.	30
3" creosoted wood flooring	15
PATENTED STRUCTURAL SYSTEMS	
Gypsteel plank-2" thick	12
Sheetrock—Pyrofill-2½" thick	12
Featherweight nailing conc.-2½" thick	19
" channel slabs-2¾" "	10
Porete roof slabs (with ½" nailing fin) 2½" "	15
Porete channel slabs-3½" thick	12
Cinder plank-2" thick	15
Aerocrete lightweight conc.-lbs. per c.f.	50-80
Nalecode-lbs. per c.f.	75
METAL TILE & JOIST 20" WIDE PANS & 5" JOISTS	
4" deep plus 2½" topping	45
6" " " " " "	50
8" " " " " "	56
10" " " " " "	64
12" " " " " "	69
14" " " " " "	75
ONE WAY CLAY TILE-16" WIDE TILE & 4" JOISTS	
4" deep with no topping	27
5" " " " " "	31
6" " " " " "	37
7" " " " " "	42
8" " " " " "	46
9" " " " " "	50
10" " " " " "	54
12" " " " " "	62
TWO WAY SLAG BLOCK-16"x16" BLOCKS & 4" JOISTS	
4½" deep with no topping	39
6" " " " " "	49
7" " " " " "	54
8" " " " " "	59
9" " " " " "	67
10" " " " " "	74
10" " " " 1" "	86
TWO WAY CLAY TILE & JOIST-16"x16" BLOCKS & 4" JOISTS	
4" deep with no topping	31
4½" " " " " "	35
5" " " " " "	39
6" " " " " "	45
7" " " " " "	52
8" " " " " "	60
9" " " " " "	68
10" " " " " "	77

PLATE V.

TABLE A - LIVE LOADS IN POUNDS PER SQUARE FOOT.*

Occupancy[41]	Dept. of Commerce 1924	Nat. Bd. of Fire Underwriters 1934	Pacific Coast Bldg. Officials Conference 1937	New York 1938	Chicago[20] 1937	Philadelphia 1929	Detroit 1936
Dwellings, apartment and tenement houses, hotels, club houses, hospitals and places of detention:							
Dwellings, private rooms and apartments	40[1]	40	40	40[11]	40	40	40
Public corridors, lobbies and dining rooms	100	100	100	100	100	100	80
School buildings:							
Class rooms and rooms for similar use	50	50	40[7]	60[12]	50	50[25]	50[25]
Corridors and public parts of the building	100	100	100	100	100	100	80
Theaters, assembly halls and other places of assemblage:							
Auditoriums with fixed seats	50	100	50	75[13]	75	60[26]	80
Lobbies, passageways, gymnasiums, grandstands, stages and auditoriums or places of assemblage without fixed seats	100	100	100[8]	100	100	100	100[33]
Office buildings:							
Office space	50[2,3]	50[2]	50[2,3]	50[11]	50[21]	60	50[34]
Corridors and other public places	100	100	100	100[14]	100	100	125[14]
Workshops, factories and mercantile establishments:							
Manufacturing—light	75	125[2]	75	120	100	120[28,27]	100[35]
" —heavy		125			100	200[28]	
Storage—light	100	125[2]	125	120	100	150[28,29]	125[36]
" —heavy	250		250		100	200[28]	
Stores—retail	75	125[2]	75	75[15]	100	110[28]	100[35]
" —wholesale	100	125[2]	100	120	100	110[28]	100[35]
Garages:							
All types of vehicles	100	125[2]	100[9]	175[16]	100[22]	100[30]	150[37]
Passenger cars only	80	125[2]	100	75[17]	50[23]	100	80[38]
All stairs and fire escapes, except in private residences	100	100	100	100	100	100	100[39]
Roofs (flat)	30	30	20	40	25	30	30
Sidewalks	250[4]	300	250[4]	300[18]		120[31]	250
Wind	10-20[5]	15-30[6]	15-20[10]	0-20[19]	25-35[24]	20[32]	20[40]

GRANDSTAND LOADING ***

LIVE LOAD

100 #/sq. ft. of gross horizontal projection.
120 #/lin. ft. for designing seats & ftboards.

HORIZONTAL FORCES

A horizontal swaying force parallel to the seats of 24 #/ft, and perpendicular to the seats of 10 #/ft. Wind = 30 #/a on vertical projection.

WIND STRESS REDUCTIONS

CONCRETE STRUCTURES:- Increase allowable stresses⅓ where wind loads are added to live and dead loads. **
STEEL STRUCTURES:- Members subject only to wind, increase allowable stresses⅓. Members subject to wind and other forces increase stresses⅓, but section to be not less than that required for dead, live and impact loads †
WOOD STRUCTURES:- Increase allowable stresses ¼, but section to be not less than required for dead and live load. ‡‡

IMPACT

For structures carrying live loads which induce impact or vibration the assumed live load shall be increased sufficiently to provide for same. If not otherwise specified the increase shall be:-

For elevator supports   100 per cent
For traveling crane supports (girders & columns)   25   "   "
For light machinery, shaft or motor driven not less than   20   "   "
For reciprocating machinery or power units not less than   50   "   "
For threaded hanger rods supporting floor & balconies   33⅓ "   "

CRANE RUNWAY FORCES

The lateral forces on crane runways to provide for the effect of moving crane trolleys shall, if not otherwise specified, be 20 per cent of the sum of the weights of the lifted load and of the crane trolley (but exclusive of other parts of the crane) applied at the top of rail, one-half on each side of runway and considered as acting in either direction normal to the runway rail.

See Page 19-9 for explanation of foot notes and for live load reductions.
* Data from Reinf. Conc. Design Handbook of the Am. Conc. Institute 1939. ** From A.C.I., 1947.
† From A.I.S.C., 1947. ‡‡ From Wood Handbook of Forest Products Lab.- U.S. Dept of Agric. 1940.
*** From National Fire Protection Bulletin #102-1949.

PLATE VI.

FOOTNOTES FOR TABLE A - ON PLATE VI[*]

1. 30 for one and two family dwellings with floors of monolithic type or of solid or ribbed slabs.
2. Or 2000 on any space 2½ feet square.
3. Additional load equivalent to a single partition placed in any position.
4. Or 800 concentrated.
5. 10 for portions below 40 ft. and 20 for portions above 40 ft.
6. 15 for portions below 40 ft. and 30 for portions above 40 ft.
7. 60 for library reading rooms and 125 for stackrooms.
8. 150 for armories.
9. Or concentrated rear wheel of loaded truck in any position.
10. 15 for portions below 60 ft. and 20 for portions above 60 ft.
11. Including corridors.
12. For rooms with fixed seats or, by special permission, other small rooms. 120 for library stackrooms.
13. 60 for churches.
14. Including entire first floor.
15. 100 for entire first floor.
16. Or 6000 concentrated. Trucking space and driveways, 24,000 concentrated. (For beams, columns and girders 120% L.L.)
17. Or 2000 concentrated.
18. Or 12,000 concentrated for driveways over sidewalks.
19. 20 for structures over 100 ft. high. Special consideration for others.
20. When dead load exceeds live load, specified live loads may be reduced by ratio of live to dead but not to less than two-thirds.
21. Or 2000 concentrated on any space 3 feet square.
22. Or 3000 concentrated on any space 4 feet square.
23. 100 on first and second floors and alternate of 3000 on area 4 feet square.
24. 25 for surfaces less than 275 ft. high with variable above.
25. Only school class rooms with fixed seats.
26. Churches only.
27. 150 for certain occupancies.
28. Every floor beam 4000 concentrated.
29. 110 for storage of household goods.
30. Or 8000 concentrated.
31. Interior courts, sidewalks, etc., not accessible to a driveway.
32. 25 for isolated structures exposed for full height.
33. 125 for dance halls and drill halls.
34. Above first floor including corridors.
35. 125 for first floor.
36. 150 for first floor.
37. Or 2500 concentrated on area 6 inches square with such concentrations spaced alternately 2 ft. 4 in. and 4 ft. 8 in. in one direction and 5 ft. and 10 ft. in the other direction.
38. Only structures with clear head room of 8 ft. 6 in. or less. Or 1500 concentrated spaced as in 37.
39. 50 for dwellings and apartments under 3 stories.
40. For buildings less than 500 ft. high.
41. *The classification used in Table A is based primarily upon that given in the Report of the Building Code Committee of the U.S. Department of Commerce entitled "Minimum Live Loads Allowable for Use in Design of Buildings."*

UPLIFT ON ROOFS

Design roofs for factories, hangars, armories, etc., which have large open interiors for an uplift of 25 lbs. per sq. ft.

SNOW LOAD

Weight of snow varies from 5# per cu ft. to 12# per cu. ft for heavy old snow. Generally roof live loads will provide for maximum snow falls, but exceptional cases such as big flat roofs and high parapets may require special attention.

LIVE LOAD REDUCTIONS.

NEW YORK CITY CODE. 1948

(a) Structures for storage purposes - all columns, piers, walls & foundations may be designed for 85% of live load.

(b) In structures intended for other purposes live load reductions for columns, piers, walls and foundations are as follows: 100% L.L. on roof, 85% top floor, 80% next floor and 5% reduction for each successive lower floor provided that in all cases at least 50% of live load is assumed.

(c) Girder members (except in roofs & as specified below) carrying floor loads the equivalent of 200 Sq. Ft. or more may be designed for 85% of live load.

(d) Trusses & girders supporting columns and for determining area of footings, the full dead load & live load may be taken with the reductions as permitted in Par. (b).

DEPT. OF COMMERCE CODE. 1924

Except in buildings for storage purposes, the following reductions in assumed total live loads are permissible, in designing all columns, piers, walls, foundations, trusses and girders.

Reduction of total L.L. carried.

Carrying		
"	1 floor	0 %
"	2 "	10 "
"	3 "	20 "
"	4 "	30 "
"	5 "	40 "
"	6 "	45 "
"	7 " or more	50 "

In determining the area of footings the full dead loads plus live loads, with reductions figured as permitted above, shall be taken; except that in bldgs. for human occupancy a further reduction of ½ L.L. as permitted above may be used.

[*]*Data from Reinforced Concrete Design Handbook of the American Concrete Institute.*

BETHLEHEM AND CARNEGIE STRUCTURAL SECTI

D	Wt	S	t	Lu	V	R	G	d	b	t'	r'	Wh
36 WF	300	1105.1	.94	38.0	451	143	22.7	36 3/4	16 5/8	1.68	3.73	
	280	1031.2	.88	35.5	420	132	21.2	36 1/2	16 5/8	1.57	3.70	790C
	260	951.1	.84	32.5	398	123	20.3	36 1/4	16 1/2	1.44	3.65	950S
	245	892.5	.80	30.5	376	115	19.2	36	16 1/2	1.35	3.62	
	230	835.5	.76	28.5	357	108	18.4	35 7/8	16 1/2	1.26	3.59	
	194	663.6	.77	20.5	365	104	18.5	36 1/2	12 1/8	1.26	2.49	
	182	621.2	.72	19.5	342	97	17.4	36 3/8	12 1/8	1.18	2.47	590C
	170	579.1	.68	18.0	320	89	16.3	36 1/8	12	1.10	2.45	710S
	160	541.0	.65	17.0	306	84	15.7	36	12	1.02	2.42	
	150	502.9	.62	15.5	291	80	15.0	35 7/8	12	.94	2.38	
33 WF	240	811.1	.83	33.0	362	118	19.9	33 1/2	15 7/8	1.40	3.52	700C
	220	740.6	.77	30.0	335	108	18.6	33 1/4	15 3/4	1.27	3.48	840S
	200	669.6	.71	27.0	307	98	17.2	33	15 3/4	1.15	3.43	
	152	486.4	.63	18.0	277	82	15.2	33 1/2	11 5/8	1.05	2.39	
	141	446.8	.60	16.5	262	76	14.5	33 1/4	11 1/2	.96	2.35	510C
	130	404.8	.58	15.0	250	72	13.9	33 1/8	11 1/2	.85	2.29	620S
30 WF	210	649.9	.77	32.5	306	108	18.6	30 3/8	15 1/8	1.31	3.38	
	190	586.1	.71	29.5	278	97	17.0	30 1/8	15	1.18	3.34	600C
	172	528.2	.65	26.5	254	87	15.7	29 7/8	15	1.06	3.30	730S
	132	379.7	.61	17.5	242	77	14.8	30 1/4	10 1/2	1.00	2.18	
	124	354.6	.58	16.0	229	72	14.0	30 1/8	10 1/2	.93	2.16	430C
	116	327.9	.56	15.0	220	69	13.5	30	10 1/2	.85	2.12	530S
	108	299.2	.54	13.0	212	66	13.2	29 7/8	10 1/2	.76	2.06	
27 WF	177	492.8	.72	30.5	257	98	17.4	27 1/4	14 1/8	1.19	3.16	510C
	160	444.5	.66	27.5	232	88	15.8	27 1/8	14	1.07	3.12	620S
	145	402.9	.60	25.0	210	78	14.4	26 7/8	14	.97	3.09	
	114	299.2	.57	17.0	202	70	13.7	27 1/4	10 1/8	.93	2.11	
	102	266.3	.52	15.0	182	63	12.4	27 1/8	10	.83	2.08	370C
	94	242.8	.49	13.5	171	59	11.8	26 7/8	10	.75	2.04	460S

D	Wt	S	t	Lu	V	R	G	d	b	t'	r'	Wh
24 WF	160	413.5	.66	32.0	211	87	15.7	24 3/4	14 1/8	1.13	3.23	470C
	145	372.5	.61	29.0	194	79	14.6	24 1/2	14	1.02	3.19	570S
	130	330.7	.56	26.0	178	71	13.6	24 1/4	14	.90	3.13	
	120	299.1	.56	23.0	176	69	13.3	24 1/4	12 1/8	.93	2.68	
	110	274.4	.51	21.0	160	63	12.2	24 1/8	12	.85	2.66	390C
	100	248.9	.47	19.0	146	57	11.2	24	12	.77	2.63	470S
	94	220.9	.52	16.0	163	61	12.4	24 1/4	9	.87	1.92	
	84	196.3	.47	14.5	147	55	11.3	24 1/8	9	.77	1.89	310C
	76	175.4	.44	12.5	137	50	10.6	23 7/8	9	.68	1.85	380S
21 WF	142	317.2	.66	33.5	184	85	15.8	21 1/2	13 1/8	1.09	3.04	390C
	127	284.1	.59	30.0	162	74	14.1	21 1/4	13	.98	3.01	470S
	112	249.6	.53	27.0	144	65	12.7	21	13	.86	2.96	
	96	197.6	.57	20.0	158	70	13.8	21 1/8	9	.93	1.97	290C
	82	168.0	.50	17.0	135	59	12.0	20 7/8	9	.79	1.93	350S
	73	150.7	.45	14.5	126	53	10.9	21 1/4	8 1/4	.74	1.76	
	68	139.9	.43	13.5	118	49	10.3	21 1/8	8 1/4	.68	1.74	250C
	62	126.4	.40	12.0	109	45	9.6	21	8 1/4	.61	1.71	310S
18 WF	114	220.1	.59	31.5	143	74	14.3	18 1/2	11 7/8	.99	2.76	330C
	105	202.2	.55	29.0	132	68	13.3	18 3/8	11 3/4	.91	2.73	390S
	96	184.4	.51	27.0	121	62	12.3	18 1/8	11 3/4	.83	2.71	
	85	156.1	.53	22.0	125	63	12.6	18 3/8	8 7/8	.91	2.00	
	77	141.7	.47	20.0	112	56	11.4	18 1/8	8 3/4	.83	1.98	240C
	70	128.2	.44	18.0	103	51	10.5	18	8 3/4	.75	1.95	290S
	64	117.0	.40	16.5	94	46	9.7	17 7/8	8 3/4	.69	1.93	
	60	107.8	.42	14.5	99	47	10.0	18 1/4	7 1/2	.69	1.63	200C
	55	98.2	.39	13.0	92	43	9.4	18 1/8	7 1/2	.63	1.61	240S
	50	89.0	.36	12.0	84	39	8.6	18	7 1/2	.57	1.59	
16 WF	96	166.1	.53	31.0	114	66	12.8	16 3/8	11 1/2	.87	2.71	300C
	88	151.3	.50	28.0	106	61	12.1	16 1/8	11 1/2	.79	2.67	360S
	78	127.8	.53	23.0	112	64	12.7	16 3/8	8 5/8	.87	1.95	
	71	115.9	.49	21.0	102	57	11.7	16 1/8	8 1/2	.79	1.93	210C
	64	104.2	.44	19.0	92	51	10.6	16	8 1/2	.71	1.91	260S
	58	94.1	.41	17.0	84	46	9.8	15 7/8	8 1/2	.64	1.88	
	50	80.7	.38	13.5	80	42	9.1	16 1/4	7 1/8	.63	1.54	
	45	72.4	.35	12.0	73	38	8.3	16 1/8	7	.56	1.52	170C
	40	64.4	.31	11.0	64	33	7.4	16	7	.50	1.50	210S
	36	56.3	.30	9.5	62	32	7.2	15 7/8	7	.43	1.45	

D	Wt	S	t	Lu	V	R	G	d	b	t'	r'	Wh
14 WF	426	707.4	1.87	134.0	455	321	45.0	18 3/4	16 3/4	3.03	4.34	670C
	398	656.9	1.77	129.0	422	295	42.5	18 1/4	16 5/8	2.84	4.31	760S
	370	608.1	1.65	122.0	386	268	39.7	18	16 1/2	2.66	4.27	
	342	559.4	1.54	115.0	353	244	37.1	17 1/2	16 3/8	2.47	4.24	590C
	314	511.9	1.41	108.0	316	217	34.0	17 1/4	16 1/4	2.28	4.20	670S
	287	465.5	1.31	99.7	286	194	31.4	16 3/4	16 1/8	2.09	4.17	570C
	264	427.4	1.20	94.1	258	175	28.9	16 1/2	16	1.94	4.14	590S
	320	492.8	1.89	104.0	413	281	45.4	16 3/4	16 3/4	2.09	4.17	570C 650S
14 WF	246	397.4	1.12	89.0	238	160	27.0	16 1/4	16	1.81	4.12	
	237	382.2	1.09	86.4	228	154	26.2	16 1/8	15 7/8	1.75	4.11	
	228	367.8	1.04	83.7	217	146	25.1	16	15 7/8	1.69	4.10	460C
	219	352.6	1.00	80.8	207	139	24.1	15 7/8	15 7/8	1.62	4.08	530S
	211	339.2	.98	78.3	201	134	23.5	15 3/4	15 3/4	1.56	4.07	
	202	324.9	.93	75.6	189	125	22.3	15 5/8	15 3/4	1.50	4.06	
	193	310.0	.89	73.1	179	119	21.4	15 1/2	15 3/4	1.44	4.05	
	184	295.8	.84	70.4	168	111	20.2	15 3/8	15 5/8	1.38	4.04	
	176	281.9	.82	67.4	163	107	19.7	15 1/4	15 5/8	1.31	4.02	400C
	167	267.3	.78	64.5	154	100	18.7	15 1/8	15 5/8	1.25	4.01	460S
	158	253.4	.73	61.7	142	93	17.5	15	15 1/2	1.19	4.00	
	150	240.2	.69	59.0	134	88	16.7	14 7/8	15 1/2	1.13	3.99	
	142	226.7	.68	55.6	130	85	16.3	14 3/4	15 1/2	1.06	3.97	
14 WF	136	216.0	.66	53.0	127	82	15.8	14 3/4	14 3/4	1.06	3.77	
	127	202.0	.61	50.2	116	75	14.6	14 5/8	14 3/4	1.00	3.76	
	119	189.4	.57	47.0	107	69	13.7	14 1/2	14 5/8	.94	3.75	310C
	111	176.3	.54	44.0	101	65	13.0	14 3/8	14 5/8	.87	3.73	370S
	103	163.6	.49	41.0	92	59	11.9	14 1/4	14 5/8	.81	3.72	
	95	150.6	.46	38.0	85	55	11.2	14 1/8	14 1/2	.75	3.71	
	87	138.1	.42	35.5	76	49	10.1	14	14 1/2	.69	3.70	
14 WF	84	130.9	.45	33.0	83	53	10.8	14 1/8	12	.78	3.02	
	78	121.1	.43	30.5	78	49	10.3	14	12	.72	3.00	
	74	112.3	.45	28.0	83	53	10.8	14 1/4	10 1/8	.78	2.48	220C
	68	103.0	.42	25.5	76	48	10.0	14	10	.72	2.46	260S
	61	92.2	.38	23.0	68	43	9.1	13 7/8	10	.64	2.45	
	53	77.8	.37	19.0	67	42	8.9	14	8	.66	1.92	
	48	70.2	.34	17.0	61	38	8.1	13 3/4	8	.59	1.91	160C
	43	62.7	.31	15.5	55	34	7.4	13 5/8	8	.53	1.89	200S
	38	54.6	.31	12.5	58	34	7.5	14 1/8	6 3/4	.51	1.49	
	34	48.5	.29	11.0	52	31	6.9	14	6 3/4	.45	1.46	
	30	41.8	.27	9.5	49	28	6.5	13 7/8	6 3/4	.38	1.41	

D	Wt	S	t	L
12 WF	190	263.2	1.06	76
	161	222.2	.90	67
	133	182.5	.75	57
	120	163.4	.71	52
	106	144.5	.62	46
	99	134.7	.58	44
	92	125.0	.54	41
	85	115.7	.49	38
	79	107.1	.47	36
	72	97.5	.43	33
	65	88.0	.39	30
12 WF	58	78.1	.36	26
	53	70.7	.34	24
	50	64.7	.37	21
	45	58.2	.34	19
	40	51.9	.29	17
	36	45.9	.30	14
	31	39.4	.27	12
	27	34.1	.24	10
	22	25.3	.26	7
	19	21.4	.24	5
	16.5	17.5	.23	4
	14	14.8	.20	3
10 WF	112	126.3	.75	57
	100	112.4	.68	52
	89	99.7	.61	47
	77	86.1	.53	41
	72	80.1	.51	39
	66	73.7	.46	36
	60	67.1	.41	33
	54	60.4	.37	30
	49	54.6	.34	28
10 WF	45	49.1	.35	[illegible]
	39	42.2	.32	[illegible]
	33	35.0	.29	[illegible]
	29	30.8	.29	[illegible]
	25	26.4	.25	[illegible]
	21	21.5	.24	[illegible]
	19	18.8	.25	[illegible]
	17	16.2	.24	[illegible]
	15	13.8	.23	[illegible]
	11.5	10.5	.18	[illegible]

COLUMN WORKING STRESSES - KIPS/SQ.IN.
A.I.S.C. MAIN MEMBERS

l/r	f	l/r	f	l/r	f	l/r	f	l/r	f	l/r	f	l/r	f	l/r	f
15	16.9	61	15.2	71	14.6	81	13.8	91	13.0	101	12.1	111	11.0	125	9.4
20	16.8	62	15.1	72	14.5	82	13.7	92	12.9	102	12.0	112	10.9	130	8.8
25	16.7	63	15.1	73	14.4	83	13.7	93	12.8	103	11.9	113	10.8	135	8.3
30	16.6	64	15.0	74	14.3	84	13.6	94	12.7	104	11.8	114	10.7	140	7.8
35	16.4	65	15.0	75	14.3	85	13.5	95	12.6	105	11.7	115	10.6	150	6.8
40	16.2	66	14.9	76	14.2	86	13.4	96	12.5	106	11.6	116	10.5	160	5.9
45	16.0	67	14.8	77	14.1	87	13.3	97	12.4	107	11.5	117	10.4	170	5.2
50	15.8	68	14.8	78	14.1	88	13.2	98	12.3	108	11.3	118	10.3	180	4.5
55	15.5	69	14.7	79	14.0	89	13.2	99	12.3	109	11.2	119	10.1	190	3.9
60	15.3	70	14.6	80	13.9	90	13.1	100	12.2	110	11.1	120	10.0	200	3.4

DEFLECTION COEFFICIENT - UNIFORM LOADS 20,000 #/□"

$$\text{DEFL. INCHES} = \frac{\text{DEFL. COEF.}}{d} = \frac{.02069\,L^2}{d}$$

L	DEFL. COEF.	L	DEFL. COEF.	L	DEFL. COEF.	L	DEFL. COEF.	L	DEFL. COEF.
21	9.124	31	19.883	41	34.780	51	53.815	62	79.532
22	10.014	32	21.187	42	36.497	52	55.946	64	84.746
23	10.945	33	22.531	43	38.256	53	58.118	66	90.126
24	11.917	34	23.918	44	40.056	54	60.332	68	95.671
25	12.931	35	25.345	45	41.897	55	62.587	70	101.381
26	13.986	36	26.814	46	43.780	56	64.884	72	107.257
27	15.083	37	28.325	47	45.704	57	67.222	74	113.298
28	16.221	38	29.876	48	47.670	58	69.601	76	119.505
29	17.400	39	31.469	49	49.677	59	72.022	78	125.878
30	18.621	40	33.104	50	51.725	60	74.484	80	132.416

SHEAR @ 15,000 — VALUE FOR POWER DRIVEN RIVETS AND TURNED BOLTS IN REAMED HOLES — BEARING SINGLE = 32,000, DOUBLE = 40,000

RIVET DIAM.	5/8"		3/4"		7/8"		1"		1 1/8"	
SINGLE SHEAR	4600		6630		9020		11780		14910	
DOUBLE SHEAR	9200		13250		18040		23560		29820	
PLATE THICKNESS	BEARING (IN KIPS)		BEARING (IN KIPS)		BEARING (IN KIPS)		BEARING (IN KIPS)		BEARING (IN KIPS)	
	32.0	40.0	32.0	40.0	32.0	40.0	32.0	40.0	32.0	40.0
1/4"	—	6.25	6.00	7.50	7.00	8.75	8.00	10.0	—	—
5/16"	—	7.81	—	9.38	8.75	10.9	10.0	12.5	11.3	14.1
3/8"	—	9.38	—	11.3	—	13.1	12.0	15.0	13.5	16.9
7/16"	—	—	—	13.1	—	15.3	—	17.5	—	19.7
1/2"	—	—	—	—	—	17.5	—	20.0	—	22.5
9/16"	—	—	—	—	—	—	—	22.5	—	25.3
5/8"	—	—	—	—	—	—	—	—	—	28.1

TENSION IN RIVETS 20,000 #/□"

DIA.	TENSION IN KIPS
1/2"	3.9
5/8"	6.1
3/4"	8.8
7/8"	12.0
1"	15.7
1 1/8"	19.8
1 1/4"	24.4

SHEAR @ 10,000 — VA[illegible] UNFIN[illegible]

BOLT DIAM.	5/8"		
SINGLE SHEAR	3070		4
DOUBLE SHEAR	6140		8
PLATE THICKNESS	BEARING (IN KIPS)		BE
	20.0	25.0	20.
1/4"	3.13	3.91	3.7
5/16"	—	4.88	—
3/8"	—	5.86	—
7/16"	—	—	—
1/2"	—	—	—
9/16"	—	—	—
5/8"	—	—	—

Sections revised according to Bulletin R-216-46 U.S. Dept. of Commerce. Dated Feb. 15, 1946.

STEEL

(cut off)	d	b	t'	r'	Wh
5.4	14 3/8	12 5/8	1.74	3.25	
.7	13 7/8	12 1/2	1.49	3.20	340C
.1	13 3/8	12 3/8	1.24	3.16	390S
7.0	13 1/8	12 3/8	1.11	3.13	
.9	12 7/8	12 1/4	.99	3.11	
.9	12 3/4	12 1/4	.92	3.09	
.1	12 5/8	12 1/8	.86	3.08	
.9	12 1/2	12 1/8	.80	3.07	230C
.3	12 3/8	12 1/8	.74	3.05	280S
.3	12 1/4	12	.67	3.04	
.4	12 1/8	12	.61	3.02	
.6	12 1/4	10	.64	2.51	180C
.3	12	10	.58	2.48	220S
.9	12 1/4	8 1/8	.64	1.96	
.1	12	8	.58	1.94	150C
.1	12	8	.52	1.94	180S
.3	12 1/4	6 5/8	.54	1.50	
.4	12 1/8	6 1/2	.46	1.47	120C
.8	12	6 1/2	.40	1.44	150S
.2	12 1/4	4	.42	.84	
.8	12 1/8	4	.35	.81	
.5	12	4	.27	.76	80C
.8	11 7/8	4	.22	.74	100S
.1	11 3/8	10 3/8	1.25	2.67	230C
.5	11 1/8	10 3/8	1.12	2.65	260S
.8	10 7/8	10 1/4	1.00	2.63	
.8	10 5/8	10 1/4	.87	2.60	
.2	10 1/2	10 1/8	.81	2.59	
.0	10 3/8	10 1/8	.75	2.58	160C
.0	10 1/4	10 1/8	.68	2.57	190S
.8	10 1/8	10	.62	2.56	
.2	10	10	.56	2.54	
.4	10 1/8	8	.62	2.00	120C
.6	10	8	.53	1.98	140S
.0	9 3/4	8	.43	1.94	
.9	10 1/4	5 3/4	.50	1.34	
.0	10 1/8	5 3/4	.43	1.31	90C
.8	9 7/8	5 3/4	.34	1.25	110S
.0	10 1/4	4	.39	.86	
.8	10 1/8	4	.33	.83	70C
.5	10	4	.27	.80	80S
.3	9 7/8	4	.20	.77	

D	Wt	S	t	Lu	V	R	G	d	b	t'	r'	Wh
8 WF	67	60.4	.57	42.9	67	67	13.8	9	8 1/4	.93	2.12	
	58	52.0	.51	37.9	58	57	12.2	8 3/4	8 1/4	.81	2.10	130C
	48	43.2	.40	32.6	45	44	9.7	8 1/2	8 1/8	.68	2.08	150S
	40	35.5	.36	27.4	39	39	8.8	8 1/4	8 1/8	.56	2.04	
	35	31.1	.31	24.0	33	33	7.6	8 1/8	8	.49	2.03	100C
	31	27.4	.29	21.5	30	30	6.9	8	8	.43	2.01	110S
	28	24.3	.29	18.5	30	30	6.8	8	6 1/2	.46	1.62	80C
	24	20.8	.24	16.0	25	25	5.9	7 7/8	6 1/2	.40	1.61	90S
	20	17.0	.25	12.0	26	25	6.0	8 1/8	5 1/4	.38	1.20	70C
	17	14.1	.23	10.0	24	23	5.5	8	5 1/4	.31	1.16	80S
	15	11.8	.24	7.5	26	24	5.9	8 1/8	4	.31	.86	
	13	9.9	.23	6.0	24	22	5.5	8	4	.25	.83	50C
	10	7.8	.17	5.0	18	16	4.1	7 7/8	4	.20	.82	60S
8C	34.3	28.9	.37	21.9	39	39	9.0	8	8	.44	1.87	100C 110S
6 WF	25	16.8	.32	21.8	27	33	7.7	6 3/8	6	.46	1.52	
	20	13.4	.26	17.8	21	26	6.2	6 1/4	6	.37	1.50	60C
	15.5	10.1	.24	13.5	19	24	5.8	6	6	.27	1.45	70S
	16	10.1	.26	13.0	21	26	6.2	6 1/4	4	.40	.96	50C
	12	7.24	.23	9.0	18	22	5.5	6	4	.28	.90	60S
	8.5	5.07	.17	6.5	13	16	4.1	5 7/8	4	.19	.87	
6C	25	15.7	.31	25.0	24	32	7.5	6	6	.50	1.43	60C
	20	12.9	.25	18.8	20	26	6.0	6	6	.37	1.39	70S
5 WF	18.9	9.5	.31	21.9	20	32	7.5	5	5	.44	1.20	40C
	18.5	9.9	.26	20.6	18	27	6.4	5 1/8	5	.42	1.28	50S
	16	8.5	.24	18.0	16	24	5.8	5	5	.36	1.26	
4B	13	5.45	.28	16.8	15	27	6.7	4 1/8	4	.34	.99	30C 40S
4C	13	5.2	.25	18.8	13	25	6.0	4	4	.37	.94	
4 WF	10	4.1	.22	13.2	11	22	5.3	4	4	.26	.97	

Junior Beams
(By Jones & Laughlin Steel Corp. Only)

D	Wt	S	t	Lu	V	R	G	d	b	t'	r'
12	11.8	12.0	.175	3.2	27.0	16.8	4.2	12	3	1/4	.53
11	10.3	9.6	.165	2.4	24.0	15.8	4.0	11	2 7/8	3/16	.50
10	9.0	7.8	.155	2.5	20.0	14.7	3.7	10	2 3/4	3/16	.48
9	7.5	5.8	.145	2.5	17.0	13.7	3.3	9	2 3/8	3/16	.42
8	6.5	4.7	.135	2.7	14.0	12.6	1.4	8	2 1/4	3/16	.42
7	5.5	3.5	.126	2.8	11.5	11.5	—	7	2 1/8	3/16	.39
6	4.4	2.4	.114	2.9	8.9	8.9	—	6	1 7/8	3/16	.36

Junior Channels
(By Jones & Laughlin Steel Corp. Only)

D	Wt	S	t	Lu	V	R	G	d	b	t'	r'
12	10.6	9.3	.19	2.0	29.6	18.6	4.5	12	1 1/2	5/16	.35
10	8.4	6.5	.17	1.9	22.1	16.0	4.0	10	1 1/2	1/4	.37
10	6.5	4.4	.15	2.3	19.5	13.9	3.6	10	1 1/8	13/32	.25

Amer. Std. Channel Sect.

D	Wt	S	t	Lu	V	R	G	d	b	t'	r'	Wh
18 [	58	74.5	.70	7.3	164	81	16.8	18	4 1/4	.62	1.04	
	51.9	69.1	.60	7.1	140	69	14.4	18	4 1/8	.62	1.06	140C
	45.8	63.7	.50	6.9	117	58	12.0	18	4	.62	1.09	170S
	42.7	61.0	.45	6.9	105	52	10.8	18	4	.62	1.10	
15 [	50	53.6	.72	8.0	140	83	17.2	15	3 3/4	.65	.87	120C
	40	46.2	.52	7.6	101	60	12.5	15	3 1/2	.65	.89	140S
	33.9	41.7	.40	7.4	78	46	9.6	15	3 3/8	.65	.91	
13 [	50	48.1	.79	10.3	133	91	19.0	13	4 3/8	.61	1.07	
	40	41.7	.56	9.8	94	65	13.4	13	4 1/8	.61	1.09	100C
	35	38.6	.45	9.5	76	52	10.8	13	4 1/8	.61	1.10	120S
	31.8	36.5	.38	9.4	64	43	9.1	13	4	.61	1.11	
12 [	30	26.9	.51	6.6	80	56	12.2	12	3 1/8	.50	.77	80C
	25	23.9	.39	6.4	60	42	9.3	12	3	.50	.79	100S
	20.7	21.4	.28	6.1	44	31	6.7	12	3	.50	.81	
10 [	30	20.6	.67	6.6	88	72	16.2	10	3	.44	.67	
	25	18.1	.53	6.3	68	56	12.6	10	2 7/8	.44	.68	70C
	20	15.7	.38	6.0	49	40	9.1	10	2 3/4	.44	.70	90S
	15.3	13.4	.24	5.7	31	26	5.8	10	2 5/8	.44	.72	
9 [	20	13.5	.45	6.1	52	47	10.8	9	2 5/8	.41	.65	60C
	15	11.3	.28	5.7	33	30	6.8	9	2 1/2	.41	.67	70S
	13.4	10.5	.23	5.6	27	24	5.5	9	2 3/8	.41	.67	
8 [	18.75	10.9	.49	6.2	51	50	11.7	8	2 1/2	.39	.60	50C
	13.75	9.0	.30	5.7	32	31	7.3	8	2 3/8	.39	.62	60S
	11.5	8.1	.22	5.5	23	23	5.3	8	2 1/4	.39	.63	
7 [	14.75	7.7	.42	6.0	38	43	10.1	7	2 1/4	.37	.57	40C
	12.25	6.9	.31	5.7	29	33	7.5	7	2 1/4	.37	.58	50S
	9.8	6.0	.21	5.5	19	22	5.0	7	2 1/8	.37	.59	
6 [	13.0	5.8	.44	6.2	34	45	10.5	6	2 1/8	.34	.53	30C
	10.5	5.0	.31	5.8	25	32	7.5	6	2	.34	.53	40S
	8.2	4.3	.20	5.5	16	20	4.8	6	1 7/8	.34	.54	
5 [	9.0	3.5	.32	6.0	21	33	7.8	5	1 7/8	.32	.49	25C
	6.7	3.0	.19	5.6	12	19	4.6	5	1 3/4	.32	.50	35S
4 [	7.25	2.3	.32	6.4	17	32	7.7	4	1 3/4	.30	.46	20C
	5.4	1.9	.18	5.9	9	18	4.3	4	1 5/8	.30	.45	30S
3 [	6.0	1.4	.36	7.2	14	35	8.5	3	1 5/8	.27	.42	
	5.0	1.2	.26	6.8	10	26	6.2	3	1 1/2	.27	.41	10C
	4.1	1.1	.17	6.4	7	17	4.1	3	1 3/8	.27	.41	10S

Amer. Std. Beam Sect.

D	Wt	S	t	Lu	V	R	G	d	b	t'	r'	Wh
24 I	120	250.9	.80	18.5	249	104	19.2	24	8	1.10	1.56	320C
	105.9	234.3	.62	18.0	195	82	15.0	24	7 7/8	1.10	1.60	380S
	100	197.6	.75	13.0	233	92	17.9	24	7 1/4	.87	1.29	280C
	90	185.8	.62	13.0	195	77	15.0	24	7 1/8	.87	1.32	330S
	79.9	173.9	.50	12.5	156	62	12.0	24	7	.87	1.36	
20 I	95	160.0	.80	16.5	208	101	19.2	20	7 1/4	.92	1.35	
	85	150.2	.65	16.0	170	82	15.7	20	7	.92	1.38	240C
	75	126.3	.64	12.5	167	78	15.4	20	6 3/8	.79	1.17	280S
	65.4	116.9	.50	12.0	130	61	12.0	20	6 1/4	.79	1.21	
18 I	70	101.9	.71	12.0	166	83	17.1	18	6 1/4	.69	1.09	190C
	54.7	88.4	.46	11.5	108	54	11.0	18	6	.69	1.15	230S
15 I	50	64.2	.55	11.5	107	63	13.2	15	5 5/8	.62	1.05	160C
	42.9	58.9	.41	11.0	80	47	9.8	15	5 1/2	.62	1.08	190S
12 I	50	50.3	.69	15.0	107	79	16.5	12	5 1/2	.66	1.05	
	40.8	44.8	.46	14.5	72	53	11.0	12	5 1/4	.66	1.08	120C
	35	37.8	.43	11.5	67	48	10.3	12	5 1/8	.54	.99	140S
	31.8	36.0	.35	11.5	55	39	8.4	12	5	.54	1.01	
10 I	35	29.2	.59	12.0	77	64	14.3	10	5	.49	.91	90C
	25.4	24.4	.31	11.5	40	34	7.4	10	4 5/8	.49	.97	110S
8 I	23.0	16.0	.44	11.0	46	46	10.6	8	4 1/8	.42	.81	70C
	18.4	14.2	.27	10.5	28	28	6.5	8	4	.42	.84	80S
7 I	20.0	12.0	.45	11.0	41	47	10.8	7	3 7/8	.39	.74	50C
	15.3	10.4	.25	10.0	23	26	6.0	7	3 5/8	.39	.78	60S
6 I	17.25	8.7	.47	10.5	36	47	11.0	6	3 5/8	.36	.68	30C
	12.5	7.3	.23	10.0	18	24	5.5	6	3 3/8	.36	.72	40S
5 I	14.75	6.0	.49	10.5	32	50	12.0	5	3 1/4	.33	.63	30C
	10.0	4.8	.21	10.0	14	21	5.0	5	3	.33	.65	40S
4 I	9.5	3.3	.33	10.0	17	32	8.0	4	2 3/4	.29	.58	30C
	7.7	3.0	.19	9.5	10	19	4.6	4	2 5/8	.29	.59	40S
3 I	7.5	1.9	.35	11.0	14	34	8.4	3	2 1/2	.26	.53	20C
	5.7	1.7	.17	10.0	7	17	4.1	3	2 3/8	.26	.53	30S

(cut off)	Bearing Single = 20,000 Double = 25,000 1"		Tension in Bolts 20,000#/□" Dia	Tension in Kips
0	7850		1/2"	2.5
0	15710		5/8"	4.0
NG (...PS)	Bearing (in kips)		3/4"	6.0
25.0	20.0	25.0	7/8"	8.3
5.47	5.00	6.25	1"	11.0
6.84	6.25	7.81	1 1/8"	13.8
3.20	7.50	9.38	1 1/4"	17.8
9.57	—	10.9	1 3/8"	21.0
0.9	—	12.5	1 1/2"	25.8
—	—	14.1	1 3/4"	34.8
—	—	15.6	2"	46.0

Equal Leg Angles

Size	S 1-1	Area	r 1-1	r 3-3	Size	S 1-1	Area	r 1-1	r 3-3
2 1/2 × 2 1/2 × 1/4	.39	1.19	.77	.49	5 × 5 × 3/8	2.4	3.61	1.56	.99
2 1/2 × 2 1/2 × 3/8	.57	1.73	.75	.49	5 × 5 × 1/2	3.2	4.75	1.54	.98
3 × 3 × 1/4	.58	1.44	.93	.59	6 × 6 × 3/8	3.5	4.36	1.88	1.19
3 × 3 × 5/16	.71	1.78	.92	.59	6 × 6 × 7/16	4.1	5.06	1.87	1.19
3 1/2 × 3 1/2 × 1/4	.79	1.69	1.09	.69	6 × 6 × 1/2	4.6	5.75	1.86	1.18
3 1/2 × 3 1/2 × 3/8	1.2	2.48	1.07	.69	6 × 6 × 3/4	6.7	8.44	1.83	1.17
3 1/2 × 3 1/2 × 1/2	1.5	3.25	1.06	.68	6 × 6 × 1	8.6	11.00	1.80	1.17
4 × 4 × 1/4	1.1	1.94	1.25	.80	8 × 8 × 1/2	8.4	7.75	2.50	1.59
4 × 4 × 3/8	1.5	2.86	1.23	.79	8 × 8 × 3/4	12.2	11.44	2.47	1.57
4 × 4 × 1/2	2.0	3.75	1.22	.78	8 × 8 × 1	15.8	15.00	2.44	1.56
4 × 4 × 3/4	2.8	5.44	1.19	.78	8 × 8 × 1 1/8	17.5	16.73	2.42	1.56

Unequal Leg Angles

Size	S 1-1	S 2-2	Area	r 1-1	r 2-2	r 3-3	Size	S 1-1	S 2-2	Area	r 1-1	r 2-2	r 3-3
2 1/2 × 2 × 1/4	.38	.25	1.06	.78	.59	.42	7 × 4 × 1/2	5.8	2.1	5.25	2.25	1.11	.87
3 × 2 1/2 × 1/4	.56	.40	1.31	.95	.75	.53	7 × 4 × 3/4	8.4	3.0	7.69	2.22	1.09	.86
3 1/2 × 3 × 1/4	.78	.59	1.56	1.11	.91	.63	8 × 4 × 1/2	7.5	2.2	5.75	2.59	1.08	.86
4 × 3 × 1/4	1.0	.60	1.69	1.28	.90	.65	8 × 4 × 3/4	10.9	3.1	8.44	2.55	1.05	.85
4 × 3 × 5/16	1.2	.73	2.09	1.27	.89	.65	8 × 4 × 1	14.1	3.9	11.00	2.52	1.03	.85
5 × 3 1/2 × 5/16	1.9	1.0	2.56	1.61	1.03	.76	8 × 6 × 1/2	8.0	4.8	6.75	2.56	1.79	1.30
5 × 3 1/2 × 3/8	2.3	1.2	3.05	1.60	1.02	.76	8 × 6 × 3/4	11.7	6.9	9.94	2.53	1.76	1.29
5 × 3 1/2 × 1/2	3.0	1.6	4.00	1.58	1.01	.75	8 × 6 × 1	15.1	8.9	13.00	2.49	1.73	1.28
6 × 4 × 3/8	3.3	1.6	3.61	1.93	1.17	.88	9 × 4 × 1/2	9.3	2.2	6.25	2.92	1.05	.85
6 × 4 × 1/2	4.3	2.1	4.75	1.91	1.15	.87	9 × 4 × 3/4	13.6	3.1	9.19	2.88	1.02	.84
6 × 4 × 3/4	6.3	3.0	6.94	1.88	1.12	.86	9 × 4 × 1	17.6	4.0	12.00	2.84	1.00	.83

Nomenclature

D = Nominal depth in inches.
Wt = Weight per foot in lbs.
S = Section modulus.
t = Web thickness in inches.
Lu = Maximum length @ 20,000 #/□" with unbraced comp. flange.
V = Maximum web shear in kips for 13,000 #/□"
R = Allowable end reaction in kips for 3 1/2" bearing (A.I.S.C.)
G = Increase in R in kips for 1" additional bearing (A.I.S.C.)
d = Actual depth in inches.
b = Flange width in inches.
t' = Flange thickness in inches.
Wh = Weight of haunch & section in #/': S = Stone conc. C = Cinder conc.
B = Bethlehem Steel Co. section.
C = U.S. Steel Corp. section.
I = American Standard section.
l = Length of member in inches.
r = Radius of gyration.
r' = Least radius of gyration.
f = Maximum allowable stress intensity per sq. inch.

Seelye, Stevenson & Value
Consulting Engineers
101 Park Ave., New York City. May 11, 1949

Diagonal lines in boxes indicate web shear governs.

EXAMPLES FOR USE OF BEAM TABLES - PLATES VIII-XI

ASSUMPTIONS FOR ALL EXAMPLES: $f_s = 20,000$ #/□", $f'_c = 3,000$, $n = 10$
$f_c = .45 \times 3000 = 1350$. DESIGN FOR d MINIMUM & BALANCED REINFORCEMENT.

EXAMPLE Nº 1. Given: Rectangular Beam, M = 90,000'#, b = 12".
Required: Effective depth "d" & Steel "As".
Solution: From Table A·Plate X the minimum effective depth "d" for moment of 90,000'# required is 20" for 12" width good for 94,200# requiring As = 3.26□. ∴ Total depth of beam = 20"+2" = 22" and required

$A_s = 3.26 \times \frac{90,000}{94,200} = 3.11$ □

∴ Use 2-#9 & 1-#10

These 3 Bars may be placed in 1 row for 12" wide Beam.
Check Shear and Bond Stresses.

EXAMPLE Nº 2. Given: Rectangular Beam with Compression Steel, M = 90,000'#, depth = 20", b = 12".
Required: Tension Steel As and Compr. Steel A's.
Solution: From Table A·Plate X the minimum effective depth "d" for moment of 90,000'# required is 18" for 12" width good for 76,300'# requiring As = 2.94□. ∴ The difference in moments = 90,000 - 76,300 = 13,700'#, which must be taken up by Compression Steel. From Table A·Pg. 1-36 Column for 1□" Compression Steel gives moment of M = 24.8'#. ∴ Required Compression Steel A's = $\frac{13.7}{24.8}$ = 0.55 □". Use 2-#5
This Compression Steel must be balanced by additional Tension Steel A_T·As = 3.45

Use 3 #10 placed in 1 row for 12" wide Beam.

Check Shear and Bond Stresses.

EXAMPLE Nº 3. Given: T·Beam, M = 105,000'#, Slab thickness 4", width b = 2'0", width of stem b'=12".
Required: Depth of Beam "d", Steel As.
Solution: From Table A·Plate X value of moment to be carried by 12" of width M = $\frac{105,000}{2}$ = 52,500'#. In same Table, in Column for 4" Slabs, the minimum effective depth "d" for moment of 52,500'# is 16" for 12" width & is good for 53,300'# requiring As = 2.23□. ∴ Total depth of Beam = 16"+2 = 18" & required As = $\frac{105,000}{53,300} \times 2.23 = 4.4$□. ∴ Use 2-#9 & 2-#10. Place 2-#10 in bottom layer & 1-#9 in 2nd layer.

EXAMPLE Nº 4. Given: T·Beam with Compression Steel. Total Moment M = 132,000'#, Slab thickness 4", b = 2'0", d = 16".
Required: Tension and Compression reinforcement.

(a). Concrete Compression in Stem neglected.
Solution: From Table A·Plate X in Col. for 4" Slab and d=16" find M = 53,300'# and As = 2.23□. ∴ The difference in moments Mc = 132,000 - 2 x 53,300 = 25,400'# which must be taken up by Compression Steel. From Table A·Plate X in Column for 1□" Compression Steel M = 20,600'# for d = 16".
Total Compression Steel required A's = $\frac{25,400}{20,600}$ = 1.23 □. ∴ Use 2-#6 & 1-#7
This Compression Steel must be balanced by additional Tension Steel. Referring to last Column in Table A·Plate X A_T = .89 per 1□" of Compression Steel. Total Tension Steel As = 2.23 x 2 + .89 x 1.23 = 5.05. ∴ Use 2-#9 & 2-#11.

Minim. width of stem for 2-#9 & 2-#11 = = b' = 17½". Use 18" and Bars may be placed in 1 row for 18" wide Beam.
Check Shear and Bond Stresses.

(b). Concrete Compression in Stem considered.
Solution: From Table A·Plate X in Col. for 4" Slab and d=16", find M = 53,300'# and As = 2.23□. Width of slab 24"-18" = 6" M = 53,300 x 6/12 = 26,700'#, A's = 2.23 x 6/12 = 1.12 □. From Table A·Plate X in Rectg. Beam Col. and d=16" find M = 60,300'# requiring Steel As = 2.61□. ∴ For 18" wide Beam and 16" effective depth M = 60,300 x $\frac{18}{12}$ = 90,500'#, As = 2.61 x $\frac{18}{12}$ = 3.92□. The difference in moments Mc = 132,000 - 26,700 - 90,500 = 14,800'#. From Table A·Plate X in Col. for 1□" Compr. Steel M = 20,600'# for d = 16". Total Compr. Steel required A's = $\frac{14,800}{20,600}$ = .72 □. This Compression Steel must be balanced by additional Tension Steel. Referring to Table A·Plate X A_T = .89 □. ∴ Use 2-#6 Total Tension Steel reqd. As = 1.12 + 3.92 + .89 x .72 = 5.68 □. ∴ Use 2-#10 & 2-#11 and Bars may be placed in 1 row for 18" wide Beam. Check Shear & Bond Stresses.

PLATE VII.

TABLE A - RESISTING MOMENTS OF CONCRETE BEAMS.*

$f_s = 20,000 \#/\square"$ $f_c = 900$
$f'_c = 2,000$ $n = 15$ $R = 157.0$

M = Moment of resistance of beam one foot wide in 1000 foot lbs.
A_s = Tensile steel area in sq. inches for moment M.
A_T = Sq. in. additional tensile steel for each $1\square"$ compression steel.

| | TEE BEAMS FOR SLAB THICKNESSES SHOWN | | | | | | | | | | | | RECTANGULAR BEAM | | MOM. $1\square"$ COMP. STEEL | | | |
| | 2" SLAB | | 2½" SLAB | | 3" SLAB | | 4" SLAB | | 5" SLAB | | 6" SLAB | | | | A.C.I. | | N.Y.C. | |
d	M	A_s	M	A_s	M	A_s	M	A_s	M	A_s	M	A_s	M	A_s	M'	A_T	M'	A_T
6"	5.5	.63											5.7	.65	1.5	.23	.73	.11
6½	6.4	.67											6.6	.71	2.3	.31	1.1	.15
7	7.2	.70	7.6	.75									7.7	.76	3.2	.38	1.5	.18
7½	8.0	.72	8.6	.79									8.8	.82	4.1	.44	2.0	.21
8	8.9	.74	9.7	.83	9.9	.87							10.0	.87	5.0	.50	2.4	.24
8½	9.7	.76	10.2	.86	11.2	.91							11.3	.92	5.9	.55	2.9	.26
9	10.6	.78	11.8	.88	12.4	.95							12.7	.98	6.8	.59	3.3	.28
9½	11.5	.80	12.8	.91	13.7	.99							14.2	1.03	7.8	.63	3.8	.30
10	12.3	.81	13.9	.93	14.9	1.02	15.7	1.09					15.7	1.09	8.8	.66	4.2	.32
10½	13.2	.83	15.0	.95	16.2	1.05	17.3	1.14					17.3	1.14	9.8	.69	4.7	.34
11	14.1	.84	16.0	.97	17.4	1.07	18.9	1.19					19.0	1.20	10.8	.72	5.2	.35
11½	15.0	.85	17.1	.99	18.7	1.10	20.5	1.23					20.8	1.25	11.8	.75	5.7	.36
12	15.8	.86	18.2	1.00	20.0	1.12	22.1	1.27					22.6	1.31	12.8	.77	6.2	.37
12½	16.7	.86	19.3	1.02	21.3	1.14	23.8	1.31					24.5	1.36	13.8	.79	6.7	.38
13	17.6	.87	20.4	1.03	22.6	1.16	25.4	1.34	26.5	1.41			26.5	1.41	14.8	.81	7.1	.39
13½	18.5	.88	21.4	1.04	23.9	1.18	27.1	1.37	28.5	1.46			28.7	1.47	15.8	.83	7.6	.40
14	19.4	.89	22.5	1.05	25.1	1.19	28.7	1.39	30.5	1.50			30.8	1.52	16.9	.84	8.1	.41
15	21.1	.90	24.7	1.07	27.7	1.22	32.1	1.45	34.6	1.58	35.3	1.63	35.3	1.63	19.0	.87	9.1	.42
16	22.9	.91	26.9	1.09	30.4	1.24	35.5	1.49	38.7	1.65	40.0	1.73	40.2	1.74	21.1	.90	10.1	.43
17	24.7	.92	29.2	1.11	33.0	1.27	39.0	1.53	42.8	1.72	44.8	1.82	45.4	1.85	23.1	.93	11.2	.45
18	26.5	.93	31.4	1.12	35.6	1.29	42.4	1.56	47.0	1.77	49.8	1.90	50.9	1.96	25.2	.95	12.2	.46
19	28.3	.94	33.6	1.13	38.3	1.30	45.9	1.60	51.3	1.82	54.7	1.97	56.7	2.07	27.3	.97	13.2	.47
20	30.0	.95	35.8	1.14	40.9	1.32	49.3	1.62	55.5	1.86	59.7	2.04	62.8	2.18	29.0	.97	14.2	.47
21	31.8	.95	38.0	1.15	43.6	1.33	52.8	1.65	59.8	1.90	64.7	2.09	69.2	2.28	30.6	.97	15.2	.48
22	33.6	.96	40.3	1.16	46.2	1.35	56.3	1.67	64.0	1.94	69.7	2.14	76.0	2.39	32.2	.97	16.3	.49
23	35.4	.96	42.5	1.17	48.9	1.36	59.8	1.69	68.3	1.97	74.8	2.19	83.0	2.50	33.8	.97	17.3	.49
24	37.2	.97	44.7	1.18	51.5	1.37	63.3	1.71	72.7	2.00	79.9	2.23	90.4	2.61	35.4	.96	18.3	.50
25	38.8	.97	46.9	1.18	54.2	1.38	66.9	1.72	76.9	2.02	85.0	2.27	98.1	2.73	37.0	.96	19.3	.51
26			49.2	1.19	56.9	1.39	70.4	1.75	81.4	2.06	90.2	2.31	106.1	2.83	38.5	.96	20.4	.51
27			51.4	1.20	59.5	1.40	74.0	1.77	86.0	2.08	94.8	2.35	114.5	2.95	40.2	.96	21.5	.51
28			53.7	1.20	62.2	1.40	77.5	1.78	90.2	2.10	100.6	2.38	123.1	3.05	41.8	.96	22.5	.52
29			55.5	1.20	64.8	1.41	80.7	1.79	94.2	2.12	105.0	2.41	132.0	3.17	43.3	.96	23.5	.52
30			58.2	1.21	67.6	1.42	84.6	1.80	99.0	2.14	111.0	2.44	141.3	3.26	44.8	.96	24.5	.53
32					73.0	1.43	91.6	1.82	107.8	2.18	121.3	2.48	160.8	3.48	48.1	.96	26.6	.53
34					78.3	1.44	98.7	1.84	116.6	2.21	131.9	2.53	181.5	3.70	51.3	.96	28.7	.54
36					83.6	1.45	105.8	1.86	125.4	2.23	142.5	2.57	203.5	3.92	54.4	.96	30.8	.54
38							113.0	1.88	134.2	2.26	152.9	2.60	226.7	4.13	57.6	.96	32.9	.55
40							120.1	1.89	143.1	2.28	163.5	2.64	251.2	4.35	60.8	.96	34.9	.55
44									160.9	2.32	184.9	2.69	303.9	4.79	67.3	.96	39.1	.56
48									178.7	2.35	206.0	2.74	361.7	5.22	73.5	.96	43.3	.56

*Adapted from Singleton, Manual of Structural Design, H.M. Ives & Sons.
See Plate VII for Examples for use of Beam Tables.

PLATE VIII.

TABLE A - RESISTING MOMENTS OF CONCRETE BEAMS.*

$f_s = 20,000 \#/\square''$ $f_c = 1125$
$f_c' = 2,500$ $n = 12$ $R = 196.2$

M = Moment of resistance of beam one foot wide in 1000 foot lbs.
A_s = Tensile steel area in sq. inches for moment M.
A_T = Sq. in. additional tensile steel for each $1\square''$ compression steel.

d	TEE BEAMS FOR SLAB THICKNESSES SHOWN												RECTANGULAR BEAM		MOM. 1" COMP. STEEL			
	2" SLAB		2½" SLAB		3" SLAB		4" SLAB		5" SLAB		6" SLAB				A.C.I.		N.Y.C.	
	M	A_s	M	A_s	M	A_s	M	A_s	M	A_s	M	A_s	M	A_s	M'	A_T	M'	A_T
6"	6.9	.79											7.1	.82	1.5	.23	.7	.11
6½	7.9	.84											8.3	.88	2.3	.31	1.1	.15
7	9.0	.87	9.5	.94									9.6	.95	3.1	.38	1.5	.18
7½	10.1	.90	10.8	.99									11.0	1.02	4.0	.44	2.0	.21
8	11.1	.93	12.1	1.04	12.3	1.09							12.6	1.09	4.9	.49	2.4	.24
8½	12.2	.95	12.8	1.08	13.9	1.14							14.2	1.16	5.8	.54	2.8	.26
9	13.2	.98	14.7	1.10	15.5	1.19							15.9	1.22	6.8	.58	3.2	.28
9½	14.3	1.00	16.0	1.13	17.1	1.23							17.7	1.29	7.8	.62	3.7	.30
10	15.4	1.02	17.3	1.16	18.7	1.27	19.6	1.36					19.6	1.36	8.7	.65	4.2	.31
10½	16.5	1.04	18.7	1.19	20.2	1.31	21.6	1.43					21.6	1.43	9.7	.68	4.7	.33
11	17.6	1.05	20.0	1.21	21.8	1.34	23.6	1.49					23.7	1.50	10.7	.71	5.1	.34
11½	18.7	1.06	21.4	1.23	23.4	1.37	25.6	1.54					26.0	1.56	11.7	.74	5.6	.35
12	19.8	1.07	22.7	1.25	25.0	1.40	27.6	1.59					28.3	1.63	12.7	.76	6.0	.36
12½	20.9	1.08	24.1	1.27	26.6	1.43	29.7	1.64					30.7	1.70	13.7	.78	6.5	.37
13	22.0	1.09	25.4	1.29	28.2	1.45	31.8	1.68	33.1	1.76			33.2	1.77	14.7	.80	7.0	.38
13½	23.1	1.10	26.8	1.31	29.8	1.47	33.8	1.71	35.6	1.82			35.9	1.84	15.7	.82	7.5	.39
14	24.2	1.11	28.2	1.32	31.4	1.49	35.9	1.74	38.1	1.87			38.5	1.90	16.7	.84	8.0	.40
15	26.4	1.13	30.9	1.34	34.7	1.53	40.1	1.80	43.2	1.97	44.2	2.04	44.2	2.04	18.8	.87	9.0	.41
16	28.6	1.14	33.7	1.36	37.9	1.56	44.4	1.86	48.3	2.07	50.0	2.16	50.2	2.18	20.9	.89	10.0	.43
17	30.9	1.15	36.5	1.38	41.3	1.59	48.7	1.91	53.5	2.15	56.1	2.27	56.7	2.31	22.9	.92	11.0	.44
18	33.1	1.17	39.2	1.40	44.5	1.61	53.0	1.95	58.7	2.21	62.2	2.36	63.6	2.45	25.0	.94	12.0	.45
19	35.3	1.18	42.0	1.42	47.8	1.63	57.3	1.99	64.1	2.27	68.3	2.45	70.8	2.58	27.1	.96	13.0	.46
20	37.5	1.19	44.8	1.43	51.1	1.65	61.7	2.02	69.4	2.32	74.6	2.54	78.5	2.72	28.8	.96	14.0	.47
21	39.8	1.19	47.5	1.44	54.5	1.66	66.1	2.06	74.7	2.37	80.8	2.61	86.5	2.86	30.3	.96	15.0	.47
22	42.0	1.20	50.4	1.46	57.8	1.68	70.4	2.09	80.0	2.42	87.1	2.67	95.0	2.99	31.9	.96	16.0	.48
23	44.2	1.21	53.0	1.47	61.0	1.70	74.8	2.12	85.4	2.46	93.5	2.73	103.8	3.13	33.5	.96	17.0	.49
24	46.5	1.21	55.9	1.48	64.4	1.71	79.2	2.14	90.9	2.50	99.9	2.79	113.0	3.26	35.1	.96	18.0	.49
25	48.8	1.22	58.8	1.48	67.5	1.72	83.8	2.16	96.3	2.54	106.3	2.84	122.5	3.39	36.6	.96	19.0	.50
26			61.6	1.49	71.0	1.73	87.9	2.18	101.8	2.57	112.7	2.88	132.7	3.54	38.2	.95	20.0	.50
27			64.2	1.50	74.4	1.74	92.4	2.20	107.4	2.60	118.7	2.93	142.9	3.67	39.8	.95	21.0	.51
28			67.1	1.50	77.8	1.75	96.8	2.21	112.8	2.62	125.7	2.97	153.8	3.81	41.4	.95	22.1	.51
29			69.5	1.50	81.1	1.76	101.8	2.23	118.5	2.65	132.0	3.00	164.9	3.95	42.9	.95	23.1	.51
30			72.8	1.51	84.3	1.77	105.7	2.24	123.7	2.67	138.8	3.04	176.6	4.08	44.4	.95	24.1	.52
32					91.1	1.79	114.5	2.27	134.7	2.72	151.7	3.10	200.9	4.35	47.6	.95	26.1	.52
34					97.8	1.80	123.4	2.30	145.7	2.76	164.9	3.15	226.8	4.62	50.8	.95	28.2	.53
36					104.5	1.81	132.3	2.32	156.7	2.79	178.1	3.20	254.3	4.90	54.0	.95	30.2	.53
38							141.3	2.34	167.7	2.81	191.2	3.25	283.4	5.17	57.2	.95	32.3	.54
40							150.1	2.36	178.9	2.85	204.4	3.30	314.0	5.44	60.3	.95	34.3	.54
44									201.1	2.90	231.2	3.37	379.9	5.98	66.5	.95	38.4	.55
48									212.2	2.92	257.2	3.42	452.1	6.53	72.8	.95	42.5	.55

* Adapted from Singleton, Manual of Structural Design, H.M. Ives & Sons.
See Plate VII for Examples for use of Beam Tables.

PLATE IX.

TABLE A - RESISTING MOMENTS OF CONCRETE BEAMS.*

$f_s = 20,000 \#/^{\square}$ $f_c = 1350$
$f_c' = 3,000$ $n = 10$ $R = 235.6$

M = Moment of resistance of beam one foot wide in 1000 foot lbs.
A_s = Tensile steel area in sq. inches for moment M.
A_T = Sq. in. additional tensile steel for each $1^{\square}$ compression steel.

d	TEE BEAMS FOR SLAB THICKNESSES SHOWN													RECTANGULAR BEAM		MOM. 1ᵃ COMP. STEEL A.C.I.		N.Y.C.	
	2" SLAB		2½" SLAB		3" SLAB		4" SLAB		5" SLAB		6" SLAB						M'	A_T	M'	A_T
	M	A_s	M	A_s	M	A_s	M	A_s	M	A_s	M	A_s	M	A_s						
6"	8.3	.94											8.5	.98		1.5	.22	.7	.11
6½	9.5	1.01											9.9	1.06		2.3	.30	1.1	.15
7	10.8	1.05	11.4	1.12									11.5	1.14		3.1	.38	1.5	.18
7½	12.1	1.08	12.9	1.18									13.2	1.22		4.0	.44	1.9	.21
8	13.3	1.11	14.5	1.24	14.8	1.30							15.1	1.31		4.9	.49	2.3	.23
8½	14.6	1.14	15.3	1.29	16.7	1.36							17.0	1.39		5.8	.53	2.8	.25
9	15.9	1.17	17.6	1.33	18.6	1.42							19.1	1.47		6.7	.58	3.2	.27
9½	17.2	1.20	19.2	1.37	20.5	1.47							21.3	1.55		7.7	.62	3.7	.29
10	18.5	1.22	20.8	1.40	22.4	1.52	23.6	1.63					23.5	1.63		8.6	.65	4.1	.31
10½	19.8	1.24	22.4	1.42	24.2	1.57	25.9	1.71					26.0	1.71		9.6	.68	4.6	.32
11	21.1	1.26	24.0	1.45	26.1	1.61	28.3	1.78					28.5	1.80		10.6	.71	5.0	.33
11½	22.4	1.27	25.7	1.48	28.0	1.65	30.7	1.84					31.1	1.88		11.6	.73	5.5	.35
12	23.7	1.28	27.2	1.50	30.0	1.68	33.2	1.90					33.9	1.96		12.5	.75	5.9	.36
12½	25.1	1.29	28.9	1.53	31.9	1.71	35.6	1.96					36.8	2.04		13.5	.78	6.4	.37
13	26.4	1.30	30.5	1.55	33.8	1.74	38.1	2.01	39.8	2.12			39.8	2.12		14.5	.80	6.9	.38
13½	27.7	1.31	32.2	1.57	35.7	1.77	40.6	2.05	42.7	2.19			43.0	2.20		15.6	.82	7.4	.39
14	29.0	1.32	33.8	1.58	37.7	1.80	43.1	2.09	45.7	2.25			46.2	2.28		16.6	.83	7.8	.39
15	31.7	1.34	37.1	1.61	41.6	1.84	48.2	2.17	51.8	2.37	53.0	2.45	53.0	2.45		18.6	.86	8.8	.41
16	34.4	1.36	40.4	1.64	45.5	1.88	53.3	2.23	58.0	2.49	60.0	2.59	60.3	2.61		20.6	.89	9.8	.42
17	37.1	1.38	43.7	1.66	49.5	1.90	58.4	2.30	64.2	2.58	67.3	2.73	68.1	2.77		22.7	.91	10.8	.43
18	39.7	1.40	47.0	1.68	53.5	1.93	63.5	2.35	70.5	2.65	74.6	2.85	76.3	2.94		24.8	.93	11.7	.44
19	42.4	1.42	50.3	1.70	57.4	1.96	68.8	2.39	76.9	2.72	82.0	2.96	85.0	3.10		26.9	.95	12.7	.45
20	45.1	1.43	53.7	1.71	61.3	1.98	74.0	2.43	83.2	2.79	89.5	3.06	94.2	3.26		28.5	.95	13.7	.46
21	47.7	1.44	57.0	1.73	65.4	2.00	79.3	2.47	89.7	2.85	97.0	3.14	103.8	3.43		30.1	.95	14.7	.46
22	50.5	1.45	60.5	1.75	69.4	2.02	84.5	2.51	96.0	2.90	104.6	3.21	114.0	3.59		31.6	.95	15.7	.47
23	53.0	1.46	63.7	1.76	73.3	2.04	89.7	2.54	102.5	2.95	112.2	3.28	124.6	3.75		33.2	.95	16.7	.48
24	55.8	1.47	67.2	1.77	77.2	2.06	95.0	2.57	109.0	3.00	119.9	3.34	135.6	3.92		34.7	.95	17.7	.48
25	58.8	1.47	70.6	1.78	81.3	2.07	100.0	2.59	115.6	3.04	127.5	3.38	147.5	4.08		36.3	.95	18.7	.49
26			73.9	1.78	85.3	2.08	105.5	2.62	122.1	3.08	135.3	3.46	159.2	4.24		37.8	.94	19.7	.49
27			77.2	1.79	89.3	2.09	110.8	2.64	128.3	3.12	142.2	3.50	172.0	4.41		39.4	.94	20.7	.50
28			80.5	1.80	93.4	2.10	116.2	2.66	135.3	3.15	150.8	3.55	184.6	4.57		40.9	.94	21.7	.50
29			84.1	1.81	97.6	2.11	121.9	2.68	141.3	3.18	158.1	3.60	198.5	4.74		42.5	.94	22.7	.50
30			87.4	1.82	101.3	2.12	126.9	2.70	148.4	3.21	166.5	3.64	211.9	4.90		44.1	.94	23.7	.51
32					109.4	2.14	137.4	2.73	161.7	3.27	182.0	3.72	241.1	5.22		47.2	.94	25.7	.51
34					117.4	2.16	148.1	2.76	174.9	3.32	197.8	3.80	272.2	5.55		50.3	.94	27.7	.52
36					125.4	2.17	158.8	2.79	188.0	3.36	213.7	3.86	305.2	5.88		53.4	.94	29.7	.52
38							169.6	2.82	201.2	3.39	229.4	3.91	340.0	6.20		56.5	.94	31.7	.53
40							180.1	2.84	214.6	3.42	245.3	3.96	376.8	6.53		59.6	.94	33.7	.53
44									241.3	3.48	277.4	4.04	455.9	7.18		65.8	.94	37.7	.54
48									268.1	3.53	309.1	4.11	542.5	7.83		72.0	.94	41.8	.55

*Adapted from Singleton, Manual of Structural Design, H. M. Ives & Sons.
See Plate VII for Examples for use of Beam Tables.

PLATE X.

TABLE A - RESISTING MOMENTS OF CONCRETE BEAMS.*

$f_s = 20,000 \#/\square"$ $f_c = 1700$
$f_c' = 3,750$ $n = 8$ $R = 298.0$

M = Moment of resistance of beam one foot wide in 1000 foot lbs.
A_s = Tensile steel area in sq. inches for moment M.
A_T = Sq. in. additional tensile steel for each 1□" compression steel.

d	TEE BEAMS 2" SLAB M	As	2½" SLAB M	As	3" SLAB M	As	4" SLAB M	As	5" SLAB M	As	6" SLAB M	As	RECT. BEAM M	As	A.C.I. M'	AT	N.Y.C. M'	AT
6"	10.5	1.22											10.7	1.24	1.5	.22	.7	.11
6½	12.0	1.26											12.6	1.34	2.3	.31	1.1	.15
7	13.5	1.30	14.4	1.43									14.6	1.44	3.1	.37	1.5	.18
7½	15.2	1.35	16.4	1.50									16.7	1.55	4.0	.44	1.9	.21
8	16.7	1.39	18.3	1.57	19.0	1.66							19.1	1.66	4.9	.49	2.3	.23
8½	18.4	1.43	20.2	1.64	21.2	1.73							21.5	1.76	5.8	.53	2.7	.25
9	19.8	1.46	22.2	1.70	23.5	1.80							24.1	1.87	6.7	.57	3.1	.27
9½	21.5	1.49	24.2	1.75	25.8	1.87							26.8	1.96	7.7	.61	3.6	.29
10	23.3	1.52	26.2	1.79	28.2	1.93							29.8	2.07	8.6	.65	4.0	.30
10½	25.0	1.55	28.3	1.82	30.6	1.99							32.8	2.17	9.6	.68	4.4	.32
11	26.8	1.58	30.4	1.85	33.0	2.05	35.9	2.28					36.0	2.27	10.5	.70	4.9	.33
11½	28.3	1.60	32.4	1.88	35.4	2.08	38.7	2.34					39.3	2.38	11.5	.73	5.4	.34
12	30.0	1.62	34.5	1.90	37.8	2.12	41.9	2.41					42.9	2.48	12.5	.75	5.8	.35
12½	31.5	1.63	36.5	1.92	40.2	2.15	44.9	2.48					46.6	2.59	13.5	.77	6.3	.36
13	33.2	1.65	38.6	1.94	42.5	2.18	48.2	2.55					50.4	2.69	14.5	.79	6.8	.37
13½	35.0	1.67	40.8	1.96	44.8	2.22	51.2	2.62					54.2	2.79	15.5	.81	7.2	.38
14	36.6	1.69	42.9	1.99	47.5	2.27	54.3	2.69	57.5	2.88			58.4	2.90	16.5	.83	7.7	.39
15	39.9	1.71	47.0	2.01	52.4	2.31	60.7	2.76	65.5	3.01			67.2	3.11	18.5	.86	8.7	.40
16	43.4	1.73	50.8	2.04	57.4	2.34	67.0	2.82	73.0	3.13	76.2	3.37	76.3	3.31	20.5	.88	9.6	.41
17	46.8	1.75	55.0	2.07	62.4	2.37	73.4	2.88	81.0	3.23	85.2	3.49	86.0	3.51	22.6	.91	10.6	.42
18	50.1	1.76	59.3	2.10	67.4	2.40	79.5	2.94	89.0	3.32	94.2	3.61	96.5	3.72	24.6	.93	11.5	.43
19	53.0	1.77	63.5	2.12	72.0	2.43	86.3	3.00	96.4	3.40	103.5	3.72	107.5	3.93	26.6	.94	12.5	.44
20	56.9	1.78	67.8	2.14	77.2	2.46	93.6	3.05	104.8	3.48	112.5	3.83	119.2	4.14	28.1	.94	13.4	.45
21	60.5	1.79	71.4	2.16	82.4	2.49	99.6	3.09	112.6	3.56	124.0	3.93	131.2	4.34	29.6	.93	14.4	.46
22	63.5	1.80	76.0	2.18	87.3	2.51	106.5	3.13	120.8	3.63	131.5	4.02	144.0	4.54	31.1	.93	15.4	.46
23	66.6	1.81	79.3	2.20	92.0	2.53	113.0	3.17	129.0	3.70	141.0	4.11	157.5	4.75	32.7	.93	16.4	.47
24	70.2	1.82	84.0	2.22	97.4	2.55	119.8	3.21	137.0	3.77	151.0	4.20	171.8	4.96	34.2	.93	17.3	.47
25			88.7	2.23	102.5	2.57	126.1	3.25	145.5	3.83	160.6	4.28	186.3	5.18	35.7	.93	18.3	.48
26			93.3	2.24	106.4	2.59	132.5	3.28	153.5	3.88	169.2	4.35	201.5	5.38	37.2	.93	19.3	.48
27			97.7	2.25	112.0	2.61	139.0	3.31	162.2	3.92	178.8	4.42	217.3	5.59	38.8	.93	20.3	.49
28			101.0	2.26	117.3	2.63	146.5	3.33	170.8	3.96	188.8	4.48	233.3	5.78	40.3	.93	21.3	.49
29			105.8	2.27	122.5	2.65	152.8	3.35	178.3	4.00	199.0	4.54	250.5	5.99	41.8	.93	22.2	.49
30			110.4	2.28	127.8	2.67	159.3	3.37	187.2	4.03	209.7	4.59	268.2	6.22	43.3	.93	23.2	.50
32					137.5	2.70	173.0	3.41	203.0	4.09	230.0	4.67	304.0	6.60	46.4	.93	25.1	.50
34					146.8	2.72	187.5	3.45	220.0	4.15	250.0	4.75	345.5	7.06	49.5	.93	27.1	.51
36					158.0	2.74	200.0	3.49	237.5	4.21	270.0	4.82	387.0	7.47	52.5	.93	29.1	.51
38							212.0	3.53	252.5	4.27	288.8	4.89	429.0	7.85	55.6	.93	31.0	.52
40							227.2	3.57	270.4	4.32	308.8	4.96	476.8	8.26	58.6	.93	33.0	.52
44							254.0	3.62	304.2	4.38	349.0	5.06	577.0	9.15	64.6	.93	37.0	.53
48							283.0	3.67	337.0	4.43	390.0	5.16	685.0	9.92	70.7	.93	41.0	.54

Column groupings: "TEE BEAMS FOR SLAB THICKNESSES SHOWN" (2" SLAB through 6" SLAB), "RECTANGULAR BEAM", and "MOM. 1□" COMP. STEEL" (A.C.I. and N.Y.C.).

* See Plate VII for Examples for use of Beam Tables.

PLATE XI.

TWO WAY FLAT SLAB DESIGN - 1951 A.C.I. CODE.

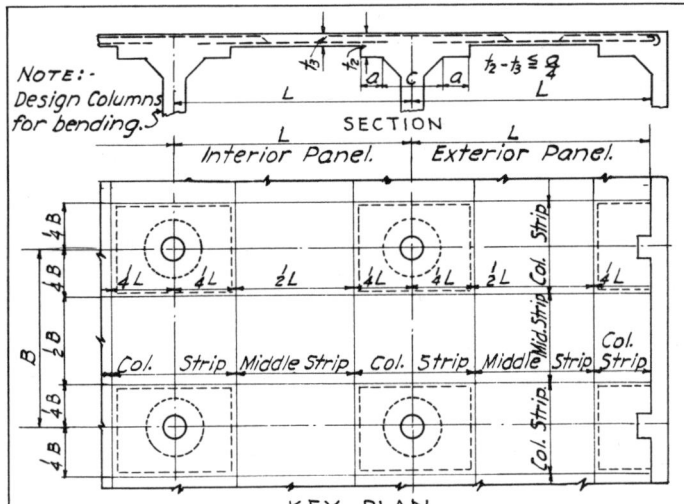

NOTE:-
Design Columns for bending.

SECTION

Interior Panel.   Exterior Panel.

KEY PLAN

$$M_o = 0.09 W \cdot L \left(1 - \frac{2C}{3L}\right)^2 \; ; \quad M_o = 0.09 W \cdot B \left(1 - \frac{2C}{3B}\right)^2$$

W = Total live and dead load uniformly distributed over a single panel area.

BENDING MOMENTS IN TWO WAY FLAT SLABS & PANELS.

DESCRIPTION	INTERIOR PANEL MOMENT COEFFICIENT	EXTERIOR PANEL. MOMENT COEFFICIENT
With Drop Panel. Column Strip.	Neg. -0.50 M_o Pos. +0.20 M_o	Exterior Neg.-0.45 M_o Pos. +0.25 M_o Interior Neg.-0.55 M_o
Middle Strip.	Neg.- 0.15 M_o Pos.+ 0.15 M_o	Exterior Neg.-0.10 M_o Pos. +0.19 M_o Interior Neg.-0.165 M_o
Without Drop Panel. Column Strip.	Neg.- 0.46 M_o Pos.+ 0.22 M_o	Exterior Neg.-0.41 M_o Pos. +0.28 M_o Interior Neg.-0.50 M_o
Middle Strip.	Neg.- 0.16 M_o Pos.+ 0.16 M_o	Exterior Neg.-0.10 M_o Pos. +0.20 M_o Interior Neg.-0.176 M_o

BENDING MOMENTS IN PANELS WITH MARGINAL BEAMS OR WALLS.

	Marginal beams with depth greater than 1½x slab thickness; or bearing walls.	Marginal beams with depth 1½x slab thickness or less.		
(a) Load to be carried by marginal beam or wall.	Loads directly superimposed upon it plus a uniform load equal to one-quarter of the total live and dead panel load.	Loads directly superimposed upon it exclusive of any panel load.		
(b) Moment to be used in the design of half column strip adjacent and parallel to marginal beam or wall.	With Drop Neg.-0.125 M_o Pos.+0.05 M_o	Without Drop Neg.-0.115 M_o Pos.+0.055 M_o	With Drop Neg.- 0.25 M_o Pos.+ 0.10 M_o	Without Drop Neg.- 0.23 M_o Pos.+0.11 M_o
(c) Negative moment to be used in design of Middle strip continuous across a beam or wall.	Neg.-0.195 M_o	Neg.-0.208 M_o	Neg.- 0.15 M_o	Neg.-0.16 M_o

The bending moments are shown for the critical sections of strips in exterior panels at right angles to the discontinuous edge where the exterior support consists of reinforced concrete columns or reinforced concrete bearing walls integral with the slab, the ratio of stiffness of the support to that of the slab being at least as great as the ratio of the live load to the dead load and not less than one.

If the flat slab is supported by a wall providing restraint at the discontinuous edge use for the negative moment at the discontinuous edge of the column strip M= -.30 M_o; and for the middle strip M= -.25 M_o.

LIMITATIONS FOR USE OF TABLE.

1. L/B = Not more than 1.33.
2. Slab continuous over 3 or more panels in each direction.
3. The successive span length in each direction differs by not more than 20% of the shorter span.

Compression due to bending.

3/4 of the width of the strip or drop panel shall be taken as the width of the section in computing compression. For positive and negative moments tension reinforcement to be distributed over entire strip.

Thickness of Slabs.

Such as not to exceed unit stresses allowed but not to be less than L/40 with drop panels or L/36 without drop panels.

Shear

Shearing unit stress v on a vertical section t_2- 1½" beyond the edge of the column capital shall not exceed:-
a- 0.03 f'_c when at least 50% of the total negative reinforcement passes directly over the column capital.
b- 0.025 f'_c when only 25% or less of negative reinforcement passes directly over the column capital.
c- For intermediate percentages interpolate for values of v.
d- In computing $v = \frac{V}{bja}$, d shall be taken as t_2- 1½".
e- V on a vertical section in a distance of t_3- 1½" from a drop panel shall not exceed 0.03 f'_c when d is taken as t_3- 1½" and at least 50% of negative reinforcement in column strip is inside the width of the drop panel.

Reinforcement.

The ratio of reinforcement in any strip shall not be less than 0.0025. Spacing of bars shall not exceed 3 times thickness of slab.

General Notes.

1. The coefficients of the table may be varied by no more than 6% provided the numerical sum of the + and - moments remains unchanged.
2. For columns without a capital the distance "c" shall be taken as the diameter of the column.
3. For columns with brackets take "c" equal to twice the distance from the ℄ of column to the point where the thickness of the bracket is 1½".
4. Panels supported by marginal beams on opposite sides shall be designed as one or two way slabs.

PLATE XII.

EXAMPLES OF NOTORIOUS FOUNDATION AREAS

At New Orleans, the soft river silt deposit contains a thin strata of gravel which have been used for pile resistance. These strata may be approximately 10 ft. thick, and long piles up to 120 ft. may be required.

In Mexico City, a fine water-bearing clay, probably originating from volcanic ash, extends to a depth of some 700 ft. or more. In this clay are thin strata of gravel at a level of 200 or 300 ft. which have been used successfully for the bringing up of piles.

In this area, wood piles with two splices have been used with success. However, the water level seems to be lowering, with the subsequent lowering of the general surface areas, so that buildings on piles appear to rise above the street level.

In Chicago, in general, there is a stratum of clay perhaps 100 ft. thick overlying the rock. This condition has given rise to the special type of footing known as the Chicago caisson, which is merely a circular wood-sheeted caisson driven down and excavated to rock with little interference from water and no air required.

However, in many cases, there is an underlying stratum of water-bearing gravel, about 25 ft. thick, which was formerly penetrated by the use of pneumatic caissons and more recently by the use of long H piles. See p. 10–9.

In Boston, there is a similar type layer of clay, where the Gow pile was developed. This is merely a method of belling out the end of the pile by hand, taking advantage of the stability of the clay in which it was placed.

On the heavier buildings such as the M.I.T. Building in Cambridge and the John Hancock Building in Boston, long H piles have been used. These have been driven 125 ft. or 150 ft. to rock. Much deeper piles have been used in special foundations.

In Detroit the plastic clays tend to bulk when piles are driven. Pressure may have to be relieved by driving a certain percentage of open-end piles.

PERMAFROST FOUNDATIONS

Definitions

Permafrost (P.F.) Ground in which the temperature remains permanently below freezing.

Permafrost Table (P.F.T.). Upper limit of permafrost.

Sporadic Permafrost. Scattered islands of permafrost occurring in an area of predominantly unfrozen ground.

Frost Action Soils. Uniformly graded soils containing more than 10% or well-graded soils containing more than 3% by dry weight of particles less than 0.02 mm. (0.0008 in.) in size.

Active Layer. Layer of ground above the permafrost that freezes and thaws seasonally.

Active Method (of Construction). A method in which the permafrost is removed permanently from the site. (Not recommended except for conditions of sporadic permafrost.)

Passive Method (of Construction). A method in which the permafrost is preserved. (Recommended for most cases.)

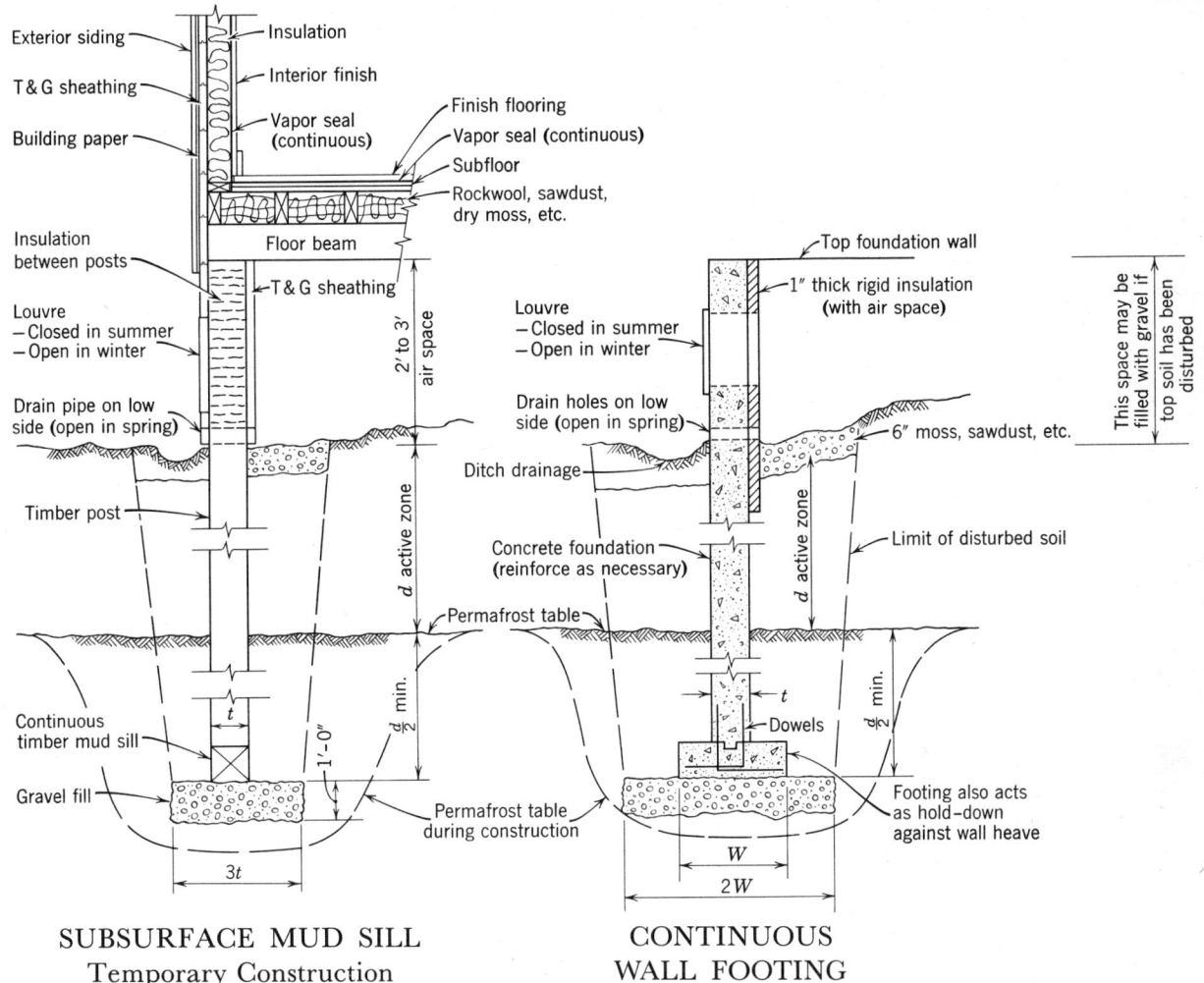

SUBSURFACE MUD SILL
Temporary Construction

**CONTINUOUS
WALL FOOTING**

Notes: Allow foundation to "freeze in" before proceeding with superstructure.
P.F.T. means permafrost table.

FIG. 2. TYPICAL FOUNDATIONS ON PERMAFROST (FOR FROST ACTION SOILS).
Passive Method.

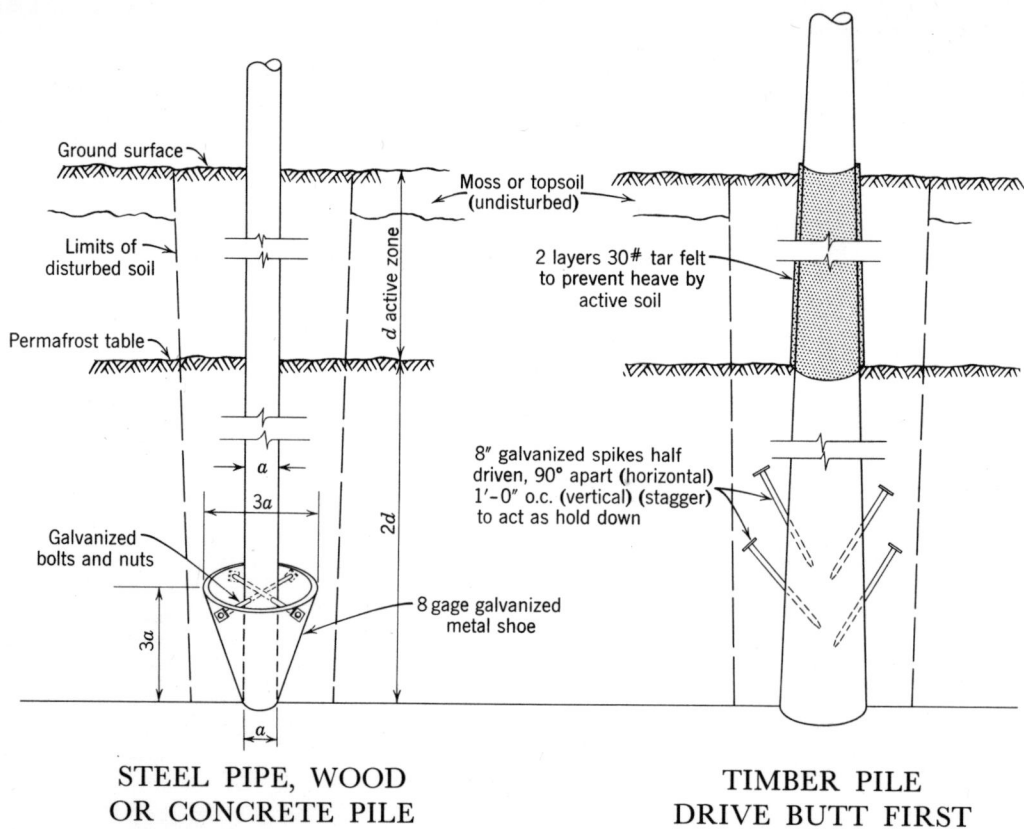

STEEL PIPE, WOOD
OR CONCRETE PILE

TIMBER PILE
DRIVE BUTT FIRST

Method for Construction

1. Excavate to P.F. level.
2. Thaw P.F. by steam jets and some hot water.   (Excessive thawing to be avoided.)
3. Drive pile (can often be done with bulldozer winch and cable).
4. Allow pile to "freeze in" before proceeding with superstructure.
5. Pile capacity same as on rock.

FIG. 3.   TYPICAL PILE FOUNDATIONS ON PERMAFROST

(FOR FROST ACTION SOILS).

Passive Method.

Red Lights (Passive Method)

1. Vegetation cover *not* to be disturbed except where absolutely necessary.   Disturbed areas must be protected to prevent lowering permafrost table.

2. Permafrost table should be located as accurately as possible, preferably by a number of test pits late in summer season.

3. Machine foundations must be isolated from building foundations.

4. Cellars not recommended except if isolated from foundations of building and insulated from above.

5. Heating plants and laundries must have special consideration as regards to:
   (*a*) Insulation of foundations.
   (*b*) Insulation of adjoining areas.
   (*c*) Disposal of hot wash water and waste steam (30 ft. minimum from any foundation and with adequate surface runoff away from foundations).

6. Allow foundations to "freeze in" before proceeding with superstructure.

7. All heated utilities systems (utilidors) to be well insulated near foundations.

8. Runways founded on frozen soil should consist of a thickness of non-frost heaving fill sufficient to insulate the base from thaw during the warmer season.*

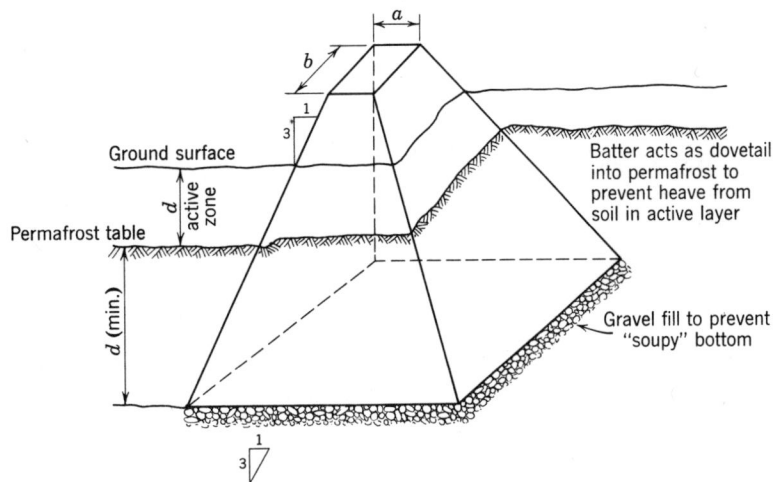

P.F.T. means permafrost table.

FIG. 4. TYPICAL PIER TYPE FOUNDATION.

CORROSION

Discussion

Water may contain corrosive chemicals. In areas of low rainfall, alkali deposits may be leached out of the soil. Such waters are very corrosive. Salt water also has a deleterious effect. The best protection is the use of a dense, rich (7-bag mix) concrete which does not allow such waters to enter.

Steel is subject to corrosion. See *Data Book for Civil Engineers*, Vol. 1, p. 4–84.

Timber below permanent ground water is not subject to rot. Timber exposed to alternate wetting and drying must be pressure-creosoted or otherwise protected.

Metal connections should not be relied upon for timber dock work, as they will rust out quickly. It is better to use scarf joints and dowels. Galvanizing is not too successful.

Extra metal should be provided to allow for corrosion of steel piles exposed to water.

Steel piling should be used with care where the piles are to be buried in cinders, garbage fill, or other organic material. In ordinary installations, it is believed that the slight surface corrosion of steel piling protects the inner part.

Steel piling exposed to electrolysis should have cathodic protection (Chapter 17).

* B. L. Trawicky, Chief Construction Division, Eastern Ocean Division, Corps. of Engineers.

Recommendations

Marine Borers (Teredo, etc.):

Creosoting. Difficult to provide complete impregnation; partial impregnation leaves heart exposed to attack if protective cover is broken.

Life of creosoted piles on Pacific Coast is increased by 1 year for each pound of creosote per cubic foot of material; * in other words, 35 lb. = 35 years.

Heavy sewage pollution protects wood piles from borers.

Earth protection: When practical, earth fill may be placed around piles to protect them against marine borers.

Concrete and steel piles are not affected.

Corrosion: *

The life of a steel pile may be estimated by the formula: $Y = W/CL$, where Y = life of metal in years; W = weight of steel per linear foot; L = perimeter of exposed steel in feet; C = value given in Table II.

TABLE II
VALUES OF C.

Foul sea air	0.1944	Pure air, or clear river water	0.0125
Clean sea air	0.0970	Air of manufacturing districts and	
Foul river water	0.1133	sea air	0.1252

Note: Cast iron has considerably more resistance than structural steel.

Concrete and Steel: Waters subject to industrial waste should be examined for corrosive action and adequate protection given.

Erosion:

Concrete structures subject to abrasion by ice, or freezing and thawing, should have protection such as sheathing or riprap.

Wood structures should be protected from ships, etc., by dolphins, fender piles, or sheathing.

Decay:

All exposed wood subject to decay above low water level should be pressure-treated with creosote preservative.

Scour:

Obstructions such as practically solid piers tend to cause river bottom scour and should be made the subject of special study.

Riprap may be used to minimize scour.

---

* Adapted by permission from *Wharves and Piers* by Carleton Greene, McGraw-Hill Book Co., 1917.

TABLE III

ANTICIPATED LIFE OF PRESSURE-CREOSOTED WOOD PILES IN MARINE WATERS *

	Years
Canadian Border to Cape May, N. J.	50
Norfolk, Virginia (Mid Atlantic)	40
East Coast of Florida	25
Gulf of Mexico	20–25
Caribbean	15
West Coast (Douglas fir piles)	25–30

* Colonel Ralph H. Mann, American Wood Preservers Association.

TABLE IV

CORROSION, DECAY, AND EROSION

Agent	Material	Correction *
	I. Steel	
Salt water		(a) Concrete casing, 7-bag dense.
Alkali		(b) Galvanizing, A.S.T.M. A–153.
		(c) Painting, 2 coats A.W.W.A. 7A6.
		(d) Cathodic protection.
	II. Miscellaneous Steel	
Air	Reinforcement for concrete casing	(a) Galvanizing, A.S.T.M.
Water	Exposed reinforced-concrete work	A–153.
	Bolts	
	III. Timber Framed	
Air		(a) Creosoting, A.W.P.A. T_1 T_2.
Water		(b) Chemical treatment.†
	IV. Timber Piles	
Air		(a) Creosoting, AW.P.A. T_1 T_5
Water		
Limnoria		
	V. Concrete	
Freezing and		(a) Density of concrete.
thawing		(b) Paint with asphalt.
		(c) Sheath with timber or steel plates.

* Listed in order of effectiveness.
† See p. 17–40.

Glossary

Abutment. A supporting or buttressing structure to sustain lateral pressure, as the thrust of an arch or vault. Usually applied to the end bearing structure of a bridge.

Anchor bolt. A round, steel bolt embedded in concrete or masonry to hold down machinery, castings, shoes, beams, plates, and engine beds.

Areaway. Area enclosed by walls to provide access to an opening in a wall located below grade.

Atterberg limits. A method of classifying soils. *See* p. 13–43.

Backfill. Soil replaced in an area that had previously been excavated.

Basalt. *See* 8–4.

Batter pile. A pile driven on a slope.

Bearing plate. Steel slab under a beam to distribute the end reaction from the beam to the supporting masonry. *See also* Billet.

Bed plane. Rock strata of sedimentary rock representing the planes on which it was laid down.

Bedding. A prepared base in soil or concrete for laying of concrete or masonry.

Bent. A structural frame composed of two or more columns and a crosspiece called a cap.

Billet. A steel slab under a steel column to distribute the load from the column to the supporting masonry.

Boils. The disturbing of ground by an upward flow of water.

Borings. Holes drilled into the ground to obtain samples of soil from every stratum encountered for purposes of investigation and soil evaluation.

Bridge abutment. Shore pier. *See also* abutment.

Bridge pier. A masonry structure supporting the superstructure.

Bulkhead. A wall of sheet piling of either steel, timber, or reinforced concrete restrained at the bottom by the soil and at the top by a wale tied back to a deadman or pile anchor. It may also be a filled crib.

Buttress. A structure of any material built against a wall to strengthen it.

Caisson. Watertight box usually of wood or steel sheeting, sometimes a cylinder of steel or concrete, used for the purpose of excavation. Caissons may be either open (that is, open to the free air) or pneumatic (that is, under compressed air). When bearing is reached it is filled with concrete.

California bearing ratio ("C.B.R."). A punching test corelation between a standard stone base and a given soil. *See* p. 15–31.

Cap. A concrete block arranged to distribute the column load, usually a concrete column, to the concrete footing. Top member on a trestle bent. *See also* pile cap and bent.

Capillary action. The phenomonon of a dry soil sucking moisture up above the ground water level.

Clay. *See* p. 8–4.

Cleavage plane. Crack at right angles to bed plane of rock.

Cofferdam. A temporary structure built to exclude earth and water from an excavation so that work may be done in the dry.

Combined footing. Two or more footings combined to act as one unit. *See* p. 1–4.

Compaction. Increasing soil density by mechanical means.

Concrete collar or doughnut. A collar of reinforced concrete placed around an existing column. The shrinkage grips the existing column enabling it to be jacked.

Counterfort. *See* buttress.

Cradle. A footing structure shaped to fit the conduit it supports.

Creep. The flow of water along contact surface between structure and soil or rock foundation, especially in dams.

Crib wall. A wall made by laying up a crib of timber or precast concrete units which is filled with soil or rock.

Cross bracing. Horizontal timbering extending across an excavation to support sheathing or cofferdam.

Culvert. A drain or channel crossing under a road, etc.; a sewer or conduit.

Deadman. A form of anchoring into the earth by burying a log-shaped element to which a tension member is fastened.

Docking. Cribs of precast concrete or timber placed to protect a bank against erosion.

Dolphin. A cluster of piles, driven in water and lashed together, for mooring purposes or for protection against floating objects.

Dowel. A short steel bar extending from one concrete element to another, as for instance from a concrete foundation to a concrete column. The dowel may or may not transfer direct stress. *See* p. 1–5.

Drain. A conduit for carrying off surplus ground or surface water.

Earth dike. A ridge of soil restraining water.

Erosion. The washing away of soil by flowing water.

Expansion joint. Joint designed to take expansion and contraction.

Feldspar. *See* p. 8–4.

Fill. *See* p. 8–6.

Footing. The lowest element of a foundation; that part which bears on the soil.

Footing drain. A drain surrounding a footing. *See* p. 3–36.

Foundation bolt. A steel bolt embedded in concrete or masonry to hold billet plates in place; also called anchor bolt.

French drain. An open joint or porous drain embedded in gravel for the purpose of removing ground water.

Friction bolt. Bolt which is held by wedge friction and bond such as Fox Bolt and Star Bolt. *See* p. 2–5.

Friction piles. Piles which obtain their support from the friction between the sides of the pile and the soil.

Frost. Ground in which the freezing of water has occurred.

Frost line. The line measuring the depth of frost penetration into the ground.

Gneiss. *See* p. 8–4.

Grade beam. A reinforced concrete beam framing between wall piers at grade elevation carrying the wall to isolated piers.

Granite. *See* p. 8–4.

Gravel. *See* pp. 1–12 and 8–3.

Grillage. A group of steel beams arranged to distribute a concentrated load to the supporting masonry or soil.

Grout. A liquid mixture of cement and water, or of cement, sand, and water.

Hardpan. *See* pp. 1–13 and 8–3.

Heave. Upthrust of frozen ground; also the rebound of piles caused by the driving of additional piles.

Hornblende. *See* p. 8–4.

Hydrostatic pressure. Pressure caused by a head of water.

Keyway. A slot for interlocking masonry walls or slabs built at different times.

Kaolinized rock. *See* p. 8–6.

Limestone. *See* p. 8–4.

Line drilling. The process of drilling holes close together so as to break the rock on a vertical line.

Loam. Sand and clay mixture. *See* p. 1–13.

Marble. *See* p. 8–4.

Mat:
1. A concrete slab of uniform thickness to withstand hydrostatic pressure.
2. A concrete slab of adequate thickness to spread column loads to allowable soil bearing, therefore acting as a combined footing.
3. Mat or mattress. Blanket of brush lumber or poles interwoven or otherwise lashed together, placed to cover an area subject to scour and weighted with rock, concrete blocks, or other means to hold it in place.

Mica. *See* p. 8–4.

Modulus of rupture. The tensile stress developed by a flexural test computed from the flexural resistance formula.

Modulus of subgrade reaction. The elastic reaction of a subgrade to a plate load test.

Muck. *See* p. 8–4.

Mud. *See* p. 10–20.

Needles. Beams piercing an existing wall to support it temporarily.

Organic silt. *See* p. 8–4.

Pavement. The top or wearing surface of a roadway.

Pavement base. The layer between wearing surface and subgrade or subbase.

Peat. *See* pp. 1–12 and 8–4.

Pedestal. An upright compression member whose height does not exceed three times its least lateral dimension.

Permafrost. Ground permanently frozen throughout the year. *See* p. 3–46.

Permeability. Ability of soil to allow water to flow through it.

Pier:
1. Synonomous with a pedestal.
2. An isolated or semi-isolated block of masonry.

Pile. A column of wood, steel, or concrete usually less than 24 inches in diameter, driven or jacked into the ground to support a load. In underpinning, piles are usually composed of steel cylinders from 12 to 24 inches in diameter, filled with concrete.

Pile cap. A slab, usually of reinforced concrete, covering the tops of a group of piles for the purpose of tying them together and transmitting to them as a group the load of the structure. Also a metal plate often welded to the top of steel piles to distribute the reaction to the concrete.

Pile tolerance. The permitted deviation of a pile in a horizontal plane or the permitted deviation from a plumb line.

Piles, master. Steel H-piles used in deep building excavation, withstanding a horizontal pull formed by arcs of steel sheet piling placed between.

Piles, soldier. Steel H-piles used in deep building excavation between which timber sheeting spans horizontally.

Predeflection. Deflecting new structural supports before loading to eliminate subsequent elastic deflection.

Pump handle footing. A footing with a strap or "pump handle" extending to an adjacent footing to remove eccentricities by lever action. *See* p. 1–4.

Pushers. Slanting timber shore giving horizontal and vertical support to a building adjacent to an excavation.

Pyrite. *See* p. 8–4.

Quartz. *See* p. 8–4.

Quicksand. Sand with water boiling up through it. *See* pp. 8–6 and 8–7.

Relieving platform. Timber structure built below water level to support masonry and fill for a slipside structure.

Retaining walls:

Gravity wall. A mass masonry wall resisting overturning its own weight.

Cantilever wall. A reinforced concrete wall resisting overturning by cantilevering out footings.

Counterfort wall. Cantilever wall reinforced with counterforts or buttresses.

Revetment. Material, such as rock, concrete blocks, log cribbing, placed on the face of a river bank to prevent or minimize erosion and to retain the earth.

Rigid frame. A structure in which the joints between the members are rigid so that stresses in one member induce stresses in the other member.

Riprap. Broken stone placed on earth surfaces for protection against the erosion of water.

Sand. *See* p. 8–3.

Sand drain. A column of gravel or sand punched through less pervious material to permit water to bleed off.

Sandstone. *See* p. 8–5.

Schists. *See* p. 8–4.

Scour. Loss of material owing to erosion by water, especially applied to river bottoms.

Seepage. The percolation of water through the soil; infiltration.

Shale. *See* p. 8–5.

Sheeting (Sheathing). Horizontal or vertical members of wood or steel placed in contact with earth, usually on a vertical plane, for the purpose of retaining an earth bank in position.

Sheet piling. A diaphragm made up of meshing or interlocking members of wood, steel, concrete, etc., driven individually to form an obstruction to percolation, for preventing movement of material, for cofferdams, for stabilizing foundations, etc.

Shims. Thin steel wedging often tapered.

Shore. Temporary strut of timber or steel.

Silt. *See* p. 8–3.

Silts, inorganic. Very fine sand.

Silts, organic. Black mud. *See* p. 8–4.

Slates. *See* p. 8–5.

Soils:

Angle of repose. Natural slope of a bank.

Cohesion. Shearing strength of a plastic soil.

Density. Weight per cubic foot.

Granular. Soils with the flow characteristics of sand.

Plastic. Soils which flow under pressure when moist. *See* Clay.

Sensitivity. Loss of strength of a plastic soil after kneading. Applied to clays.

Shearing strength. The shearing resistance of a plastic soil or the angle of internal friction of a granular soil.

Spillway. Overflow channel for a dam.

Spud. A rugged false pile (generally steel) used to force obstructions out of line to facilitate driving permanent piles.

Spur shores. Slanting timber holding a cofferdam around a building excavation.

Starling. That portion of bridge pier which is sloped as it intersects the water level to protect pier nose from floating objects.

Stub pile. A short, thick pile.

Subbase. The layer between base and subgrade.

Subdrain. A drain draining a subgrade.

Subfloor drain. Drain under a floor.

Subgrade. The soil below pavement or subbase.

Sump. A low spot from which to pump.

Surcharge. Extra load on the surface immediately behind a retaining wall or over a conduit.

Swales. Open, shallow hollows used for draining or ponding at the sides of highways or runways.

Termites. Antlike insects which attack wood.

Top soil. *See* p. 8–6.

Thrust block. Anchor for pipes at critical locations such as joints and elbows consisting of a small mass of concrete placed against the earth.

Trap rock. *See* p. 8–4.

Tremie. A closed chute funneling concrete between different elevations to avoid segregation and also to place concrete under water.

Underpinning. Art of placing new foundations under old foundations.

Varved clay. *See* p. 8–4.

Wales. Horizontal timbers or beams to support sheeting or concrete forms.

Waterproofing:

Membrane waterproofing. Felt membrane set in bituminous cement applied to outside of wall to stop water.

Hydrolithic waterproofing. Cement compound mortar applied and bonded to the inside surfaces of concrete to stop water.

Integral waterproofing. A water repellent compound mixed with concrete.

Waterstop. A plate or dam placed in a joint to prevent flow of water along the contact surface.

Wave action. Scouring effect as waves travel up and down a slope or beach.

Wearing surface. Top surface of a pavement. Often an extra replaceable surface on top to prevent wear.

Weep holes. Openings left in retaining walls, aprons, linings, foundations, etc., to permit drainage and reduce pressures.

Well point. Perforated pipe sunk into sand to permit the pumping of ground water and the exclusion of sand.

Index

Date Due